The Basic Science of
Oncology

Pergamon Titles of Related Interest

Bragg/Rubin/Youker ONCOLOGIC IMAGING
Kallman RODENT TUMOR MODELS IN EXPERIMENTAL
CANCER THERAPY
Gross ONCOGENIC VIRUSES, THIRD EDITION
Mizer/Scheller/Deye RADIATION THERAPY SIMULATION WORKBOOK
Bentel/Nelson/Noell TREATMENT PLANNING & DOSE CALCULATION IN
RADIATION ONCOLOGY, FOURTH EDITION
Turner ATOMS, RADIATION, AND RADIATION PROTECTION
Hall RADIATION AND LIFE, SECOND EDITION

Related Journals
(Free sample copies available on request)

INTERNATIONAL JOURNAL OF RADIATION
ONCOLOGY/BIOLOGY/PHYSICS
JOURNAL OF CANCER EDUCATION
EUROPEAN JOURNAL OF CANCER & CLINICAL ONCOLOGY
MEDICAL ONCOLOGY AND TUMOR PHARMACOTHERAPY
JOURNAL OF FREE RADICALS IN BIOLOGY AND MEDICINE
ADVANCES IN FREE RADICAL BIOLOGY AND MEDICINE

The Basic Science of
Oncology

Edited by

Ian F. Tannock, MD, PhD
Richard P. Hill, PhD

The Ontario Cancer Institute
and
The University of Toronto
Toronto, Ontario
Canada

PERGAMON PRESS

New York • Oxford • Beijing • Frankfurt
São Paulo • Sydney • Tokyo • Toronto

Pergamon Press Offices:

U.S.A. Pergamon Press, Maxwell House, Fairview Park, Elmsford, New York 10523, U.S.A.

U.K. Pergamon Press, Headington Hill Hall, Oxford OX3 0BW, England

PEOPLE'S REPUBLIC OF CHINA Pergamon Press, Qianmen Hotel, Beijing, People's Republic of China

FEDERAL REPUBLIC OF GERMANY Pergamon Press, Hammerweg 6, D-6242 Kronberg, Federal Republic of Germany

BRAZIL Pergamon Editora, Rua Eça de Queiros, 346, CEP 04011, São Paulo, Brazil

AUSTRALIA Pergamon Press (Aust.) Pty., P.O. Box 544, Potts Point, NSW 2011, Australia

JAPAN Pergamon Press, 8th Floor, Matsuoka Central Building, 1-7-1 Nishishinjuku, Shinjuku-ku, Tokyo 160, Japan

CANADA Pergamon Press Canada, Suite 104, 150 Consumers Road, Willowdale, Ontario M2J 1P9, Canada

---

First printing 1987

Library of Congress Cataloging in Publication Data

The basic science of oncology.

    1. Cancer. 2. Oncology. I. Tannock, Ian. II. Hill, Richard P., 1942-   . [DNLM: 1. Neoplasms. QZ 200 B3115]
RC267.B3 1986   616.99'4   86-16946
ISBN 0-08-032389-8
ISBN 0-08-032388-X (soft)

Printed in the United States of America

Contents

PART 3: BIOLOGY UNDERLYING CANCER TREATMENT

Preface

An understanding of the basic science which underlies oncology is important both to clinicians treating cancer patients and to scientists engaged in cancer research. The editors have organized a course on "The Basic Science of Oncology" for several years at the Ontario Cancer Institute/Princess Margaret Hospital (OCI/ PMH) in Toronto. The course is attended by clinical trainees in radiation and medical oncology, by medical students, graduate students and postdoctoral fellows who desire an overview of the field, and occasionally by nurses, pharmacists, technicians and other health professionals. The course is supported by money raised by Terry Fox's heroic attempt to run across Canada.

This book arises from our wish to provide students with a comprehensive reference to the material covered in our course. We hope that it will also be a suitable reference for trainees and practitioners in all branches of oncology. Although we believe that the book provides a comprehensive overview of the basic science relating to oncology we deliberately chose to exclude any discussion of pathology. There are a number of other texts which adequately cover this topic.

In organizing this volume we have tried to achieve a uniform level of content and style. We invited various members of the University of Toronto, who had taught segments of the course, to contribute chapters. We specified that these should be written to a predetermined format, and subjected the original chapters to considerable editing to achieve our goal. After this initial editing we obtained at least four reviews of each chapter. Two of these were by international experts who were asked to comment on the content and accuracy of the information. The other two reviews were by trainees in clinical oncology and basic research, who were asked to consider the relevance of the information for their needs and to comment on its clarity.

The above process has depended on the assistance of a large group of people, without whose good will this volume would never have appeared. We thank first our authors, who responded to our frequent demands to produce, modify, and modify again. Second, we thank our expert reviewers (listed below) and our students whose suggestions led to many improvements. Next we thank our colleagues, and in particular Dr. Ray Bush, Director, OCI/PMH, Dr. Daniel Bergsagel, Chief of Medicine, OCI/PMH, and Dr. Gordon Whitmore, Head of Physics, OCI/PMH, who warned us of the folly of this endeavour yet allowed us to forego some of our usual duties in order to complete the volume. Our secretaries, Chris Beaney and Anne Marie Watson, undertook the enormous task of typing and retyping many of the chapters. Mr. Doug McCourt and Mr. Alan Connor, respectively heads of the Art and Photography Departments at OCI/PMH, produced the many diagrams in this volume, often starting only with a rough sketch. Finally we thank our wives Rosemary and Lyndel, and our children (in descending age) Michael, Stuart, Peter, Lisa, Kirsty and Steven, for their support and encouragement to complete this book.

The expert reviewers who kindly consented to read and comment upon the various chapters are listed below. Many of their comments and suggestions led to improvements in the chapters but the final decision concerning content lay with the authors and editors. Any errors or inaccuracies are our responsibility.

I. F. Tannock
R. P. Hill

EXPERT REVIEWERS

S. Bacchetti	R. J. M. Fry	A. Marks	S. Rockwell
B. H. Barber	A. Fuks	M. J. Mastrangelo	D. S. R. Sarma
J. C. Barrett	F. L. Graham	G. E. McKeown–Eyssen	D. W. Siemann
S. Benchimol	G. H. Heppner	A. B. Miller	G. G. Steel
A. Bernstein	F. W. Hetzel	R. T. Mulcahy	T. C. Stephens
P. E. Branton	R. S. Kerbel	D. Osoba	J. R. Stewart
G. P. Browman	I. G. Kerr	M. G. Pallavicini	R. M. Sutherland
N. Bruchovsky	A. G. Knudson	J. L. Pater	S. R. Tannenbaum
J. M. Collins	J. E. Kudlow	A. J. Pawson	J. M. Trent
W. Duncan	V. Ling	B. H. Robinson	L. Weiss
H. A. Fritsche			G. F. Whitmore

1

Introduction: Cancer as a Cellular Disease

Richard P. Hill and Ian F. Tannock

1.1 HISTORICAL PERSPECTIVE

Malignant tumors have been described in pictures or writings from many ancient civilizations, including those of Asia, South America and Egypt. Bone cancers (osteosarcomas) have been diagnosed in Egyptian mummies. Cancer also occurs in all known species of higher animals.

Early cultures attributed the cause of cancer to various gods, and this belief was held generally until the Middle Ages. Hippocrates, however, described cancer as an imbalance between the black humor (from the spleen) and the other three bodily humors: blood, phlegm and bile.. Although incorrect, the theory was the first (~400 BC) to attribute the origin of cancer to natural causes. The suggestion that cancer might be an inherited or environmental disease appeared later: writings from the Middle Ages made reference to "cancer houses," "cancer families," and "cancer villages" which were shunned at all costs.

One of the first scientific enquiries into the cause of cancer dates from 1775 when Sir Percival Pott, an English physician, carried out what would now be described as an epidemiological study. At that time young boys were used as chimney sweeps in London, since they were small enough to climb the chimneys. Pott observed that young men in their twenties who had been chimney sweeps as boys had a high rate of death due to cancer of the scrotum. He suggested that the causative agent might be chimney soot (now known to be the tar) and recommended frequent washing, and changing of clothing that trapped the soot, to reduce exposure to the "carcinogen." Pott's study not only

identified a putative carcinogenic agent but also demonstrated that a cancer may develop many years after exposure to the causative agent, ie, that there can be an extended latent period.

Pott's deductions about the origin of scrotal cancer in chimney sweeps were made with little knowledge of the biological properties of tumors. The recognition that the growth of cancer results from a disordered proliferation of cells followed the development of the microscope. Microscopic examination of tumors allowed Virchow, the eminent 19th century pathologist, to declare that "every cell is born from another cell." Thus cancer was established as a cellular disease, and most of the research into its causation, biological properties and treatment is based on this underlying concept.

1.2 CANCER CAUSATION

Epidemiological studies have established associations between a number of environmental factors and the incidences of different types of cancer. Some of these associations are very strong (eg, smoking and lung cancer) and almost certainly represent cause-and-effect relationships. Doll and Peto (1981) have estimated that about 35% of cancer incidence in the United States may be due to dietary factors and about 30% due to smoking. From these epidemiological studies has come the recognition that many types of cancer are potentially preventable.

The most direct evidence for the carcinogenicity of environmental factors is an increase in cancer incidence in animals exposed to these factors. Such exposure has

1

shown that a variety of different and seemingly unrelated factors can cause cancer. They include viruses, a wide variety of chemicals, and both ionizing and ultraviolet radiation. Most of these agents share another important biological property: they can cause damage to or alteration of the DNA in cells. This common property suggests that DNA is the essential target of all carcinogenic agents, and that cancer arises as a result of changes in cellular DNA.

Further evidence to support this concept is (a) the existence of some (rare) forms of cancer whose incidence is directly dependent on hereditary factors; (b) a high incidence of cancer in individuals who have an inherited deficiency in their ability to repair lesions in DNA; (c) the incidence of several well-defined chromosomal changes in the cells of specific types of cancer; and (d) the existence of a number of genes ("oncogenes") which can transform normal cells into cancer cells.

The genetic analysis of cancer cells is advancing rapidly at the present time due to the recent development of techniques which allow study of the base sequence of DNA and the cloning of genes. These techniques have shown that normal mammalian cells contain genes ("proto-oncogenes") which are similar in base sequence to the transforming genes ("oncogenes") that are carried by some tumor viruses. One or more of these proto-oncogenes may be altered in malignant cells. The introduction of such altered genes into cells of immortalised normal cell lines may induce transformation of the cells to a malignant state. Some types of chromosomal rearrangement, such as the translocation which leads to the Philadelphia chromosome in cells of chronic myelogeneous leukemia, have been shown to involve proto-oncogenes, with resultant changes in the protein products of these genes. In hereditary tumors such as Wilms' tumor or retinoblastoma, there is a strong association with deletion of a specific cellular gene (not associated with any known viral oncogene), suggesting loss of important genetic information in these cancer cells.

All of these observations have helped to identify specific genes which appear to be involved in the causation of different types of cancer. Despite the above observations, however, specific genetic lesion(s) have not been identified in most spontaneous cancers, and the actual role of oncogenes in the causation of such cancers remains an area of hypothesis and speculation. The identification of genetic changes in malignant cells, and of the role that the protein products of involved genes play in cancer causation, is a central focus of current cancer research.

The normal development and growth of any multicellular organism requires controlled interactions between cells in the organism. The growth of a cancer demonstrates the failure of such control mechanisms. This could occur because the cancer cell does not respond to the control signals, possibly because of damage to its DNA or to the presence of the products of oncogenes. Alternatively, it may be the homeostatic control mechanisms themselves which are disturbed or inappropriate. An example of how different homeostatic control mechanisms can influence cancer growth is provided by the events that can occur following the transplantation of cancer (teratocarcinoma) cells which arise in mouse testis into the blastocyst of a normal mouse embryo (Mintz and Fleischman, 1981). Such transplantation may result in the development of an apparently normal mouse, whose tissues contain cells derived from both the normal embryo and the cancer cells.

Induction of hormonal changes in animals can also lead to the development of tumors which will often regress when normal hormone balance is restored. Similarly, tumors induced by the insertion of inert plastic sheets into connective tissue may regress if the sheets are removed. Persistence of the disturbed environment, however, leads to progressive alterations which transform the initial response into irreversible cancer growth. Many of the alterations observed in cancer cells might represent a response to an altered environment in the tissue and/or arise during such a process of progression.

1.3 CANCER BIOLOGY

Most normal cells are differentiated, a term that indicates that they have developed specific morphology and function. During the process of differentiation, normal cells tend to lose their ability to proliferate, but many tissues of the body undergo a process of renewal in which the loss of mature cells is replaced by proliferation of less mature precursor cells (in renewal tissues, known as stem cells), followed by differentiation of their progeny. Most cancers probably originate from these precursor cells.

There is evidence that cancers may arise from the transformation of a single precursor cell, which proliferates to form a clone, since all of the cells in the tumor may share some particular feature(s) of the original precursor cell. Despite the presence of such clonal markers the cells in the clone are not necessarily identical; indeed, the cells in most tumors are quite heterogeneous with respect to their properties, suggesting that cancer cells continually modify their properties during the growth of the tumor.

In a cancer, cell proliferation usually continues independent of a requirement for new cells, and differentiation is impaired. Considerable differentiation may still occur in a cancer, however, and this usually allows the pathologist to recognize the tissue of origin. Thus an adenocarcinoma arises from glandular epithelium (*adeno* = gland, *carcinoma* = tumor in tissue of epidermal origin) and an osteosarcoma arises from bone (*osteo* = bone, *sarcoma* = tumor in tissue of mesenchymal origin). The word "anaplastic" is used to describe a tumor with little or no evidence of differentiation.

The ability of cancer cells to invade other tissues and to spread to other parts of the body where they can generate new tumors (metastases) is their major property that leads to death of the host. The mechanisms involved in this process of metastasis are poorly understood, but recent research suggests that specific cellular properties, possibly expressed by only a small proportion of the cells in most tumors, are involved in the formation of metastases. Similarly, it has been found that a small proportion of cells in tumors may develop resistance to one or more drugs during growth of the tumor. An active area of research is the elucidation of changes in the expression of genes associated with features such as drug resistance or metastasis.

From the earliest studies of the biology of cancer, investigators have tried to find properties of cancer cells (known as their "phenotype") that are *consistently* different from properties of normal cells. This has been a daunting task where the recurring theme has been failure to uphold claims for the specificity of any given property. An early example was the hypothesis of Warburg (1930) that cancer cells have a change in their metabolism, leading to an increased rate of glycolysis. This and many other phenotypic changes that were thought to characterize cancer cells were instead simply a function of the increased cellular proliferation.

The cells in some spontaneous tumors, including those in man, have surface antigens that can be identified by monoclonal antibodies, and which are not found in the corresponding normal tissue. Such antigens are often found in fetal tissue and appear to relate to the degree of cellular differentiation. Their specificity may be sufficient, however, to allow improvements in cancer diagnosis and imaging through the use of radio-labeled monoclonal antibodies, and in rare instances might permit the design of specific therapy targeted against the tumor cells.

The many differences that have been observed between the properties of normal and cancer cells are not surprising when viewed in the light of the many types of genetic change that have been associated with cancer. It is possible that future research will discover some common links between these genetic changes, but at present, none of the differences has been shown to be unique.

1.4 CANCER TREATMENT

The absence of specific identifiable differences between normal and malignant cells is a major barrier that has limited the development of specific anticancer therapy. Treatment has had to rely on spatial separation of tumor and critical normal tissue (surgery or radiotherapy), or on minor and empirical differences in the responses of tumors and normal tissues to systemic treatments such as chemotherapy. Thus almost all types of cancer treatments cause significant damage to normal tissue; this is in marked contrast with the use of antibiotics to treat bacterial diseases such as pneumonia, where cures can be achieved with little or no toxicity.

Tumor cure requires that the treatment causes all of the tumor stem cells to lose the ability to generate progeny that can regrow the tumor. Thus the most important assay for cell "survival" after treatment tests the cell's ability to form a colony or clone of progeny (ie, a colony-forming or clonogenic assay). Cell survival, defined in this way, is often found to be exponentially related to radiation or drug dose over a wide range of doses. This observation implies that repeated identical courses of therapy kill a given fraction of the cells, rather than a given number. A clinically detectable tumor weighing 10 g may contain 10^{10} cells. Complete clinical remission (ie, tumor shrinkage such that there is no longer evident tumor by physical examination or X-rays) is still consistent with a surviving fraction of as many as 10^8 cells ($\sim$0.1 g tumor). Thus a dose of radiation or drugs which causes complete remission may be much smaller than the dose required to produce cure.

If a cancer is diagnosed before metastasis has occurred, it is often curable by local treatment with surgery and/or radiotherapy. The choice of appropriate local treatment depends largely on the morbidity involved. Surgical removal of a tumor must include an adequate margin of normal tissue to allow for local invasive spread. Radiation treatment kills mammalian cells mainly by causing damage to DNA, but it is not specific for malignant cells. A major aim of research in experimental radiotherapy is thus to maximize the effect of radiation treatment on the tumor while minimizing the damage to the surrounding normal tissue. Current interest is focussed on drugs which can radiosensitize specific subpopulations of tumor cells and on modifying fractionated treatment schedules to reduce normal tissue damage.

Many localised treatments fail because of the growth of metastases that were present but undetected at the time of treatment. Systemic treatment with cytotoxic drugs is often the only treatment that may influence all sites of metastatic disease. At tolerated doses, such treatment can be highly effective for certain types of cancer (eg, lymphomas and testicular cancer), but it is rarely effective for many of the common types of solid tumors (eg, colo-rectal or lung carcinoma). A major limitation to the success of drug treatment is the presence in the tumor of drug-resistant cells which convey either initial resistance to treatment, or subsequent resistance after the tumor has initially responded. There is considerable research interest in understanding the mechanisms involved in drug resistance; this research may lead to the design of new and better drugs or to the use of available drugs in more effective combinations.

Alternative approaches to cancer treatment include the use of hormones, which may be effective in inducing remission, but not cure, of some cancers that arise in hormone-sensitive tissues such as breast and prostate. Hyperthermia is being investigated as an alternative or auxiliary treatment which can be combined with ionizing radiation or chemotherapy, but it remains unclear whether heat can provide selective toxicity to tumor cells. Various approaches to immunotherapy have been tried clinically but classical approaches involving attempted immunization have met with minimal success. The development of monoclonal antibodies and of a number of agents which can stimulate specific components of the immune response (eg interferons, interleukins, tumor necrosis factor) has rekindled hopes for specific killing of tumor cells via immune-mediated effects.

All new treatments depend on therapeutic trials to investigate their efficacies in man. Erroneous conclusions can be drawn if clinical trials are poorly designed or performed, and several types of bias can make it difficult to interpret the results. The scientific method must be applied carefully in the design of such trials, and should allow for better evaluation of new treatments.

Cancer is a progressive disease which is responsible for a high proportion of all deaths. Our current understanding of the basic biological processes underlying the development, growth and treatment of cancer is explored in the subsequent chapters.

REFERENCES

Doll R, Peto R: The causes of cancer: quantitative estimates of avoidable risks of cancer in the United States today. *J Natl Cancer Inst* 1981; 66:1191–1308.
Mintz B, Fleischman RA: Teratocarcinomas and other neoplasms as developmental defects in gene expression. *Adv Canc Res* 1981; 34:211–278.
Warburg O: *The Metabolism of Tumours.* F. Dickens (trans). London, Arnold Constable, 1930.

PART 1

CANCER CAUSATION

2

The Epidemiology of Cancer: Principles and Methods

Norman F. Boyd

2.1 INTRODUCTION

2.1.1 GENERAL PRINCIPLES

Epidemiology seeks to explain the distribution of disease. The subject is concerned with explaining, in Acheson's phrase, why "this patient, developed this disease, at this time," as well as with explaining why different populations of individuals are at different risks for different diseases. The subject is therefore of concern to clinicians, clinical researchers, and laboratory scientists.

Clinicians must advise patients about any risk of cancer that is associated with their lifestyle, and with medical procedures or treatments. Thus, they need to understand how data describing such risks are generated, to be able to assess the quantitative importance of the risks described, and to be able to appraise critically the credibility of reports of cancer risk.

Cancer epidemiologists seek ultimately to identify the causes of cancer and thus share their goal with clinical researchers and laboratory scientists. Epidemiological descriptions of the distribution of cancer, and the identification of groups of individuals at different risks for the development of cancer, provide basic information that is required to test hypotheses concerning the causes of cancer.

Laboratory and clinical science, by developing improved methods of measuring exposure to potential causes of cancer, or the biological consequences of such exposure, can also contribute substantially to the epidemiological study of disease. Some of the most striking examples of recent progress in the understanding of the causes of cancer have come from such collaborative work (see, for example, section 3.2).

Other chapters in this volume give detailed accounts of specific etiological associations, and no attempt will be made in this chapter to provide a comprehensive description of the epidemiology of cancer. Rather, the general principles used in the epidemiological study of cancer will be described. Examples of the epidemiology of selected cancers will be cited to illustrate these general principles or particular issues in methodology.

Table 2.1. Measures of Disease Frequency

Measure	Definition	Examples
Prevalence	The number of cases of a disorder present in a defined population at a particular *point* in time.	Number of women with breast cancer in Ontario today.
		Number of undiagnosed cancers found at autopsy.
		Number of smokers in the population.
Incidence	The number of *new* cases of a disorder developing in a defined population over a defined *period* of time.	Number of women who develop breast cancer in Ontario each year.
		Number of individuals dying of cancer each year.
		Annual death rate among smokers.

Relationship: Prevalence α incidence $\times$ duration of illness.

2.1.2 FREQUENCY OF CANCER

The general approach taken by epidemiologists to the study of cancer etiology is to first describe the frequency of cancer in terms of its geographical distribution (place), the age and sex characteristics of the affected individuals (person), and any temporal associations such as changes in frequency of disease that occur over time. The basic attributes of place, person and time provide a general description of the manner in which the frequency of specific cancers varies between populations, or between groups within populations, and indicate whether these differences are stable or changing with time.

Incidence and prevalence are the principal measures of disease frequency used in epidemiology (Table 2.1). *Incidence* is defined as the frequency of new events, such as deaths or the diagnosis of disease, occurring in a defined population during a specified period of time. *Prevalence* is defined as the frequency of disease in a defined population at a particular point in time.

An incidence rate has three components: (a) the population who form the denominator of the rate, (b) the interval of time over which the population is followed, and (c) the number of individuals who experience the event of interest, who form the numerator of the rate.

A prevalence rate has two components: (a) the population under study who form the denominator, and (b) the number of individuals with the attribute of interest who form the numerator.

Table 2.1 shows some examples of these different rates. As the table shows, the numerator in prevalence rates may refer to present attributes, such as the number of patients with leukemia who are in a hospital on a particular day, or to past attributes such as the number of patients with breast cancer who were previously exposed to ionising radiation. Some useful sources of information about the distribution of cancer are listed in Table 2.2.

Table 2.2. Sources of Information about the Distribution of Cancer

1. Segi M, Kurihara M: *Cancer Mortality for Selected Sites in 24 Countries. No 6.* Japan Cancer Society, 1972.

   A comparison of cancer mortality in several European, North and South American countries, Japan and New Zealand.

2. Waterhouse J, Muir C, Shanmugarathnam K, Powell J: *Cancer Incidence in 5 Continents.* IARC Scientific Publications, 1982.

   Cancer incidence for several countries, according to age. Attempts to assess the quality of data in terms of the comparability of methods of coding and registration in the countries providing information.

3. *Cancer Surveillance, Epidemiology, and End Results Reporting Program Descriptions and Data Format. National Cancer Institute, Biometry Branch, Bethesda, MD. NCI Monograph No 57.* US Dept of Health and Human Resources, Public Health Service, National Institutes of Health.

   Age-, sex- and race-specific incidence and mortality rates for cancer from population-based cancer registries that include some unique population subgroups.

4. *Statistics Canada, Cancer in Canada.* Ottawa, Supply and Services, 1970 on.

   Cancer incidence according to site, age, sex, and method of diagnosis, reported by provincial cancer registries (does not include Ontario). Published annually.

2.2 METHODS OF EPIDEMIOLOGICAL INVESTIGATION

2.2.1 GENERATION OF HYPOTHESES ABOUT CANCER CAUSATION

Populations or groups identified by descriptive data as being at different risks for the development of specific cancers can be examined for differences in their exposures to agents suspected of causing cancer. For many common cancers these comparisons of high- and low-risk populations involve two scientifically distinct phases.

The first of these steps involves the generation of hypotheses about cancer etiology. Ideas about the causes of cancer may come from several sources. Alert clinical observers have frequently been the first to draw attention to etiological associations. Examples include scrotal cancer, which Sir Percival Pott noted to be common in chimney sweeps, breast cancer, which was observed to be common among nuns by Ramazzini in 1713, and the more recently described associations of smoking and lung cancer, of nasopharyngeal cancer with the manufacture of wood furniture, and of maternal exposure to the drug diethylstilbestrol and clear-cell carcinoma of the vagina in offspring.

Other hypotheses may be developed from epidemiological data collected for purely descriptive purposes. Thus, for example, descriptions of the geographic distribution of malignant melanoma led to the observation that the frequency of the disease was associated with latitude, and to the hypothesis that the disease might be caused by exposure to the ultraviolet components of sunlight (section 2.3.4).

For many types of cancer there is often insufficient information to formulate prior hypotheses about causative factors, and epidemiological studies may be required to generate leads to further investigations. In such studies, populations or groups at high and low risk for a particular cancer may be contrasted, in the first instance, for as many attributes as it is feasible to examine. In analyzing the collected data these attributes will be compared in a search for differences between the groups that might be causally related to their different risks for developing cancer. Such exercises, while necessary and important in the preliminary search for the causes of cancer, can do no more than generate hypotheses. They do not distinguish between causative factors, and factors which are merely associated with the development of cancer. Hypotheses about the causes of cancer, generated by one or more of these several methods, need to be tested formally before any firm conclusions can be drawn about their etiological significance.

The epidemiological approach to the study of the causes of cancer is based upon a comparison of cancer risks. The risk of cancer in individuals exposed to some factor suspected of causing (or protecting against) cancer is compared to the risk of cancer in individuals not so exposed. These two risks are then compared to determine the extent, if any, to which exposure to the suspect factor has increased the risk of disease.

The most important methods available for assembling the information required to make these comparisons of risk are cohort and case-control studies. The design of such studies and their major variants will be described in the sections that follow.

2.2.2 COHORT STUDIES

The general design of cohort studies is to identify a defined population of individuals who have been exposed to a factor suspected of increasing or decreasing the risk of cancer, and a population not so exposed, and to follow both groups forward in time and observe them for the development of cancer. After some suitable interval of time, sufficient for a number of cancers to have developed, the incidence of cancer in the exposed is then compared to the incidence in the nonexposed (Fig 2.1). The major types of cohort studies are experimental trials and observational studies.

Experimental trials provide the strongest evidence available about etiological relationships, but they can be applied only rarely in cancer epidemiology. They have the advantage that the subjects taking part in the trial can be selected according to specified criteria, and they can be characterized according to any features that influence their risk for developing the cancer of interest. The exposure that is under investigation can be allocated randomly and the subjects can then be followed at predetermined intervals and examined for the devel-

INITIAL CLASSIFICATION	SUBSEQUENT CLASSIFICATION	
	DISEASED	NONDISEASED
EXPOSED	A	B
NON-EXPOSED	C	D

RISK OF DISEASE WITH EXPOSURE = A/A+B

RISK OF DISEASE WITH NON-EXPOSURE = C/C+D

RELATIVE RISK OF EXPOSURE = A/A+B ÷ C/C+D

Figure 2.1. The general design of cohort studies. A population is identified which has been exposed to a factor suspected of increasing or decreasing the incidence of cancer. This population, and controls without such exposure, are followed and observed for the development of cancer.

opment of cancer. Ethical considerations limit the use of experimental trials to the investigation of exposures that may be protective against cancer, and some trials are now either underway or planned to examine the influence of dietary modification, vitamin supplements, and other possible means of reducing cancer risk.

Observational cohort studies differ from experimental trials in that the allocation of the exposure under investigation is not in the control of the investigator. Genetic influences, occupational exposures, habits like cigarette smoking, medical treatments, and exposure to atomic explosions are among the many types of exposures that have been investigated by this type of study.

In observational cohort studies the investigator can specify and apply criteria for the inclusion of subjects in the cohort and in the control, nonexposed population; he or she can characterize baseline risk factors for the development of the disease of interest, and can arrange for regular surveillance for the detection and enumeration of cancers. However, inability to control the allocation of exposure means that the results of observational cohort studies are often open to more than one interpretation. Exposure to many potential causes of cancer, such as occupation, cigarette smoking, and dietary practices, is self-selected. The finding of an association between these exposures and cancer risk may therefore mean either that these exposures are causally related to the risk of cancer or alternatively, that some other attribute of the individual determined both the decision to select exposure and independently influenced the risk of cancer. For example, it was at one time argued that a genetic factor influenced both the risk of lung cancer and the decision to smoke cigarettes. Studies in identical twins, discordant for smoking habits, have now shown this suggestion to be incorrect and that smoking and not genetic makeup is the major determinant of lung cancer risk, but the original observational cohort data linking cigarette smoking and risk of lung cancer were open to both interpretations.

Many studies that are reported as cohorts were not planned as such, but were assembled in retrospect. Such an approach is possible if a population that had been exposed to a potential cause of cancer can be defined, some time has elapsed after exposure, and the development of cancer is observed in some subjects. Studies of this type have been used to examine such questions as the risk of breast cancer in women who earlier had been biopsied for benign breast disease, the risk of cancer among former shipyard workers, and the risk of cancer after exposure to diethylstilbestrol during pregnancy. In all of these examples it was possible for the investigators to assemble a defined population in retrospect, and to then determine their subsequent inci-

dence of cancer. It is not possible with this approach to arrange for the population to be examined with a predetermined frequency, as can be done in experimental trials or prospective observational cohort studies. For those diseases where investigation is required to detect the presence of disease this is a major shortcoming. However, many types of cancer can be expected to declare their presence even when not sought deliberately, and in these circumstances the retrospective approach to cohort studies may give valid estimates of risk.

The data collected in a cohort study comprise a cancer incidence rate, calculated for the exposed and for the nonexposed. The contribution of exposure to cancer risk is examined by calculating the ratio of these rates, which is called the relative risk (Fig 2.1). Statistical tests are then used to calculate the probability of determining the relative risks observed if exposure were in reality irrelevant to risk (Anderson et al, 1980).

The major advantage of cohort studies is that they address directly the etiological sequence of cause preceding effect that is being investigated. When carried out prospectively they also allow the characterization of baseline risk for cancer and the possibility of regular surveillance of the population for the development of cancer. However, even the most common human cancers are still relatively infrequent events and cohort studies often need very large numbers of subjects in order to have a good chance of finding an increase in risk associated with a particular exposure. Table 2.3 shows the required number of subjects according to the incidence of cancer in the nonexposed and the magnitude of the relative risk that is being sought. Thus if cancer occurred at a rate of 1/10,000 in the nonexposed, and an investigator wishes to be able to detect or rule out a tripling of risk (ie, a relative risk of 3) with reasonable certainty, he would need to assemble 70,000 individuals in the exposed group and an equal number in the nonexposed. These requirements, as well as other considerations, have led to the development of the

Table 2.3. Sample Sizes Required to Investigate Causes of Cancer in Cohort Studies*

Relative Risk	1 per 10,000	1 per 1,000	1 per 500	1 per 100
2	100,000	10,000	5000	1000
3	70,000	7000	3500	700
4	40,000	4000	2000	400
5	25,000	2500	1250	250
10	10,000	1000	500	100

Note: Adapted from Lilienfeld and Lilienfeld, 1980.

*Cohort studies require large numbers of subjects to evaluate possible causes of disease. The number of patients required to detect various levels of relative risk is indicated for given rates of incidence in the control group, during the period of study.

more economical case-control study as a means of investigating etiological relationships.

2.2.3 CASE-CONTROL STUDIES

Whereas cohort studies follow individuals from exposure to the development of disease, case-control studies begin with individuals who either have disease (cases) or do not have disease (controls) and then assess previous exposure (Fig 2.2). Cases may be drawn from several sources including hospital diagnostic indices, cancer registry files or from the files of one or more physicians. Controls may also be selected from hospitals, outpatient facilities, or from the general population using random-sampling techniques. The selection of cases and appropriate controls presents the major problem in case-control studies since there are many ways of introducing bias into the assessment of the relationship between exposure and disease (see section 2.2.5). The measurement of exposure in case-control studies depends on the type of information that is sought. The most frequent method of obtaining information about exposure in case-control studies is by use of a questionnaire to assess factors such as occupational history or cigarette smoking. Other factors, such as prior exposure to viruses or the influence of some aspect of the individual's phenotype on disease risk, may be assessed by blood tests or by direct examination.

Relative risk cannot be calculated directly in case-control studies, but it can be approximated by a measure called the odds ratio. The relationship between the relative risk and the odds ratio is shown in Figure 2.3. Figure 2.3a shows the results of a hypothetical cohort study in which the incidence of disease has been compared in 5000 exposed and 5000 nonexposed subjects. The relative risk of exposure as well as the odds of exposure in diseased and nondiseased individuals have been calculated. Figure 2.3b shows the result of a hypothetical case-control study in which exposure was compared in cases and randomly selected controls drawn from the cohort study illustrated above it. As can be seen in Figure 2.3a, in the cohort study the ratio of the odds of disease in the exposed and nonexposed (the relative risk), and the ratio of the odds of exposure in the diseased and nondiseased, are virtually identical. The reason for this similarity in the ratios of two dissimilar pairs of rates lies in their algebraic relationship which is given in Figure 2.3c. This relationship is valid if the disease is uncommon in the population, something that is true of even the most common human cancers. In addition, the subjects in the case-control study must be selected in such a way that no distortion is introduced into the relationship between disease status and exposure; thus sampling must be free of bias in that the

SUBSEQUENT CLASSIFICATION	INITIAL CLASSIFICATION	
	DISEASED (CASES)	NONDISEASED (CONTROLS)
EXPOSED	A	B
NONEXPOSED	C	D
ODDS OF EXPOSURE IN CASES	: A/C	
ODDS OF EXPOSURE IN CONTROLS	: B/D	
ODDS RATIO	: AD/BC	

Figure 2.2. The general design of case-control studies. Individuals are identified who either have disease (cases) or do not have disease (controls). They are then assessed for previous exposure to an agent suspected of increasing or decreasing the incidence of cancer.

selection of cases and controls must not be influenced by their exposure status.

Case-control studies can be performed more quickly and involve fewer subjects to detect a given level of risk than cohort studies. Case-control studies may be used to investigate diseases that are rare or those that have a long interval between exposure and the development of cancer. However, exposure must often be measured by the recollection of the subjects and there are frequently no means available to check the accuracy of this information. Also, as discussed in section 2.2.5, there are many types of potential biases in the selection of subjects and in the measurement of exposure that are often easier to avoid, or to detect, in cohort than in case-control research. Despite these disadvantages, case-control studies are frequently the only feasible means of assessing, in human populations, the validity of new claims about cancer risk.

Some epidemiological designs may allow the advantages of both cohort and case-control studies. One such design is known as a case-control study within a cohort. In some circumstances, a cohort of individuals at risk for cancer may exist where information can be obtained which allows assessment of their exposure to some putative risk factor. An example is the influence of certain types of benign breast lesions on subsequent development of breast cancer. Thus a cohort is provided by women who have had breast biopsies for benign disease, but classification of their exposure status will be time consuming if complex histologic classification of the biopsied material is needed. A considerable saving in labor and expense can be realised if, rather than classifying all individuals at the start of the study period, the cohort is followed until some cancers have developed. Those subjects, and a group of controls from the original cohort who have not developed cancer, are then compared with respect to their initial histology.

a) HYPOTHETICAL COHORT STUDY

		DISEASED		ODDS OF DISEASE	RELATIVE RISK
		YES	NO		
EXPOSED	YES	40	4960	0.0081	
	NO	10	4990	0.0020	4.0
ODDS OF EXPOSURE		4	1.0		

b) HYPOTHETICAL CASE CONTROL STUDY
(A SAMPLE OF DISEASED AND NONDISEASED SUBJECTS TAKEN FROM THE COHORT IN (A)).

		DISEASED	
		YES	NO
EXPOSED	YES	40	50
	NO	10	50
ODDS OF EXPOSURE		4	1

c) ALGEBRAIC RELATIONSHIP OF RELATIVE RISK AND ODDS RATIO

		DISEASED		ODDS OF DISEASE	RELATIVE RISK
		YES	NO		
EXPOSED	YES	A	B	A/B	A/A+B
	NO	C	D	C/D	÷ C/C+D
ODDS OF EXPOSURE		A/C	B/D		

IF DISEASE IS UNCOMMON A AND C ARE SMALL AND: $A/B \simeq A/A+B$

AND $C/D \simeq C/C+D$

THEN THE RATIO OF ODDS OF DISEASE : $A/B \div C/D$ AND THE
RELATIVE RISK : $A/A+B \div C/C+D$ ARE THE SAME

Figure 2.3. Illustration of the algebraic relationship between the relative risk of developing disease in cohort studies and the odds ratio for exposure in case control studies (see text).

2.2.4 ERROR

In common with other forms of scientific enquiry, the results of epidemiologic studies can be distorted by features in their design. The common sources of distortion are error, bias and confounding, and an understanding of the origins and effects of these factors will help in the interpretation of epidemiologic data.

Errors may occur through the random misclassification of subjects, according to either exposure status or their disease status. Exposure status in either cohort or case-control studies is often determined by questioning subjects about events that took place many years earlier, and some inaccuracies in the classification of exposure are to be expected. Disease status, even when based upon histologic material, as is usually the case in cohort epidemiology, is also subject to error, and some

incorrectly classified diseased and nondiseased individuals may be included in a study. Preliminary testing and validation of questionnaires and the use of independent assessments of disease status are important parts of epidemiologic research. These procedures can do much to reduce error but are unlikely to eliminate it entirely.

The usual effect of methodological error upon the results of a study is to conceal, or reduce, the magnitude of true associations, rather than to give rise to associations that are spurious. For example, if questioning is unable to distinguish correctly between smokers and nonsmokers, or the customary methods of diagnosing lung cancer are so inefficient that large numbers of unidentified cases are present in the population, it is very unlikely that enquiry will reveal an association between smoking and lung cancer.

2.2.5 BIAS AND CONFOUNDING

Like error, bias also refers to the misclassification of subjects. It differs from error, however, in that the misclassification is systematic, whereas in error it is random. The importance of this distinction is that, while error is likely to conceal true associations, bias distorts the truth by giving rise to results that either systematically overestimate or underestimate associations. Bias can therefore create associations where none exist, or magnify or diminish associations that are genuine.

Studies must be designed in such a way that bias is either prevented, or if this is impossible, that checks are introduced to determine whether bias has occurred and to estimate the influence of bias on the result obtained. A full discussion of the problem is beyond the scope of this chapter and details should be sought in Sackett (1979).

The most frequent causes of bias are those that affect the selection of subjects and the measurement of exposure. Types of bias that may influence the selection of subjects include those that result in the referral of diseased individuals with atypical characteristics to the center performing the research; those that influence the performance of diagnostic tests with the result that exposed individuals are more frequently tested and thus have disease more frequently detected than the nonexposed; and those that arise from the special characteristics of volunteers.

Admission rate bias. This bias affects individuals (either cases or controls) drawn from hospital populations and arises from the differential rates of admission that may apply to those with cancer who were exposed to a putative risk factor, as opposed to those with cancer who had no such exposure. The result of the bias is that subjects with cancer who are in hospital may have a higher (or lower) frequency of exposure than subjects with the same disease who are not in hospital. Figure 2.4 illustrates this source of bias for some hypothetical data. The example assumes that a defined population, shown in section *a* of the figure, contains 1000 individuals with bladder cancer, and 1000 individuals with diseases other than bladder cancer. Further, it assumes that 10% of each of these two groups regularly takes saccharin.

Assume now that a study of the association between bladder cancer and saccharin is to be carried out in the hospital that serves this population, and that the rates of admission to hospital shown in section *b* of Figure 2.4 apply to individuals in the population. Patients may be admitted to hospital from each of the four groups specified in section *a* of Figure 2.4 (bladder cancer present, other disease present, saccharin user, saccharin nonuser). The use of an agent like saccharin could be a cause of hospitalization because of the diseases for which it is prescribed, such as diabetes or obesity and associated conditions. The key point about the admission rates shown in the table is that they differ for these four states.

Knowing these rates of admission we can calculate the probability that an individual in any of the four cells in Figure 2.4 will enter the hospital. The probability (P) that someone who both has bladder cancer and takes saccharin will enter hospital is $P = P$ (Bladder cancer causes admission) + P (Bladder cancer does not cause admission but saccharin taking causes admission) = $(0.2) + (1 - 0.2) (0.5) = (0.2) + (0.4) = 0.6$. The probability of admission for someone with a disease other than bladder cancer, who takes saccharin, is P (other disease causes admission) + P (other disease does not cause admission, but saccharin use is associated with admission) = $(0.8) + (1 - 0.8) (0.5) = 0.9$. For the two cells not associated with saccharin use the

HYPOTHETICAL ILLUSTRATION OF ADMISSION RATE BIAS

a) GENERAL POPULATION

		BLADDER CANCER	OTHER DISEASE
SACCHARIN	USER	100	100
	NONUSER	900	900
	% TAKING SACCHARIN	10%	10%

b) ADMISSION RATES

BLADDER CANCER	0.2
OTHER DISEASE	0.8
SACCHARIN USE	0.5

c) PROBABILITY OF ADMISSION

		BLADDER CANCER	OTHER DISEASE
SACCHARIN	USER	100 (0.6)	100 (0.9)
	NONUSER	900 (0.2)	900 (0.8)

d) HOSPITAL POPULATION

		BLADDER CANCER	OTHER DISEASE
SACCHARIN	USER	60	90
	NONUSER	180	720
	% TAKING SACCHARIN	25%	11%

Figure 2.4. Hypothetical illustration of admission rate bias (see text). *a*, 1000 patients with bladder cancer and 1000 patients with other disease are selected from the general population. Saccharin use in both groups is 10%. *b*, The relative rates of hospital admission among the subgroups of patients. *c*, Calculation of the probability of hospital admission of the various subgroups. *d*, Numbers of patients who are in hospital and might form the subjects of a hospital-based case-control study. In this example admission-rate bias has led to a spurious association between saccharin use and bladder cancer.

probabilities of admission are 0.2 and 0.8 respectively, for those with bladder cancer and other diseases.

The composition of the group observed in hospital can then be determined as shown in section *d* of Figure 2.4. We now find, in contrast to the situation observed in the population, that saccharin use is associated with bladder cancer.

These data are of course hypothetical, but the existence of admission biases of the type illustrated here have been demonstrated empirically (Roberts et al, 1978), and may affect any hospital-based etiologic study.

Prevalence-incidence bias. This refers to distortion in the estimation of exposure that would arise if exposure and survival after diagnosis were related. Exposure would be either over- or underrepresented, according to its effect upon survival, in a group of surviving patients with disease. Neyman first recognized this possible source of bias and raised it as a possible explanation for the association observed between smoking and lung cancer. He reasoned that if smokers with lung cancer had a better survival after diagnosis than did nonsmokers with the same disease, then smokers would be overrepresented in the population of subjects with lung cancer, giving rise to an apparent association between smoking and the disease. However, studies of patients with newly diagnosed lung cancer have shown that the association with smoking persists, and is thus not explained by the better survival of smokers. The possibility that exposure might influence survival is nonetheless important and is the reason that newly diagnosed (ie, incident) cases are selected for case-control studies of disease etiology (eg, Sackett, 1979).

Detection bias. Some exposures may themselves give rise to clinical symptoms or signs that resemble those of cancer, and may thus cause clinicians to initiate a search for cancer. Examples include drugs that can cause lymph node enlargements, such as phenytoin, and drugs like stilbestrol that can cause endometrial bleeding. It has been suggested that the association found between estrogens and endometrial cancer arises because estrogens can cause endometrial bleeding which then causes occult cancers to be detected. Although there is at present no general agreement on whether detection bias is an important contributor to the association observed between estrogens and endometrial cancer, it is likely to be an important potential source of bias for those diseases that regularly have a long subclinical course and may escape detection in the absence of a diagnostic search.

Other types of bias that may distort the assessment of exposure include those of recall (diseased subjects are more likely to think about and recall previous exposure than nondiseased controls). A special case of this phenomenon is bias in information about illnesses in other family members: family members who are themselves diseased are more likely to know about other disease in other members of the family than are those who are not diseased.

When present behavior, such as eating habits, rather than past exposure is the subject of investigation, the act of carrying out a study may itself alter the behavior of the subjects of the study in a way that systematically changes results. Thus subjects who are recruited as controls in a cohort study of the influence of dietary fat on breast cancer may decrease their fat intake even though they have been asked to continue their usual diet.

Confounding. Confounding, like bias, can either give rise to spurious associations or mask associations that are real. A confounding variable must satisfy two criteria: (a) it must itself be related to risk for the disease under study and (b) it must be associated with the exposure of interest (but not be a consequence of exposure).

One example of a confounding variable is ingestion of alcohol, when the risk of oropharyngeal cancer following exposure to cigarettes is under investigation. Alcohol ingestion, as well as smoking, is a risk factor for this disease. In addition, smokers are more likely to ingest alcohol than nonsmokers. Thus confounding leads to uncertainty as to how much risk is due directly to smoking, and how much is attributable to associated alcohol use. A second example might be the number of pregnancies in the investigation of the influence of age at first pregnancy on risk of breast cancer. Both a lower age at first pregnancy and a high number of pregnancies are associated with a lower incidence of breast cancer. Yet women who have more pregnancies are likely to have the first of them at a younger age.

Confounding can be dealt with either in the design or in the analysis of a study. Selection of matched cases and controls that are alike with respect to the confounder ensures that any difference between them in the exposure of interest is not due to confounding. However, matching may cause an increase in both the cost and the difficulty in doing the study and prevents an examination of the relationship between the confounder and the disease. In analysis, confounding can be examined by assessing the frequency of exposure among cases and controls, among those with and without the potential confounding variable.

2.2.6 CRITERIA FOR INFERRING THAT EPIDEMIOLOGICAL ASSOCIATIONS ARE CAUSATIVE

Epidemiologic research can often show no more than an association between certain exposures and the risk of cancer, but because not all associations are causal, there is a need for guidelines that will help to identify exposures that are causally related to disease. The guidelines given below are those proposed by Bradford Hill (1971) and are in descending order of importance.

Evidence from true experiments in humans. Studies in which humans are assigned randomly to receive or not to receive a putative cause of cancer and are then followed and observed for the development of cancer would provide the strongest evidence of cause, but for ethical reasons cannot be performed. Randomized studies of potential protective factors are feasible and trials on the role of vitamins and other dietary factors are likely to provide the most convincing epidemiological evidence available on the effect of these agents on cancer risk.

Strength of association. The stronger an association between an exposure and risk of cancer the less likely is it to be due to chance, error, or bias. This does not mean that chance and bias cannot give rise to spurious associations that are strong, but simply that they are more likely to give rise to weak associations. The quantitative magnitude of a relative risk or odds ratio is thus a rough guide to the probability that the observed relationship is causal.

Consistency. Associations between an exposure and cancer that are demonstrated repeatedly, by different investigators using different research methods, are more likely to be causal than those where different methods have generated different results. However, the same result obtained repeatedly from one research method does not necessarily strengthen it, since the same mistake may occur repeatedly.

Temporal association. For an association to be causal the exposure must precede the disease. This rather obvious requirement is always met in cohort studies by virtue of their design, but is often difficult to establish in case-control studies. Increasing risk with increasing duration of exposure, however, can be examined in case-control studies (see, for example, the data on use of oral contraceptives and hepatocellular adenoma shown in Table 2.4).

Gradient of risk. Exposure to possible causes of cancer is seldom an all-or-none phenomenon, and the incidence of cancer can usually be related to the level of exposure. Finding a relationship between increasing level of exposure and increasing risk strengthens a causal interpretation (see, for example, the association between smoking and risk of lung cancer discussed in section 2.3.4).

Biological sense. Associations between exposure and disease that agree with present knowledge about the reaction of cells and tissues to the exposure make it more plausible that the association is causal. Thus, the results of animal experiments showing that estrogen induces hyperplasia, and on continued exposure carcinoma in situ and eventually invasive cancer of the endometrium, make it more likely that the association between estrogen use and endometrial cancer in humans is causal.

The dependence of this criterion upon the present state of knowledge means that, while the existence of supporting biological information adds to the credibility of causal arguments, the absence of such support may arise from the incomplete state of available information and does not necessarily detract from causal interpretations. This limitation is illustrated by the difficulties that have been experienced in demonstrating in the laboratory the teratogenic effects of thalidomide and the carcinogenic effects of cigarette smoke, both exposures whose causal association with human disease has been amply demonstrated.

Epidemiological sense. The existence of supporting epidemiological evidence on the distribution of the

Table 2.4. Dose Response in Cancer Etiology: Oral Contraceptives and Hepatocellular Adenoma*

Months of OC** Use	Cases	Controls	RR†
0–12	7	121	1.0
13–36	11	49	3.9
37–60	20	23	15.0
61–84	21	20	18.1
≥85	20	7	49.3
Total	79	220	

Note: Adapted from Rooks et al, 1979.

*The case-control study shows that increasing duration of use of oral contraceptives is associated with increasing risk of hepatocellular adenoma.

**OC = Oral contraceptives.

†RR = Relative risk of hepatocellular adenoma.

causes of disease also makes causal interpretations of associations more likely to be correct. The observed association between obesity and endometrial cancer thus gains credibility because of the associations of obesity with diabetes and hypertension, both disorders that are also associated with endometrial cancer.

Specificity. An association between a single type of exposure and one disease may make it easier to infer causality. This only contributes to causal reasoning when it is present, as for example in the association between maternal exposure to diethylstilbestrol and clear-cell carcinoma of the vagina in offspring. The absence of specificity is of no importance at all, as is shown by the multitude of diseases that have now been found to be associated with cigarette smoking, and the growing number of disorders that are associated with nutritional factors.

2.3 DESCRIPTIVE EPIDEMIOLOGY OF HUMAN CANCER

2.3.1 GEOGRAPHICAL DISTRIBUTION

Information on the incidence and prevalence of cancer in many geographical areas is available from several sources and some of the most useful are listed in Table 2.2. The influence of sex and site of disease on mortality from cancer is illustrated for Ontario in Figure 2.5. Epidemiological observations show a striking international variation in the frequency of specific types of cancer. Some examples of this variation are shown in Figures 2.6, 2.7 and 2.8. Breast cancer, colon cancer, and prostatic cancer all show an incidence and mortality that is generally low in Eastern and African countries, and high in North America. For example, there is a sevenfold variation in breast cancer incidence between North America and Japan, and similar or greater variation in rates can be seen for other tumors. In contrast, hepatocellular carcinoma is one of the most common cancers worldwide, but is uncommon in Europe and North America. Other types of cancer that are more common in developing countries include cancers of the stomach, esophagus and cervix.

International differences in cancer incidence appear not to be due to inherited differences between populations. Strong evidence for the importance of environmental as compared to heritable factors comes from the study of migrant populations. Migrants from countries where the incidence of cancers such as breast and colon is low, who move to countries where the incidence of these tumors is high, eventually acquire the cancer incidence of the country to which they have moved. An example of this phenomenon is seen in the changing frequency of breast cancer in Japanese migrants to Hawaii (Fig 2.9). The rate at which this change in fre-

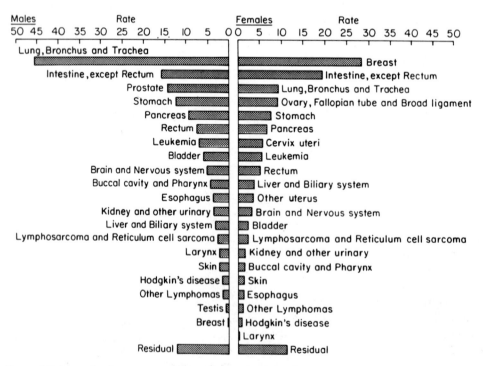

Figure 2.5. Mortality from various types of cancer in Ontario. Data indicates mortality rate per 100,000 population from the years 1971–1975. (Adapted from *Cancer in Ontario,* 1977.)

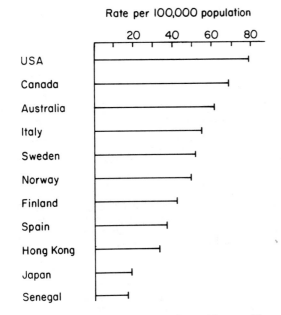

Figure 2.6. International variation in the incidence of breast cancer. (Adapted from Waterhouse et al, 1982.)

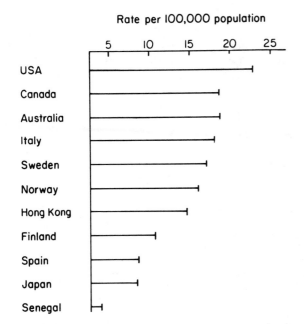

Figure 2.7. International variation in the incidence of colon cancer. (Adapted from Waterhouse et al, 1982.)

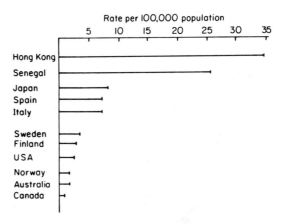

Figure 2.8. International variation in the incidence of liver cancer. (Adapted from Waterhouse et al, 1982.)

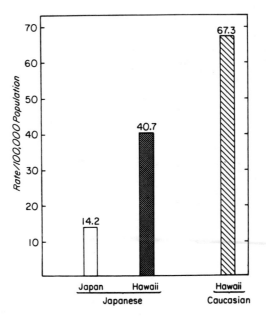

Figure 2.9. The incidence of breast cancer in Japanese women born in Japan, Japanese women born in Hawaii, and Caucasians born in Hawaii. Breast cancer incidence in Japanese migrants is substantially higher than in Japanese women living in Japan, indicating that environmental factors exert a strong influence on the frequency of this disease. (Adapted from Reddy et al, 1980.)

quency of cancer takes place varies according to the type of cancer and the migrant group. Japanese migrants to North America acquire within one generation an incidence of colon cancer typical of North America, but take two generations to show a substantial change in the incidence of breast cancer. In contrast, Italian migrants to Australia show a change in the incidence of breast cancer within the migrant group. The reasons for these differences are unknown, but may be related to the rate at which migrant groups abandon their old culture and adopt that of the country to which they have moved. The implication of these migrant studies is that the international variation in cancer rates is not due to comparison of inherited differences between the individuals who live in the countries but rather to some feature of life in those countries. Further evidence in support of this conclusion is provided by observed changes in cancer rates within countries that have experienced rapid changes in their diet or lifestyle. An example is the rapid rise in incidence of breast cancer, and adoption of a more "Western" diet that has occurred in Japan since World War II.

2.3.2 AGE DISTRIBUTION

Age exerts a strong influence upon the incidence of most common cancers. Figure 2.10 shows the relationship between age and incidence of cancer of the lung, breast, and colon and of Hodgkin's disease in Canada. For cancer of the lung, breast, and colon, the frequency of disease rises sharply with increasing age, and for Hodgkin's disease a bimodal age distribution is seen with peaks of incidence occurring in early adult life and in old age. Analysis of these age–incidence curves has suggested implications for their causation. For example, the shape of the age–incidence curves in Figures 2.10 (*a–c*) may be explained by a process involving two or more distinct mutations (section 3.2; Knudson, 1973). The bimodal age distribution of Hodgkin's disease suggests that two etiologically distinct forms of the disease may exist (MacMahon and Pugh, 1970), a suggestion that is supported by the different age distribution of the histologic subtypes of Hodgkin's disease.

2.3.3 ENVIRONMENTAL FACTORS AND CANCER

The evidence described above suggests that environmental, rather than genetic, factors are chiefly responsible for the variation in cancer rates throughout the world. Some of the many environmental factors that have been associated with an increased risk of cancer are listed in Table 2.5. A review of these factors and their associated risks of cancer has led Doll and Peto

Table 2.5. Some Environmental Causes of Cancer

Agent	Site of Cancer
Aflatoxin	liver
Alcohol	mouth, pharynx, esophagus, larynx
Alkylating agents	bladder, bone marrow
Aromatic amines	bladder
Asbestos	lung, mesothelium
Benzene	marrow
Estrogens	endometrium, vagina
Polycyclic hydrocarbons	skin, lung
Tobacco smoking	mouth, pharynx, esophagus, larynx, lung, bladder, lip
UV light	skin, lip
Vinyl chloride	liver (angiosarcoma)
Hepatitis virus	liver (hepatoma)

Note: Adapted from Doll and Peto, 1981.

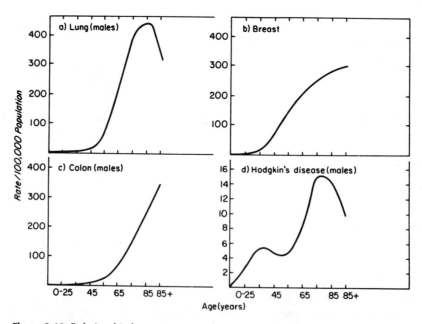

Figure 2.10. Relationship between age and cancer incidence for four Canadian sites. Different neoplasms have different associations with age. For some tumors (eg, Hodgkin's disease) the relationship may suggest different causes at different ages. (Adapted from *Cancer in Canada*, 1983.)

(1981) to conclude that most common cancers in the Western world are potentially avoidable (Fig 2.11).

Tobacco use is the environmental exposure most widely known to be associated with an increased risk of cancer, in addition to several nonmalignant diseases. The associated cancers include lung (numerically the most important, Fig 2.12), larynx, pharynx, esophagus, bladder, pancreas and cervix. Epidemiological studies have suggested that up to 35% of human cancer may be due to the effects of smoking.

Alcohol is associated with many cancers of the upper respiratory and digestive tracts in its own right, but more importantly, shows evidence of an interaction with tobacco in the etiology of these cancers. An interaction is inferred from evidence that the combined effect of tobacco and alcohol on the risk of these cancers exceeds the separate additive effects of these agents (Fig 2.13).

Many dietary factors have been associated with cancer risk (see Ames, 1983, and Willet and McMahon, 1984 for recent reviews). Dietary factors include major constituents such as fat, which appears to be closely associated with risk for breast, colon and endometrial cancer, and possibly also with prostatic, ovarian, and pancreatic cancers. Vitamins and trace minerals such as selenium are currently under investigation as factors that may influence the risk of cancer but no definitive conclusions about their influence on causation of cancer can be drawn at present.

Dietary variables are not only strongly associated with risk of cancer but may also explain the changing frequency of cancer seen in migrants, who eventually change their diets to that of the country to which they move. Further, changing rates of cancer within countries can be correlated with changes in dietary practices. Examples are the fall in both cancer mortality and fat consumption in Europe during World War II, or the rise in frequency of breast cancer rates and fat consumption in Japan after the war.

The possible risks of cancer associated with chemicals that are added to food, for the purpose of preservation or decoration, have been a source of great concern. However, despite intensive investigation there is at present little evidence to suggest that food additives are an important cause of human cancer. Saccharin has received considerable publicity as a possible risk factor, but there is now evidence that it is not associated with an increased risk of bladder cancer in humans, although it does seem to cause cancer in animals when given in very large doses. Nitrites, which are used as food preservatives, are of potential importance because they are known to be converted in the body to nitroso compounds that are potent carcinogens in animals (see section 6.3.3). However, epidemiological investigation

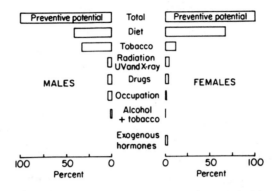

Figure 2.11. Estimates of the proportion of cancer incidence that is potentially avoidable. (Adapted from Wynder, 1977.)

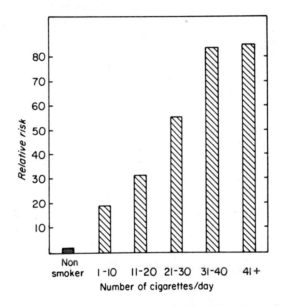

Figure 2.12. Lung cancer risk in males according to number of cigarettes smoked. The relative risk of lung cancer increases with the amount smoked. (Adapted from Schottenfeld and Fraumeni, 1982.)

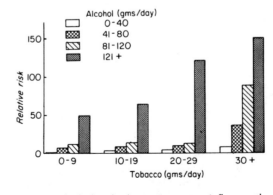

Figure 2.13. Alcohol and tobacco interact to influence the risk of esophageal cancer. (Adapted from Doll and Peto, 1981.)

has so far not shown a major role for nitrite in the causation of human cancer.

Reproductive and sexual behavior influences risk for cancer of the cervix, breast, and endometrium. The risk of cervical cancer is increased by the number of sexual partners and the early onset of sexual activity. These features of the disease suggest a transmissible agent and there have been reports of an association between cervical cancer and exposure to herpes or to papilloma viruses (see section 4.3). The risk of breast and endometrial cancer is reduced in women who have had several pregnancies. In breast cancer this influence appears to be due to a protective effect of a pregnancy resulting in a live birth early in a woman's life.

Several occupational exposures are associated with an increased risk of cancer, and some of these are listed in Table 2.6 with the agents known or suspected of causing cancer (see also section 6.6). Important examples of industrial exposure include asbestos, which increases the risk of cancer of the lung and mesothelioma, and vinyl chloride, which increases the risk of angiosarcoma of the liver.

Exposure to ionising radiation of any type is a rare but widely recognised cause of cancer. At present there is debate about the safety of low doses of irradiation, but as there is no convincing evidence for a "threshold" of carcinogenic effect, it seems prudent to regard any exposure as potentially damaging, and to expect the risk of cancer to increase with increasing dose. Radiation carcinogenesis is discussed in detail in chapter 7. Exposure to ultraviolet light is known to be associated with risk of skin cancer of all types (basal cell, squamous cell, and melanoma), leading to a high incidence in people who have a prolonged exposure to sunlight.

The role of viruses in the etiology of cancer is discussed in chapter 4. Despite substantial evidence from animals that viruses can cause cancer, a definite causal relationship between viruses and human tumors has been established for only a few types of tumors such as hepatocellular carcinoma (see section 2.3.4) and Burkitt's lymphoma. The association of disease with serological evidence of prior viral infection also suggests a possible role for viruses in the causation of nasopharyngeal cancer, cervical cancer, and some other lymphomas, particularly those that develop soon after renal transplantation.

In summary, numerous environmental factors may influence the risk of cancer. A major task of environmental protection agencies is to evaluate the role of these factors, and to set guidelines that are both socially acceptable and that will lead to a reduction in the incidence of cancer.

2.3.4 SPECIFIC TYPES OF CANCER

A description of the epidemiology of four types of human cancer is presented in this section to illustrate some of the factors described previously.

Hepatocellular carcinoma. This is one of the most common forms of cancers in the world, with most of the cases occurring in the developing countries (Fig 2.8). The incidence of the disease is about 40/100,000 per year in the areas of highest risk in Asia and Africa, and is more common in men than in women. The incidence is less than 4/100,000 per year in low-risk areas such as Europe and North America. The frequency of disease falls in migrants from high-risk countries.

The geographic distribution of hepatocellular carcinoma closely follows that of hepatitis. It is believed that about 80% of hepatocellular carcinoma is associated with exposure to hepatitis B virus. A prospective study

Table 2.6. Some Occupational Exposures that Influence Cancer Risk

Occupation	Agent	Site of Disease
Dye manufacturers, rubber workers	aromatic amines	bladder
Asbestos mining and handling	asbestos	lung, mesothelium
Cadmium workers	cadmium	prostate
Uranium miners	ionizing radiation	lung
Coal gas manufacturers, asphalter and others	polycylic hydrocarbons	skin, lung
Farmers, sailors	UV light	skin, lip
Hardwood furniture manufacturers	unknown	nasal sinuses

Note: Adapted from Doll and Peto, 1981.

in Taiwan has shown that the relative risk of developing disease after exposure to the virus is about 200, with virtually all cases of the disease occurring in people who were carriers of the virus. Integration of viral DNA into the genome of the tumor can be demonstrated (section 4.3.4). Efforts are now being made to prevent hepatocellular cancer through the use of a vaccine that will prevent infection with hepatitis B.

Another etiological factor is aflatoxin, a strong carcinogen produced by a mould that may contaminate peanuts and other food. Animal feed contaminated by aflatoxin was found to be responsible for outbreaks of liver tumors among poultry. Other experiments have shown that aflatoxin may cause hepatocellular carcinoma in experimental animals. International comparisons have shown a strong correlation between contamination by aflatoxin of food for human consumption and the incidence of the disease.

Hepatocellular carcinoma has been associated with alcoholic cirrhosis, but the association may be due to accompanying infection with hepatitis B. In Western women there is also an association of this type of cancer with use of oral contraceptives, but the disease remains uncommon.

Melanoma. The incidence of melanoma varies from more than 15/100,000 per year in high-risk areas of Australia, New Zealand and South Africa, to about 0.2/100,000 per year in low-risk areas such as Japan (Fig 2.14). The disease occurs equally in men and women, but has a better prognosis in women.

There is an international gradient in the incidence and mortality of melanoma, with increasing risk as the equator is approached. A similar gradient can be seen within the United States. These observations led to the suggestion that exposure to the sun was a major determinant of risk. There are, however, anomalies in the distribution of disease that cannot be explained simply on the basis of exposure to sunlight. Melanoma is more common in some parts of northern Europe than in the south, for reasons that are quite unclear at present.

White-skinned races are at higher risk than pigmented races, and whereas in Caucasians melanoma occurs most often on the trunk or legs, in Africans the disease occurs most frequently on the soles of the feet. Furthermore, among blacks there is no variation in frequency of disease with latitude. The ability to tan appears to be protective, and the association of the disease with social class (it is more common in professionals than in manual workers) suggests that intermittent exposure to the sun may be more hazardous than continuous exposure, which may allow a protective tan to develop. Avoidance of the sun or the use of barrier creams may reduce the frequency of disease.

Rarer forms of melanoma are associated with a familial predisposition that may be associated with a recognizable precursor lesion called the dysplastic nevus. Xeroderma pigmentosum is an inherited disease characterized by a deficiency in the repair of lesions induced in DNA by ultraviolet light. As expected, it predisposes to melanoma as well as other skin cancers.

Breast cancer. The incidence of breast cancer varies between about 100/100,000 per year in high-risk areas to less than 20/100,000 in low-risk areas. The geographic variation in incidence of breast cancer has been described in Figure 2.6. Northern Europe, North America and Australia are high-risk areas; Asia and Africa are low-risk areas. Table 2.7 shows the major demographic and reproductive variables that have been found to be associated with risk of breast cancer. Most of the variables listed are associated with only a modest increase in risk, and do not appear to explain the considerable international variation in the incidence of disease.

Several studies show that benign breast disease, in which there is hyperplasia associated with atypia in breast lobules, increases the risk for subsequent breast cancer. There is a strong international correlation between dietary fat consumption and breast cancer incidence and mortality. Diet also influences other risk factors such as age at menarche, age at menopause, and obesity. Support for a causal role of dietary fat is

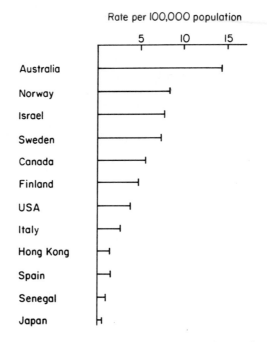

Figure 2.14. International variation in the incidence of melanoma. (Adapted from Waterhouse et al, 1982.)

Table 2.7. Demographic, Reproductive, and Other Risk Factors for Breast Cancer

Risk Factor	Higher Risk	Lower Risk	Relative Risk
Age	older	younger	5–7
Country of residence	N. America, Europe	Asia, Africa	5–7
Age at first birth	older	younger	2–3
Number of births	none	some	2–3
Age at menarche	earlier	later	1.5–2
Age at menopause	later	earlier	1.5–2
Oophorectomy	none	when young	1.5–2
Body weight	increased	decreased	1.5–3
Height	increased	decreased	1.5–3

obtained from studies in experimental animals, where fat may promote the activity of carcinogens.

Some studies have shown elevated levels of urinary estrogen in populations at increased risk for breast cancer, and others have found high levels of free estradiol (unbound to sex-hormone-binding globulin) in groups at high risk. It remains to be seen whether these findings can be replicated and to what extent they are explained by differences in diet which are known to affect hormone levels. An increased understanding of the relationship between diet, hormones, and the histological changes known to be associated with an increased risk of breast cancer might lead to the development of preventive strategies.

Lung cancer. For males, high and low rates of lung cancer are approximately 100/100,000 and 25/100,000 per year respectively. Europe and North America are high-incidence areas, whereas incidence is lower in India and Asia. Incidence increases with age, and the disease is at present 5–6 times more common in men than women. Lung cancer is increasing in incidence, however, in most Western countries, largely due to a very rapid rate of increase in women.

The relationship between cigarette smoking and lung cancer is the most extensively documented etiological relationship in cancer epidemiology. Large numbers of studies have shown a consistent association between cigarette smoking and risk of lung cancer. These studies have also shown a dose–response relationship in that the risk of lung cancer increases with the amount smoked and the duration of smoking. An example of data showing the association has been shown in Figure 2.12. The current increase in lung cancer in women follows a considerable increase in the number of women who smoke. The risk of smoking may be somewhat less

with low tar and nicotine cigarettes. Recent studies have suggested that passive smoking (ie, the exposure of nonsmokers to the cigarette smoke from smokers) is also associated with an increase in the risk of lung cancer.

Several occupational exposures, including asbestos, uranium mining, and smelting of iron ore, contribute to an increased risk of lung cancer. Some of these factors may interact with cigarette smoking. Some studies have shown that reduced intake of vitamin A may increase risk among smokers, and trials are now in progress to determine whether vitamin A supplementation reduces cancer risk.

2.4 SUMMARY

Epidemiology is concerned with explaining the distribution of disease in individuals and in populations. Descriptive epidemiology gives an account of the distribution of disease in terms of its frequency (incidence or prevalence) in different geographical regions, the age and sex of affected individuals, and any associations with time. Analytic epidemiology attempts to explain observed variations in disease frequency by identifying factors that are associated with the development of disease. The principal methods of analytical epidemiology are the observational (nonexperimental) cohort study, experimental trials (which rarely can be performed), and case-control studies. The application of these methods to the study of human cancer has shown large variations throughout the world in the incidence and mortality of most common cancers. This variation is not due to inherited differences between populations because cancer rates change in migrant groups and are thus largely influenced by environmental factors. The methods of analytical epidemiology have shown several features of the environment to be related to the risk of most common cancers, which are therefore, in principle, potentially avoidable.

REFERENCES

Ames BN: Dietary carcinogens and anticarcinogens. Oxygen radicals and degenerative diseases. *Science* 1983; 221: 1256-1264.

Anderson S, Auquier A, Hauch WW, et al: *Statistical Methods for Comparative Studies.* John Wiley and Sons, New York, 1980.

Bradford Hill A: *Principles of Medical Statistics*, ed 9. Oxford University Press, New York, 1971.

Cancer in Canada, 1980. Statistics Canada, Minister of Supply and Services, Canada, 1983.

Cancer in Ontario. Ontario Cancer Treatment and Research Foundation, Toronto, 1977.

Doll R, Peto R: *The Causes of Cancer: Quantitative Estimates of Avoidable Risks of Cancer in the United States.* Oxford University Press, Oxford, 1981.

Knudson AG, Jr: Mutation and human cancer. *Adv Cancer Res* 1973; 17:317-352.

Lilienfeld AM, Lilienfeld DE: *Foundations of Epidemiology*, ed. 2. Oxford University Press, Oxford, 1980.

MacMahon B, Pugh TF: *Epidemiology: Principles and Methods.* Little Brown & Co, Boston, 1970.

Reddy BS, Cohen LA, McCoy GD, et al: Nutrition and its relationship to cancer. *Adv Cancer Res* 1980; 32:237-345.

Roberts RS, Spitzer WO, Delmore T, Sackett DL: An empirical demonstration of Berkson's Bias. *J Chron Dis* 1978; 31:119-128.

Rooks JB, Ory HW, Ishak KG, et al: Epidemiology of Hepatocellular adenoma. The role of oral contraceptive use. *JAMA* 1979; 242:644-648.

Sackett DL: Bias in analytic research. *J Chron Dis* 1979; 32:51-63.

Schottenfeld D, Fraumeni JF, Jr (eds): *Cancer Epidemiology and Prevention.* W.B. Saunders Co., Philadelphia, 1982.

Waterhouse J, Muir C, Shanmugarathnam K, Powell J: *Cancer Incidence in 5 Continents.* IARC Scientific Publications, Lyons, 1982.

Willet WC, MacMahon B: Diet and cancer—an overview. *N Engl J Med* 1984; 310:633-638; 697-703.

Wynder EL: Cancer prevention: a question of priorities. *Nature* 1977; 268:284.

BIBLIOGRAPHY

Doll R, Peto R: *The Causes of Cancer: Quantitative Estimates of Avoidable Risks of Cancer in the United States.* Oxford University Press, Oxford, 1981.

Feinstein AR: *Clinical Epidemiology: The Architecture of Clinical Research.* W.B. Saunders, Philadelphia, 1985.

Hiatt HH, Watson JD, Winsten JA (eds): *Origins of Human Cancer, Book A: Incidence of Cancer in Humans.* Cold Spring Harbor Laboratory, Cold Spring Harbor, NY, 1977.

Lilienfeld AM, Lilienfeld DE: *Foundations of Epidemiology*, ed 2. Oxford University Press, Oxford, 1980.

MacMahon B, Pugh TF: *Epidemiology: Principles and Methods.* Little Brown & Co., Boston, 1970.

Sackett DL, Haynes RB, Tugwell P: *Clinical Epidemiology: A Basic Science for Clinical Medicine.* Little Brown & Co., Boston/Toronto, 1985.

Schottenfeld D, Fraumeni JF, Jr (eds): *Cancer Epidemiology and Prevention.* W.B. Saunders Co., Philadelphia, 1982.

3

The Genetic Basis of Cancer

Robert A. Phillips

3.1 INTRODUCTION

There is overwhelming evidence that mutations can cause cancer. In this context mutations are broadly defined to include any changes in the genome such as point mutations, deletions, insertions, translocations and amplifications. Major evidence for the genetic origin of cancer (Table 3.1) includes the observation of Ames (1983) that almost all carcinogens induce mutations, and the finding that genetically determined traits associated with a deficiency in the enzymes necessary to repair lesions in DNA are associated with an increased risk of cancer. Factors affecting the integrity of the genome also increase the probability of malignant disease; thus several inherited diseases associated with increased chromosome breakage have an increased incidence of cancer. If mutations can cause cancer, and if some mutations occur in the germline, then some cancers should be inherited like other genetic traits. There are many examples of heritable human cancers. Finally, since mutations are rare events, tumors should also be rare events with each tumor arising from a sin-

Table 3.1. Evidence that Mutations Cause Cancer

- Most carcinogens are mutagens
- Susceptibility to certain carcinogens is dependent on the ability of cellular enzymes to convert it to a mutagenic form
- Defects in DNA repair increase the probability of cancer
- Chromosome instability is observed in many types of cancer
- Some cancers are inherited
- Malignant tumors are clonal
- Some tumors contain mutated oncogenes

gle mutant cell; in fact, there is much evidence for the clonal origin of human malignancies (see section 8.2.3).

The number of mutations required to convert a normal cell into a malignant cell is unknown, but the results of many studies suggest that two or more mutations are required to induce tumor formation. Thus in most malignant diseases, the question is not "Does mutation cause cancer?" but rather "How many mutations cause this cancer?" and "What is the nature of the genes affected by mutation?"

Unequivocal answers to the above questions are not available for any human or animal tumors, but recent advances in epidemiology, and in cellular and molecular biology, have allowed progress in understanding these problems. This chapter will review information about the genetic nature of cancer deduced from epidemiological studies, and will describe the common chromosomal abnormalities that are observed in some tumors. Studies of two heritable cancers, retinoblastoma and Wilms' tumor, will then be discussed as examples of multidisciplinary approaches to understanding genetic aspects of cancer. Many of the studies described in this and subsequent chapters have made use of re-

cently developed techniques of chromosome analysis and molecular biology. These techniques are described in an Appendix.

3.2 BASIC CONCEPTS OF CANCER GENETICS

3.2.1 RELATIONSHIP BETWEEN CANCER INCIDENCE AND AGE

The overall incidence of cancer varies strikingly with age, increasing as the fourth to sixth power of age for most cancers (Fig 3.1). The simplest mathematical analysis of such data suggests that 5–7 mutations are necessary for malignant transformation of a normal cell. However, there are difficulties with models requiring many mutations for induction of cancer. To create the necessary age–incidence curves, multihit models assume that all of the cells are present for the lifetime of the individual, that cells with fewer than the required number of mutations have no growth advantage, that each tissue has a very large number of targets for malignant transformation and that the presence of a putative envi-

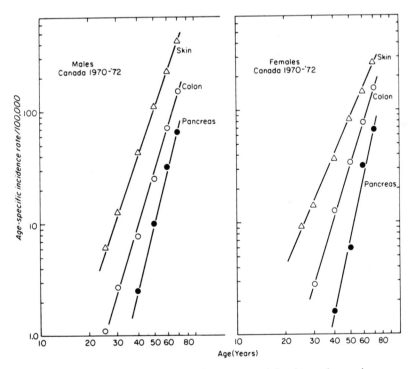

Figure 3.1. Age-specific incidence rates for cancers of the skin, colon and pancreas in males and females in Canada for the years 1970 to 1972. All of these curves are straight lines fitting the multihit models for induction of cancer. According to these models, the above cancers require between 5 (skin) and 7 (pancreas) mutations for induction of the malignant state. (From *Cancer Patterns in Canada, 1931–1974*. Published by the authority of the minister of National Health and Welfare, Bureau of Epidemiology. Laboratory Centre for Disease Control, Health Protection Branch, 1982.)

ronmental carcinogen leads to unusually high mutation frequencies. For example, Ashley (1969) had to postulate 10^9 target cells in the stomach and a mutation frequency of 10^{-3} per cell per generation in order to derive an incidence curve for gastric cancer that increased as the fifth power of age. While it is difficult to estimate the actual number of cellular targets in the lining of the stomach, it is unlikely that 10^9 progenitors remain for the lifetime of the individual. Spontaneous mutations occur at a frequency of 10^{-6}–10^{-7} per cell per generation. High concentrations of mutagens can increase this frequency 10–100-fold, but it is unlikely that tolerable doses of any known carcinogen can increase the mutation frequency to the levels required by a simple multihit model.

Because of the apparent requirement for an unobtainable frequency of mutation, some investigators have proposed that cancer does not arise by mutation, but that other events modify the expression of existing genes. For example, some results indicate that changes in patterns of DNA methylation can turn genes on or off and that the frequency of these events can be as high as 10^{-3} mutations per cell per generation. One difficulty with such epigenetic models is that the high frequency of genetic changes will make the malignant phenotype highly unstable. Nevertheless, there is evidence that at least some murine teratocarcinomas can totally revert at high frequency to normal functioning cells (Mintz and Illmensee, 1975; also section 8.2.6). In this instance, either the mutant genes initiating the tumor are turned off and are not required for normal function, or the initiating events involve inappropriate gene expression rather than mutation. Thus, reversion to a normal phenotype is probably associated with turning off a mutant gene or the alteration of abnormally expressed genes to give normal, tissue-specific expression. Despite the possible induction of teratocarcinomas by nonmutational events, most cancers appear to result from stable genetic changes and the remainder of the chapter will summarize findings related to these stable events.

3.2.2 CELLULAR AND GENETIC BASES OF CANCER

Analysis of the number of mutations responsible for malignant disease requires some understanding of the cellular basis for transformation. In addition to the requirement for unrealistically high frequencies of mutation, multihit models requiring 5–7 mutations also ignore the dynamics of proliferating cell populations. Almost all cancers arise in renewing cell populations where the differentiated cells are derived from progenitors with extensive proliferative potential. However,

even these progenitors have a limited life span and disappear after some number of divisions. Therefore, realistic models for the induction of cancer must take into account the following properties of cell renewal systems (section 8.2).

1. The immature progenitor cells, which are the probable targets for transformation, are only a small proportion of the total number of cells in that tissue or organ.
2. The limited life span of proliferating progenitors means that mutations which accumulate in a progenitor cell will disappear when this cell completes its life span and when it and its progeny disappear from the animal.
3. Most organs and tissues show marked variations in their proliferative rate during the lifetime of the animal. Some tissues proliferate early in childhood, others during puberty, and others (eg, bone marrow, intestine and skin) contain proliferating cells during the entire life span of the individual. These changes in proliferative rate can markedly influence the number of cells that are targets for malignant transformation.

Moolgavkar and Knudson (1981) have proposed a model for carcinogenesis (Fig 3.2) which takes into account the above properties of normal cells. In their model, conversion of a normal progenitor cell into a malignant cell requires only two mutations. Both normal stem cells and "initiated" stem cells, which have accumulated one of the two mutations necessary for transformation, retain normal ability to differentiate.

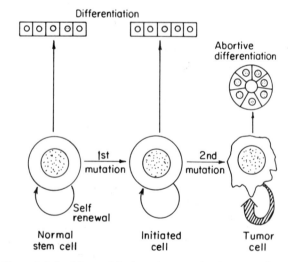

Figure 3.2. In this model of carcinogenesis, the normal stem cells and initiated cells have similar properties; both differentiate normally and self-renew normally. Following a second mutation, however, self-renewal potential is greatly increased and differentiation becomes grossly abnormal.

Susceptibility to transformation depends primarily on the relative rates of differentiation and self-renewal of initiated stem cells. If most stem cells differentiate rapidly and have limited potential for self-renewal, most mutations will be eliminated from the stem cell pool when the stem cells differentiate. An important assumption in this model is that only mutations in stem cells lead to malignant disease; mutations in differentiated cells with little or no potential for self-renewal cannot cause malignant transformation.

A feature of the above model is that the rate of transformation is more dependent on the growth kinetics of the tissue than on the frequency of mutation. At any cell division a stem cell has two choices: differentiation or self-renewal. In this model, it is the difference between the probability of self-renewal and the probability of differentiation which determines the slope of age-specific incidence curves of the type shown in Figure 3.1. The incidence of cancer at any age is directly proportional to the number of initiated stem cells accumulated at that age. In some cancers, there are indications that the initiating event (eg, smoking in lung cancer) alters the growth kinetics of the target tissue; these changes can be accommodated by the model. Other cancers occur in target tissues which normally change during the lifetime of the animal; examples are embryonic cells which differentiate and disappear early in life, and breast tissue which changes both at puberty and at menopause. The model proposed by Moolgavkar and Knudson accurately models the unusual age–incidence curves of childhood cancers and breast cancer (see Moolgavkar and Knudson, 1981 for a detailed discussion).

3.2.3 TYPES OF GENETIC RISK FACTORS FOR CANCER

Occasionally mutations which can cause cancer occur in the germline, giving rise to a heritable predisposition to malignant disease. However, changes in genes other than those directly responsible for malignant disease can lead to an increased risk of cancer. Peto (1980) has suggested that mutations predisposing to malignant disease be grouped into three categories depending on the level of risk involved (Table 3.2). In the first category are those mutations which give a 1,000-fold or greater increase in the risk of malignant disease (see section 3.2.5); only a very small proportion of total cancers fall into this group. The second category consists of mutations which increase the risk of cancer 10–100 times. The last category of mutations give less than a tenfold increase in risk. In his analysis, Peto demonstrated the extreme difficulty of identifying factors which increase the risk of cancer by as much as 10–100-fold above that

in the control population. The major difficulty in detecting unknown genetic risk factors is the identification of a suitable control group. Unless the genetic risk factor can be identified by its effects on normal cellular function (eg, inhibition of DNA repair in xeroderma pigmentosum) all control groups will be a mixture of normals and high-risk individuals. The presence of the latter reduces the difference between the experimental and control groups, making identification of the high-risk group difficult. It is probable that many cancers are associated with genetic risk factors which have not yet been identified.

3.2.4 MUTATIONS LEADING TO INTERMEDIATE DEGREES OF GENETIC RISK

One approach to detecting risk factors is to study defined, partially inbred populations. In such populations it is possible to correlate the incidence of particular malignancies with the degree of relatedness. For example, studies of the Mormon population in Utah have identified several types of human cancer with probable genetically determined risk factors (Skolnick et al, 1981). The combination of accurate genealogical data, a good cancer registry, large families and a relatively stable, homogeneous population makes possible the identification of genetic risk factors that cannot be detected in other populations. In initial studies, members of the Mormon population with specific malignancies were identified, and the degree of relatedness of individuals with the malignancy was calculated. Skolnick argued that if genetic factors were important in a specific cancer, individuals with that malignancy would be more closely related than an age-matched control population chosen at random from the Mormon population. The degree of relatedness of two individuals is expressed as a kinship coefficient which is essentially the probability that randomly selected homologous

Table 3.2. Categories of Genetic Risk

Increase in Risk of Malignant Disease	Examples	Ease of Identifying Existence of Risk/Factor
>1000	Retinoblastoma, polyposis coli, xeroderma pigmentosum	easy
10–100	Breast cancer?	difficult
<10	?	almost impossible

Note: Adapted from Peto, 1980.

chromosomes are identical by descent from a common ancestor; the genealogical index (GI) describes the average relatedness of specific groups in the population. The larger the GI value, the more closely related is the population; the GI for the control Mormon population is 1.39×10^{-5}. Table 3.3 shows the GI obtained for groups of patients with several common malignancies. Of the malignancies shown, only lymphoma shows no familial clustering; all others have a GI value significantly greater than that of the controls, indicating possible genetic risk factors in their etiology. In these studies, one cannot rule out the possible involvement of environmental or dietary factors which may show familial clustering because families often share the same environment and diet. Nevertheless, this method has identified malignancies that merit detailed investigation for the presence of genetic risk factors characterizing the second of Peto's categories.

3.2.5 MUTATIONS LEADING TO HIGH DEGREES OF GENETIC RISK

Mulvihill (1977) reviewed over 200 mutations which predispose to malignancy in humans. Most of these mutations cause substantial increases in risk and fall into the first category described by Peto. Some mutations cause tumors by indirect mechanisms, but at least 100 of them probably act directly to cause tissue-specific tumors. The best-characterized mutations lead to cancers inherited as autosomal dominant traits; two examples of such mutations are described in detail in section 3.4. Relatively few of these mutations have been mapped to a chromosomal location, and in no case has the specific gene been identified or characterized.

As described in chapter 5, all species have numerous genes, called oncogenes, which are homologous to transforming oncogenes carried by specific RNA retroviruses. Some human tumors have mutations in these oncogenes which may have led to their activation. Such genes appear to be probable candidates for direct-acting germline mutations predisposing to malignancy. However, there is no evidence for germline mutations in oncogenes. Mutations in oncogenes appear restricted to somatic cells; perhaps such mutations in the germline are lethal even in the heterozygous state.

Many mutations result in instability of the genome and lead indirectly to high degrees of risk, presumably because the initial germline mutation increases the likelihood of somatic mutations occurring in direct-acting genes. The following well-characterized autosomal recessive diseases strongly predispose to malignant disease: xeroderma pigmentosum (XP), Fanconi's anemia, ataxia telangiectasia (AT) and Bloom's syndrome. Patients with XP have a well-documented defect in

Table 3.3. The Genealogical Index Among Groups of the Mormon Population with Specified Types of Cancer

Site	Mean Genealogical Index ($\times 10^{-5}$)
Lip	3.84
Melanoma	3.36
Ovary	3.07
Prostate	2.59
Colon	2.31
Breast (<50 yr)	2.23
Breast (>50 yr)	2.11
Lymphoma	1.27
Control population	1.39

Note: Adapted from Skolnick et al., 1981.

their ability to repair DNA damage caused by ultraviolet light and by some chemical agents (section 7.4). This defect leads to a high incidence of various types of skin cancer, presumably because of failure to repair lesions caused by ultraviolet components of sunlight. The AT mutation results in a threefold increase in sensitivity to ionizing radiation, an increase in spontaneous chromosome breakage, and increased susceptibility to lymphoreticular tumors. The other two syndromes are also characterized by chromosomal instability and by an increased susceptibility to lymphoreticular tumors, but they produce no known defect in DNA repair. It is not clear why the chromosome breakage syndromes predispose to tumors in lymphatic tissue, and not in other organs that are more common sites of cancer in unaffected individuals.

Other mutations may predispose to malignant disease, but in most cases the data are only circumstantial. Since many carcinogens must be metabolized before they can cause mutations (section 6.3.3), mutations in genes which code for enzymes in the activation pathways could lead to changes in the incidence of malignant disease caused by these carcinogens. In inbred mice, differences in the activity of aryl hydrocarbon hydroxylase (AHH) in different strains appear to account for the marked differences in susceptibility to cancers induced by methylcholanthrene, a carcinogen which depends on AHH for activation (for review, see Nebert, 1980).

Various mechanisms of host resistance are probably important in preventing malignant disease, and mutations in genes which determine host resistance might predispose to cancer. While immune suppression can accelerate the development of chemically or virally induced tumors in experimental animals, immune suppression does not always lead to marked increases in tumor incidence. For example, nude mice, which lack a thymus and are unable to reject foreign tumor grafts, do not have an increased incidence of malignant disease. In contrast, patients with immune deficiency disease, of either genetic or acquired origin, have an increased incidence of lymphoid tumors. However, since tumors develop within the system which is defective, it is unclear whether the malignancies occur because of immune suppression or because of the abnormality in the development of lymphocytes.

Viruses can cause malignant tumors in experimental animals, and numerous genetic factors influence susceptibility to transformation by these viruses. For example, Friend leukemia virus (FLV) induces erythroleukemia in many inbred strains of mice. Resistance to infection and tumorigenesis is regulated by as many as six different genetic loci in mice (Shibuya and Mak, 1982). Viruses have also been implicated in human malignancies, such as Burkitt's lymphoma and a rare type of T-cell leukemia (see chapter 4). Although there is no evidence for genetic predisposition to infection with these putative human tumor viruses, this may reflect the current limited state of knowledge in the field of human tumor viruses rather than the absence of genetic risk factors.

3.3 CHROMOSOME ABNORMALITIES IN TUMORS

3.3.1 OVERVIEW

Important genetic changes in cells are often manifested as gross chromosomal alterations which can be detected by examination of mitotic cells (see section A3.2 for techniques used to analyze chromosomes). Because of the ease with which leukemic cells can be obtained and analyzed, most studies of karyotypic abnormalities have been performed on leukemias. Initial studies simply characterized the types of abnormalities observed in different types of malignancy. Recently, molecular rearrangements that are associated with some common chromosomal abnormalities have been characterized. These rearrangements are frequently associated with oncogenes, and some of them are discussed in chapter 5. The data in the following section will summarize results obtained for various tumors and will stress that common chromosomal abnormalities are found in many malignancies. This important observation suggests that common genetic mechanisms might be involved in the induction or progression of specific tumors.

In general, chromosomal changes observed in tumors fall into three categories. The first category is reciprocal translocation, in which there is no loss of genetic information since portions of two chromosomes are sim-

ply exchanged (Fig 3.3). The result is that genes on one chromosome are placed near genes on another. This rearrangement can result in aberrant expression of genes in their new location, or it can alter the structure of genes at the site of the translocation.

The second general category of chromosomal changes involves nonreciprocal exchanges (Fig 3.4). These exchanges can result in either deletion or addition of chromosome regions. Although such changes are frequently observed in tumors, the consequences are known in only a few instances (for example, deletions in 13q or 11p in retinoblastoma and Wilms' tumor, respectively; see section 3.4).

The last category involves an increase in the amount of DNA from a specific region of a chromosome. The increased genetic material results in areas on chromo-

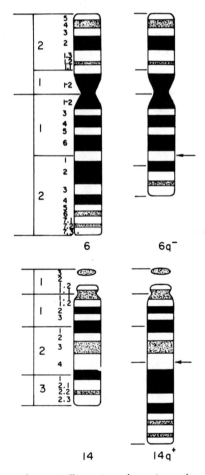

Figure 3.3. Schematic illustration of a reciprocal translocation found in ovarian carcinoma and other tumors. On the left-hand side are shown a normal chromosome 6 (*top*) and a chromosome 14 (*bottom*). On the right-hand side, arrows indicate the break points on each chromosome. The bottom half of chromosome 6 is transferred to chromosome 14, and the bottom part of chromosome 14 is translocated to the bottom part of chromosome 6.

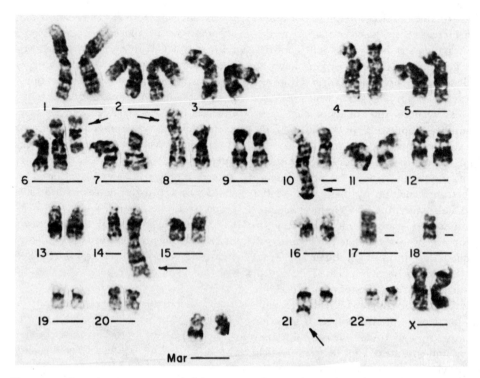

Figure 3.4. Complex, nonreciprocal chromosome abnormalities often observed in tumors are illustrated. This karyotype from a retinoblastoma tumor is simpler than that found in many solid tumors, but it nevertheless illustrates the complex nature of chromosome abnormalities. There is an abnormal chromosome 6 and an abnormality on the short arm of chromosome 8. In addition, there are abnormalities in chromosomes 10, 14 and 21; 2 chromosomes (indicated by Mar) cannot be identified and are simply designated as marker chromosomes. Finally, there is a loss of one copy of chromosome 17 and of one copy of chromosome 18. (Figures 3.4, 3.5 and 3.6 are courtesy of J. Squire, Department of Medical Biophysics, University of Toronto, Canada.)

somes referred to as homogeneously staining regions (HSR) or abnormally banding regions (ABR) (see Fig 3.5, *top*). HSRs and ABRs are associated with extensive gene amplification, commonly associated with drug resistance and oncogenes. It is important to note that HSRs and ABRs can occur at any site in the genome; peculiarly, they often occur at sites other than the usual chromosomal location of the amplified gene. Another form of gene amplification leads to chromosome abnormalities called double minutes (DMs). DMs appear as two small dots of dark-staining material in a metaphase preparation (see Fig 3.5, *bottom*). Unless a careful examination is made, these DMs may be dismissed as debris on the slide. In some instances, the number of DMs can be very large, approaching several hundred. It is generally believed that DMs represent the first stage in gene amplification and that some HSRs result from the integration of DMs into the chromosome.

In most tumors, a variety of chromosome abnormalities can be observed. The mechanisms by which somatic chromosome changes occur remain unknown. However, many chromosomes have regions known as frag-

ile sites where the chromosome is uniquely susceptible to breakage. In some instances these fragile sites are also sites for chromosome rearrangement. In the following sections, those abnormalities which are reproducible and representative of a specific disease are discussed. Some of the chromosome abnormalities have provided clues about basic genetic mechanisms, and others have been found to have prognostic significance.

3.3.2 MYELOID LEUKEMIAS

Chronic myelogenous leukemia (CML) was the first malignancy in which a reproducible chromosome abnormality was described. In almost all patients with CML, the leukemic cells contain a unique small chromosome, called the Philadelphia chromosome (commonly abbreviated Ph[1] or simply Ph). For many years, arguments raged over whether the marker chromosome was a defective chromosome 21 or chromosome 22. With the advent of detailed chromosome banding (section A3.2), it became clear that the abnormality involved chromosome 22. In 1973, Rowley (1973) suggested that the Ph chromosome resulted from a reciprocal translocation between chromosomes 22 and 9 (Fig 3.6). With usual banding techniques, the tip of the long arm of chromosome 22 stains faintly, and most investigators did not detect the translocated fragment at the tip of the long arm of chromosome 9. The precise location of the break on chromosome 22 has been identified, and there is now unequivocal evidence that the rearrangement is indeed a reciprocal translocation and that it alters the structure of the abl oncogene (section 5.3).

The Ph chromosome has also provided information about the patterns of hematopoietic differentiation. During periods of remission, when malignant cells are undetectable, all of the dividing myeloid cells (ie, erythrocytes, granulocytes and megakaryocytes) contain the Ph chromosome. This finding indicates that the Ph chromosome arose in a pluripotent stem cell with high self-renewal ability, allowing this clone to dominate the entire hematopoietic system. Whether or not the translocation leading to the Ph chromosome initiates this clonal dominance is unclear. Fialkow and his colleagues (Martin et al, 1982), using both glucose-6-phosphate dehydrogenase isozymes and the Ph chromosome as clonal markers, have shown that B lymphocytes in CML patients can be derived from the malignant clone without having the Ph chromosome. Thus, it is likely

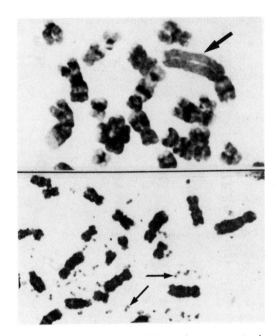

Figure 3.5. A portion of two different karyotypes is shown. The top photograph shows an abnormally long chromosome. The extended region of this chromosome has no identifiable bands and is called a homogeneously staining region (HSR). The bottom photograph shows multiple paired dots of chromatic material. These chromosomal abnormalities are called double minutes (DM). Both abnormalities are associated with gene amplification.

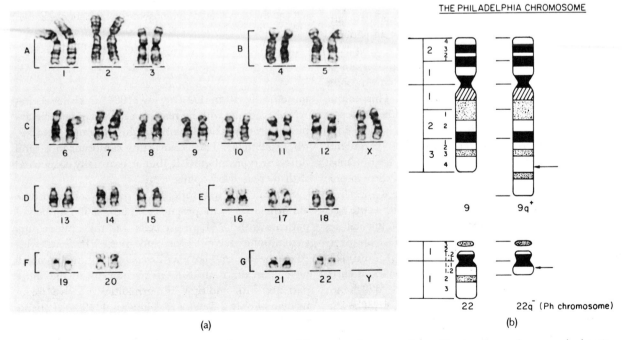

Figure 3.6. The photograph on the left, *a*, shows a typical karyotype from a patient with chronic myelogenous leukemia. Note the loss of material from the long arm of one copy of chromosome 22 and its addition to the long arm of one copy of chromosome 9. In *b*, a schematic diagram illustrates the precise location of the chromosomal break points in this reciprocal translocation.

that dominance of the abnormal clone occurs before the appearance of the Ph chromosome.

In the chronic phase of the disease, the tumor cells in CML are diploid with the Ph chromosome translocation being the only detectable karyotypic abnormality. When patients enter the blast crisis phase, other chromosome abnormalities frequently appear. Among the most common changes are the appearance of a second Ph chromosome, an iso(17q) chromosome (see section A3.2.4 for notation) or an extra copy of chromosome 8.

For many years, investigators have recognized chromosome abnormalities in the tumor cells from patients with acute nonlymphocytic leukemia (ANLL), but only recently has a consistent picture of chromosome changes appeared. Early studies indicated that only a small proportion of patients with acute leukemia had chromosome abnormalities associated with their tumor, but these studies were limited by technical factors; in particular, many of the metaphases observed in acute leukemia represent normal cells in the bone marrow. A recent study by Yunis et al (1984) indicates that at least 93% of patients with ANLL have gross chromosomal abnormalities. Many of these abnormalities are characteristic of the type of tumor, and some have prognostic significance. However, none of the markers in ANLL are as common as the Ph chromosome detected in CML. Some of the more common chromosomal markers found in ANLL are described below and summarized in Figure 3.7.

The most common chromosome abnormality occurs in acute promyelocytic leukemia. In almost all patients, the malignant cells have a translocation involving chromosomes 15 and 17. The translocation appears to be reciprocal, occurring at the q25 band on chromosome 15 and the q22 band on chromosome 17. This unique abnormality has not been observed in other types of ANLL.

In acute myelogenous leukemia 30% of patients show abnormalities of chromosome 8. The two most common changes detected are a trisomy of chromosome 8 or a translocation between chromosome 8 and chromosome 21, t(8;21)(q22;q22). Patients with acute myelomonocytic leukemia frequently have abnormalities affecting chromosome 16. Some patients have an inversion of part of chromosome 16 between p13 and q22, and there is often a deletion of the q22 band on chromosome 16. Both abnormalities affect the q22 band, but the significance of this finding is not clear. The leukemic cells in acute monocytic leukemia frequently have rearrangements of the long arm of chromosome 11; breaks tend to occur at q13 or q23. The most common translocation is between chromosome 9 and chromosomes 6, 10 or 17. Rowley (1984) has shown that ANLL patients with increased basophils almost always have a translocation involving chromosomes 6 and 9, t(6;9)(p23;q34). This abnormality can occur in several different types of ANLL, but it is usually associated with increased basophils.

Several investigators have related chromosome abnormalities with prognosis. The small number of patients with CML whose cells lack the Philadelphia chromosome have a poor prognosis. Patients with ANLL whose cells have an inversion of chromosome 16 have a median survival of 25 months, while those patients with multiple abnormalities survive for a median of only 2.5 months (Yunis et al, 1984). Patients with trisomy 8 (Yunis et al, 1984) or with the t(6;9) translocation respond poorly to treatment (Rowley, 1984). Another bad prognostic factor is multiple chromosome abnormalities (Yunis et al, 1984).

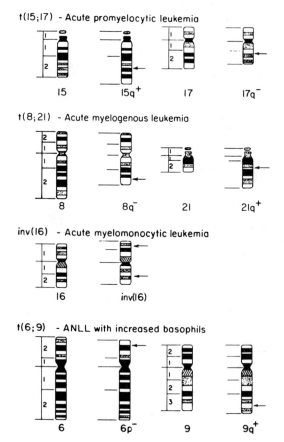

Figure 3.7. Some of the most common chromosome markers found in acute nonlymphocytic leukemia (ANLL). In each pair of chromosomes, the normal chromosome is shown on the left and the translocated chromosome on the right; the arrows indicate the positions of the break points.

3.3.3 LYMPHOID TUMORS

Burkitt's lymphoma was the first tumor where a chromosome abnormality was demonstrated to involve the translocation of a specific gene. The common translocations involving chromosome 8 and chromosomes 2, 14 or 22 result in the relocation of the myc oncogene near to genes which code for immunoglobulin molecules (see also section 5.3.4). The most common abnormality is a reciprocal translocation between chromosomes 8 and 14 (see Fig 3.8). The myc oncogene moves from chromosome 8 to a location near the constant region of the immunoglobulin heavy-chain gene on chromosome 14; the variable region of the immunoglobulin gene is transferred from chromosome 14 to chromosome 8. Similar rearrangements involving the light-chain loci are involved in translocations with chromosomes 2 (κ chain) and 22 (λ chain). The possible role of translocations in activating oncogenes is discussed in chapter 5.

Other B cell tumors also have translocations involving chromosome 14, although these translocations do not occur as frequently as the translocations described above for Burkitt's lymphoma. Two translocations involve the immunoglobulin locus and the rearrangement occurs at precise locations on chromosomes 11 and 18. It is speculated that these sites on chromosomes 11 and 18 are loci for unknown oncogenes.

The isolation and mapping of the genes for the T-cell receptor has allowed analysis of chromosome abnormalities in T-cell tumors to determine whether there are rearrangements involving genes which code for the T-cell receptor. Although chromosome abnormalities affecting chromosome 7 (location of the gene encoding the β chain of the T-cell receptor) and chromosome 14

(location of the α-chain gene) occur in T-cell tumors, they are not common. However, those abnormalities that do occur appear to involve the genes for T-cell receptors. One may speculate that the genes translocated next to the T-cell receptor genes are new oncogenes involved in the pathogenesis of T-cell tumors.

Prognostic significance in lymphoid leukemia is associated with the frequency of abnormal cells and total chromosome number rather than with specific abnormalities. Thus, a patient with a large number of normal metaphases in the bone marrow has a better prognosis than one with a high proportion of abnormal cells. Surprisingly, patients whose leukemic cells are pseudodiploid, containing near-normal chromosome numbers with only a single translocation, have a poor prognosis. A hyperdiploid karyotype with more than 50 or 51 chromosomes is a good prognostic sign.

3.3.4 SOLID TUMORS

Relatively little information is available about chromosome abnormalities in solid tumors. The major reason for this lack of data is the difficulty in obtaining suitable cellular preparations for chromosome analysis. In contrast to leukemias, which grow naturally as single-cell suspensions or are easily disrupted into single cells, cells in solid tumors are held together by tight junctions. Disruption of tumors into a single-cell suspension suitable for karyotype analysis often results in cell death. For this reason, it is often necessary to grow solid tumors in tissue culture before a suitable preparation can be obtained for analysis of chromosomes, but satisfactory growth can be difficult to achieve. Other problems also complicate karyotype analysis of solid tumors. Nevertheless, many solid tumors have been

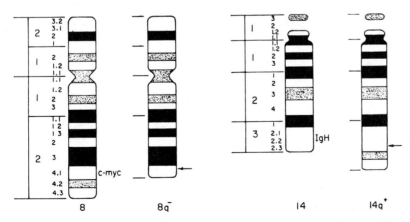

Figure 3.8. The common translocation between chromosomes 8 and 14 in Burkitt's lymphoma is illustrated. As in the other figures, the arrows indicate the position of the break points in the translocated chromosomes shown on the right of each pair.

found to have gross chromosome abnormalities with a highly variable number of chromosomes. The following paragraphs describe some tumors where a common abnormality can be observed.

Ovarian tumors often have a common translocation involving chromosomes 6 and 14 t(6;14)(q21;q24) (see Fig 3.3). The significance of this translocation, which can also be found in other tumors, is unclear. Several other solid tumors appear to have reproducible chromosomal deletions. Almost all meningiomas have a single chromosome 22. There is no evidence that the missing copy of chromosome 22 is involved in a chromosome translocation, and the tumors are probably haploid for all genetic loci on chromosome 22. Small-cell carcinoma of the lung appears to have a reproducible deletion in a portion of the short arm of chromosome 3, del(3p) (p14p23); similarly, neuroblastomas frequently have a deletion on the short arm of chromosome 1, del(1p) (p31p36). By analogy with retinoblastoma and Wilms' tumor (section 3.4), these chromosomal deletions in meningioma, small-cell carcinoma of the lung and neuroblastoma suggest the presence of genetic loci where mutations are critically involved in the initiation of the tumor. If the mutation is recessive, the deletion might represent a loss of the normal allele, allowing expression of the remaining mutated allele.

A common chromosomal abnormality observed in solid tumors is an increased copy of a portion of the long arm of chromosome 1. The region most commonly increased in number is the portion distal to 1q25. This abnormality is not characteristic of any particular tumor, since it has been observed in tumors of the breast, colon, ovary, and testis, and in retinoblastoma. Its significance is unclear. Its presence in many tumors suggests that it is associated with progression of tumors rather than their initiation (see chapter 6 and section 8.3). For example, genes on the long arm of chromosome 1 might be involved in cell proliferation, and an increase in the number of gene copies would give those cells a selective growth advantage.

In addition to translocations and deletions, tumor cells often show increases in genetic material. Solid tumors frequently have large numbers of chromosomes, often approaching a tetraploid number, and increases in specific chromosomes or in portions of a chromosome are also detected. Cells from many tumors show double minutes (DMs), which are diagnostic of gene amplification. Only a small number of gene amplifications have been studied in detail, and these include oncogenes, as found in neuroblastoma where the N-myc oncogene is frequently amplified, and those genes involved in drug resistance. It is impossible by karyotypic studies to predict which genes are amplified since

DMs apparently can integrate to form HSRs at any site in the genome.

3.4 DOMINANTLY INHERITED CANCERS

The best-documented examples of dominantly inherited cancers are listed in Table 3.4. The strong penetrance of the mutations leading to these malignancies has allowed a careful documentation of their mode of inheritance. However, the rarity of these syndromes has made detailed studies of the genetic defect difficult. Fundamental information on the nature and location of the germline mutations are known for only two tumors, retinoblastoma and Wilms' tumor; these tumors are discussed in more detail below.

3.4.1 RETINOBLASTOMA

Retinoblastoma is a tumor of the eye found exclusively in young children. It occurs in both hereditary and nonhereditary forms. The nonhereditary form is always unilateral; 60% of tumors are nonhereditary. The remaining 40% of patients have a germline mutation which predisposes to retinoblastoma. About 80% of people with the germline mutation have bilateral disease (ie, tumors arise independently in both eyes), about 15% have unilateral tumors, and 5% of individuals are asymptomatic carriers of the retinoblastoma mutation.

The high cure rate in this malignancy has allowed analysis of its inheritance. In most families the penetrance of the mutation is 90–95%, and it is inherited as an autosomal dominant trait. In some other families the penetrance is lower with several individuals being asymptomatic or having only unilateral tumors. In these families, inheritance of the retinoblastoma mutation still follows an autosomal dominant pattern, but other factors such as delayed mutation, host resistance or unusual chromosome translocations may affect the expression of the mutation and the pattern of inheritance.

Table 3.4. Syndromes with a Dominant Inheritance

- Retinoblastoma
- Adenopolyposis of the colon and rectum
- Wilms' tumor
- Basal-cell nevus syndrome
- Neurofibromatosis
- Multiple-endocrine-adenomatosis syndromes
- Neuroblastoma
- Family cancer syndrome

Two types of analyses place the germline mutation on the long arm of chromosome 13. The first suggestion for this location came from analysis of individuals having a congenital deletion of part of chromosome 13. Such individuals have multiple congenital abnormalities, and when the deletion involves the q14 region of chromosome 13, the patient is at very high risk for development of retinoblastoma. A detailed analysis of a variety of deletions from this part of chromosome 13 has placed the retinoblastoma locus (RB1 locus) at the 13q14.11 band. The second indication that the RB1 locus is at this location came from studies of multiple families, which show close linkage of this mutation to the enzyme esterase D (ESD) (see section A3.4.3 for detection of linkage between genes). Both the RB1 and ESD loci appear to be in the same subband in the 13q14 region (see Fig 3.9). These linkage studies demonstrate that in individuals with normal karyotype, the retinoblastoma mutation is located on chromosome 13 within the region identified by congenital deletion. In all individuals where it has been possible to investigate the germline mutation, it has been mapped to the long arm of chromosome 13; there is no evidence that mutations at other loci can produce retinoblastoma. However, when the mutation was first mapped to chromosome 13, the locus was called RB1 to allow for the possible future discovery of other loci involved in retinoblastoma.

In addition to retinoblastoma, individuals inheriting a germline mutation at RB1 are at high risk for developing other primary tumors, particularly osteosar-

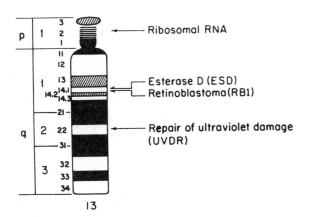

Figure 3.9. The location of the genetic loci unequivocally mapped to chromosome 13 is shown. The location of esterase D (ESD) proximal to the centromere and retinoblastoma (RB1) distal is based on a chromosome deletion which separates the two loci (see section A3.4.2). The only other functional marker mapped unequivocally to the long arm of chromosome 13 is a gene involved in the repair of UV damage to DNA (UVDR).

comas. If the patients received radiation as part of their therapy for the initial retinoblastoma tumor, they develop other tumors more rapidly than those patients who were not irradiated, and the second tumors frequently appear within the irradiated field.

The normal cells that are able to transform into retinoblastoma tumor cells probably disappear with age. The most likely explanation for the disappearance of these cells is that they are embryonic cells which differentiate into mature photoreceptors. Once the cells are terminally differentiated they are no longer at risk for transformation by mutations. Knudson (1971) has presented convincing evidence that the transformation of these embryonic target cells into tumor cells requires two mutations. For nonhereditary unilateral retinoblastoma, both mutations are somatic and must occur in the same cell. Because mutation frequencies are low and because the putative target cells gradually disappear from the eye, it is not surprising that retinoblastoma is a very rare malignancy. However, when the first mutation occurs in the germline, every potential target cell in the retina has undergone first mutation and is an "initiated cell" in terms of the model shown in Figure 3.2. A second mutation in any of the target cells will lead to malignancy. The large number of target cells in the retina almost guarantees that one or more will undergo the second mutation and develop into a tumor cell; in fact, most patients develop more than two tumors. However, it is important to realize that because the proposed second event is stochastic, some individuals with a germline mutation will not develop any tumors and others will develop only a single tumor. Approximately 5% of people with a germline mutation develop no tumor and are asymptomatic gene carriers, while 15% develop only a single tumor and are usually incorrectly diagnosed as having nonheritable, unilateral retinoblastoma.

On the basis of the two-hit model and the occurrence of retinoblastoma in patients with deletion of large portions of the long arm of chromosome 13, the first mutation in both hereditary and nonhereditary tumors probably occurs on this chromosome and involves loss of gene function. There are two possible sites for the second mutation: it could occur at the remaining normal RB1 locus on the other chromosome, or it could occur at other sites in the genome. In the former case, the mutation would be considered recessive at the cellular level since the mutant phenotype (ie, retinoblastoma) requires mutant alleles at the RB1 loci on both chromosomes.

The precise nature of the second mutation has not been unequivocally confirmed, but the majority of evidence favors a mutation in the remaining normal allele at the RB1 locus. Although most tumors retain two normal copies of chromosome 13, a detailed genetic analysis of chromosome 13 using restriction-fragment-length polymorphism (RFLP; section A3.3.5) shows that in 60% of tumors the long arm of chromosome 13 becomes homozygous at almost all loci (Fig 3.10). Cavenee et al (1985) showed that most tumors retain two copies of the chromosome carrying the RB1 mutation and lose the chromosome carrying the normal allele. Many tumors are homozygous for all RFLP examined on chromosome 13. A few tumors remain heterozygous at loci near the centromere and become homozygous for all distal loci; in these tumors, mitotic recombination probably creates the observed pattern of homozygosity (see Fig 3.11). The majority of tumors do not have polymorphic RFLP near the centromere, and

it is not possible in these tumors to determine whether homozygosity is generated by mitotic recombination or by loss of the normal chromosome and duplication of the chromosome with the retinoblastoma mutation. Ten percent of tumors have only a single copy of chromosome 13; they have presumably retained the chromosome carrying the mutant allele at the RB1 locus and lost the one with the normal allele. Thirty percent of retinoblastoma tumors remain heterozygous at all loci tested on chromosome 13; presumably in these tumors a second independent mutation inactivated the normal allele. Figure 3.11 summarizes the four mechanisms thought to be important for generating homozygosity at the RB1 locus.

The generation of homozygosity on chromosome 13 occurs in both heritable and sporadic forms of retinoblastoma, indicating that the same mutations are

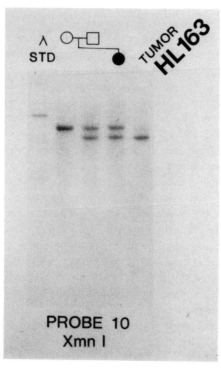

Figure 3.10. The usefulness of restriction fragment-length polymorphisms (RFLP) to identify the loss of genetic information in a retinoblastoma tumor is illustrated. In this particular example, DNA probe 10 detects an RFLP (with restriction enzyme Xmn 1) in chromosome 13. As shown in the figure, the mother is homozygous for this marker (lane 2) and the father (lane 3) heterozygous. The child inherited one allele from each parent and is also heterozygous in the majority of her cells (lane 4). However, the retinoblastoma which arose in the child (lane 5) has lost the allele inherited from the mother and retains only the chromosome inherited from the father. Lane 1 contains labeled fragment DNA from phage λ; this fragment of known size provides a molecular weight standard. (From Dryja et al, 1984. Reprinted with permission of the *New England Medical Journal*.)

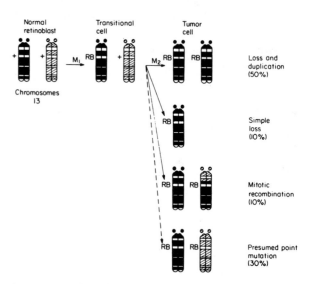

Figure 3.11. Retinoblastoma tumors appear to occur when two independent mutations, M1 and M2, inactivate both normal alleles at the RB1 (RB) locus on chromosome 13. In most cases, the first mutation, M1, is localized to the RB1 locus. Four different mechanisms generate the second mutation, M2, in the remaining normal allele at the RB1 locus. In 50% of the cases, the chromosome carrying the normal allele appears to be lost entirely, and the mutant chromosome is duplicated. In 10% of the cases, the normal chromosome is lost and the mutant chromosome remains as an apparent monosomic chromosome. In an additional 10% of the cases, there is a detectable mitotic recombination such that the proximal part of chromosome 13 retains the maternal and paternal markers, but the distal portions of chromosome 13 contain only the markers characteristic of the chromosome carrying the retinoblastoma mutation. In 30% of the cases, there is no molecular or cytogenetic evidence for changes in the markers on either the maternal or paternal chromosome 13. It is presumed in these patients that two independent mutations have occurred at the RB1 locus, resulting in inactivation of both copies of the gene(s) at the RB1 locus.

involved in both forms of the disease. In addition, homozygosity develops only on chromosome 13; all other chromosomes retain the same heterozygous state detected in normal cells from the same individuals. Interestingly, osteosarcomas arising in patients with the germline mutation at the retinoblastoma locus are also homozygous for chromosome 13, and there is an increased incidence of a similar homozygosity in osteosarcoma patients who do not have the germline mutation. Thus, mutations at the RB1 locus appear responsible for at least two different tumors, retinoblastoma and osteosarcoma, and for both tumors identical genetic mechanisms appear responsible for tumor formation. The mutation is recessive at the cellular level and only appears dominant in the individual because of the large number of target cells at risk for a second somatic event.

Detailed karyotypic studies of retinoblastoma tumors have identified two frequent chromosomal changes in addition to the changes affecting chromosome 13. Sixty percent of tumors contain a small marker chromosome identified as an iso(6p). Such isochromosomes have been observed in other malignancies, but the isochromosome affecting the short arm of chromosome 6 has only been observed at high frequency in retinoblastoma. Since most tumors also have two normal copies of chromosome 6, the presence of the isochromosome represents an amplification of all of the genes on the short arm of this chromosome. In 80% of tumors there are extra copies of the long arm of chromosome 1. Many different tumors show similar amplification of the long arm of chromosome 1, and this change, as well as the presence of the iso(6p), are probably tertiary changes associated with progression.

3.4.2 WILMS' TUMOR

Wilms' tumor has many characteristics in common with retinoblastoma. It is a kidney tumor of childhood, and occurs in both a heritable and a nonheritable form; the heritable form is frequently bilateral. The Wilms' tumor locus is known to be located on the short arm of chromosome 11, close to the gene for the enzyme catalase (Fig 3.12). A detailed analysis of patients with congenital deletions indicates that the precise location is at 11p1305-11p1306. Although the cure rate for Wilms' tumor now approaches 90%, patients with the heritable form of the disease appear to be at risk for second tumors. Thus, mutations at this complex genetic locus are probably involved in several types of malignancies; recent evidence implicates mutation at this locus in hepatoblastoma and rhabdomyosarcoma (Koufos et al, 1985).

Analysis of the short arm of chromosome 11 in

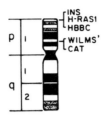

Figure 3.12. Many genes have been mapped to the short arm of chromosome 11. Indicated is the location of the best characterized of these genetic loci. At the tip of the short arm are three genes, insulin (INS), the ras oncogene (H-ras1) and the human β globin cluster (HBBC). In the p13 band are two loci, one for Wilms' tumor and one for the catalase (CAT).

Wilms' tumor cells has revealed a mechanism of tumorigenesis similar to that observed for retinoblastoma. By using RFLP (see section A3.3.5), several investigators have observed a reduction to homozygosity in many loci on the short arm of chromosome 11. Thus, it is likely that the Wilms' tumor gene is a recessive mutation, and both alleles must become mutant for the malignant phenotype to be expressed.

Patients with a congenital deletion of 11p13 usually have both aniridia (lack of the iris of the eye) and Wilms' tumor, and frequently also have a congenital urinary abnormality and mental retardation. The occurrence of this grouping of abnormalities has led to the suggestion that mutations at the same locus are responsible for all the abnormalities. However, a family has been observed whose cells have a reciprocal translocation between chromosomes 4 and 11, t(4;11) (q22;p13). Members of this family have aniridia but none of the individuals with this translocation have developed Wilms' tumor; also, families with heritable Wilms' tumor and without chromosome 11 deletion do not have aniridia. Thus, aniridia and Wilms' are caused by mutations in different genes.

3.5 SUMMARY

There is strong evidence to support the conclusion that cancer is a genetic disease of somatic cells. Development of a tumor probably requires two or more mutations in the stem cells of the tissue but expression of the mutations as a tumor likely depends strongly on the kinetics of cellular proliferation and numerous host factors, such as availability of growth factor, presence of host resistance, and so forth. A few rare tumors, such as retinoblastoma and Wilms' tumor, are frequently heritable, and in these two tumors a precise chromosomal location has been established for genes where mutation leads to malignancy. In fact, most cancers probably have a heritable subgroup. Studies of partially inbred populations, such as the Mormon population in Utah, suggest that the risk of developing most of the common cancers is associated with genetic factors. However, mutations associated with this increase in risk have not been identified, and it remains possible that the observations can be explained by environmental factors.

Chromosome abnormalities are associated with many types of tumors. Some of these, such as the rearrangements of Burkitt's lymphoma and the Philadelphia chromosome of CML, involve breakage of chromosomes close to known oncogenes. Others involve amplification of genes or addition or deletion of chromosomal material. Analysis of common abnormalities may give clues to the sites of genes that are involved in cancer causation and progression.

REFERENCES

Ames BN: Dietary carcinogens and anticarcinogens. *Science* 1983; 221:1256–1264.

Ashley DJB: The two "hit" and multiple "hit" theories of carcinogenesis. *Br J Cancer* 1969; 23:313–328.

Cavenee WK, Hansen MF, Nordenskjold M, Kock E et al: Genetic origin of mutations predisposing to retinoblastoma. *Science* 1985; 228:501–503.

Dryja TP, Cavenee WK, White R, Rapaport JM et al: Homozygosity of chromosome 13 in retinoblastoma. *N Engl J Med* 1984; 310:550–553.

Knudson AG Jr: Mutation and cancer: statistical study of retinoblastoma. *Proc Natl Acad Sci USA* 1971; 68:820–823.

Koufos A, Hansen MF, Copeland NG, Jenkins NA et al: Loss of heterozygosity in three embryonal tumours suggests a common pathogenetic mechanism. *Nature* 1985; 316:330–334.

Martin PJ, Najfeld V, Fialkow PJ: B-lymphoid cell involvement in chronic myelogenous leukemia: Implications for the pathogenesis of the disease. *Cancer Genet Cytogenet* 1982; 6:359–368.

Mintz B, Illmensee K: Normal genetically mosaic mice produced from malignant teratocarcinoma cells. *Proc Natl Acad Sci USA* 1975; 72:3585–3589.

Moolgavkar SH, Knudson AG Jr: Mutation and cancer: a model for human carcinogenesis. *J Natl Cancer Inst* 1981; 66:1037–1052.

Mulvihill JJ: Genetic repertory of human neoplasia, in Mulvihill JJ, Miller RW, Fraumeni JF Jr (eds), *Genetics of Human Cancer*. New York, Raven Press, 1977, pp. 137–143.

Nebert DW: Pharmacogenetics: an approach to understanding chemical and biologic aspects of cancer. *J Natl Cancer Inst* 1980; 64:1279–1290.

Peto J: Genetic predisposition to cancer, in Cairns J, Lyon JL, Skolnick M (eds), *Banbury Report 4: Cancer Incidence in Defined Populations*. Cold Spring Harbor, NY, Cold Spring Harbor Laboratory, 1980, pp. 203–213.

Rowley JD: A new consistent chromosomal abnormality in chronic myelogenous leukemia identified by quinacrine fluorescence and Giemsa staining. *Nature* 1973; 243:290–293.

Rowley JD: Biological implications of consistent chromosome rearrangements in leukemia and lymphoma. *Cancer Res* 1984; 44:3159–3168.

Shibuya T, Mak TW: Host control of susceptibility to erythroleukemia and to types of leukemia induced by Friend murine leukemia virus: initial and late stages. *Cell* 1982; 31:483–493.

Skolnick M, Bishop DT, Carmelli D, Gardner E et al: A population-based assessment of familial cancer risk in Utah Mormon genealogies, in Arrighi FE, Rao PN, Stubblefield E (eds), *Genes, Chromosomes and Neoplasia*. New York, Raven Press, 1981, pp. 477–500.

Yunis JJ, Brunning RD, Howe RB, Lobell M: High resolution chromosomes as an independent prognostic indicator in adult acute nonlymphocytic leukemia. *N Engl J Med* 1984; 311:812–818.

BIBLIOGRAPHY

Knudson AG Jr: Hereditary cancer, oncogenes, and antioncogenes. *Cancer Res* 1985; 45:1437–1443.

Sandberg AA: *The Chromosomes in Human Cancer and Leukemia*. New York, Elsevier, 1980.

APPENDIX: METHODS OF GENETIC ANALYSIS

A3.1 HISTORICAL PERSPECTIVE

The level of understanding of any scientific phenomenon depends on the sophistication of the technology available for its investigation. Technological advances in the analysis of chromosomes and genes have occurred rapidly, and this Appendix describes some of the more important techniques applied to understanding genetic changes in cancer cells. The rapidity with which changes have occurred is well illustrated by studies on the Philadelphia (Ph) chromosome, which is found in chronic myelogenous leukemia (CML).

Nowell and Hungerford first described the Ph chromosome in CML in 1960; they detected it as a deletion in one of the small chromosomes in the G group of chromosomes. At that time, it was possible to place chromosomes in groups, but it was not possible to unequivocally identify them. Nevertheless, with the relatively crude techniques of chromosome analysis, the Ph chromosome could be identified easily and was shown to have clinical significance in that CML patients whose cells contained the Ph chromosome had better survival than those whose cells did not. In 1970, when staining techniques allowed the visualization of unique bands on every chromosome, the Ph chromosome was identified as chromosome 22 with a deletion of its long arm. The subsequent careful study by Rowley (1973) revealed that the missing material from chromosome 22 was probably translocated to chromosome 9. The advent of molecular genetics and the cloning of various oncogenes has permitted another level of understanding. It is now clear that in all cases of CML with the Ph chromosome the c-abl oncogene normally present on chromosome 9 is translocated to a specific region (bcr) on chromosome 22, confirming that there is a reciprocal translocation. Prior to the molecular studies the exact nature of the translocation was not known. The banding techniques could not determine whether or not the translocation was reciprocal because the exact amount of chromosomal material exchanged between chromosome 9 and chromosome 22 cannot be defined precisely by microscopic techniques; molecular studies show unequivocally that a reciprocal translocation has occurred.

In all cases examined, the translocation break point on chromosome 9 disrupts the c-abl oncogene, leaving behind some of the coding sequences on chromosome 9. The remaining portion of the gene that is translocated to chromosome 22 can be transcribed, but the protein produced is larger than normal. However, the altered abl protein has an unusual property; it has tyrosine kinase activity. This enzyme activity has been associated with several transforming oncogenes (see section 5.4). Although amino acid analysis of the c-abl oncogene revealed structural homology to other oncogenes with protein kinase activity, the normal c-abl product has little detectable kinase activity. Whether or not this new enzyme activity is relevant to the induction of CML must await further cellular and molecular studies. Nevertheless, this example illustrates how advances in technology have allowed progression from a relatively crude analysis of a chromosome abnormality to the precise identification of the genes altered in the chromosome aberration.

A3.2 CHROMOSOMAL ANALYSIS

A3.2.1 OVERVIEW

Chromosomes are recognized in preparations of metaphase cells by their size and shape, and by the pattern of light and dark bands observed after staining by specific procedures. With current methods, all 22 autosomes and the sex chromosomes can be identified unequivocally. By international agreement the chromosomes have been assigned specific numbers, and chromosome analysis, called karyotypic analysis, has been standardized worldwide (see Yunis, 1981).

A3.2.2 COLLECTION OF CELLS

Normal cells are usually obtained from peripheral blood for karyotypic analysis. After isolation of the white blood cells by density-gradient centrifugation, the lymphocytes are stimulated to proliferate by exposure to the T-lymphocyte mitogen, phytohemagglutinin. The cells begin to divide after approximately 1 day in tissue culture and sufficient mitotic cells for karyotypic analysis can be harvested after three or four days of incubation. Alternatively, small biopsies of skin or of amniotic fluid can be used as a source of fibroblasts which grow in culture and are also suitable for chromosomal analysis. However, lymphocytes offer the simplest procedure and usually the best preparations.

Many different techniques are used to obtain dividing tumor cells for karyotypic analysis. Leukemias and lymphomas are easily dispersed into single cells suitable for chromosome analysis; for this reason, there are more data available for these diseases than for solid tumors. Sources of lymphoid tumors can be peripheral blood, bone marrow, or lymph node biopsies. Since one property of malignant cells is their ability to proliferate autonomously, it is usually not necessary to stimulate them to divide or to incubate the cells in tissue culture prior to analysis.

In contrast to leukemias and lymphomas, karyotypic analysis of solid tumors presents several difficulties. First, the cells are tightly bound together and cannot be easily dispersed by simple mechanical means. Rather, samples of tissue must be digested with proteolytic enzymes in order to release single cells for analysis. These procedures can cause disruption of cells. Second, the mitotic index in solid tumors is often low, making it difficult to find enough mitotic cells to obtain a good karyotypic analysis. Third, lymphoid and myeloid cells often infiltrate solid tumors as part of an inflammatory or immune response against the tumor. Since it is often difficult to distinguish tumor cells from normal cells, especially in preparations for chromosome analysis, it is desirable to separate the tumor cells from the normal cells. Separation may be attempted by growing the tumor cells in tissue culture or in immune-deficient animals. One difficulty with cell culture in a liquid medium is that normal fibroblasts grow well; growth of fibroblasts may be prevented if the tumor cells will form colonies in a semisolid medium such as methylcellulose. Many tumors will grow in immune-deprived mice, and large numbers of dividing tumor cells can be obtained from xenografts. Normal cells of the mouse which may infiltrate the tumor pose no problem for karyotypic analysis since mouse chromosomes can easily be distinguished from human chromosomes. The normal cells within a tumor will not proliferate in immune-deficient animals. This technique works well for many solid tumors, although some types of tumors (eg, breast cancer) are difficult to grow as xenografts.

A3.2.3 PREPARATION OF CHROMOSOME SPREADS

Chromosome spreads can be prepared from populations of proliferating cells incubated in tissue culture for a short period of time in the presence of a drug which arrests cells in mitosis (Worton and Duff, 1979, for review); colchicine and vinblastine are used most often. As well as increasing the number of mitotic cells, the drugs also cause compaction of the chromosomes, thus allowing easier identification. Following exposure to hypotonic saline solution and fixation in acetic acid and methanol (or ethanol), the cells are broken open on a glass slide by rapid drying. This process leads to disruption of the cells and release of the chromosomes onto a small area of the glass slide. With practice (and luck) the chromosomes will be distributed and not overlap each other.

Various stains are used to distinguish the chromosomes. The most common is Giemsa stain. If the chromosomes are stained directly after fixation, the chromosomes will appear as solid entities with few distinguishing characteristics. To obtain banded chromosomes, the unstained cells are first exposed for a brief period to proteolytic digestion with trypsin. When trypsinized chromosomes are stained with Giemsa, bands, called G bands, appear. It is not clear why exposure to trypsin creates the bands on chromosomes. Although there are several other methods for staining chromosomes to produce bands, the G-banding technique is the most popular and the bands observed are the ones on which the internationally agreed nomenclature is based.

Stained preparations must be examined under oil emersion with a high-quality microscope. When satisfactory chromosome spreads are observed, the field is photographed. Detailed karyotypic analysis is made from the enlarged photographs. Generally, the chromosomes are cut from the photographs and placed in numerical order. A typical karyotype from a normal human cell is shown in Figure A3.1.

A3.2.4 NOMENCLATURE

The chromosomes and their bands have been numbered by a universally accepted nomenclature (Fig A3.2). The short and long arms of each chromosome are referred to as p and q, respectively. The number of bands detectable depends on the quality of the chromosome spread and the stage of the cell in mitosis. Cells spread at prophase can have over 800 identifiable bands. However, the standard metaphase spread (Fig A3.1) has approximately 550 bands (Yunis, 1981). Rules for naming various abnormalities in the karyotype are listed in Table A3.1. If tumors contain chromosomes which cannot be identified, the unidentified chromosomes are simply called markers, often indicated as M1, M2. . . , etc. In designating a karyotype, one usually indicates the number of chromosomes, the sex chromosomes, and then lists the abnormalities. If a chromosome is not mentioned in the list of abnormalities, one can assume that the karyotype contains two copies of a normal-appearing chromosome. An example of a hypothetical karyotype is

$$47,XY,-21,+1q-,5p+,t(2;6)(p13;q24),+16.$$

This designation means that the karyotype contained 47 chromosomes with one X chromosome and one Y chromosome. In addition, there was only a single copy of chromosome 21. Two extra chromosomes were observed; one was an apparently normal chromosome 16, the other was an extra copy of chromosome 1, but the extra copy was deleted for a portion of the long arm. One of the copies of chromosome 5 contained an unidentified addition to the short arm. Finally, there was

Table A3.1. Nomenclature for Describing Chromosome Abnormalities

Description	Meaning
-1	Loss of one chromosome 1
$+7$	Gain of extra chromosome 7
$2q^-$ or del2q	Deletion of part of long arm of chromosome 2
$4p^+$	Addition of material to short arm of chromosome 4
t(9;22)(q34;q11)	Reciprocal translocation between chromosomes 9 and 22 with break points at q34 on chromosome 9 and q11 on chromosome 22
iso(6p)	Isochromosome with both arms derived from the short arm of chromosome 6
inv(16)(p13q22)	Part of chromosome 16 between p13 and q22 is inverted

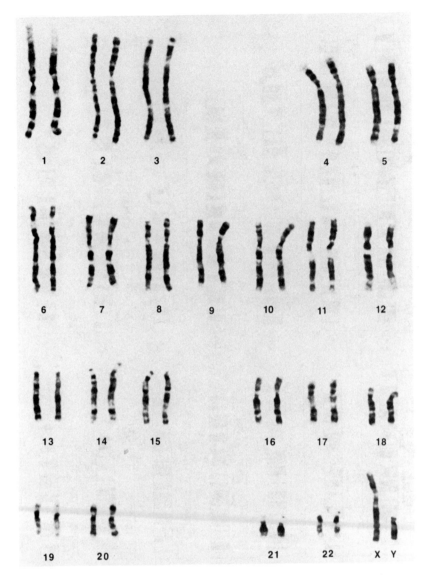

Figure A3.1. The chromosomes are arranged in pairs according to their banding pattern. By international agreement, the chromosomes are numbered according to their appearance. See Figure A3.2 for a schematic illustration of the accepted band pattern for each chromosome. (Figures A3.1 and A3.2 are from Yunis, 1981. Reprinted with permission of W.B. Saunders Co.)

a reciprocal translocation involving chromosomes 2 and 6 with breakpoints at the p13 band on the short arm of chromosome 2 and the q24 band on the long arm of chromosome 6. While it is difficult for a novice to visualize the karyotypic abnormalities from the abbreviated form, the shorthand method is simple and almost as informative as the photographic representation. Nevertheless, the interpretation of chromosome abnormalities involves a significant subjective evaluation, and most investigators give photographic confirmation to the typical karyotypic abnormalities observed in their studies.

A3.3 MOLECULAR ANALYSIS

A3.3.1 OVERVIEW

The advances in technology which allow an analysis of genes at the nucleotide level have revolutionized the study of genetics, including the analysis of genetic changes in tumor cells. It has become possible to identify and isolate specific genes, and it is often easier to isolate a gene than its protein product. The nucleotide sequence can be determined from an isolated gene, and from the nucleotide sequence one can deduce the amino acid sequence of its putative product. It is possible to

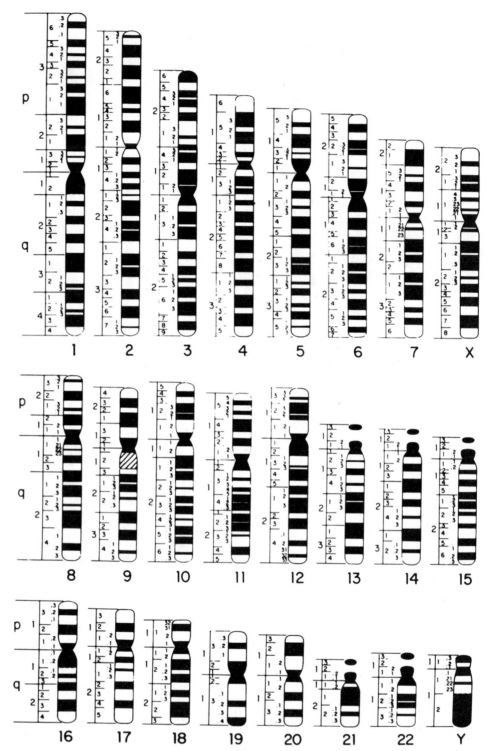

Figure A3.2. Cytogeneticists have agreed to group the chromosomes and to number the bands in a standard fashion. Indicated are the bands which everyone has agreed exist, and the method used to number the bands for purposes of describing abnormalities.

synthesize small peptides corresponding to the proposed amino acid sequence of the product and to make antibodies against this peptide sequence. Often the antibodies will react with the complete protein, allowing the subsequent isolation and purification of the gene product. The following sections will not describe all of the molecular techniques, but will concentrate on those techniques commonly used for the genetic analysis of tumors. For additional information, the reader is referred to the books on molecular genetics that are listed in the Bibliography(eg, Maniatis et al, 1982).

A3.3.2 RESTRICTION ENZYMES

Perhaps the single most important discovery which has allowed the widespread use of molecular genetics in the routine analysis of mutations in normal and malignant cells was that of restriction enzymes. These enzymes are nucleases which have the ability to cut DNA, but they recognize only specific sequences of nucleotides and always cut the DNA at exactly the same place within the designated sequence.

Restriction enzymes were first discovered in bacterial cells where their functions include protection against infecting viruses and perhaps participation in DNA repair and DNA recombination. Similar enzymes probably exist in mammalian cells, but few have been characterized. Figure A3.3 lists some of the more commonly used restriction enzymes together with the sequence of nucleotides that they recognize and the position at which they cut the sequence.

The importance of restriction enzymes is that they allow DNA to be cut into reproducible segments which can be analyzed with great precision. For example, in the study of the gene for the T-lymphocyte receptor, human DNA may be cut with the restriction enzyme BamH1, and the C_β gene will be found on a DNA fragment of 22 kilobase pairs. Any exception to this observed size will indicate either mutation or rearrangement near this gene.

An important feature of many restriction enzymes is that they create "sticky ends." These ends occur because the DNA is cut in a different place on the two homologous strands. When the DNA molecule falls apart, the cut end has a small single-stranded portion which can hybridize to other fragments having compatible sequences (ie, fragments prepared by digestion with the same restriction enzyme). The presence of sticky ends allows investigators to "cut and paste" pieces of DNA together, as described below.

A3.3.3 MANIPULATION OF CLONED GENES

The numerous techniques used to isolate genes are beyond the scope of this presentation. Once a gene has been isolated, it is usually placed in a bacterial virus or plasmid to facilitate its manipulation and propagation. Figure A3.4 indicates schematically how a gene, once isolated, can be inserted into a viral host, such as the bacterial phage λ. This phage has genes which are not essential for its replication; these genes can be removed by cutting λ DNA with the appropriate restriction enzyme and separating the fragments containing these

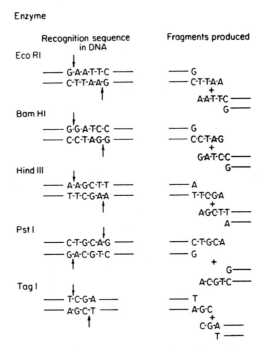

Figure A3.3. The nucleotide sequence recognized by five different restriction endonucleases is shown. On the left-hand side, the sequence recognized by the enzyme is shown; the sites where the enzymes cut the DNA are shown by the arrows. On the right side, the two fragments produced following digestion with that restriction enzyme are shown. Note that each recognition sequence is a palindrome, ie, the first two or three bases are complementary to the last two or three bases. For example, for EcoR1 GAA is complementary to TTC. Also note that following digestion, each fragment has a single stranded tail of DNA. This tail is useful in allowing fragments cut with the same restriction enzyme to anneal with each other.

genes by electrophoresis. If λ is digested with the same restriction enzyme as that used to prepare the cloned gene, all of the fragments will have compatible "sticky ends" and can be hybridized (spliced) back together. The spliced fragments can be sealed with the enzyme DNA ligase, and the reconstituted molecule can be packaged in vitro into an infectious virus particle. These in-vitro-constructed virus particles will infect bacterial cells and propagate to very large numbers. By this technique, large quantities of a gene can be obtained (ie, "cloned") for analysis in Southern blots (see section A3.3.4), nucleotide sequencing, transfer into other cells (see section A3.3.6), or other applications.

To recover the cloned gene, one simply has to isolate the λ phage, remove the DNA, cut it with the original restriction enzyme and isolate the fragments by electrophoresis. Figure A3.5 shows a gel in which a λ phage carrying a cloned gene was separated and stained with ethidium bromide to allow easy visualization. To use the cloned gene, the portion of the gel containing the

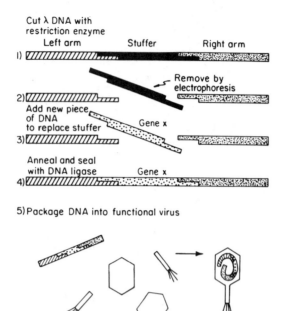

Figure A3.5. If a λ phage carrying a piece of foreign DNA is isolated and cut with a restriction enzyme which digests DNA as shown in Figure A3.4, the fragments can be easily separated by electrophoresis. Shown are the results of such an experiment. Lane A contains DNA from λ bacteria phage, after digestion with a restriction enzyme. The top and bottom bands are the left and right arms of λ, and the middle band is the fragment of foreign DNA. For comparison, lane B contains the intact λ phage. (Figures A3.5 and A3.10 are courtesy of Dr. BL Gallie, Hospital for Sick Children, Toronto, Canada.)

Figure A3.4. Insertion of foreign DNA into λ phage. This bacterial virus can still replicate when several of the genes in the middle of the virus (indicated by "Stuffer") are removed. Thus, to insert foreign DNA into this virus, one digests viral DNA with a restriction enzyme which cuts only at the borders of the stuffer region. The fragments of DNA can be separated by electrophoresis and the left and right arms of the viral DNA can be mixed with the new piece of foreign DNA (gene X). If the DNA containing gene X has been digested with the same enzyme used to remove the stuffer region, it can reanneal with the single-stranded ends to form a linear molecule. The gaps in the DNA can be sealed with an enzyme called DNA ligase. The reconstructed gene can be packaged into a functional virus particle by simply mixing the gene with preformed heads (shown as hexagons) and tails. Under appropriate conditions, the DNA, heads and tails will form into intact, functional virus particles.

appropriate fragment of DNA is cut out, and the DNA eluted from it.

A3.3.4 SOUTHERN BLOTS

A widely used method for analyzing the structure of DNA is the technique described by Southern (1975), which involves "blotting" of DNA onto a supporting matrix. The Southern blot technique is outlined schematically in Figure A3.6. The DNA to be analyzed is cut into defined lengths using a restriction enzyme, and the fragments are separated by electrophoresis through an agarose gel. Under these conditions the DNA fragments are separated according to size with the smallest fragments migrating farthest in the gel and the longest remaining near the origin. Pieces of DNA of known

size are electrophoresed at the same time for comparison. The gel is then laid on top of nitrocellulose paper and paper towels are placed on top of the nitrocellulose to draw fluid through the gel into the nitrocellulose paper. This blotting technique causes the DNA to migrate from the gel to the nitrocellulose paper, where it is immobilized and cannot diffuse.

A common application of Southern blots is to determine the size of the fragment in the DNA which carries a particular gene. For such an analysis, a cloned gene, propagated in λ phage as described above, can be isolated and made radioactive by allowing the replication of its DNA to occur in the presence of radioactively labeled nucleotides. The nitrocellulose paper containing all of the fragments of DNA cut with a restriction enzyme is subjected to conditions which denature DNA, but do not cause the DNA to be removed from the filter paper. The filter paper is then incubated in a solution containing the radioactively labeled gene. Under these conditions the gene, usually called a probe, will anneal with homologous DNA sequences present on the piece of filter paper. Gentle washing will remove the single-stranded, unbound probe; the only DNA fragments on the filter paper containing radioactively labeled material will be those homologous sequences which hybridized with the labeled probe. To detect the region of the filter paper containing the radioactive material, the filter is simply placed on top

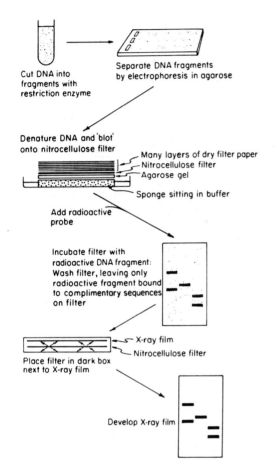

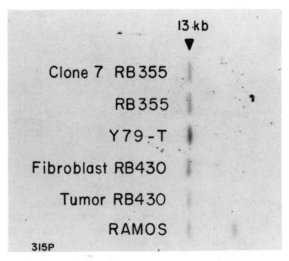

Figure A3.7. In the experiment shown, DNA was extracted from a normal fibroblast and from cells from three different retinoblastoma tumors (RB430, RB355, RB355–clone 7 and Y79-T); in addition, DNA was extracted from a Burkitt's lymphoma (Ramos). The DNA was digested with the restriction enzyme EcoR1 and probed with a DNA fragment specific for the c-myc oncogene. As shown in the figure, all of the samples have the usual germline-sized piece of DNA at 13 kb. However, in the Ramos tumor in which the t(8;14) translocation occurs in the middle of this oncogene, there is a new fragment of smaller size. Such an analysis illustrates the ease with which abnormalities in DNA can be detected by the Southern blot technique. (Figures A3.7 and A3.9 are courtesy of J. Squire, Department of Medical Biophysics, University of Toronto, Canada.)

Figure A3.6. Schematic outline of the procedures involved in analyzing DNA fragments by the Southern blotting technique. The method is described in more detail in the text. A typical Southern blot is shown in Figure A3.7.

of a piece of X-ray film, enclosed in a dark container and placed at −70°C for several hours to expose the film. The film is then developed and the places where the radioactive material are located show up as dark spots on the X-ray film. Figure A3.7 shows a typical Southern blot using a probe for one of the known oncogenes, c-myc; it shows that the gene is located on a piece of DNA approximately 13000 basepairs (or 13 kilobases [kb]) in length.

An almost identical procedure can be used to characterize messenger RNA. In this case, RNA is separated by electrophoresis, transferred to nitrocellulose and probed with a labeled, cloned fragment of DNA; the technique is called a "Northern blot." An analogous procedure has also been devised to characterize proteins. Following separation by electrophoresis, the proteins are immobilized by transfer to nitrocellulose. To identify specific proteins, the nitrocellulose filter is incubated in a solution containing a specific antibody labeled with [125]I. The antibody will bind only to the

region of the filter containing the protein used to induce the antibody. The region of radioactivity can be located by the exposure of X-ray film described in Figure A3.6. This method is called a "Western blot." Despite attempts by several investigators to describe their new technique as an "Eastern blot," there is not yet a universally accepted method with this name.

A3.3.5 RESTRICTION-FRAGMENT-LENGTH POLYMORPHISMS (RFLP)

Restriction enzymes recognize specific sequences in DNA; thus any mutation within a recognition sequence will prevent that sequence from being recognized by that restriction enzyme. Mutations at sites recognized by restriction enzymes therefore lead to changes in the length of the fragments that are obtained after digestion of DNA with such enzymes. These polymorphisms at restriction enzyme sites are very useful for genetic analysis. The method is illustrated in Figure A3.8. In a normal cell, there are two copies of each piece of DNA, one derived from the maternal chromosome, and one from the paternal chromosome. The restriction sites for

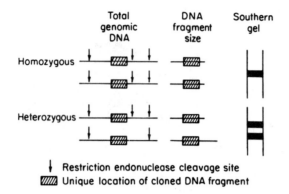

↑ Restriction endonuclease cleavage site
▨ Unique location of cloned DNA fragment

Figure A3.8. The principle of the method of detection and analysis of restriction-fragment-length polymorphisms (RFLP) is illustrated. The individual labeled homozygous contains two identical chromosomes with respect to the specific fragment of cloned DNA. In the individual indicated as heterozygous, one of the restriction enzyme sites has mutated; this results in the cloned DNA fragment appearing on a larger piece of DNA in that individual. It is important to note that with this technique it is unnecessary to know the function of the fragment of DNA used in the analysis. The only requirement for RFLP analysis is that the cloned DNA fragment be unique, ie, be present in only a single copy at a single location in the human genome.

a specific restriction enzyme (designated by the arrows) are shown for each chromosome. Suppose that in an individual, the first restriction site to the right of a unique DNA sequence on the paternal chromosome has mutated and is missing. The result of this mutation is that the gene will be found on a smaller fragment of DNA from the maternal chromosome than from the paternal chromosome. Thus, a Southern blot of DNA from the cells will show two bands, one identifying the maternal chromosome and one identifying the paternal chromosome. Because the polymorphism leads to a difference in length of the fragments carrying the piece of DNA used for analysis, the technique is referred to as restriction-fragment-length polymorphism (RFLP). Mutations at restriction sites are inherited as any other genetic trait and can be used for linkage analysis as described below (see section A3.4.3).

A3.3.6 PUTTING NEW GENES INTO CELLS

The function of a gene can often be studied most effectively by placing it into a cell different from the one from which it was isolated. For example, one may wish to place a mutated oncogene, isolated from a tumor cell, into a normal cell to determine whether it causes malignant transformation (section 5.2). There are several methods for introducing DNA into animal cells (Table A3.2). For transfection to be successful the efficiency of transfer must be high enough for detection

Table A3.2. Methods of Transfer of Genes into Animal Cells

Microinjection of cloned DNA fragments into cells.[a]

Incubation of cells with DNA precipitated with calcium phosphate.[b]

Hybridization with bacterial protoplasts carrying a cloned gene(s) in a plasmid.[c]

Infection with RNA or DNA virus carrying cloned gene.[d]

Electroporation—exposure of cells to voltage pulse enhances uptake of DNA.[e]

[a]Palmiter and Brinster, 1985.
[b]Graham and van der Eb, 1973.
[c]Shaffner, 1980.
[d]Bernstein et al, 1985.
[e]Potter et al, 1984.

and there must be a method for recognition and selection of cells containing the newly introduced gene.

The most efficient method for introducing a new gene into cells is to insert the cloned gene into an RNA virus and allow the virus to infect the cell (see Bernstein et al, 1985, for review). The major disadvantage of this technique is that only relatively small pieces of DNA (up to 10 kb) can be transferred. The most common method is the calcium phosphate precipitation technique (Graham and van der Eb, 1973). In this method, calcium phosphate is used to precipitate DNA in large aggregates; for unknown reasons, some cells take up large quantities of such DNA. Although this technique is less efficient than the use of retrovirus, it allows the introduction of large numbers of large pieces of DNA into single cells. Some transferred genes, such as those conveying resistance to drugs, allow easy selection of the cells into which they are introduced. When the newly introduced gene offers no selective advantage to the recipient cell, a selectable gene, such as the gene encoding resistance to the antibiotic neomycin or to the anticancer drug methotrexate, can be introduced simultaneously by taking advantage of the fact that frequently cells which can take up one gene will also take up another.

A3.4 MAPPING GENES TO SPECIFIC CHROMOSOMES

A3.4.1 OVERVIEW

Once a gene or gene function has been identified, it is necessary to map it to a specific chromosome. Mapping of genes may provide clues about which genes are affected by chromosome breaks or other abnormalities. Genes whose chromosomal locations are known can also be used to map additional genes. Many of the studies on tumors have depended on knowledge of the location of genes. For example, the observation that the abl oncogene was located on chromosome 9 near the region of the break point in the Philadelphia chromosome stimulated investigators to examine the tumor cells for possible involvement of the abl oncogene in this rearrangement (Heisterkamp et al, 1983). The following sections describe several methods used for mapping a specific gene or gene function to a specific chromosome.

A3.4.2 DELETION ANALYSIS

Congenital abnormalities involving deletion of parts of a chromosome almost invariably lead to severe congenital anomalies. These defects are often useful in identifying missing genes within the deleted chromosome. For example, the genes responsible for causing retinoblastoma and Wilms' tumor were mapped to chromosomes 13 and 11, respectively, because whenever deletions involved the 13q14 region of chromosome 13 the affected individuals developed retinoblastoma, and whenever the deletion involved the 11p13 region the individuals developed Wilms' tumor. In addition to the tumors, the affected individuals had several other congenital anomalies, indicating that many genes were affected by the deletion. If many individuals with a particular abnormality and chromosomal deletion are available for study, one can define precisely the location of a specific gene. Figure A3.9 shows a series of deletions affecting chromosome 13 in individuals with retinoblastoma (Ward et al, 1984). The only common region of overlapping deletion involves a small portion of the q14 band, thus localizing the retinoblastoma gene to this region. It should be emphasized that this method of mapping has limited resolution since each band in a chromosome contains on the average 3 million base pairs of DNA.

A3.4.3 LINKAGE ANALYSIS

If two genes are close together on a chromosome, they tend to be inherited as a single unit (ie, they appear "linked" together). Of course, any two markers on a single chromosome can segregate through the phenomenon of meiotic recombination, but the closer the two genes are together on a chromosome the less likely they are to be separated by a crossover during meiosis. Thus, one can attempt to map a new gene by looking for its linkage with other previously mapped genes. If several large families are available for analysis, one can also look for meiotic recombination and obtain an esti-

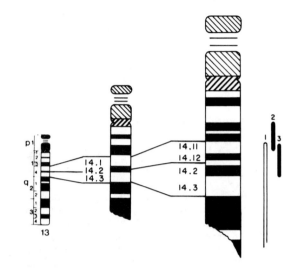

Figure A3.9. Cytogenetically detectable deletions in human chromosome 13 used to map the RB1 and ESD loci. Three different patients with deletions affecting chromosome 13 are indicated. All patients had the eye tumor, retinoblastoma. From examination of these three patients, the smallest region of overlap is in the upper part of the q14.11 band. Thus, the RB1 locus must be in this region of chromosome 13. In addition, these deletions give information about the location of the enzyme esterase D (ESD). In the patient whose deletions are indicated by the solid bars, ESD activity is lost from the deleted chromosome. In contrast, in patient 1, indicated by the open bar, ESD is normal. Although the deletions in patients 1 and 3 appear to begin at the identical place, the deletion in patient 1 must start distally to ESD, while the deletion in patient 3 includes ESD. Thus, these series of deletions allow the mapping of both ESD and RB1 to a small region of chromosome 13 and indicate that ESD is closer to the centromere than RB1.

mate of the distance of separation of two linked genes. In fact, the distance between genes in a linkage map is given in recombination units or centiMorgans (1 cM = a meiotic recombination frequency of 1% in offspring).

The assignment of the retinoblastoma gene to chromosome 13 was confirmed by its close linkage to an enzyme, esterase D (ESD), which had been mapped previously to chromosome 13. ESD exists as isozymes that may be separated by electrophoresis, and many individuals are heterozygous for type 1 and type 2 of the enzyme. Figure A3.10 shows a family in which both the retinoblastoma genes and the esterase D genes can be followed. This small family shows the close linkage between retinoblastoma and ESD. There has never been an observed recombination between the two loci, indicating that they are probably less than 1 cM apart. If the assays for the genes being investigated are simple, and if there are several families or a very large family available for investigation of linkage, this technique can provide rapid and accurate information

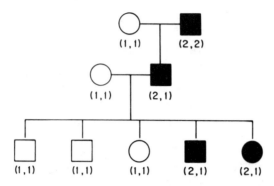

Figure A3.10. This pedigree shows the segregation of retinoblastoma (solid symbols) and esterase D isozymes (indicated in parentheses below each symbol). It is obvious that the chromosome with the retinoblastoma mutation must be linked to the chromosome containing isozyme type 2. In the second generation, the male with retinoblastoma is heterozygous for the ESD isozymes. In the third generation, only the children inheriting chromosome 13 with the type 2 isozyme developed retinoblastoma. This family illustrates the linkage of the retinoblastoma phenotype with the ESD locus.

about gene localization. However, reliable results require the examination of many members of several families.

A3.4.4 SEGREGATION AND SOMATIC CELL HYBRIDS

One of the most useful methods for mapping genes involves the use of somatic cell hybrids. A hybrid cell can easily be formed from a rodent cell, such as a mouse fibroblast, and a human cell, such as a human fibroblast. The hybrid cells usually express most of the genes expressed by the two parent lines. As the human-rodent hybrid cells are propagated in tissue culture, the hybrids tend to lose human chromosomes and retain the rodent chromosomes. Shortly after hybridization, loss of chromosomes occurs rapidly but the hybrid cell becomes more stable after some chromosomes have been lost. If a series of subclones are derived from an original hybrid cell line after the period of maximum chromosome loss, the cells in these clones will contain close to a full complement of mouse chromosomes and a random sample of human chromosomes. In principle, it is possible to obtain hybrids with only one or two human chromosomes, and a gene can be mapped by simply examining the subclones for the presence or absence of the human gene in question. The presence of the gene may be detected through its product, or by the use of Southern blot analysis if the gene has been isolated and a labeled probe is available. By correlating the presence of the gene with the chromosomes present in these hybrids, it is possible to identify the human chromosome on which the gene is located. The data in Table A3.3 show an example of data obtained using such hybrids to map a gene whose product is involved in the repair of UV-irradiated DNA. In this example it is clear that the DNA repair gene is present on chromosome 19 because it is expressed only when that chromosome is present in cell hybrids (Rubin et al, 1985).

The technique as described above simply locates the gene somewhere on the chromosome, but other refinements in the hybridization techniques can allow more precise localization of the gene. For example, it is possible to make a series of hybrids beginning with parental lines having chromosomal deletions or translocations. After loss of human chromosomes, some of the hybrids will then contain only a portion of one or more chromosomes.

A3.4.5 IN SITU HYBRIDIZATION

This recently developed technique localizes a cloned DNA fragment to a specific band on a chromosome. The rationale for the procedure is that a highly radioactive fragment of DNA from the gene to be mapped will hybridize to its homologous sequences on a chromosome under appropriate conditions. Metaphase chromosomes are treated gently to denature the DNA and the slides are incubated with radioactive DNA from the gene to be studied. The radioactive DNA will reanneal to the piece of DNA in the precise location of the chromosome. After washing, the slides are dried, overlaid with a photographic emulsion and placed in the dark to allow sufficient time for radioactive decay to occur. The majority of silver grains in the emulsion should be located above the precise chromosomal location of the radioactive probe. For an accurate identification of the location of the gene, it is necessary to examine a large number of silver grains that are located precisely above chromosomes and to plot their location on a schematic karyotype similar to that shown in Figure A3.2. Most grains will occur in the region where the gene is located. Figure A3.11 shows an example of in situ hybridization of a probe for the N-myc oncogene to its location on chromosome 2.

A3.4.6 SORTED CHROMOSOMES

It is possible to isolate large numbers of intact chromosomes from mitotic cells of a rapidly growing cell line. When these chromosomes are stained with a fluorescent dye (Hoechst 33258) and passed through a fluorescence-activated cell sorter (section 9.4.1), they produce the fluorescence profile shown in Figure A3.12 (Fantes et al, 1983). Many chromosomes give unique fluorescence signals, and they may be separated on the basis of the intensity of their fluorescence signals. A

Table A3.3. Distribution of Human Chromosomes in Rodent–Human Somatic-Cell Hybrids Segregating Sequences Homologous to the DNA Repair Gene

Hybrid	Hybridization with DNA Repair Gene Probe	Presence of Human Chromosome										
		1	2	3	4	5	6	7	8	9	10	11
A	+	+	−	+	−	−	−	+	+	−	+	+
B	−	−	−	−	−	+	−	+	−	−	+	+
C	−	−	−	+	−	−	−	+	−	−	−	+
D	−	−	−	+	+	+	−	+	+	−	+	*
E	+	+	+	+	−	+	−	−	−	−	*	+
F	−	−	−	−	−	−	−	−	−	−	−	−
G	−	+	−	+	−	+	+	+	−	−	−	−
H	−	−	−	−	−	+	−	−	−	−	−	−
I	−	−	−	−	−	+	−	−	−	−	−	+
J	+	−	−	−	−	−	−	−	−	−	−	−
K	+	−	+	−	+	+	+	+	−	−	+	+
L	+	+	+	−	+	+	+	+	−	−	+	+
M	+	−	−	−	+	−	−	+	−	−	−	−
N	+	−	+	+	−	−	−	−	−	+	−	−
O	−	−	−	−	+	−	+	−	−	+	−	−
P	+	+	−	+	+	−	−	−	−	+	−	+
Q	+	−	−	+	+	−	−	−	−	−	−	−
No. of discordant clones		6	5	7	6	11	9	9	9	8	7	7

Hybrid	Hybridization with DNA Repair Gene Probe	Presence of Human Chromosome										
		12	13	14	15	16	17	18	19	20	21	22
A	+	+	−	+	+	+	−	−	+	+	−	−
B	−	−	−	−	−	−	−	+	−	+	+	−
C	−	−	−	−	−	−	−	+	−	+	+	−
D	−	+	−	+	−	+	−	+	−	−	+	−
E	+	−	−	−	+	−	−	+	+	−	+	−
F	−	−	−	−	−	−	−	−	−	−	−	−
G	−	+	+	+	−	+	+	−	−	+	+	−
H	−	−	−	−	−	−	+	+	−	+	+	−
I	−	−	−	−	−	−	+	+	−	−	+	−
J	+	−	+	+	−	−	+	−	+	+	−	−
K	+	−	+	+	−	−	+	+	+	+	+	−
L	+	−	+	+	+	−	+	+	+	+	+	−
M	+	−	−	+	−	−	−	−	+	−	−	−
N	+	−	+	+	−	+	−	−	+	−	+	+
O	−	+	−	+	+	−	−	−	−	−	+	−
P	+	+	−	+	−	+	−	−	+	−	−	−
Q	+	+	−	+	−	−	−	−	+	−	−	+
No. of discordant clones		9	6	4	7	8	9	11	0	9	12	7

Note: From Rubin et al, 1985, with permission.

*Indicates that the designated chromosome in the hybrid was involved in a rearrangement in the human parental cells and in the hybrid and was not scored.

recently developed technique allows for individual chromosomes to be sorted directly onto nitrocellulose paper (Lebo et al, 1985). The DNA is concentrated in a tiny spot and the resulting filter can be used directly for hybridization studies to determine whether or not a specific gene can hybridize to the DNA in the spot. The advantage of this technique is that it requires relatively little material, only 30,000 chromosomes per spot, and

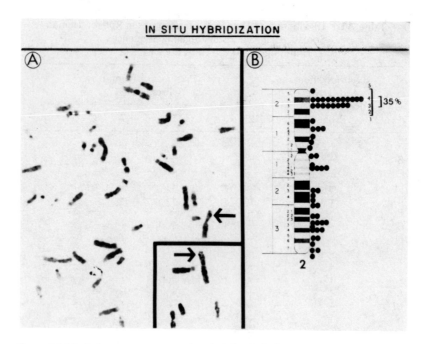

Figure A3.11. A chromosome spread with individual silver grains lying on top of the short arm of chromosome 2 (arrows) is shown (*left*). In this instance, the radioactive probe was for the N-myc oncogene. After examining 100 chromosome spreads and counting 57 silver grains, these investigators found 35% of the silver grains at the P23 to P24 bands on chromosome 2. Although the technique has some background, it generally gives an unequivocal localization of a gene. (From Schwab et al, 1984. Reprinted with permission from Macmillan Journals Limited.)

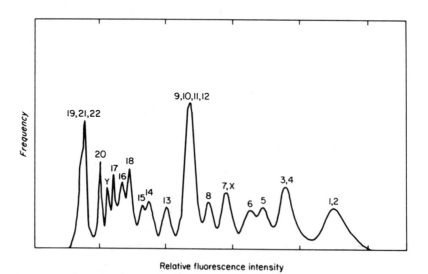

Figure A3.12. The fluorescence profile obtainable from the chromosomes of a particular individual is illustrated. As indicated, many chromosomes are found singly in individual peaks of fluorescence. Because chromosomes can be sorted on the basis of their fluorescence intensity, it is possible to deflect droplets containing individual chromosomes onto nitrocellulose filters. Accumulation of 30,000 chromosomes on a single filter provides sufficient DNA to allow a Southern blot type of analysis.

it is rapid and objective. Although a few human chromosomes, such as some members of the C group (chromosomes 9–12), do not separate cleanly, most of the other chromosomes give a unique peak. Recent developments in technology suggest that it will soon be possible to uniquely identify and separate each of the human chromosomes. It is probable in the future that all mapping of cloned genes will be performed using sorted human chromosomes.

REFERENCES

Bernstein A, Berger S, Huszar D et al: Gene transfer with retrovirus vectors, in Setlow JK, Hollander A (eds), *Genetic Engineering: Principles and Methods*. New York, Plenum, 1985, Vol 7, pp. 235–261.

Fantes JA, Green DK, Cooke HJ: Purifying human Y chromosome by flow cytometry and sorting. *Cytometry* 1983; 4:88–91.

Graham FL, Van der Eb AJ: A new technique for the assay of infectivity of human adenovirus 5 DNA. *Virology* 1973; 52:456–467.

Heisterkamp N, Stephenson JR, Groffen J et al: Localization of the *c-abl* oncogene adjacent to a translocation break point in chronic myelocytic leukemia. *Nature* 1983; 306:239–242.

Lebo RV, Tolan DR, Bruce BD et al: Spot-blot analysis of sorted chromosomes assigns a fructose intolerance disease locus to chromosome 9. *Cytometry* 1985; 6:478–483.

Maniatis T, Fritsch EF et al: *Molecular Cloning. A Laboratory Manual*. Cold Spring Harbor, NY, Cold Spring Harbor Laboratory, 1982.

Nowell PC, Hungerford DA: A minute chromosome in human chronic granulocytic leukemia. *Science* 1960; 132:1497.

Palmiter RD, Brinster RL: Transgenic mice. *Cell* 1985; 41:343–345.

Potter H, Weir L, Leder P: Enhancer-dependent expression of human kappa immunoglobulin genes introduced into mouse pre-B lymphocytes by electroporation. *Proc Natl Acad Sci USA* 1984; 81:7161–7165.

Rowley JD: A new consistent chromosomal abnormality in chronic myelogenous leukaemia identified by quinacrine fluorescence and Giemsa staining. *Nature* 1973; 243:290–293.

Rubin JS, Prideaux VR, Willard HF et al: Molecular cloning and chromosomal localization of DNA sequences associated with a human DNA repair gene. *Molec Cell Biol* 1985; 5:398–405.

Schaffner W: Direct transfer of cloned genes from bacteria to mammalian cells. *Proc Natl Acad Sci USA* 1980; 77:2163–2167.

Schwab M, Varmus HE, Bishop JM et al: Chromosome localization in normal human cells and neuroblastomas of a gene related to c-myc. *Nature* 1984; 308:288–291.

Southern EM: Detection of specific sequences among DNA fragments separated by gel electrophoresis. *J Mol Biol* 1975; 98:503–517.

Ward P, Packman S, Loughman W et al: Location of the retinoblastoma susceptibility gene(s) and the human esterase D locus. *J Med Genet* 1984; 21:92–95.

Worton RG, Duff C. Karyotyping. *Meth Enzymol* 1979; 58:322–344.

Yunis JJ: Chromosomes and cancer: new nomenclature and future directions. *Hum Pathol* 1981; 12:494–503.

BIBLIOGRAPHY

Lewin BM: *Genes*, ed 2. John Wiley & Sons, New York, 1985.

Maniatis T, Fritsch EF et al: *Molecular Cloning. A Laboratory Manual*. Cold Spring Harbor, NY, Cold Spring Harbor Laboratory, 1982.

Thompson JS, Thompson MW: *Genetics in Medicine*, ed 4. Philadelphia, WB Saunders, 1986.

4

Viruses and Cancer

Rose Sheinin, Tak W. Mak and Stephen P. Clark

4.1 INTRODUCTION

The study of tumor viruses began in 1908 when Ellerman and Bang (1908) demonstrated that an extract from circulating blood cells of leukemic chickens induced leukemia when injected into normal chickens. In 1911, Peyton Rous (1911) performed the same kind of experiment with a "filterable agent" from a fibrosarcoma. Studies over two decades by Shope and coworkers, beginning in 1913, led to the discovery of two viruses which were established as the etiologic agents for fibromas and malignant papillomas in wild and domestic rabbits on three continents (cf Shope, 1966). These successes in transferring neoplastic disease by viruses had little influence on the medical and scientific communities, partly because of the novelty of viruses as infectious agents and partly because of skepticism about the relevance of tumors in birds and rabbits to those in human beings. Also, a major difficulty with this work was lack of experimental reproducibility.

Reproducible results were obtained by Bittner (1942), who discovered a factor which was passed from nursing mothers to newborn mice in the milk. This caused a high incidence of mammary tumors in female C_3H mice. Susceptibility to this virus, mouse mammary tumor virus (MMTV), is strain-specific and therefore genetically determined. Newborn and very young animals were found to be sensitive to the virus, but older animals were resistant, a finding which is related to the immunocompetence of the animals. The action of MMTV was found to be dependent upon host physiology, and in particular upon stimulation by estrogen. Female C_3H mice were highly susceptible to breast cancer mediated by MMTV, whereas male mice only developed tumors when treated with estrogen.

These early studies suggested strongly that neoplastic disease in animals could be caused by viruses. Skeptics remained, however, because the results were variable and the available experiments did not always satisfy Koch's postulates (Table 4.1), which are regarded as the definitive test of whether a disease is caused by an infectious agent.

4.2 EXPERIMENTAL METHODS AND DEFINITIONS

4.2.1 IN VIVO ASSAY FOR TUMOR VIRUSES

In the early 1950s Gross (1983) recognized the following recurring themes in the older literature, with regard to tumor induction by viruses:

Table 4.1. Koch's Postulates for Identifying an Infectious Agent as the Cause of a Specific Disease

1. From a specific diseased tissue one should be able to isolate a unique infectious agent.

2. This microorganism, upon inoculation into a susceptible host, should produce the same disease or disease state.

3. The disease should be indefinitely transmissible by the recovered unique infectious agent.

4. Antibody to the unique infectious agent should prevent transmission of disease by this organism.

1. Young or newborn animals are more susceptible to deliberate infection by the Rous sarcoma virus, MMTV, Shope fibroma and Shope papilloma viruses.

2. Susceptibility is inversely dependent upon immunocompetence; ie, the more immunocompetent, the less sensitive is the animal to viral oncogenesis.

3. Adult animals are totally resistant, except under conditions such as treatment with chemicals, radiation or immunosuppression.

Based on these observations, Gross set out to isolate the virus which he believed to be the cause of leukemia which occurred spontaneously at 100% incidence in AKR and C58 strains of mice. During these studies he developed a reproducible test for tumor induction by viruses, which is now used routinely (Fig 4.1). Gross prepared a cell-free extract of leukemic cells from AKR mice, and injected it into newborn C_3H mice, not normally susceptible to leukemia. He found that 100% of these mice developed the disease later in life. Eventually the virus responsible, a murine leukemia virus (MuLV), was isolated.

This simple test of preparing a cell-free extract of tumor cells, injecting it into newborn hosts and watching for the development of a tumor, has since been used to identify more than 2000 tumor virus isolates. The method satisfies Koch's postulates (Table 4.1) and provides definitive evidence for the action of the infectious agent in naturally occurring cancer.

4.2.2 VIRAL INFECTION

The productive infection of host cells by any virus proceeds in a number of stages. First, the virus adsorbs to plasma membrane receptors, usually specific to that microorganism. The virus penetrates the cell by a process of endocytosis, or pinocytosis. Once inside the cell the virus undergoes a process of "uncoating," by which the viral nucleoprotein is made accessible to enzymes

which transcribe m-RNA and/or replicate the viral genome.

The "early stage" of virus production is that characterized by the formation of what are termed the "early proteins." They include sets of regulatory proteins and enzyme proteins which participate in replication of the viral genome and induction of the cellular machinery that may be necessary for viral DNA replication. The early stage ends with the onset of replication of the viral genome, and heralds the "late stage" of virus multiplication. This is usually linked with the synthesis of viral nucleoproteins, which become associated with the replicating genome. The capsid proteins, viral membrane glycoproteins and any other virion peptides made after initiation of viral genome synthesis are termed "late proteins."

Nonproductive or abortive infection occurs if there is no formation of infectious virus or of virus particles. During such infection some of the early proteins are made but usually no viral DNA or late proteins are produced.

4.2.3 IN VITRO PLAQUE ASSAY FOR VIRUS

In vitro cultivation of a tumor virus was first achieved with polyoma virus (described in Eddy, 1969). Mouse embryo cells were infected with a cell-free extract of murine tumor tissue and viral multiplication in these permissive cells was found to cause cell death (Fig 4.2a). The amount of virus can be determined using a plaque assay (Fig 4.2b). Permissive cells, grown

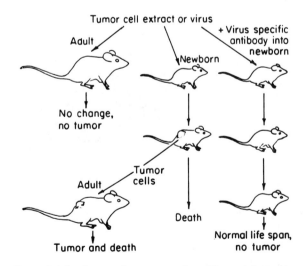

Figure 4.1. In vivo test for a tumor virus. Viruses injected into adult animals rarely cause tumors. Viruses injected into newborn animals cause tumors, but this may be prevented by specific immunization. Cells from the tumors which develop in newborn animals can be transplanted to form tumors in adult animals. (Adapted from Sheinin, 1975.)

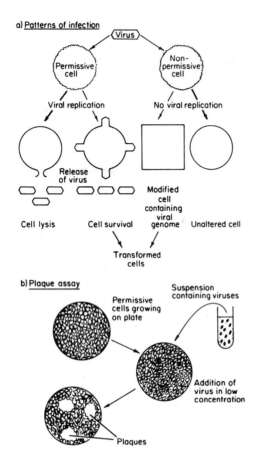

Figure 4.2. *a*, Patterns of viral infection of cells which permit, or do not permit, viral multiplication. (Adapted from Sheinin, 1975.) *b*, Schematic diagram of a plaque assay used to determine the number of infectious viruses in a suspension.

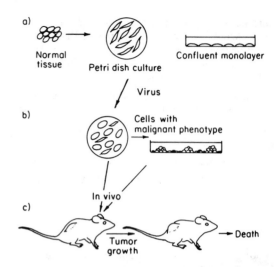

Figure 4.3. *a*, Normal cells usually grow in culture attached to a surface until they form a confluent layer. *b*, Infection with a virus may cause transformation of some of the cells which proliferate and pile up to form identifiable foci (see Fig 4.4). *c*, Injection of such transformed cells into syngeneic animals leads to tumor formation. (Adapted from Sheinin, 1975.)

almost to confluence on a solid surface, are exposed to virus at a concentration of less than one viral particle per cell. Every infected cell then produces virus and causes cell lysis. The virus particles that are released infect adjacent cells, and the process continues. When the cell culture is stained a few days later, the plaques (or holes) due to virus-killed cells can be seen and counted. Each plaque derives from a single infectious virus particle.

4.2.4 IN VITRO ASSAY FOR TUMOR VIRUS: TRANSFORMATION

When normal mouse fibroblasts are cultured in vitro on a solid substratum, they grow until they make contact with another cell. In a confined vessel, growth ultimately ceases as a result of contact inhibition (Fig 4.3a). The resulting confluent layer of cells exhibits a characteristic pattern, determined by cell type. Malignant cells show little or no contact inhibition in vitro

and give rise to multilayered and disorganized colonies (see also section 8.4.2). These properties were used to develop the in vitro transformation assay which is shown schematically in Figure 4.3b.

If normal cells are infected with a tumor virus under conditions which do not result in lysis of all the cells, some may undergo viral transformation (Fig 4.2b). Cell morphology is altered and the pattern of cell growth is modified because of loss of contact inhibition. As a result, transformed cells form multilayered, disorganized colonies, or foci, of cells on the surface of the culture dish (Figs 4.3b and 4.4). To demonstrate that these foci contain malignant cells, the transformed colonies are dissociated into single cells, and injected into adult animals of the appropriate syngeneic background. Under such condition the host adult animals, which are resistant to the free virus (Fig 4.1), will permit the transformed cells to grow to form a transplantable tumor (Fig 4.3c).

The in vitro transformation assay for a tumor virus demonstrates its ability to alter the characteristic growth properties of susceptible cells in a stable, heritable fashion. The assay has been used to detect a large number of tumor viruses, and many of these have been shown to satisfy Koch's postulates (Table 4.1). Not all putative tumor viruses, nor all virus-transformed cells identified by this test, have been examined for their ability to cause tumors in animals. However, in vitro cell transformation has facilitated study of the mode of action of tumor viruses, and also of chemical and phys-

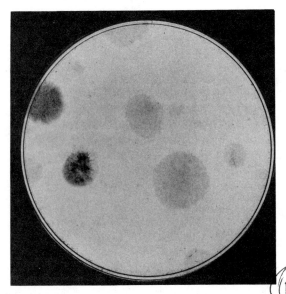

Figure 4.4. Photograph of colonies of normal or SV40-transformed Swiss 3T3 mouse fibroblasts. The palely stained flat colonies of normal cells can be readily distinguished from the heavily stained, disorientated and overgrown colonies of virus-transformed cells.

ical carcinogens (see sections 6.5 and 7.5). In vitro transformation is an important assay for the study of human tumor viruses, which cannot ethically be evaluated by the in vivo test shown in Figure 4.1. Transformed human cells can be tested for tumor induction in susceptible experimental animals, such as the nude mouse (see section 17.4.2).

4.2.5 THE FAMILIES OF TUMOR VIRUSES

The development of reproducible assays allowed the demonstration that many different forms of spontaneous or experimentally induced tumors are caused by viruses in plants, reptiles, amphibians, birds and mammals. The tumor viruses fall into two major classes: DNA-containing, "oncodnaviruses" (Tooze, 1981) or RNA-containing, originally called "oncornaviruses," but now referred to as oncogenic retroviruses (Weiss et al, 1985).

Six of the seven known families of DNA viruses have been shown to contain oncogenic members (Table 4.2). In contrast, only 1 of the 9 or 10 groups of RNA viruses are known to act as tumor-inducing agents. This group contains the B-, C-, and D-type retroviruses.

Table 4.2 highlights the heterogeneity of the seven different classes of tumor viruses. The viral genome may be DNA or RNA (in one of many physical forms), and it may be replicated in the nucleus (most often) or in the cytoplasm of infected cells. In some viruses the

nucleic acid codes for almost all known enzymes required for their genome duplication. In others, it encodes a single protein essential for such replication and depends on the host cell to supply the rest.

4.3 DNA TUMOR VIRUSES

4.3.1 INTEGRATION OF VIRAL DNA

The usual property which distinguishes tumor viruses from all others is their ability to effect stable integration of their viral genome into the genomic DNA of the host cell (Fig 4.5). Thus viruses may become chromosomal parasites and give rise to genetically transformed cells carrying one or more copies of part or all of the viral genome.

Various interactions of viruses with cells, some of which can lead to stable integration of viral DNA, are illustrated in Figure 4.2. Those cell–virus outcomes which yield a surviving cell are of relevance to the induction of cancer. Surviving cells may harbor viral genetic material. Some of these make and release viral particles. It is from genetically transformed cells that malignant cells may emerge in the host.

Many types of virus-transformed cells and cells from

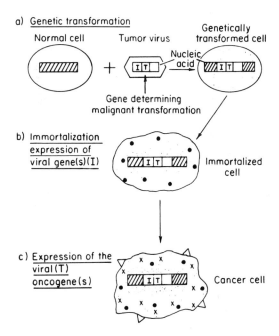

Figure 4.5. Schematic diagram to illustrate transformation of cells by a tumor virus. *a*, Integration of viral DNA into chromosomal DNA. *b*, Expression of one or more viral genes (indicated by I) leading to immortalization of the cells. *c*, Expression of a viral gene (indicated by T) or cellular oncogene leading to malignant transformation. New antigens are formed on the surfaces of the cells during this process.

Table 4.2. Families of Tumor Viruses

Virus Group	Examples	Natural Cancers: Host	Natural Cancers: Disease	Genome Molecular Weight	Site of Multiplication	In Vitro Transformation
Hepadna	hepatitis B	human woodchuck duck	primary hepato-cellular carcinoma (PHC)	DNA ~2×10^6 d	nucleus	+
	ground squirrel	squirrel	PHC			
Papilloma (Papova A)	Shope papilloma canine papilloma equine papilloma human papilloma	rabbit dogs horses human	benign papilloma papillomata papillomata papillomata, cervical carcinoma	DNA ~5×10^6 d	nucleus	+
Papova B	polyoma SV40 human papova	mouse monkey human	unknown unknown unknown	DNA ~3×10^6 d	nucleus	+
Adenovirus	human adeno-12-31 ovine adeno-	human sheep	unknown adenoma	DNA ~20×10^6 d	nucleus	+
Herpes	Marek's disease pig herpes cattle herpes Epstein–Barr	chicken guinea pig cattle human	lymphosarcoma leukemia lymphoma Burkitt's lymphoma nasopharyngeal carcinoma	DNA ~90×10^6 d	nucleus	+
Pox	Shope fibroma Yaba *Molluscum contagiosum*	rabbit monkey human	benign fibroma benign histiocytoma benign molluscum bodies	DNA ~120×10^6 d	cytoplasm	–
Retrovirus				RNA ~6×10^6 d	cytoplasm	+
type B	mouse mammary tumor	mouse	mammary adenocarcinoma			
type C	leukemia–sarcoma complex	reptiles, fish, birds, rodents, cattle, cats, dogs, primates	leukemia–lymphosarcoma diseases			
type D	human T-cell leukemia (HTLV)	human	leukemia–lymphoma			

virally induced tumors have been studied using the methods of molecular biology (section A3.3). In most instances it has been shown that at least one copy of part or all of the viral genome is present in covalent linkage with the high-molecular-weight cellular genomic DNA. In some cells there is single copy insertion. In others, analysis of their DNA has revealed multiple copies of the viral genome. In some cells these are distributed randomly in single copy throughout the cellular genome; in others the viral DNA exists in polymeric form in which single units are linked head-to-tail in tandem array.

Excision of the integrated viral DNA from a chromosome can occur autonomously or following treatment with drugs, radiation, or manipulation of the growth environment. The result is the formation of an episome: a double-stranded, covalently closed DNA molecule which is extrachromosomal. Such episomal DNA may continue to replicate, or it may initiate the formation of new infectious virus by transcription and subsequent translation of the mRNA. Viral DNA may also be packaged into virions which are released for horizontal infection of other cells. This process is known as viral induction (Fig 4.6).

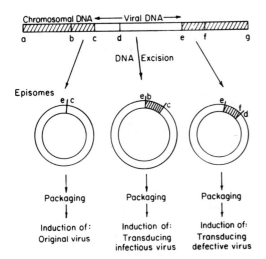

Figure 4.6. Viral induction is the process by which integrated viral DNA gives rise to mature virus particles. The viral DNA is excised from the chromosomal DNA to form an episome. Transduction results when incorrect excision removes part of the cellular DNA with all or part of the viral DNA. Episomes may continue to replicate in the cell, and/or may initiate the formation of mature virus which can be released to infect other cells. This model is derived from studies of bacteriophages.

Sometimes incorrect excision leads to the removal of segments of cellular DNA along with the viral DNA (transduction) and/or to loss of some of the viral DNA (eg, Bourgaux et al, 1982; Pellegrini et al, 1984). Such DNA may be encapsidated, thereby giving rise to transducing particles, which are capable of moving segments of cellular DNA from one host cell to another.

4.3.2 EXPRESSION OF VIRAL GENES

Viral oncogenesis is a complex process. A simplified model identifying three stages which can be studied in cell cultures is shown in Figure 4.5. In the first, the host cell undergoes genetic transformation, during which viral DNA is stably integrated into the cellular genome. In the second stage, the genetically transformed cells express one or more viral genes which allow them to grow indefinitely in cell culture (immortalization). In most instances these two events appear to be essential but not sufficient to produce a cancer cell. This requires expression of one or more viral transforming genes or cellular oncogenes (section 5.1).

Each neoplastic outcome of a virus–cell interaction is uniquely determined by the virus involved and by the nature of the infected cell. There is, however, a general pattern of modifications of cellular processes which occur during viral oncogenesis. Some of these are listed in Table 4.3. Specific determinants of a virus-transformed cell are a result of the expression of one or more viral genes, or are derived from the impact of integrated viral DNA on expression of the genome of the host cell (Fig 4.7). Presence of the viral DNA may lead to derepression of genes which are normally expressed only during fetal development, leading to synthesis of oncofetal antigens (section 12.2). In addition, a family of cellular proteins may be produced, which interact with virus-encoded transforming proteins (Hunter, 1984). Of these, the 53,000-d-molecular-weight (P_{53}) proteins have been most extensively studied. As yet, the precise action of the viral transforming protein/cellular P_{53} complex in oncogenesis is not understood (Crawford, 1983).

Several changes are observed in virus-transformed cells, at the level of mRNA transcription and the formation of proteins in the cell and on the cell surface (Fig 4.7). Important modified antigenic properties are mediated by molecules associated with the plasma membrane of the cell. These surface antigens are glycolipids, glycoproteins and/or proteins. Malignant cells which derive from infection by the same tumor virus tend to express the same surface antigens, at least some of which are encoded by viral genes. These anti-

Table 4.3. Cellular Processes Modified by Viral Oncogenesis

Process Affected	Modification
Multiplication of single cells	regulation altered
Contact inhibition	disrupted or abolished
Differentiation	interrupted or modified
Cell recognition, homing, adhesion and organogenesis	disrupted, resulting in potential to form metastases
Immunogenicity	enhanced and/or modified
Chromosomal replication	aberrant: rearrangements, transformation, aneuploidy, polyploidy

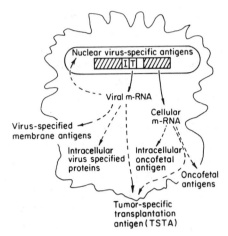

Figure 4.7. Antigenic changes which may occur in virally transformed cells. (Adapted from Sheinin, 1975.)

gens can be recognized by the host immune system, particularly when they are associated with cellular antigens of the major histocompatibility complex (section 14.2.8). This may lead to immune destruction of the tumor cells. If the immune system is unable to kill all

the tumor cells the outcome is neoplastic growth, and usually death of the animal (see also section 14.3.1).

Because naturally occurring and laboratory-produced virus-transformed cells derive from a very broad range of target cells, their phenotypes are equally diverse. A number of tests are available to detect the presence of viral components in cells (Table 4.4), and these are adaptable, with appropriate probes, to the study of human tumor viruses.

4.3.3 HUMAN TUMORS AND VIRUSES

The foregoing discussion summarizes the methods which have been used to provide evidence that a large number of different tumors, in a broad spectrum of animal species, have a viral etiology. This information suggests that some types of cancer in the human animal may also involve tumor viruses. It has been difficult to obtain definitive evidence for this hypothesis for the following reasons:

1. Experiments performed in outbred animals have demonstrated nonreproducibility of detection of tumor viruses, and variable rates of tumor inci-

Table 4.4. Tests for The Presence of Viral Components in Cells*

Component	Nature of Test	Requirement
Virus particle		
Intact virus	infectious virus assay	permissive cells
Particle defective for multiplication	helper virus assay	cell culture system
Transforming particle	transformation assay electron microscopy	in vivo or in vitro system for detecting a tumor virus
Viral nucleic acids		
Integrated viral genome	molecular hybridization	molecular probes, consisting of radioactively labeled viral nucleic acids or transcripts or parts thereof
Viral messenger RNA	molecular hybridization	
Virus-specified cellular components		
Nuclear antigens	immunological assays	specific antisera
Cell-surface antigens	immunological assays	specific antisera
Intracellular antigens	immunological assays	specific antisera
Viral protein		
Structural proteins	immunological assays	antisera to virus particle or specific components thereof
	physicochemical assays	physicochemical procedures for identification of specific viral proteins
Viral enzymes	enzymatic	specific enzyme assay, specific antibody

*Modified from Sheinin (1975).

dence, upon subsequent inoculation with virus. Most reproducible information about tumor viruses in other animals has been obtained in experiments using highly inbred strains, thereby minimizing problems imposed by the immune response.

2. Highly malignant, virus-induced tumor cells do not normally carry free virus at biopsy, nor do they produce or release such virus. Isolation of virus requires induction during extended periods of in vitro cultivation of the tumor cells. The mechanisms involved are poorly understood.

3. Many tumor viruses show rigorous cell, tissue, organ and species specificity, which is retained in vitro. It has been difficult to culture many of the normal human cells which are the suspected targets of viral transformation, thus limiting the application of in vitro assays.

4. The target cell for acute infection and viral multiplication may differ from that which undergoes neoplastic conversion by the tumor virus.

It has been difficult to identify human tumor viruses by the direct application of techniques which were developed for the isolation of tumor viruses of other animals. Nevertheless, the presence of human tumor viruses has been implicated by epidemiological analysis (see chapter 2) and by indirect approaches suggested by the analysis of virally induced tumors in other animal systems (cf Essex et al, 1980). These approaches have led to the isolation of the human viruses which are the probable causes of Burkitt's lymphoma (see section 4.3.9), hepatocellular carcinoma (section 4.3.4) and T-cell leukemia (section 4.4.5). In the following sections, each family of DNA tumor viruses with known oncogenic members is reviewed, with particular reference to human cancer.

4.3.4 HEPATITIS B VIRUS AND HEPATOCELLULAR CARCINOMA

The human hepatitis B virus (HBV) was the first identified member of a virus family which now includes isolates from woodchucks, squirrels and ducks (cf Blumberg, 1980). These viruses are structurally homologous but genetically unique. Each virus infects hepatocytes, and may cause cancer of the liver. The initial infection gives rise to acute hepatitis, which may persist as chronic hepatitis, and may eventually progress to cirrhosis of the liver and to hepatocellular carcinoma (cf Kew, 1984).

HBV is an enveloped DNA-containing virus, whose structure is shown in Figure 4.8. The genome is housed in a nucleoprotein complex, within the viral core (Fig 4.8b). The envelope carries a surface-exposed glycoprotein, which functions as the hepatitis B surface antigen (HBsAg). This molecule interacts with a specific

HBV receptor on the plasma membrane of susceptible hepatocytes in the first step of infection.

The DNA genome of ~2 × 10^6 d molecular weight is circular and partially double stranded (Fig 4.8b).

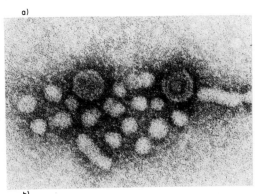

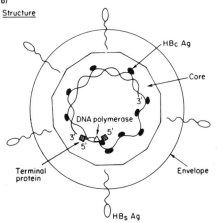

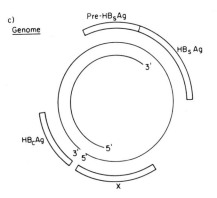

Figure 4.8. *a*, Electron micrograph of hepatitis B virus (HBV), showing two 42-nm complete virus particles and many spherical and filamentous incomplete forms of virus surface antigen particles. (Courtesy of Frances W. Doane, Department of Microbiology, University of Toronto, Canada.) *b*, Structure of the HBV. Note the long and short DNA strands with complementary sequences which overlap at their 5' ends. *c*, Schematic illustration of the genome illustrating the DNA segments encoding the core and surface antigens on the long strand. The region denoted by X may encode a transforming protein. The pre-HBsAg sequence encodes a protein somewhat larger than the surface antigen, produced by subsequent processing.

One strand carries the complete genetic information, whereas the other lacks 15–50% of the complement depending on the virus isolated. When extracted from the virion the DNA retains a circular configuration, because of the base pairing of an overlapping region of some 250 nucleotide residues at the 5′ end of both strands. The resulting structure resembles an episomal DNA (see Fig 4.6).

The viral DNA is associated with the core protein antigen (HBcAg), within the central subunit of the virion. The HBV genome encodes the HBV DNA polymerase, which is thought to be the previously identified HBeAg. It is not known whether the HBV genome contains a specific transforming gene but the X locus (Fig 4.8c) may encode such a protein. The HBV DNA shares some features with other oncogenic viruses, including sequences analogous to long-terminal repeats. These have been most extensively studied in the oncogenic retroviruses (see section 4.4). One potential mechanism for transformation is through promotion or enhancement of cellular oncogenes.

Primary and chronic infection by HBV can be detected by the presence of the HBsAg-carrying envelope fragments, which circulate in the blood (see Fig 4.8a). Electron-microscopic analysis has revealed viral cores in cirrhotic scars. In contrast, the cells from tumors induced by the virus are devoid of any evidence of intact virus, core or HBsAg particles. However, using radiolabeled probes obtained with cloned viral DNA (see section A3.3), it has been shown that HBV-transformed cancer cells carry the double-stranded HBV DNA, covalently linked to the DNA of the cellular chromatin. The mechanism of this integration of HBV DNA into the host genome is not known.

A number of HBV-induced cancer cells have been grown in vitro. Examination of these cells by restriction enzyme analysis (see section A3.3) has revealed that the HBV DNA, in whole or in part, is integrated randomly at multiple, but limited (perhaps six) numbers of sites in the cellular genome. The viral DNA is present as inverted tandem repeats, or as duplicated segments and sequences lacking parts of the genome. Each hepatic cancer can be shown to arise by clonal growth of one unique virus-transformed cell. None of the cells from human liver cancers established in culture has yielded fully infectious HBV, but they have been induced to make specific HBV products, in particular the HBsAg.

For any given hepatic cancer, integrated HBV DNA can be detected not only in the hepatocytes, but also in nontumorous segments of liver. These findings suggest that the tumor may have arisen during an abortive process of liver regeneration in response to destruction of cells by chronic HBV infection. The liver serves as the major organ for detoxification of many chemicals which

enter the body. It is possible that HBV oncogenesis is enhanced by, or even dependent upon, the presence of toxic chemicals or free radicals produced in the course of their metabolism by the liver (see section 6.3).

HBV is endemic in countries of the Far East and Africa. It is transmitted horizontally, primarily from chronically infected mother to young child. It has been estimated by the World Health Organization to induce 80% of all human cancers in these regions. HBV vaccines under test in China have shown promise in prevention of primary infection and its subsequent evolution into cancer. The vaccines presently in use were prepared against HBsAg obtained from the blood of infected individuals, or against virus particles induced in vitro from hepatocellular cancer cell lines (cf Sun et al, 1980; Szmuness et al, 1980). Vaccines against proteins encoded by HBV DNA sequences are being developed using recombinant DNA technology. It is hoped that they will lead to safer and more effective prevention of HBV-induced hepatitis and cancer.

4.3.5 HUMAN PAPILLOMAVIRUSES, WARTS AND CERVICAL CANCER

The human papilloma viruses (HPV), currently classified as type A papovaviruses, cause warts and papillomas which occasionally become malignant (Lutzner, 1983). The viral etiology of human warts was demonstrated in 1917 when cell-free extracts from warts were found to induce similar pathology in host individuals. The HPVs are spherical viruses (Fig 4.9a) with double-stranded, covalently closed DNA of ~5×10^6 d molecular weight. The viral DNA resembles cellular DNA, in that it is associated with cellular histone proteins in the form of a viral minichromosome.

The HPV genome is organized so that transcription of the early and late viral genes proceeds sequentially from opposite strands (Fig 4.9b). Genes encoding the early proteins are designated E1–E8. The early proteins carry information for immortalization and transformation of a target cell. At least one of these proteins can complement polyoma and adenoviruses, which are defective in the immortalizing gene or gene product.

Papillomaviruses exhibit specificity with respect to target cells in their natural hosts, and produce benign warts in differentiating cells of the epithelium. HPV maintains a latent infection in the lower layers of the epidermis and of the mucosal epithelium (Bunney, 1982). Productive infection occurs in the differentiating cells of the skin and internal mucosae, where virus particles can be seen in large numbers using electron microscopy. Progression of warts and papillomata is usually limited and temporary or permanent regression is frequently observed. This may be mediated, in part,

a) Human papilloma virus

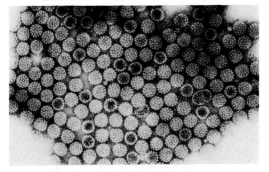

b) Genome organisation of human papilloma virus

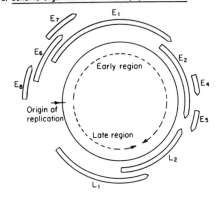

c) Genome organisation-human papova(BK)virus

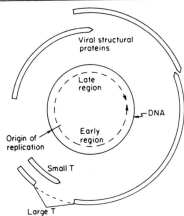

Figure 4.9. *a*, Electron micrograph showing human papillomaviruses which are approximately 50 nm in diameter. (Courtesy of Frances W. Doane, Department of Microbiology, University of Toronto, Canada.) *b*, Diagram illustrating major features of the genome of a human papillomavirus; E and L designate early and late proteins. *c*, Diagram illustrating major features of the genome of the human BK papovavirus.

by an immune response to the virus and/or to transformed cells. Restriction-enzyme analysis indicates that a wart or papilloma derives from a single papillomavirus-transformed cell. HPV DNA remains free within the host-cell nucleus and replicates as an episome in nonproducer cells of benign papillomata.

Laryngeal papillomas have been linked to HPV types 2 and 6 and tend to occur in children whose mothers were infected with genital warts at the time of delivery, suggesting horizontal transmission of virus. In some cases of juvenile laryngeal papillomas, malignant conversion of the disease has been reported. These patients had received radiation to the affected area, suggesting a synergistic effect between the HPV virus and X-irradiation. In adults the cocarcinogen is postulated to be heavy smoking. Recently, skin cancers and widespread wart infections have been observed in kidney transplant patients receiving immunosuppressive drug therapy.

Recent evidence has suggested that HPVs may be involved in the etiology of cervical carcinoma, and of other tumors of the anogenital tract. Molecular probes from several types of HPVs were used to seek the presence of viral DNA segments of a variety of benign and malignant tumors of the genital area. DNA sequences from HPV-6 and HPV-11 were found commonly in condylomas (anogenital warts) but in only 5–10% of cervical cancers (Gissman et al, 1983; Ferenczy et al, 1985). DNA sequences from HPV-2 and HPV-10 have been detected in occasional cervical cancers (eg, Green et al, 1982), but HPV-16 sequences have been found in more than 80% of cervical tumors and 25% of penile and vulvar tumors, in patients from different geographical regions. DNA sequences from HPV-18 have also been detected in cervical cancer. Several cell lines derived from human cervical cancer have been found to harbor HPV genomes.

Cervical cancer cells do not produce mature virus. Serological evidence for HPV capsid protein is found in 50–70% of pure condylomas, and 10–45% of condylomas with associated dysplasia, but is not found in invasive carcinoma of the cervix (eg, Kurman et al, 1983). Thus malignant transformation appears to correlate with loss of the ability to produce mature papillomavirus, perhaps associated with a transition of the HPV DNA from episomal state to integration into the cellular genome.

4.3.6 THE HUMAN PAPOVAVIRUSES

It has been estimated that most humans have been infected with a human papovavirus (type B) by the age of 5 years (cf Howley, 1980). These viruses are usually latent but may be released in large amounts into the urine in immunosuppressed patients.

Transformation of cells by the human papovaviruses has been demonstrated using the in vitro transformation assay (Fig 4.3), followed by injection of cells into nude mice. In recent years the presence of DNA sequences from human papovavirus has been sought in human tumors, using the tools of molecular hybridization. Many samples from a wide range of the most common human tumors were examined (Wold et al, 1978). To date there is no evidence that any of these tumors carry segments of human papovavirus DNA.

Human papovaviruses (Fig 4.9c) encode early proteins referred to as the T antigens. The large T antigen is present in the nucleus of infected cells, where it stimulates cellular DNA replication. It is essential for initiation of viral genome replication, for initiation of transformation and for maintenance of the transformed state. A small T antigen is also made early, but it is incorporated into the plasma membrane. In association with the histocompatibility antigens, it forms the molecular complex which is recognized as the tumor-specific transplantation antigen (TSTA) of papova-virus-transformed cells.

The large T antigens of many of the papovaviruses show sequence homology. In particular, the human papovaviruses are related to the SV40 (simian virus 40) papovavirus (Eddy, 1964) which is able to transform cells from a number of different species (including humans) in vitro, and causes tumors when injected into newborn rodents and rabbits. It has not yet been demonstrated to cause tumors in monkeys, the animal of origin. In the late 1950s, a large number of people around the world (in excess of 10 million) received a live vaccine of attenuated poliovirus. The poliovirus had been grown in monkey kidney cells which were subsequently found to be carrying the SV40 viral genome and could be induced to produce SV40 virus. This virus has been induced in humans by immunosuppressive therapy but does not appear to spread amongst human beings. Of concern is the possibility that the SV40 virus might contribute to the causation of cancer in individuals who have received the infected poliovirus vaccine.

4.3.7 HUMAN ADENOVIRUSES AND NEOPLASTIC DISEASE

The human adenoviruses (Fig 4.10) were first isolated from adenoid tissue. Acute infection with members of this large group may cause respiratory disease, lymphoid infection, conjunctivitis and gastroenteritis. Experimental studies have indicated that some of the human adenoviruses may induce tumors in rodents, and many of them have been shown to cause transformation of cells in vitro (cf Graham, 1984). The genetic organization of the transforming region of a representative adenovirus is indicated in Figure 4.10c. This fragment of viral DNA, comprising 12–14% of the genome, carries all of the information essential for oncogenic transformation (Graham, 1984). The gene

a) Electron micrograph

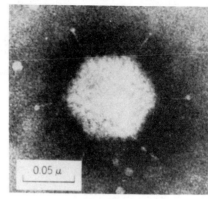

b) Intact virus

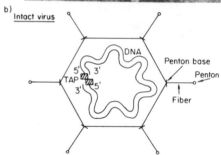

c) Genome

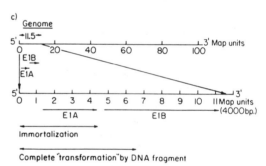

Figure 4.10. *a*, Electron micrograph of an adenovirus. (Modified from Valentine and Pereira, 1965.) *b*, Diagram illustrating some components of a human adenovirus. TAP is the terminal adenoviral protein, which acts as a primer for DNA replication by the adenovirus DNA polymerase. *c*, Schematic illustration of the genome of a human adenovirus indicating the early transforming region (E1A and E1B), which is required for immortalization and transformation of infected cells.

products of this region are required for immortalization and transformation.

Many samples from commonly occurring human tumors have been screened for the presence of integrated or episomal DNA of transforming human adenoviruses, using molecular hybridization (eg, Green et al, 1979). These experiments yielded negative results but the limit of detection was 0.2 adenovirus genome copies per cellular genome. Despite these negative results it remains possible that human adenoviruses play a role in the etiology of rarer types of human cancer. It may be relevant that DNA sequences of human adenoviruses have been found integrated into the cellular DNA of tonsillar tissue (Green et al, 1979). At the present time there is a major interest in adenoviruses because they are a useful tool in the study of the molecular biology of transformation and control of gene expression.

4.3.8 THE ONCOGENIC POXVIRUSES

A poxvirus was identified in 1932 as the etiological agent of rabbit fibromatosis by Shope (1966). Since then only three other poxviruses have been shown to cause tumors. One of these, molluscum contagiosum, was demonstrated to be the causative agent of the benign plantar wart, by direct infection of human beings. Other poxviruses, like vaccinia, cause an increase in the incidence of malignant tumors in animals treated with the chemical carcinogen methylcholanthrene, suggesting a possible cocarcinogenic interaction of virus and chemicals. In addition, poxviruses have been shown to cause in vitro transformation of mouse embryo cells. Shope fibroma and variola viruses promote the growth of cells in vitro and produce persistently infected cells. Taken together, these observations suggest that the poxvirus genomes may have the potential to induce neoplasia under appropriate conditions. The fact that genome replication takes place within the cytoplasm, rather than in the nucleus, of infected cells may limit the ability of the viral DNA to integrate into the cellular genome.

4.3.9 HUMAN HERPES VIRUSES, BURKITT'S LYMPHOMA AND NASOPHARYNGEAL CARCINOMA

In humans, herpes viruses have been implicated in the etiology of Burkitt's lymphoma and nasopharyngeal carcinoma (NPC). Herpes simplex virus II has been associated with cervical cancer but a direct etiological role for this virus now seems less likely.

The herpes viruses are large, complex particles which carry a linear, double-stranded DNA genome of about 10^8 d molecular weight (Fig 4.11). The herpes virus DNA is replicated in the nucleus of the infected cell. The viral genome encodes enzymes that are necessary for viral DNA synthesis, and for induction of formation of cellular proteins required for integration of viral DNA into cellular chromosomes. As shown in Figure 4.11c the viral genome contains a number of regions of repeat sequences. The terminal repeat sequences are involved in viral DNA replication and integration.

a) Electron micrograph

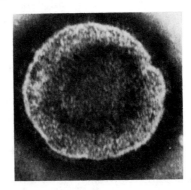

b) Structure

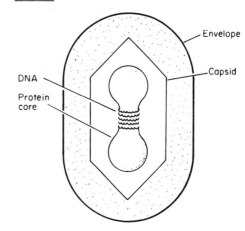

c) Genome of EBV

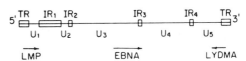

Figure 4.11. *a*, Electron micrograph of a herpes virus. The diameter of the complete virus is about 140 nm. (Courtesy of Frances W. Doane, Department of Microbiology, University of Toronto, Canada.) *b*, Diagram illustrating the important components of a human herpes virus. (Modified from Ginsberg, 1980.) *c*, Schematic illustration of the genome of the Epstein–Barr virus. The linear double-stranded DNA molecule has a number of unique sequences (U_1–U_5) and a number of repeated DNA sequences located both at the 3' and 5' termini of the molecule (TR) and at internal sites (IR1–IR4). The approximate coding regions for the E-B nuclear antigen (EBNA), and two membrane antigens (LMP, LYDMA), are indicated.

In 1958, Burkitt identified a lymphoma in African children which is now known as Burkitt's lymphoma (cf Burkitt, 1958; Glemser, 1970). Epstein and Barr (1964) isolated the causative agent for this lymphoma by in vitro induction from cultured tumor cells. The Epstein–Barr virus (EBV) particles are morphologically indistinguishable from other herpes viruses. Subsequent studies showed that whereas biopsied material was devoid of virus particles, cultured cells yielded large amounts of virus.

Virus production in EBV-transformed cells, irrespective of their origin, can be induced in any one of several ways. These include long-term culture in vitro, X- or UV irradiation, superinfection with virus, and treatment with chemicals such as the promoter 20-tetra-decanoyl-phorbol-13-acetate (TPA), or with bromodeoxyuridine or other nucleotide analogues which disrupt nucleic acid formation and structure.

EBV is transmitted horizontally, infecting >90% of the human population by the age of 20, often without manifestation of disease. EBV is naturally restricted to humans but can infect the marmoset. The host range for EBV replication is confined to a few specific cell types such as B lymphocytes and epithelial cells of the pharyngeal mucosa. The virus may remain latent in, and transform such target cells. EBV induces B lymphocytes to grow in vitro in media which will not support the growth of normal cells. Such lymphoblastoid cell lines can be generated from patients with infectious mononucleosis, the acute phase of infection by EBV, and also by in vitro infection of human B lymphocytes with the virus.

Infectious mononucleosis is usually a benign lymphoproliferative disease and after recovery patients continue to produce antibodies against EBV. The EBV virus establishes a latent infection in B lymphocytes, nasopharyngeal mucosal cells and perhaps other cells. Viral DNA may remain integrated in cellular DNA for the lifetime of that person. In rare circumstances, acute infection by EBV may give rise to a B-cell malignancy which presents like acute leukemia.

Many African children are infected with EBV within the first year of life. There is strong epidemiological evidence for an association between such infection and the later development of Burkitt's lymphoma (de Thé, 1982). The etiology of this disease probably involves additional factors of continuous mitogenic stimulation of B lymphocytes by constant exposure to malarial parasites. The disease is characterized by a translocation of part of chromosome 8 to chromosomes 14, 2 or 22. This translocation may lead to activation of the c-myc oncogene (see section 3.3.3).

There is also epidemiological and molecular evidence for an association between EBV infection and nasopharyngeal carcinoma (NPC), particularly in southern China (de Thé, 1982). The pathogenesis of this disease remains unknown but may relate to an interaction between the viral DNA and unidentified environmental cocarcinogens.

The EBV genome contains enough information to code for some 100–200 average-size proteins. These include the major polypeptides of the nucleocapsid and essentially all of the proteins which participate in EBV DNA replication. An important nonvirion protein is the EBV nuclear antigen (EBNA) which is diagnostic of EBV infection (Fig 4.11c). It is present in large amount in the cell nucleus where it is tightly bound to the chromatin at the site of integration of EBV DNA into the cellular genome. Originally the EBNA antigen was detected in the nucleus of all Burkitt's lymphoma cells, even though there was no evidence of virus particles. It was subsequently demonstrated in the epithelial cells of NPC and in B lymphocytes in the circulation of patients with acute infectious mononucleosis. The EBNA antigen, a DNA-binding protein, appears to regulate initiation of replication of viral DNA and derepression of host-cell DNA synthesis.

Recently, it has been suggested that the EBV DNA carries a transforming gene which encodes a 200-amino-acid plasma-membrane protein with six hydrophobic transmembrane domains (Wang et al, 1985). Its expression, which occurs only in transformed cells (including latently infected, immortalized lymphocytes) results in the loss of contact inhibition, an altered cell morphology and the loss of serum dependence associated with normal lymphocytes. The gene is designated as LMP in Fig 4.11c to denote that it encodes the latent membrane protein. EBV-infected cells also express another membrane antigen known as lymphocyte-determined membrane antigen (LYDMA), which may be recognized by the host as a transplantation antigen.

Various vaccines, directed against the envelope glycoprotein of EBV which is involved in virus–cell interaction, are being tested for their efficacy against infectious mononucleosis, Burkitt's lymphoma and NPC. The purified glycoprotein has been derived from the virus, or has been generated by recombinant DNA technology (see section A3.3) from a cloned sequence of EBV DNA.

4.4 RNA TUMOR VIRUSES

4.4.1 CHARACTERISTICS OF RETROVIRUSES

All oncogenic RNA tumor viruses are retroviruses, the extracellular, infectious forms of which fall into three morphologically distinct classes: B, C, and D (Weiss et al, 1985). The A form is an intracellular, immature stage of one of the other mature types. The B-type retroviruses are implicated in mammary carcinoma; the C-type in carcinomas, sarcomas, leukemias and lymphomas. There are very few D-type isolates, but two are implicated in mammary carcinoma, and another in acute T-cell infection.

The retroviruses are enveloped viruses of about 120 nm diameter (Fig 4.12). Their envelope consists of a lipid bilayer, derived from the plasma membrane, with which are associated functional glycoproteins, proteins and lipoproteins. Internal to the viral envelope is a matrix layer surrounding the core of the virion. This comprises the viral RNA, its associated nucleoprotein and other proteins. The virus contains two single-stranded RNA genomes which are noncovalently linked together near their 5' end.

Interaction of a glycoprotein on the viral envelope with a specific protein on the surface of the cell to be infected results in penetration of the virus into the cytoplasm, where the RNA is converted into double-stranded DNA through the activity of reverse transcriptase (Baltimore, 1970; Temin and Mizutani, 1970) (Figs 4.12 and 4.13). A fraction of the linear molecules migrate to the nucleus where they may be converted to circular forms and integrated into the host DNA. This integrated DNA is known as a provirus. The RNA viral genome is regenerated by transcription of the provirus, by a cellular RNA polymerase. Viral sequences encode proteins necessary for virion assembly and replication. The virus exits from the cell by budding, a process which encloses the capsid within a membrane envelope (Fig 4.12).

4.4.2 THE RETROVIRUS GENOME

The genome of the retroviruses consists of two identical single-stranded RNA molecules with a total molecular weight of about 6×10^6 d. Each RNA strand can serve as a direct template for reverse transcription. Also found in the retrovirus core is a low-molecular-weight transfer RNA (t-RNA), which acts as a primer for RNA-dependent DNA polymerase (reverse transcriptase) during the synthesis of the first strand of the DNA copy of the RNA genome.

The retrovirus genome consists of the following elements reading from left to right in Figure 4.13: the cap

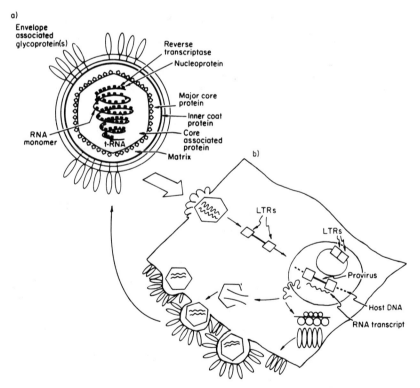

Figure 4.12. *a,* Schematic diagram illustrating the structure of a retrovirus. The virus contains two identical RNA strands, only one of which is shown for clarity. (Adapted from Bolognesi et al, 1978.) *b,* Illustration of the life cycle of a retrovirus. After penetrating the plasma membrane, the single-stranded viral RNA genome is reverse transcribed (copied) to a double-stranded DNA form which has at its extremities a duplication called the long-terminal repeat (LTR). The viral DNA migrates to the nucleus and is converted to a circular form which can integrate into the chromosomal DNA. The single viral transcript can form the genome for daughter viruses, or can be processed and translated to generate viral structural proteins.

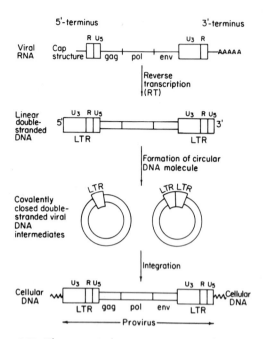

Figure 4.13. The retroviral genome contains three coding regions with two terminal sequences (see text). The pol sequence encodes the enzyme reverse transcriptase, which generates a double-stranded DNA homologous to the original RNA strand. This DNA molecule is flanked by identical long-terminal-repeat (LTR) sequences, as shown. The DNA molecule assumes a circular form prior to integration into cellular DNA, where it is referred to as a provirus. (The relative lengths of the genes and LTRs are not drawn to scale.)

structure, the 5'-terminal sequence, the coding region, the 3'-terminal segment and the polyadenylic acid (poly-A) tail. Both the cap structure and the poly-A tail are present on most cellular messenger RNA molecules. The 5'-terminal region is composed of a segment called R, a repeated sequence of 20–80 nucleotides that is present at both extremities of the genome, and a unique segment (U5) of about 70–100 nucleotides. Adjacent to U5 is the t-RNA primer binding site from which reverse transcriptase initiates DNA synthesis. At the 3' end of the viral RNA is the second copy of the R segment, next to a unique sequence of between 170 and 1260 nucleotides, called U3. Between the protein-coding region and U3 is a stretch of about 15 purine residues which is involved in initiation of the synthesis of the second DNA strand. The gag coding region carries genetic information for the virion core proteins which determine group-specific antigenicity. The pol sequence encodes the reverse transcriptase and a protein involved in proviral integration. The env gene encodes the envelope proteins, which determine the species specificity of the virus.

Figure 4.13 outlines the mechanism by which the reverse transcriptase participates in replication of the viral

genome, and ultimately in its integration into the host cell DNA. A DNA strand complementary to the viral RNA is synthesized. The resulting RNA–DNA hybrid serves as template for the formation of a linear double-stranded DNA molecule which is colinear in physical and genetic structure with the viral RNA, with the exception of the terminal UR sequences. These are modified during the process of reverse transcription such that each terminus is extended by the addition of the U segment of the opposite end. These enlarged segments are referred to as the LTRs or long-terminal repeats. Ultimately a double-stranded, covalently closed viral DNA molecule with one or two LTR segments is formed. The latter serves as the substrate for the event which gives rise to integration into the cellular genome. Integrated retroviral proviruses can be detected at many sites in the cellular DNA. The position of the integration site does not appear to depend on the local DNA sequence of the host chromosome.

The LTR regions are important, since they interface with the cellular flanking DNA, and have promotor and enhancer sequences for the synthesis of viral RNA. Recent evidence indicates that LTR sequences can strongly influence the tropic properties of the virus (ie, the nature of the target cells for malignant transformation) (cf Fields, 1984), and that they may promote or enhance transcription of adjacent, and more distant, cellular genes.

4.4.3 MECHANISMS OF TRANSFORMATION BY RETROVIRUSES

Transforming C-type retroviruses can be separated into groups based on their different mechanisms of transformation. The more intensely studied group consists of viruses which contain a viral oncogene (v-onc). Viruses of this category are almost always defective in replication owing to replacement of some sequences that are required for replication (eg, gag, pol and env sequences) by the viral oncogene (Fig 4.14). They require the presence of a replication-competent "helper" virus in the cells in order to produce new intact viral particles. Analysis of the genome of these retroviruses with labeled probes of known sequence (section A3.3) has indicated that the oncogenes carried by different retroviruses have homologous sequences present in the DNA of all normal vertebrate cells. These normal genes, termed cellular proto-oncogenes (c-onc), are believed to be involved in control of cellular growth and differentiation (see section 5.4).

There is strong evidence that the v-onc genes in retroviruses are derived from their homologous c-onc sequences (see section 5.1.2) by transduction following infection of a cell (Figs 4.6 and 4.14). Because the v-

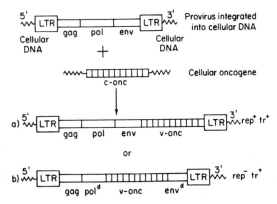

Figure 4.14. Retroviruses may incorporate cellular oncogenes (c-onc) into their genome. The exact mechanism by which this recombination occurs is not known. These viral oncogenes (v-onc) are integrated into different parts of the viral genome without *a*, or with *b*, deletion of viral sequences (indicated by pol^d and env^d). Such viruses may be replication proficient (rep$^+$; *a*) or deficient (rep$^-$; *b*). Replication-deficient viruses require the presence of replication-proficient helper viruses to produce the proteins necessary for forming mature virus particles. The presence of the v-onc may allow rapid transformation of infected cells (tr$^+$). (The relative lengths of the genes and LTRs are not drawn to scale.)

onc genes have come under the control of the efficient retroviral promotor and are no longer tightly regulated by cellular mechanisms, these genes can be expressed at a high level in the virally infected cell. The viral oncogenes are frequently mutated because of the poor fidelity of retroviral replication, with point mutations, deletions, substitutions and insertions as compared to the original cellular oncogene. Some retroviruses which contain oncogenes can transform fibroblasts in cell culture and can induce sarcomas or leukemias from a few days to about 2 months after infection of animals or birds. Such viruses have been termed rapidly transforming, although it is now apparent that retroviruses which contain oncogenes can vary widely in the time at which induced tumors become evident.

A large number of viral oncogenes have been identified and sequenced (see Table 5.1). Evidence for the transforming ability of these oncogenes includes the following: (a) Deletions in the genes may lead to loss of transforming ability of the virus. (b) Identification of viruses, containing temperature-sensitive mutations of the genes, which can transform cells only at certain permissive temperatures. (c) Transformation of cells by introduction of the cloned gene by DNA transfection (see section A3.3).

Another group of transforming C-type retroviruses do not contain known viral oncogenes but appear to act through integration of the provirus near a cellular oncogene (Fig 4.15). These viruses cannot transform fibroblasts in cell culture but they induce leukemias which usually develop from one to several months after an animal is infected. The viruses are replication competent and have been referred to as slow leukemia viruses.

The presence of the strong retroviral promotor in the vicinity of a c-onc gene can lead to increased transcription of this cellular gene, and this probably results in transformation of the cell. The elevated level of transcription of the c-onc gene can be the result of a direct process whereby the retrovirus integrates close to the c-onc gene on the 5′ side in the same transcriptional orientation, a process known as "promotor insertion" (Fig 4.15). Transcription can then initiate in the LTR that is at the 3′ end of the provirus and continues out of the LTR into the adjacent cellular sequences, and through the cellular oncogene. Transformation can also occur if the retrovirus integrates 5′ to the oncogene but in the opposite transcriptional orientation, or if the retrovirus integrates 3′ to the gene. In these situations transcription cannot initiate normally in the LTR and proceed through the cellular oncogene in the usual 5′ to 3′ direction. The strong enhancer properties of the LTRs, which can act at a considerable distance from the point of initiation of transcription, are then believed

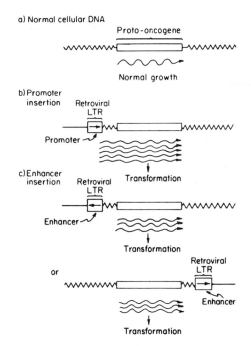

Figure 4.15. Retroviruses which do not carry a v-onc gene may cause cellular transformation by integration of the provirus close to a cellular proto-oncogene (c-onc). The retroviral LTR can then act to increase the transcription of the c-onc gene by *b*, direct promotion or *c*, indirectly as a result of its enhancing properties.

to be responsible for activation of transcription. This mechanism of transformation is known as "enhancer insertion" (Fig 4.15).

4.4.4 RETROVIRUSES AND MAMMARY CANCER

It has been established that mammary tumors in mice may have a viral etiology. The virus involved, the mouse mammary tumor virus (MMTV), is a B-type retrovirus. It is carried endogenously in the mouse genome and can be transmitted in milk from mothers to the offspring in those strains of mice that produce the virus. The life cycle and genome of MMTV is similar to that of other retroviruses. The viral genome does not contain a known oncogene. An interesting feature of the LTR region of the genome is that it contains a promoter sequence which is sensitive to glucocorticoids (see section 13.5.4).

Most strains of inbred mice carry endogenous virus but it is the exogenously acquired virus which appears to be responsible for tumor formation (Hynes et al, 1984). Thus offspring of mice that produce virus in the milk usually do not develop tumors if they are foster-fed by mothers of a strain that does not produce the virus. In mice that develop tumors, a large percentage of mammary gland cells become productively infected with the virus. The viral DNA can apparently integrate at random sites into the host genome of these cells. The fact that only a few of the cells become transformed and form tumors suggests that specific integration sites may have to be involved for the process of tumorigenesis to occur. Analysis of the integration sites of MMTV in a number of murine mammary tumors has indicated that 80–90% of the tumors have proviral DNA integrated into one of two regions known as int-1 and int-2 (Dickson et al, 1984). These regions do not contain known cellular oncogenes but it has been suggested that they may contain unidentified oncogenes. There is evidence that insertion of the proviral DNA can activate transcription of RNA from these regions by an indirect mechanism, possibly as a result of an enhancer property of the proviral LTR.

A few strains of mice may develop tumors without exogenous infection from mother's milk. Endogenously carried MMTV can be detected at various locations in the cellular genome and two of these sites (Mtv-1 and Mtv-2) appear to be directly related to mammary tumor development. A possible link between these observations and those related to virus that is exogenously acquired in mother's milk is that early expression of the MMTV provirus associated with the Mtv-2 locus increases the likelihood that mammary gland cells will produce virus that can infect other cells. Thus, if

random integration of the MMTV into the cellular genome occurs in the infected cells, there is a higher probability that this could occur in the mammary glands of mice in which the provirus is associated with the Mtv-2 locus (see Hynes et al, 1984).

Considerable effort has been expended in the search for a virus which might be the cause of human mammary cancer. These studies have included the use of molecular probes and technology developed during studies of MMTV. To date these studies have not provided convincing evidence for a viral etiology of this disease. Studies of DNA from MMTV-induced mouse mammary tumors and from a human mammary tumor cell line (MCF-7), however, have demonstrated homology between the DNA responsible for transformation of NIH/3T3 cells derived from the two sources.

4.4.5 HUMAN T-CELL LYMPHOTROPIC VIRUSES

Epidemiological studies of adult T-cell leukemia revealed clustering of this disease in some parts of Japan and the Caribbean. A member of the HTLV group of viruses was isolated from a patient with this disease (Hinuma, 1985; Wong–Staal and Gallo, 1985). This virus, HTLV-I, and a related virus isolated from a patient with hairy cell leukemia, HTLV-II, are retroviruses whose host range is restricted to human beings and higher apes. A third member of this group is lymphadenopathy virus (LAV; Montagnier et al, 1984) or HTLV-III (Wong–Staal and Gallo, 1985) which is the probable cause of acquired immune deficiency syndrome (AIDS); a new name has been proposed for this virus—human immunodeficiency virus (HIV). All these viruses infect helper T lymphocytes expressing the OKT4 surface antigen(s). Current evidence suggests that a part of this antigen may function as a component of the HTLV receptor. HTLV-I and HTLV-II can genetically transform these lymphocytes in culture while LAV/HTLV-III (HIV) either causes them to lyse during acute infection or induces a state of chronic infection.

The HTLV group of viruses (Fig 4.16) has some properties which differ from those of other oncogenic retroviruses. The LTR region of the HTLV family is longer than in most other oncogenic retroviruses and the HTLV genome (RNA) has additional genetic information for cellular targetting. The genomes of HTLV-I and HTLV-II contain a locus, known as pX or tat, which is not closely homologous to cellular sequences and hence is not a classical onc gene (Fig 4.16b). The pX gene product is recognised by antibodies in the sera of patients with virus-induced leukemia, and there is

a) Electron micrograph of LAV/HTLV III

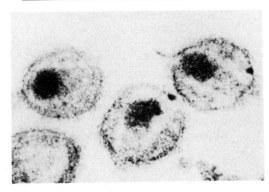

b) Genome of HTLV-I (Leukemia)

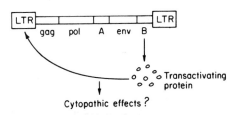

c) Genome of LAV/HTLV III (AIDS)

Figure 4.16. *a*, Electron micrograph of LAV/HTLV-III. The diameter of the viruses is approximately 100 nm. (Courtesy of Dr. Frank Murphy, Centers for Disease Control, Atlanta, GA, and Frances W. Doane, Department of Microbiology, University of Toronto, Canada.) *b*, Schematic illustration of the genome of HTLV-I integrated into cellular DNA. The locus pX encodes a protein (the transactivating protein, tat) which can stimulate the expression of the viral genome after initial activation. *c*, The genome of LAV/HTLV-III encodes a closely related tat protein. The tat mRNA is derived mainly from the region denoted by B. (The relative lengths of the genes and LTRs are not drawn to scale.)

evidence that this protein (now known as the transactivating protein, tat) is critical for the process of transformation (Wong–Staal and Gallo, 1985). The site of integration of the HTLV-I provirus is the same in all leukemic cells of a given patient with adult T-cell leukemia, but the site varies among different patients. These observations indicate that the disease is clonal in nature. The absence of a known oncogene in the genome of HTLV-I suggests that the virus might trans-

form cells through a protein product which would activate cellular oncogenes. Transfection of the pX or tat gene has now been shown to cause transcriptional activation of the HTLV LTR in the recipient cell. This property of the transactivating protein may provide a mechanism that is partly responsible for transformation by HTLV-I, if tat can also activate cellular genes.

Cells transformed by HTLV-I carry one or two copies of proviral DNA integrated into the cellular genome, whereas LAV/HTLV-III (HIV) exists in two forms within infected cells. Multiple copies of LAV/HTLV-III (HIV) provirus are integrated into the cellular DNA and coexist with free circular or linear forms (Wong–Staal and Gallo, 1985). The presence of a large amount of unintegrated viral DNA appears to be characteristic of cytotoxic retroviruses. Genetic information homologous to pX is rearranged in LAV/HTLV-III (HIV) into two regions A and B (Fig 4.16c), and a protein encoded mainly by the B region appears to act as a transactivating protein. The activation produced by this tat gene of LAV/HTLV-III (HIV) is much higher than that of HTLV-I, but it is not known if this is causally related to the cytopathic activity of the virus.

Evidence that LAV/HTLV-III (HIV) is the cause of AIDS has accrued from seroepidemiological studies, and from isolation of the virus in more than 100 patients who either have the AIDS syndrome or are members of a high-risk group (Wong–Staal and Gallo, 1985). The virus has been isolated from blood, plasma, bone marrow, lymph nodes, spleen, semen and saliva of such patients. Patients with AIDS develop adenopathy, multiple infections and often a sarcoma involving the skin known as Kaposi's sarcoma. Virus has not been isolated from these tumors. Kaposi's sarcoma is also observed in other immunosuppressed patients (eg, kidney transplant recipients) and it is unlikely that LAV/HTLV-III (HIV) is a direct cause of the malignant transformation that leads to this tumor.

Genetic analysis and sequencing of LAV/HTLV-III (HIV) isolates has demonstrated that they form a continuous spectrum of related viruses with up to 8% variability in nucleotide sequences (Wong–Staal and Gallo, 1985). The most divergent part of the genome lies in the env gene encoding the exterior glycoprotein where there is a 10–20% difference in amino acids. The development of a suitable vaccine to protect against HTLV viruses is currently under intensive study. Variability in envelope proteins and other problems to be overcome in producing such a vaccine are discussed by Francis and Petricciani (1985). The current best option appears to be incorporation of the env gene into a suitable host (mammalian cell, bacterium, yeast, or nonpathogenic virus) by recombinant DNA technology. The new host would then produce the major envelope glycoprotein, which could be used as a purified antigen to produce a vaccine. It may be necessary to use mammalian cells as the host for the env gene because the protein must be appropriately glycosylated, and to select antibodies against the part of the molecule that shows little or no variation among members of the LAV/HTLV-III (HIV) family. The work on developing a vaccine for AIDS will undoubtedly have a major impact on the development of a vaccine against HTLV-I, HTLV-II and associated T-cell leukemias.

4.5 SUMMARY

Tumors which occur spontaneously in a variety of animals have been shown to be caused by DNA- or RNA-containing tumor viruses. Viruses can be detected in cell-free extracts of cancer cells by infection of newborn animals, in experiments which satisfy Koch's postulates for an infectious agent for disease. In vitro, these viruses can cause genetic and morphological transformation of infected cells. Such cells will generate tumors when injected into a suitable host.

An essential step in malignant transformation of normal cells by most tumor viruses is integration of all or part of the viral DNA (or DNA copy of retroviral RNA) into the host-cell genome. Such viral DNA then acquires immortality as a chromosomal parasite. Expression of specific viral genes leads to the synthesis of new polypeptide(s) which may cause malignant transformation directly, if that protein is the product of a viral oncogene. The viral genes or their protein products may also act indirectly by activating a cellular oncogene. The outcome is a loss of regulation of cellular proliferation, and antigenic changes on the cell surface which modify a cell's interaction with the immune system of the host.

Six of the seven known families of DNA-containing viruses have members which can induce tumors in animals and/or cause genetic transformation and immortalization of cells in vitro. There is evidence that (a) the human hepatitis B virus is a major cause of primary hepatocellular carcinoma, (b) the human papilloma viruses cause benign warts and papillomas and are implicated in the etiology of cervical cancer, and (c) the Epstein–Barr herpes virus is the etiological agent of Burkitt's lymphoma, and possibly nasopharyngeal carcinoma.

Retroviral oncogenes, which may have been derived initially from cellular DNA, may undergo mutational events which enhance their expression and therefore the oncogenicity of the virus which houses them. Oncogenic viruses which induce rapid formation of tumors in animals have acquired oncogenes which are regulated by the viral promotor and enhancer sequences.

Other viruses induce tumors after a longer latency period and are active because they promote expression of cellular oncogenes adjacent to, or even remote from, their site of insertion into the cellular genome. There is evidence that retroviruses cause adult T-lymphocytic leukemia and acquired immunodeficiency syndrome in humans.

Major research efforts are currently directed toward the development of vaccines against these viruses; such vaccines hold promise for reducing the incidence of specific types of human cancer.

REFERENCES

Baltimore D: RNA-dependent DNA polymerase in virions of RNA tumor viruses. *Nature* 1970; 226:1209–1211.

Bittner JJ: Milk-influence of breast tumors in mice. *Science* 1942; 95:462–463.

Blumberg BS: The hepatitis B virus. *Public Health Rep* 1980; 95:427–435.

Bolognesi DP, Montelaro RC, Frank H, Schafer W: Assembly of Type C oncornaviruses: A model. *Science* 1978; 199:183–186.

Bourgaux P, Sylla BS, Chartrand P: Excision of polyoma virus DNA from that of a transformed mouse cell: identification of a hybrid molecule with direct and inverted repeat sequences at the viral–cellular joints. *Virology* 1982; 182:84–97.

Burkitt D: A sarcoma involving the jaws in African children. *Br J Surg* 1958; 46:218–223.

Bunney MH: *Viral Warts: their Biology and Treatment.* Oxford University Press, New York, 1982.

Crawford L: The 53,000 dalton cellular protein and its role in transformation. *Int Rev Exp Pathol* 1983; 25:1–50.

de Thé G: Epidemiology of Epstein-Barr virus and associated diseases in man, in Roizman B (ed): *The Viruses: the Herpesviruses.* Plenum Press, New York, 1982, vol 1, pp 25–103.

Dickson C, Smith R, Brookes S, Peters G: Tumorigenesis by mouse mammary tumor virus: proviral activation of a cellular gene in the common integration region int-2. *Cell* 1984; 37:529–536.

Eddy BE: Simian virus 40(SV40): an oncogenic virus. *Prog Exp Tumor Res* 1964; 4:1–26.

Eddy BE: Polyoma virus. *Virol Monogr* 1969; 7:1–114.

Ellerman V, Bang O: Experimentelle leukamie bei Huhnern *Zentralbl Bakteriol* 1908; 46:595–609.

Epstein MA, Barr YM: Cultivation in vitro of human lymphoblasts from Burkitt's malignant lymphoma. *Lancet* 1964; 1:252–253.

Essex M, Todaro G, zur Hausen H (eds): *Viruses in Naturally Occurring Cancer.* Cold Spring Harbor Laboratory, Cold Spring Harbor, NY, 1980.

Ferenczy, A, Mitao M, Nagai N et al: Latent papillomavirus and recurring genital warts. *N Engl J Med* 1985; 313:784–788.

Fields B: Viral genes and tissue tropism, in Notkins AL, Oldstone MB (eds): *Concepts in Viral Pathogenesis*. Springer Verlag, New York, 1984, pp 102–108.

Francis DP, Petricciani JC: The prospects for and pathways toward a vaccine for AIDS. *N Engl J Med* 1985; 313: 1586–1590.

Ginsberg HS: Herpesviruses, in Davis BD, Dulbecco R, Eisen HN, Ginsberg HS (eds): *Microbiology*, ed 3. Harper and Row, Hagerstown, 1980, pp 1061–1076.

Gissmann L, Wolnik L, Ikenberg H et al: Human papillomavirus types 6 and 11. DNA sequences in genital and laryngeal papillomas and in some cervical cancers. *Proc Nat Acad Sci USA* 1983; 80:560–563.

Glemser B: *Mr. Burkitt and Africa*. World Publishing Co., New York, 1970.

Graham FL: Transformation by and oncogenicity of human adenoviruses, in Ginsberg HS (eds): *The Adenoviruses*. Plenum Press, New York, 1984, pp 339–398.

Green M, Brackmann KH, Sanders PR et al: Isolation of a human papillomavirus from a patient with epidermodysplasia verruciformis. Presence of related viral DNA genomes in human urogenital tumors. *Proc Natl Acad Sci USA* 1982; 79:4437–4441.

Green M, Wold WSM, Mackey JK, Rigden P: Analysis of human tonsil and cancer DNAs and RNAs for DNA sequences of group C (serotypes 1, 2, 5 and 6) human adenoviruses. *Proc Natl Acad Sci USA* 1979; 76:6606–6610.

Gross L: *Oncogenic Viruses*, ed 3. Pergamon Press, New York, 1983.

Hinuma Y: Natural history of the retrovirus associated with a human leukemia. *Bioassays* 1985; 3:205–209.

Howley PM: Molecular biology of SV40 and the human polyoma viruses BK and JC, in Klein G (ed): *Viral Oncology*. Raven Press, New York, 1980, pp 489–550.

Hunter T: The proteins of oncogenes. *Sci Amer* 1984; 251: 70–79.

Hynes NE, Groner B, Michalides R: Mouse mammary tumor virus: transcriptional control and involvement in tumorigenesis. *Adv Canc Res* 1984; 41:155–184.

Kew MC (ed): *Hepatic Tumors: Seminars in Liver Disease 4*. Thieme Stratton, New York, 1984.

Kurman RJ, Jenson AB, Lancaster WD: Papillomavirus infection of the cervix. II. Relationship to intraepithelial neoplasia based on the presence of specific viral structural proteins. *Am J Surg Pathol* 1983; 7:39–52.

Lutzner MA: The human papillomaviruses: a review. *Arch Dermatol* 1983; 119:631–635.

Montagnier L, Chermann JC, Barre-Sinoussi F et al: A new human T-lymphotropic retrovirus: characterization and possible role in lymphadenopathy and acquired immune deficiency syndromes. Gallo RC, Essex ME, Gross L (eds): *Human T-Cell Leukemia/Lymphoma Virus*. Cold Spring Harbor Laboratory, Cold Spring Harbor, NY, 1984.

Pellegrini S, Dailey L, Basilico C: Amplification and excision of integrated polyoma DNA sequences require a functional origin of replication. *Cell* 1984; 36:943–949.

Rous P: A sarcoma of the fowl transmissible by an agent separable from the tumor cells. *J Exp Med* 1911; 13:397–413.

Sheinin R: Viruses: Causative agents of cancer. *Laryngoscope* 1975; 85:468–486.

Shope RE: Evolutionary episodes in the concept of viral oncogenesis. *Perspect Biol Med* 1966; 9:258–274.

Sun Z, Wang L, Xia Q et al: Immunological approach to natural history, early diagnosis and etiology of human primary hepatocellular carcinoma, in Essex M, Todaro G, zur Hausen H (eds): *Viruses in Naturally Occurring Cancer*. Cold Spring Harbor Laboratory, New York, 1980, pp 471–480.

Szmuness W, Stevens CE, Harley EJ et al: Hepatitis B vaccine: demonstration of efficacy in a controlled clinical trial in a high-risk population in the United States. *N Engl J Med* 1980; 303:833–841.

Temin HM, Mizutani S: RNA-dependent DNA polymerase in virions of Rous Sarcoma Virus. *Nature* 1970; 226: 1211–1213.

Tooze J (ed): *DNA Tumor Viruses*, ed 2. Cold Spring Harbor Laboratory, Cold Spring Harbor, NY, 1981.

Valentine RC, Pereira HG: Antigens and structure of the adenovirus. *J Mol Biol* 1965; 13:13–20.

Wang D, Liebowitz D, Kieff E: An EBV membrane protein expressed in immortalized lymphocyes transforms established rodent cells. *Cell* 1985; 43:831–840.

Weiss R, Teich N, Varmus H, Coffin J (eds): *RNA Tumor Viruses*. Cold Spring Harbor Laboratory, Cold Spring Harbor, NY, 1985.

Wold WSM, Mackey JK, Brackmann KH et al: Analysis of human tumors and human malignant cell lines for BK virus-specific DNA sequences. *Proc Natl Acad Sci USA*, 1978; 75:454–458.

Wong-Staal F, Gallo RC: Human T-lymphotropic retroviruses. *Nature* 1985; 317:395–403.

BIBLIOGRAPHY

Essex M, Todaro G, zur Hausen H (eds): *Viruses in Naturally Occurring Cancer*. Cold Spring Harbor Laboratory, Cold Spring Harbor, NY, 1980.

Fields BN (ed): *Virology*. Raven Press, New York, 1985.

Notkins AL, Oldstone MB (eds): *Concept in Viral Pathogenesis*. Springer-Verlag, New York, 1984.

Tooze J (ed): *DNA Tumor Viruses*, ed 2. Cold Spring Harbor Laboratory, Cold Spring Harbor, NY, 1981.

Varmus HE, Levine AJ (eds): *Readings in Tumor Virology*. Cold Spring Harbor Laboratory, Cold Spring Harbor, NY, 1983.

Weiss R, Teich N, Varmus H, Coffin J (eds): *RNA Tumor Viruses*. Cold Spring Harbor Laboratory, Cold Spring Harbor, NY, 1985.

5

Oncogenes

Mark D. Minden

5.1 INTRODUCTION

5.1.1 ONCOGENES AND VIRAL GENES

The concept that there are genes capable of causing cancer (oncogenes) is based largely on studies carried out with transplantable tumors in chicken, mice and rats. In 1911, Rous described a transmissible sarcoma in chickens (Rous, 1911). The original tumor found in an adult bird could be transmitted to other chickens either by the injection of tumor cells or by the injection of a cell-free filtrate of the tumor. Cell-free extracts made from the secondary tumors were also capable of inducing tumor formation. Later, similar observations were made for tumors arising in mice, rats and hamsters.

The causative agent for such tumors was found to be an RNA virus. Based on the highly efficient manner in which the viruses were able to cause tumors it was proposed that the virus carried genetic information responsible for transforming a normal cell into a tumor cell. However, there is little evidence that such viruses have a major role in the causation of human cancer (see chapter 4).

In 1969 Huebner and Todaro proposed the oncogene hypothesis of cancer (Huebner and Todaro, 1969). They based this hypothesis on the following observations: (a) RNA-virus-type particles had been observed by electron microscopy in all types of vertebrate cells; (b) viruses could cause cancer in several types of animals, and (c) cells that were apparently free of viruses could be induced to produce viruses following exposure to radiation or chemical carcinogens. They proposed that the cells of many, if not all, vertebrates contained information for producing RNA-type viruses. They postulated that the DNA which coded for viral information (the virogene), including the portion of the virus responsible for malignant transformation (the oncogene), is present in all cells and is passed on from one generation to the next through germ cells. Under normal circumstances the viral genes were thought to be inactive; however, as the result of irradiation, chemical carcinogens or aging there could be complete or partial activation of the virus resulting in the development of cancer (Fig 5.1a).

The above hypothesis was developed at a time when it was supposed that all RNA viruses carried onco-

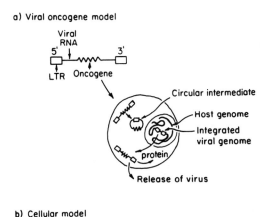

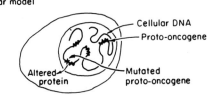

Figure 5.1. *a*, In the viral oncogene model, an RNA virus carrying an oncogene enters a cell. Double-stranded DNA is made from viral RNA, using the enzyme reverse transcriptase, and may integrate into the host genome. This genetic information may be transcribed to produce an mRNA which is packaged as a mature virus, or is translated into a protein that leads to malignant transformation. *b*, In the cellular-oncogene model, proto-oncogenes are seen as normal genes in mammalian cells. Alterations by mutation, amplification or translocation may lead to gene products that cause malignant transformation.

genes. In the following decade it was found that RNA viruses could be classified into rapidly transforming and slowly transforming viruses (section 4.4.3). The rapidly transforming viruses carry genetic information capable of inducing tumors directly (oncogenes). The slowly transforming viruses do not carry oncogenes; rather they induce tumors by inserting next to host cellular genes, and in some way alter the transcription of the adjacent cellular gene. At this time 20 or more viral oncogenes have been identified (Table 5.1).

5.1.2 CELLULAR ORIGIN OF ONCOGENES

Once oncogenes in RNA tumor viruses were recognized, a number of investigators sought to determine the origin of these sequences. Were they genes that had evolved wholly within the virus or had they been acquired from another genome? To determine which of these hypotheses was correct cDNA fragments of the oncogene region from Rous sarcoma virus were isolated and used to probe DNA from various tissues of the chicken (section A3.3.4).

Using this approach it was found that sequences homologous to the oncogene region of the virus were present in the DNA of all tissues of virus-free chickens. More extensive investigations have revealed that there are homologous sequences in yeast, drosophila, mice, rats and humans. The normal cellular sequences have been referred to as proto-oncogenes (Bishop, 1983;

Table 5.1. Proto-Oncogenes That Have Been Deleted in RNA Viruses

Proto-oncogene/ Oncogene	Species of Origin	Possible Subcellular Location(s) of Gene Product	Possible Function of Gene Product
abl	mouse	Plasma and cytoplasmic membranes	Protein–tyrosine kinase
erb-A	chicken	Cytoplasm	?
erb-B	chicken	Plasma and cytoplasmic membranes	Protein–tyrosine kinase
ets	chicken	Nucleus (fused with product of v-myb)	?
fes/fps	cat	Plasma and cytoplasmic membranes	Protein–tyrosine kinase
fgr	cat	Plasma and cytoplasmic membranes	Protein–tyrosine kinase
fms	cat	Plasma and cytoplasmic membranes	Protein–tyrosine kinase
fos	mouse	Nucleus	?
kit	mouse	?	?
mil/raf	mouse	Cytoplasm	Protein–serine/threonine kinase
mos	mouse	Cytoplasm	Protein–serine/threonine kinase
myb	chicken	Nucleus	?
myc	chicken	Nucleus	?
ras	mouse, rat	Plasma membrane	Regulator of adenylate cyclase
rel	chicken	Cytoplasm	?
ros	chicken	Plasma and cytoplasmic membranes	Protein–tyrosine kinase
sis	mouse	Cytoplasm/secreted	Analogue of PDGF-β*
ski	mouse	Nucleus	?
src	chicken	Plasma and cytoplasmic membranes	Protein–tyrosine kinase
yes	chicken	Plasma and cytoplasmic membranes	Protein–tyrosine kinase

*β-chain of platelet-derived growth factor (see section 5.4.2).

Varmus, 1984; Fig 5.1b); at the level of nucleic acids and their protein products there is a high degree of homology between the viral oncogenes and the cellular proto-oncogene. The oncogene carried by a virus is referred to as v-onc, while the proto-oncogene is referred to as c-onc.

Investigations aimed at determining whether oncogenes developed initially in viruses or in cells of higher organisms have concluded that the cellular proto-oncogenes most likely developed first. The evidence for this is presented below.

Eukaryotic genes have the unique feature of being composed of coding regions (exons) and noncoding spacer regions (introns). When mRNA is made, both the introns and the exons of a gene are transcribed and then processed so that the introns are spliced out. This results in mRNA that is composed of exons and thus is substantially shorter than the gene itself. The proto-oncogenes have such an intron–exon structure, while the viral oncogene is composed entirely of exons (that is, it more closely resembles the RNA form of the gene rather than the genomic form of the gene). It is unlikely that the virus infected the cells and then developed an intron–exon structure for the following reasons:

1. The number and size of introns and exons are relatively conserved between species.
2. The chromosome localization and linkage of proto-oncogenes is conserved between species: a proto-oncogene linked to genes A and B in one species is linked to the same genes in another species. If the viral oncogene was introduced into cells after speciation one would not expect to find such conserved structure and linkage.
3. Animals infected with RNA viruses that do not contain an oncogene may on occasion develop a tumor. In some cases these tumors have been found to produce virus derived from the infecting virus, except that they now carry an oncogene (Fig 5.2; Rapp et al, 1983).

5.1.3 THE PROTO-ONCOGENES

More than 20 different viral oncogenes have been identified; each of these has been found to have a counterpart in normal cells (Table 5.1). In normal cells these genes are expressed, but do not result in the development of malignancy. In the normal cell, the expression of proto-oncogenes is well controlled and appears to play a role in the growth and development of the organism. The function of some of these genes has been determined, while for others a close association between cell proliferation and gene expression has been established; this is presented below and in Figure 5.3.

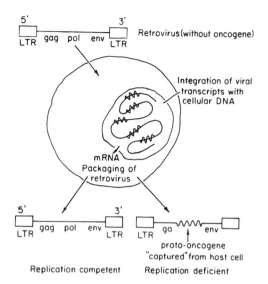

Figure 5.2. Probable origin of oncogenes in RNA viruses. A replication-competent virus enters the cell and its complementary DNA integrates into the genome. During the transcription of messenger RNA, mature replication-proficient virus may be packaged and released. Alternatively, viral sequences may be lost and replaced by a cellular proto-oncogene that is then packaged as a virus. Because this virus has lost the reverse transcriptase gene (pol), it is no longer replication proficient.

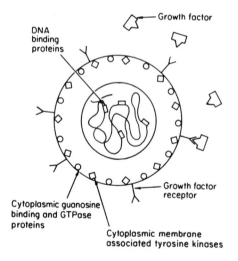

Figure 5.3. The site of action of oncogene products in different parts of the mammalian cell.

Stimulation of a nonmalignant cell into a proliferative state often depends on an external signal. This signal is received by a receptor on the cell membrane which then transfers the signal through the membrane into the cytoplasm and ultimately to the nucleus, where DNA synthesis is initiated; proto-oncogenes have been found that function at each step of this pathway. The c-sis proto-oncogene encodes for a polypeptide chain of platelet-derived growth factor (PDGF). Cells such as fibroblasts in tissue culture require the presence of PDGF to enter cell division. The erb-B oncogene is homologous to the gene encoding for cell membrane receptor of epidermal growth factor (EGF). The interaction of EGF with its receptor induces the proliferation of epidermal cells such as breast epithelium, etc. The protein products of the proto-oncogenes, src, abl, and ras, are cytoplasmic in location. These proteins have been found to function as protein kinases or GTPases. As such, they likely act as second messengers to transfer the signal for growth to the nucleus. The proto-oncogene products of myc, fos, ski and myb are nuclear in location and are believed to play an important role in the control of cell division. In cells that have been stimulated to divide there is a coordinated and transient rise in the amount of myb, myc and fos. The expression of these genes may be responsible for the entry of the cell into DNA synthesis.

The proto-oncogenes appear to play an important role in the normal cell (see also section 5.4). Alteration of these genes either in form or expression may result in the development of a malignant cell. The manner in which the altered gene has been detected and the type of alteration is described below.

5.2 DETECTION OF ONCOGENES IN HUMAN CANCER CELLS

5.2.1 GENETIC BASIS OF MALIGNANCY

There is strong evidence that induction of malignancy is associated with genetic changes in the cell. Examples of this are the finding of specific chromosome abnormalities in malignant cells, the association of tumor development with DNA-damaging agents such as ionizing irradiation and chemical carcinogens, and the increased incidence of cancer in hereditary disease such as Bloom's syndrome, ataxia telangiectasia and xeroderma pigmentosum (see chapter 3). In some experiments where cell hybrids were formed between malignant and nonmalignant cells, it was shown that hybrid cells were also malignant. Thus some genes in tumor cells appear to act in a dominant manner to produce the malignant phenotype. To investigate the nature of such genes a number of investigators turned to the technique of gene transfer.

5.2.2 TRANSFECTION OF DNA

Techniques have been developed for transferring genes from one cell to another with reasonable efficiency (see section A3.3.6). The essential components

of such an experiment are (a) a recipient cell deficient in the trait being sought, (b) a donor cell proficient in the desired trait, and (c) a selection system. Genetic material in the form of naked chromatin or chromosomes from the donor cell are precipitated in the presence of calcium phosphate, and applied to the recipient cells. The precipitate is taken up by the recipient cell and some of the DNA finds its way to the nucleus, where it is replicated and transcribed and in some cases integrated into the chromosomes of the recipient cell. In the presence of selection, the cells that express the necessary genes will survive while the other cells will die. For example, cells deficient in the enzyme thymidine kinase will be killed by the drug methotrexate much more efficiently than normal cells; however, cells that have had the thymidine kinase gene introduced into them by gene transfer will survive the selection (ie, treatment with methotrexate) and form colonies.

The possibility that such a system could detect dominantly acting transforming genes in tumor cells was tested by extracting DNA from either chemically transformed rodent cells or human tumor cell lines, and transferring the DNA to nonmalignant mouse or rat cells. A cell line designated NIH/3T3, derived from mouse embryo fibroblasts, was used as the recipient in most of these experiments. Although this cell line has a normal phenotype in culture it was selected for its ability to propagate indefinitely (ie, it is immortal). Following transfection the cells were assayed for the development of a transformed phenotype (Fig 5.4). Three different assays have been used (see section 8.4.2).

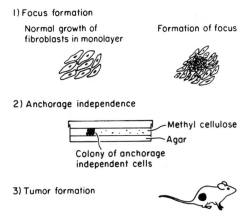

Figure 5.4. Assays of the malignant phenotype. Malignant transformation of a cell may be recognized in tissue culture, *a*, by cells piling up on the bottom of the culture dish to form a focus; *b*, by growth under anchorage-independent conditions in semisolid media such as methylcellulose or agar; or *c*, by tumor formation in syngeneic or immune-deprived animals.

1. *The focus assay.* Normal fibroblasts are contact inhibited and will stop growing when they become confluent. Transformed cells are not contact inhibited and continue to grow. This results in the development of a focus of cells on a background of contact-inhibited fibroblasts.

2. *Anchorage-independent growth.* Normal fibroblasts will not grow unless they are adherent to a supporting matrix such as glass or plastic. In contrast, transformed cells do not need such attachment and are capable of growing when suspended in a semisolid medium such as agar that prevents adherence to the bottom of the culture vessel.

3. *Tumor formation.* Normal fibroblasts will not form tumors in syngeneic or immunologically deficient animals, while transformed fibroblasts can. Each of these assay systems has been used to detect transforming genes.

Several laboratories have used the technique of gene transfer to detect dominantly acting transforming genes. In the initial experiments, transfection of DNA from chemically transformed cells led to transfer of the malignant phenotype to mouse cells (Shih et al, 1979), but at that time the DNA sequences responsible for transforming activity could not be determined. Transforming activity was also detected in the DNA from some virally transformed tumor cell lines. Moreover, acquisition of the malignant phenotype correlated with the transfer of viral sequences (Copeland et al, 1979). Transformation appeared to be specific to DNA from tumor cell lines since transfer of DNA from normal cells did not induce a malignant phenotype.

5.2.3 TRANSFECTION OF DNA FROM HUMAN TUMORS

Initial experiments which sought the presence of transforming activity in DNA from human tumor cells were mostly unsuccessful, but a few positive results were obtained. Three groups were able to detect transforming activity using DNA obtained from the EJ cell line derived from human bladder cancer (this cell line is also designated T24 or MGH-U1 in other laboratories). If the DNA from the transformed cells was used in a further transfection assay it was able to generate further transformants (eg, Shih and Weinberg, 1982).

At the same time that transfection experiments were being performed, Gusella et al (1980) reported that it was possible to detect human DNA sequences from a human–rodent hybrid cell. Their technique took advantage of the fact that there are repetitive sequences in human DNA that can be distinguished from analogous sequences present in rodent DNA. When radiolabeled

human DNA is hybridized to human DNA immobilized on a filter, hybridization will occur between the complementary base pairs of the repetitive sequences (see section A3.3.4 for details of hybridization). In contrast, no detectable hybridization will occur between radiolabeled human DNA and filter-bound rodent DNA (Fig 5.5). This technique can detect very small amounts of human DNA in a rodent cell that has had human DNA transferred into it. One of the most frequent human repeat sequences is the "alu" family, and maximum sensitivity is obtained when a radioactively labeled cloned alu sequence is used to probe a Southern blot of DNA derived from a rodent cell that contains human DNA. These are 300-base-pair repetitive units that are dispersed evenly throughout the human genome. There are approximately 300,000 such repeats in each cell, and so on the average a fragment of human DNA that is 5000 bp long will contain one such repeat (most genes are more than 5000 bp). If the fragment of human DNA present in the transfectant contains an alu sequence it will be detected in the Southern blot (see section A3.3.4 for a description of this method).

The Southern blotting technique for detecting human DNA in a rodent cell was used to study the transformants obtained after transfer of genes from human malignant cells to murine fibroblasts. Using either radioactively labeled total human DNA or a cloned alu probe, primary transformants were found to have varying amounts of human DNA. Some samples showed extensive hybridization, indicating the presence of a large amount of human DNA, while in other samples discrete bands were evident, indicating that only a small amount of human DNA was present in the transformant. The complex pattern seen in primary transformants was simplified in secondary and tertiary transformants. Following DNA transfection a transformant may contain up to 0.1% donor DNA. When analyzed with an alu probe, a Southern blot of a mouse cell that has taken up this amount of human DNA would show hybridization to the entire lane. In a secondary transfection the recipient cell may again take up 0.1% of the donor DNA; this results in a dilution of the amount of human DNA present in the secondary transformant. When Southern blots of DNA from secondary transformants were probed with an alu sequence discrete bands were seen (Fig 5.5). Independent transformants derived from the same source of DNA contained the same pattern of bands, indicating that in each case the same gene had been transferred. Transformants derived from different sources of tumor DNA revealed a few different patterns of bands; this suggested that the same gene was being transferred from different sources of DNA and that a limited number of genes were being detected as active in the transfection assay.

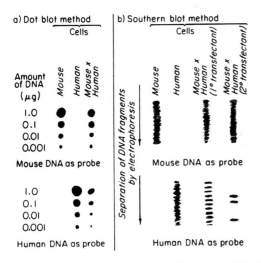

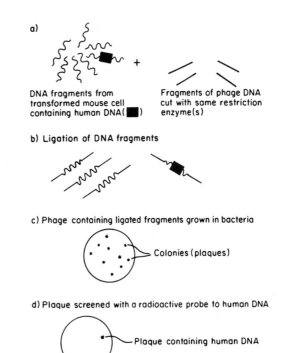

Figure 5.5. Methods for the detection of human DNA following transfection into rodent cells, or in hybrid cells between rodent and human cells. *a*, In the dot-blot method either labeled-murine DNA or labeled-human DNA is used as a probe for serial dilutions of DNA extracted from murine cells, human cells, or hybrid cells. *b*, In Southern blots, the separation of DNA on electrophoretic gels allows specific DNA sequences to be recognized as bands. Unique bands may be recognized, particularly in secondary transfectants.

Figure 5.6. Cloning of transforming sequences. In *a*, DNA from a murine cell which contains human DNA is mixed with DNA from a bacteriophage. When the same restriction enzymes are used to cut the DNA, spontaneous ligation between the different types of DNA may occur, as shown in *b*. The ligated DNA, *c*, is then packaged into mature bacteriophages which form colonies or "plaques" on a plate containing bacteria. *d*, The plaques are then screened with a radioactive probe which recognizes the specific human DNA of interest.

To determine which gene was being transferred, the DNA of a secondary transformant was cloned into a bacteriophage and individual plaques (ie, colonies of bacteriophage) which contained human DNA (detected by hybridization) were isolated (Fig 5.6). DNA from some of the clones isolated in this manner was found to be extremely efficient in inducing malignant transformation of NIH/3T3 cells. Thus a gene had been isolated from a malignant cell which was capable of inducing a transformed phenotype in nonmalignant cells.

5.2.4 CRITIQUE OF THE TRANSFECTION ASSAY

DNA from almost all histological types of human tumors has been able to transform NIH/3T3 cells to a malignant phenotype; however, only a small percentage (in general <10%) of any tumor type score as positive in the transfection assay. Exceptions are the leukemias and lymphomas, in which up to 70% of tumors score as positive (Eva et al, 1983). Three possible reasons for this low rate of positive results are (a) the majority of tumors do not have an activated oncogene, (b) the assay system is insensitive, and (c) the activated oncogenes may be sufficiently large that they are broken during the extraction and transfer of tumor cell DNA. The last two alternatives are most likely. The transfection assay is highly variable, being positive one day and negative

the next, even when the same sample of DNA is tested. Important factors in this variability include the nature of the DNA precipitate, the "well being" of the recipient cells, and the quality of the DNA. Also, the end-point of focus formation is somewhat subjective. For example, foci derived from different tumor types may have different morphologies; therefore the person who is scoring for foci must be aware of subtle differences in the appearance of the cells. Finally, the transfected gene may not be active in NIH/3T3 cells. Genes show tissue specificity: genes that are expressed in one cell type may not be expressed or may not function to produce a transformed phenotype in a cell of another type. Evidence that this may be the case is derived from recent experiments in which "nonimmortalized" cell lines other than NIH/3T3 have been used as recipients in the transfection assay. DNA extracted from tumors that was unable to transform NIH/3T3 cells was found to transform other types of cell. The pattern of bands containing human DNA detected on Southern blots of DNA derived from these transformants differ from the pattern of bands containing human DNA in NIH/3T3 transformants; this suggests that a set of genes different from those detected with NIH/3T3 cells are being identified in the new recipient cells.

5.2.5 THE RELATIONSHIP BETWEEN TRANSFECTED DNA AND VIRAL ONCOGENES

The nature of the transfected DNA in the transformed cells was studied using labeled DNA probes derived from RNA tumor viruses in Southern blot analysis. Surprisingly, the transfected DNA in many of the transformants was found to be homologous (ie, to share many common base sequences) to the viral oncogenes of the Harvey and Kirsten sarcoma viruses (Parada et al, 1982; Chang et al, 1982; Santos et al, 1984). These two genes, known as H-ras and K-ras, both encode proteins of molecular weight 21,000 d that are strikingly similar in amino acid sequence; in fact, some antibodies against the two proteins cross-react. These proteins are referred to as p21 ras proteins, and are located in the cytoplasm adjacent to the cell membrane. Though the precise function of the proteins is unknown it has been determined that they bind to GTP and have GTPase activity (see section 5.4).

A large number of cells that were transformed by DNA from human tumor cells contained human DNA which was found to hybridize to either the H-ras or K-ras gene. However, there were some that did not. One example of such a transformant was derived following transfection with DNA from a neuroblastoma. When the gene responsible for the transforming activity was isolated it was found that there was weak homology between the 5' portion of the gene with either K-ras or H-ras (Taparowsky et al, 1983). Moreover, the predicted amino acid sequence for the protein coded by this new gene had an almost identical amino terminal end to the proteins coded by the other ras genes. Analysis of the protein produced by this gene revealed that it had a molecular weight of 21,000 d and that the protein cross-reacted with antibodies against the H-ras and K-ras proteins. This new gene has therefore been included in the family of ras genes, and as it was derived from a neuroblastoma it has been named N-ras. N-ras has since been found in a number of other transformants, especially those derived by transfection of DNA from leukemias and lymphomas. Cells from up to 70% of acute leukemia have an activated N-ras gene (Eva et al, 1983).

Most tumors that are positive in the transfection assay have been found to contain a ras gene. However, a few cells that have been transformed by DNA from human tumors contain human DNA, yet do not con-

tain a transfected ras gene. Some of the genes isolated from such transformants have been designated B-lym, met, neu and mam. At the present time less is known about these genes than about the ras genes.

5.3 ACTIVATION OF ONCOGENES

5.3.1 POINT MUTATION AS A MECHANISM OF ACTIVATION

The ras gene from the bladder tumor cell line was active in transfection/transformation assays, while a ras gene cloned from a normal cell was inactive. To determine what change might be responsible for the activation of this gene a series of elegant recombination experiments were carried out (Tabin et al, 1982; Reddy et al, 1982). Using different restriction enzymes to cut the DNA at different sites, pieces of the normal gene were joined to pieces of the active gene in such a manner that a whole gene was reconstructed (Fig 5.7). These constructs were then used in the transfection assay. Constructs that contained the 5' end of the activated gene were active in such an assay, while genes that had the 5' end of the normal gene were inactive. The 5' ends of both genes were then sequenced and it was found that there was a change in a single base pair in the 12th codon that resulted in substitution of valine (val) for glycine (gly) in the corresponding p21 ras protein. The significance of this point mutation was confirmed in a number of ways. First, a mutation at the same position was found in ras genes derived from other tumors. Second, when genes were synthesized that were specifically mutated at this point, transforming activity was found. Thus a single point mutation can significantly alter the biological behavior of a normal gene.

A number of other members of the ras gene family that are active in the transfection assay have been cloned and sequenced. In addition to changes in the 12th amino acid, changes in the 13th and 61st amino acids have been found to convey the ability to transform fibroblasts to a malignant phenotype (Capon et al, 1983). The proteins produced by the mutated genes have been studied by protein electrophoresis. These proteins migrate more slowly, and appear to have decreased GTPase activity as compared to the p21 protein derived from the normal ras gene (see also section 5.4).

5.3.2 POINT MUTATIONS MAY BE DUE TO CHEMICAL CARCINOGENS

The role of the mutated ras gene in the development of tumors has been investigated by Barbacid and his

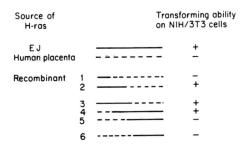

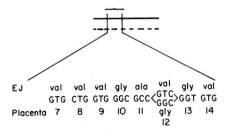

Figure 5.7. Detection of the region of DNA in the H-ras gene from the EJ bladder carcinoma cell line that was responsible for transforming activity was determined as follows. Recombinant techniques were used to exchange fragments of DNA from the normal gene which is inactive in transformation with fragments of DNA from the active gene. This results in a number of different recombinants that could be tested in the transformation assay and allowed the determination of the region of DNA that was responsible for transforming activity. This region was subsequently sequenced and it was found that transforming activity was due to a single mutation in the 12th codon.

colleagues (Zarbl et al, 1985). They used rats from a strain which will develop mammary carcinoma at a high frequency when injected with the carcinogens dimethylbenzanthracene (DMBA) or nitrosomethylurea (NMU) (see also section 6.3.2). Tumors that developed were excised, and their DNA was extracted and tested for transforming activity in the transfection assay. The majority of the tumors contained an activated ras gene. There was no consistent point mutation in the gene in DNA from tumors induced by DMBA; however, in all NMU-induced tumors the normal guanine base in the 12th codon was replaced by adenine. The probable explanation is that NMU causes O^6 methylation of the guanosine; if this is not repaired it will result in replacement of guanine by adenine upon DNA replication (see Fig 5.8).

5.3.3 GENE DOSAGE

A number of mechanisms other than point mutation of an endogenous gene have been implicated in the development of malignancy. Cytogeneticists have recog-

nized a large number of chromosomal abnormalities in malignant cells (see section 3.3); they include breaks and translocations, homogeneously staining regions (HSRs) and double minute chromosomes (DMs). Schimke et al (1980) have demonstrated that HSRs and DMs are the result of amplification of genes.

Malignant cells are sometimes found to contain HSRs and/or DMs. The genes contained in these HSRs and DMs have been studied using Southern blots and/or in situ hybridization (section A3.3). Amplification of a proto-oncogene (c-myc) was first reported for the HL-60 cell line derived from a patient with acute promyelocytic leukemia (Collins and Groudine, 1982). Cells from neuroblastomas often contain HSRs which contain amplified copies of the N-myc gene (eg, Schwab et al, 1983); N-myc is a gene that bears homology to myc but is located on a different chromosome. Amplifications of c-myc have also been found in cell lines derived from small-cell cancer of the lung, where they seem to correlate with biological subtypes showing aggressive clinical behavior (Little et al, 1983). Amplifications of H-ras, N-ras, and K-ras have been reported in various tumors. The role of these amplified genes in the development of a tumor and its subsequent biological behavior is not yet known, but a role for gene amplification in the development of malignancy is supported by the following observations. The normal ras gene will not induce transformation; however, when the promoter of the gene is altered so that higher levels of the ras p21 protein are produced, one can observe the development of a malignant phenotype (Chang et al, 1982). Thus, increased production of the normal protein products of amplified proto-oncogenes may contribute to the development of the malignant phenotype.

The mechanisms which lead to amplification of genes are unknown. Gene amplification in lower animals such as the silk worm and frog is important during their development. Amplification of genes during the normal development of higher animals has not been described, but transient amplification at certain stages of development could easily be missed. Gene amplification has been well characterized as a mechanism which conveys resistance of cells to drugs such as methotrexate or colchicine (section 19.2): it may occur on a random basis or because the drugs interfere with DNA synthesis, but the amplified gene is presumably retained because it conveys a selective advantage to the cell. It is probable that other genes also become amplified on a random basis, and that amplification of some proto-oncogenes may also be retained as they provide a selective advantage to the cell. Such events may be involved in the primary development of the tumor or in secondary changes which are associated with progression.

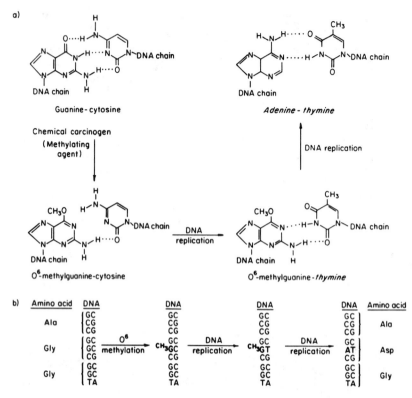

Figure 5.8. The action of chemical carcinogens to produce point mutation. Carcinogens may cause O^6 methylation of guanine as shown in *a*. This methylation causes faulty DNA replication, leading eventually to the replacement of a guanine–cytosine DNA base pair with an adenine–thymine base pair. The sequence shown in *b* corresponds to the 11th to 13th codon of the H-ras gene and indicates how a mutation might occur in the 12th codon after treatment with a chemical carcinogen (see Zarbl et al, 1985).

5.3.4 CHROMOSOME TRANSLOCATIONS

Chromosome translocations occur at a high frequency in some types of tumors, suggesting that they may play a role in the development of these tumors. Examples of recurring translocations are the Philadelphia chromosome (a 9;22 translocation) in chronic myelogenous leukemia (CML), the 15;17 translocation in promyelocytic leukemia, and the several translocations involving chromosome 8 that occur in lymphoid malignancies (see section 3.3). Klein (1981) proposed that chromosomal breaks might lead to activation of oncogenes located close to the break points. Recently, several genes situated at sites of common translocations have been identified; many of these genes are known oncogenes, thus supporting this hypothesis.

The chromosomal location of human oncogenes has been established by using two different methods. The first method uses panels of mouse–human or hamster–human hybrid cells. These cells contain a full complement of rodent chromosomes but a reduced number of human chromosomes. By hybridizing labeled DNA from the cloned human oncogene to DNA from these cells on Southern blots it is possible to identify those cells that carry the gene and those that do not. This information is then correlated with the known human chromosomes in the hybrid cells; in this manner it is possible to determine on which chromosome a gene is resident (see section A3.4.4). The second method of assigning a gene to a chromosome is through in situ hybridization. The cloned gene is hybridized directly to metaphase chromosomes and visualized by autoradiography. This technique gives precise localization on a specific chromosome; however, there is a chance of error from cross-hybridization to closely related genes. A combination of these two techniques has led to localization of many of the known proto-oncogenes. Figure 5.9 illustrates the chromosomal localization of known proto-oncogenes and the common sites of chromosome translocations in malignant cells. It is evident that break points are frequently found near an oncogene (Rowley, 1984).

A number of investigators have cloned genes from the sites of chromosomal translocations (Fig 5.10,

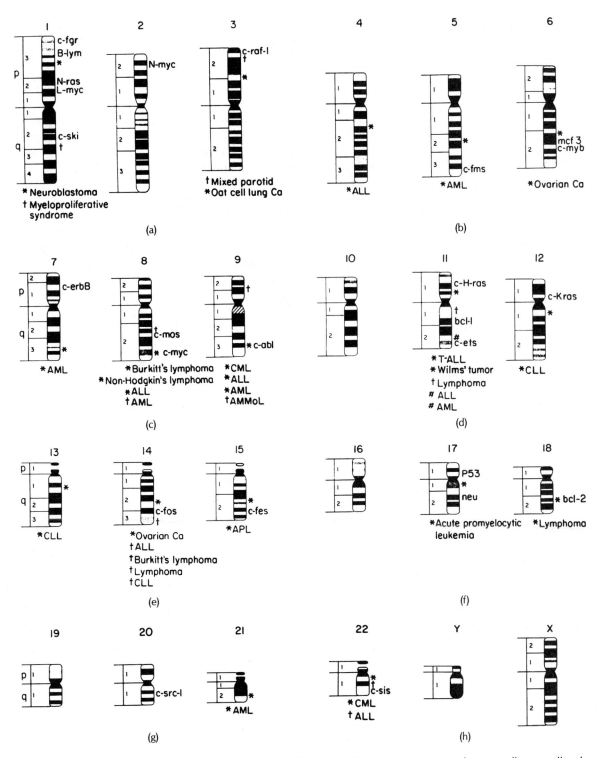

Figure 5.9. Schematic diagram indicating the chromosomal location of known oncogenes in human cells, as well as break points that are involved in translocations associated with human malignancy.

Groffen et al, 1984). This can be illustrated by analysis of genes at the site of translocation between chromosomes 9 and 22 in the Philadelphia chromosome. The proto-oncogene abl is normally on chromosome 9, and the proto-oncogene sis on chromosome 22. Using in situ hybridization the location of these genes was determined in cells from patients with Ph⁺ CML. The abl gene had moved from chromosome 9 to 22 and sis had

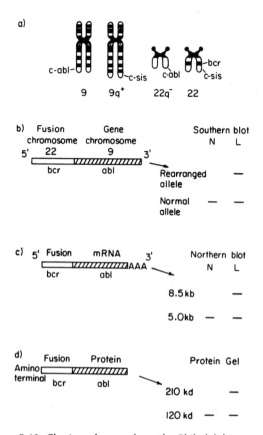

Figure 5.10. Cloning of genes from the Philadelphia translocation. *a,* A schematic presentation of the normal chromosomes 9 and 22, and of the chromosomes 9q⁺ and 22q⁻ following translocation in CML. The Philadelphia chromosome is 22q⁻. *b,* Rearrangement of the c-abl oncogene was found in a patient. A probe derived from this rearranged region (see text) was used to probe Southern blots from normal cells (N) and those from patients with CML (L). Rearrangement was found in almost all patients with CML. *c,* Schematic diagram of the mRNA from the fused region, and of a Northern blot demonstrating an increase in size of the mRNA from the abl oncogene in Ph-positive cells. *d,* Schematic diagram of the protein product of the fused gene, and of a polyacrilamide gel electrophoresis demonstrating the increased size of the c-abl protein in Philadelphia-positive CML cells. Note that CML cells contain both the abnormal enlarged (210 kd) protein and the normal (120 kd) protein.

moved from 22 to 9. These genes were then examined to determine if they had been disrupted in any manner. Using cloned probes for the genes and their flanking regions it was found that in some patients with CML the abl gene was rearranged. The DNA from the leukemic cells of one such patient was cloned into a bacteriophage and the clone containing the rearranged fragment of the abl gene was isolated. Analysis of this clone revealed that one end of the insert was derived from chromosome 9 while the other end was derived from chromosome 22. This clone therefore rep-

resents the point at which the abl gene on chromosome 9 joins to a gene on chromosome 22. When a probe, derived from the region of chromosome 22 involved in the translocation, was used in Southern-blot analysis of a large number of samples of DNA from patients with CML, rearrangement of this fragment was found in almost all cases of Philadelphia-positive CML (Groffen et al, 1984; Konopka et al, 1984, 1985). This result is significant for two reasons. First, the probe derived from chromosome 22 provides a simple means for detecting the presence of the Philadelphia chromosome. Second, the finding that almost all patients with a Philadelphia chromosome show rearrangement indicates that the translocation involves a limited region on chromosome 22; this has been referred to as the break-point cluster region, and is abbreviated as bcr.

The structure of the mRNA corresponding to the abl gene has been determined in CML cells (Shtivelman et al, 1985). In normal cells the abl mRNA gives a transcript of 5 kb (ie, 5000 base pairs long), but in cells from CML the transcript is 9 kb in length. This change in length is due to the production of mRNA from a fusion between a gene on chromosome 22 and the abl gene that is translocated from chromosome 9 (Fig 5.10). This enlarged message has been found to produce a novel form of the abl protein that has a molecular weight of 210 kilodaltons (kd) rather than the normal 120 kd. In addition to its altered size the gene product has increased the ability to phosphorylate the amino acid tyrosine in other proteins.

In the above example a translocation results in the production of a new protein. In other translocations, such as those involving immunoglobulin genes and the myc gene (8;14 translocation) which have been observed in lymphomas, the regulation of the myc gene is altered (Feo et al, 1985). The myc gene appears to be involved in the control of differentiation and proliferation (section 5.4.8). Normally the expression of this gene is tightly regulated, but in cells in which a translocation has occurred the gene is constitutively expressed; that is, rather than being regulated, the gene product is always being produced. It seems possible that this alteration in the expression of the gene contributes to development of the malignant phenotype.

5.3.5 OTHER ONCOGENES

At the beginning of this chapter oncogenes were described as the genetic material carried by RNA tumor viruses that results in rapid malignant transformation of target cells. From the material presented above it is now clear that oncogenes are normal cellular genes that may contribute to the development of the malignant cell if their expression is altered through mutation, translocation, amplification or some other mechanism. With this expanded definition of an oncogene, genes such as N-ras, which have not been found to be associated with an RNA tumor virus but were detected in transformation assays, should also be considered as oncogenes. A list of oncogenes not associated with RNA tumor viruses but recognized either by their activity in transformation assays or by their association with chromosome translocations is presented in Table 5.2.

5.3.6 COMPLEMENTATION BETWEEN ONCOGENES

The previous discussion of the various ways in which oncogenes might become activated has not addressed whether any one of these changes is sufficient to produce the malignant phenotype. Evidence reviewed in section 3.2 suggests that at least two genetic changes are needed to produce a cancer cell, and studies of oncogenes support this view. Some cell lines contain two activated oncogenes. For example, the cell line HL-60 contains an amplified myc gene as well as an activated N-ras gene, while some cell lines derived from Burkitt's lymphoma contain a rearranged myc gene and an activated N-ras gene. Support for the involvement of two oncogenes in malignant transformation has also been obtained in experiments using gene transfer.

The DNA transfection experiments described in section 5.2.2 all used NIH/3T3 cells as recipients; this cell line has a normal phenotype but has been selected for its ability to be propagated indefinitely in tissue culture. Normal fibroblasts obtained fresh from an individual or an animal, referred to as primary fibroblasts, do not have this property, and will die after approximately 20 generations in culture. When primary rat embryo fibroblasts are transfected with a rearranged myc gene it is possible to obtain permanent cell lines; however, they are phenotypically normal. If an activated ras gene is used instead, morphologic transformation may occur, but these cells are unable to grow indefinitely nor will they form tumors in animals. Transfection with both an activated ras gene and a rearranged myc gene leads to morphologic transformation, the development of permanent cell lines and the development of tumors upon injection into animals (Land et al, 1983). However, these tumors grow to only a limited size and then stop growing; this suggests that yet another event may be needed to produce a tumor that can grow to kill the animal.

In the above example myc and ras oncogenes can complement each other in the development of tumors. It is possible to replace one of these genes with a second oncogene and to get the same effect. For example, myc can be replaced by myb or p53 while ras can be replaced by src or abl. Thus there appear to be two classes of oncogenes: those that produce immortalization and those that produce morphologic transformation (Table 5.3). In general, the gene products of the former class are located in the nucleus of cells, while those of transforming oncogenes are located in the cytoplasm.

Table 5.2. Proto-Oncogenes That Have Not Appeared in Retroviruses

Proto-oncogene	Method of Identification	Original Source
bcl-1	Translocation	B-cell leukemia
bcl-2	Translocation	B-cell lymphoma
Blym	Transfection	B-cell lymphoma
int-1	Insertional mutagenesis	mammary carcinoma
int-2	Insertional mutagenesis	mammary carcinoma
L-myc	Amplification	lung carcinoma
mcf2	Transfection	mammary carcinoma
mcf3	Transfection	mammary carcinoma
met	Transfection	chemically transformed osteosarcoma cells
Mlvi-1	Insertional mutagenesis	T-cell lymphoma
Mlvi-2	Insertional mutagenesis	T-cell lymphoma
Mlvi-3	Insertional mutagenesis	T-cell lymphoma
neu	Transfection	neuroblastoma
N-myc	Amplification	neuroblastoma
N-ras	Transfection	neuroblastoma
onc-D	Transfection	colon carcinoma
pim-1	Insertional mutagenesis	T-cell lymphoma
tcl-1	Translocation	T-cell leukemia
Tlym-1	Transfection	T-cell lymphoma
Tlym-2	Transfection	T-cell lymphoma

Table 5.3. Complementation Groups of Oncogenes

Immortalizing Function	Morphologic Transformation
myc	H-ras
myb	N-ras
p53	src
ElA of adenovirus	abl
Large T of SV40	
Middle T of polyoma virus	

5.4 ROLE OF (PROTO) ONCOGENES IN NORMAL AND TRANSFORMED CELLS

5.4.1 PROTO-ONCOGENE PRODUCTS

The role of proto-oncogenes in the growth and development of normal and malignant cells is not yet well defined, but is an area of intensive investigation. In this section current knowledge of the structure and function of the protein products of oncogenes and proto-oncogenes will be reviewed. The proteins can be grouped into several classes based upon their location and their reactivities (see Fig 5.3); they are (a) nuclear, (b) cytoplasmic and membrane protein kinases, (c) cytoplasmic GTP binding proteins, (d) growth factors, and (e) others not yet characterized. Examples of proteins that fall into each of these classes are presented in Table 5.4.

5.4.2 GROWTH FACTORS

Growth factors are proteins that act at the cell surface to stimulate the growth of cells (see section 8.4.5). Much of the evidence supporting the existence and role of growth factors comes from studies carried out in tissue culture. Two examples in which the physiologic importance of a growth factor has been demonstrated

Table 5.4. Protein Products of Oncogenes

1. *Nuclear*
   c-myc
   N-myc
   L-myc
   myb
   fos
   ski
   p53

2. *Cytoplasmic and membrane protein kinases*
   erb-B (EGF receptor)
   fms (CSF-1 receptor)
   src
   yes
   fes
   ros
   fgr
   raf

3. *Cytoplasmic GTP-binding proteins*
   H-ras
   K-ras
   N-ras

4. *Growth factors*
   sis

5. *Others*
   B-lym
   T-lym-1
   mcf3
   bcl-1
   bcl-2

in vivo are (a) the glycoprotein erythropoietin, which is important in the regulation of the production of red blood cells, and (b) nerve growth factor (NGF), which is important in development of the nervous system. Thus, if the action of NGF is blocked by injecting newborn animals with antibodies against it, the development of the nervous system is impaired.

Despite the important role played by growth factors in controlling cell proliferation there is no evidence that the in vivo production of a growth factor induces malignancy. To date only one of the viral oncogenes has been recognized as being homologous to a gene whose protein product is a growth factor; this is the sis oncogene, which is homologous to the gene for the β-chain of platelet-derived growth factor (PDGF; Waterfield et al, 1983). PDGF is required for the growth in culture of normal fibroblasts and acts by binding to its cell surface receptor; this in turn induces the tyrosine kinase activity of the receptor (see section 5.4.4). In cells that have been transformed by the sis oncogene it appears that the sis protein acts within the cytoplasm of the transformed cell and not by binding to a cell-surface receptor. It is of note that PDGF does not induce a malignant phenotype when added to cells in culture. Thus the observation that PDGF and the protein product of the sis oncogene are homologous raises more questions than answers as to how the sis oncogene produces a malignant cell.

5.4.3 PROTEIN TYROSINE KINASES

The activity of proteins and other biologic molecules can be affected by the presence or absence of phosphate groups (see section 11.3.1). The phosphate is added to serine, threonine or tyrosine by a specific kinase and is removed from the protein by a phosphatase. The majority of phosphorylation occurs on serine and threonine with only a small percentage occurring on tyrosine. The possible importance of tyrosine phosphorylation came to light with the observation that v-src had tyrosine kinase activity (Hunter and Cooper, 1985). Other viral oncogenes and normal cellular proteins have also been found to have tyrosine kinase activity. All proteins with tyrosine kinase activity share a common catalytic site. The members of this family of proteins have been found either as transmembrane receptors or as cytoplasmic proteins associated with membranes.

5.4.4 MEMBRANE RECEPTORS WITH PROTEIN KINASE ACTIVITY

There are a number of transmembrane receptors that have protein kinase activity (Hunter and Cooper, 1985); examples are epidermal growth factor receptor (EGFR), platelet-derived growth factor receptor (PDGFR), insulin receptor, insulin-like growth factor 1 receptor, and colony-stimulating factor 1 (CSF-1) receptor. These proteins can themselves be phosphorylated on serine, threonine and tyrosine. The binding of the ligand to the receptor increases the tyrosine kinase activity of the receptor molecule; this results in autophosphorylation of the receptor protein on tyrosine, and to the phosphorylation of other proteins on tyrosine. The region of the receptor protein with tyrosine kinase activity is towards the carboxy terminal end of the molecule and resides on the cytoplasmic side of the membrane.

Two of the viral oncogenes are homologous to genes encoding growth-factor receptors; the gene product of v-erb-B is homologous to EGFR and that of v-fms is homologous to the CSF-1 receptor (Downward et al, 1984; Sherr et al, 1985). The protein products of these genes are present in normal cells and yet do not result in malignant transformation. The reason for this may be that, though homologous, both viral oncogenes are significantly different from the cellular genes. Thus the v-erb-B protein is missing both extracellular and intracellular regions of the EGFR, while the v-fms protein is of a lower molecular weight than the CSF-1 receptor, although the precise structures have not been elucidated. As a result of these modifications the viral protein behaves differently than the normal cellular protein. Upon binding of EGF, the EGFR is internalized; this may protect the cell against overstimulation by EGF. However, the protein product of v-erb-B cannot bind EGF and thus remains in the cell membrane. Second, the tyrosine kinase activity of EGFR is stimulated by the binding of EGF while preliminary evidence suggests that the tyrosine kinase activity of the v-erb-B protein is always being expressed. The fact that v-erb-B protein is confined to the cell membrane and is constitutive for protein kinase activity may account for its ability to transform cells.

5.4.5 CYTOPLASMIC PROTEINS WITH TYROSINE PROTEIN KINASE ACTIVITY

A second type of tyrosine protein kinase is associated with the inside of cell membranes. Examples of these kinases are the protein products of the v-src, c-src, v-abl and v-fes genes.

The v-src protein was the first of the oncogene products recognized to have tyrosine kinase activity, and consequently the most is known about this protein (Hunter and Cooper, 1985). Src protein is associated with cytoplasmic membranes through its amino terminal end. This attachment appears to be essential for its function, since mutations that block binding to the membrane inhibit the transforming activity of the pro-

tein. The second domain that is essential for the function of v-src is the tyrosine kinase catalytic site at the carboxy terminal end of the molecule. Within this domain is a tyrosine molecule (tyrosine 416) that is capable of being phosphorylated. This tyrosine appears to be important in the transforming capacity of v-src, since either substitution of tyrosine 416 with phenylalanine or lack of phosphorylation of this tyrosine in temperature-sensitive mutants leads to the loss of tumor formation. In cells containing v-src a number of proteins phosphorylated on tyrosine have been identified. These proteins are either associated with the cell membrane and cytoskeleton or are soluble in the cytoplasm. It is not known at the present time whether phosphorylation of any of these proteins is important in producing the transformed phenotype or whether the critical phosphoproteins have still to be detected.

The cellular homologue of v-src, c-src, also encodes a phosphoprotein that has protein kinase activity; however, the c-src product does not produce transformation unless present at very high levels (Shalloway et al, 1984). This is probably due to point mutations and a genetic substitution that differentiate v-src and c-src. The normal protein is not phosphorylated on tyrosine 416 nor does it phosphorylate the proteins that are phosphorylated by v-src, even when expressed at high levels. It is possible that the transforming ability of v-src is due to changes within the gene that result in the attachment to and phosphorylation of alternative substrates by the src protein.

5.4.6 GTP-BINDING PROTEINS

The ras family of proto-oncogenes produce a 21,000-d-molecular-weight cytoplasmic protein that binds to and acts as a phosphatase for GTP. Two similar genes are present in yeast and produce proteins which also have GTP binding and GTPase activity. Much more is known about these two genes, known as RAS 1 and RAS 2 (Defeo-Jones et al, 1985; Kataoka et al, 1985). In yeast the RAS 1 and 2 proteins in their activated form, when bound to GTP, stimulate adenylate cyclase. The submembrane position of the RAS proteins and their ability to stimulate adenylate cyclase suggest that they may act as an intermediate between a receptor on the cell surface and adenylate cyclase. As yet such a physiologic function has not been assigned.

The v-ras and activated c-ras proteins (activated by a point mutation involving amino acids 12, 13, or 61) also bind GTP but have reduced GTPase activity (Gibbs et al, 1984). The inability to remove the phosphate of GTP might lead to the protein always being in an active state. There is no indication that v-ras or the activated c-ras protein interacts with adenylate cyclase, but both v-ras and c-ras can substitute for RAS

1 and 2 in yeast and a mutant of RAS 1 can transform NIH/3T3 cells. Also, microinjection into cells of antibodies directed against the p21 ras protein has been found to inhibit the entry of such cells into DNA synthesis. The physiological function of ras proteins will almost certainly be determined in the next few years.

5.4.7 OTHER PROTEIN KINASES

In addition to phosphorylation of tyrosine, phosphorylation of serine and threonine may alter the activity of a protein. The protein products of the viral oncogenes mil and mos may possess such activity. These proteins reside in the cytoplasm of the cell rather than in or closely associated with cell membranes.

5.4.8 NUCLEAR PROTEINS

The nuclear proteins coded by myc, myb, fos, and other oncogenes of this type appear to function in normal cells to control the proliferation and self-renewal capacity of a cell. Self-renewal occurs when cell division leads to two daughter cells which are identical to the parent cell and which maintain the capacity for extensive proliferation. This is in contrast to cell division that results in daughter cells that differentiate and lose or have reduced capacity for proliferation (section 8.2.1). The ability to control the self-renewal capacity of a population of precursor cells is important for the homeostasis of any renewal tissue. For example, if self-renewal declines in the hemopoietic system it is likely that aplastic anemia will develop, while if self-renewal increases a state similar to leukemia may develop. Evidence that the level of myc mRNA correlates with cell proliferation and, more importantly, with self-renewal comes from a number of experimental systems.

The acute promyelocytic cell line HL-60, which has an amplified myc gene, is a model system for studying aspects of self-renewal and differentiation. When HL-60 cells are exposed to dimethyl sulfoxide (DMSO) they differentiate to become granulocytes and after a few cell divisions stop dividing. Cell division by HL-60 can also be arrested by serum starvation or by the inhibition of polyamine production (growtharrested cells); the addition of serum or polyamines results in rapid recovery of cell division. When the level of myc mRNA was measured in untreated, growtharrested, or DMSO-treated HL-60 cells, it was found that there were high levels of myc mRNA in the untreated and growth-arrested cells but undetectable levels in the DMSO-treated cells (Westin et al, 1982; Filmus and Buick, 1985). The fall in the level of myc mRNA in the DMSO-treated cells occurred rapidly, long before cell proliferation ceased. The decline in myc

mRNA appeared to be specific; it was associated with differentiation (and hence loss of the property of selfrenewal), rather than with change in the overall rate of proliferation of the cells. A parallel result has been obtained with a different human leukemic cell line (ML-1) where differentiation induced by a phorbol ester was associated with a decrease in the expression of the c-myb oncogene (Craig and Bloch, 1984).

A similar situation is found in mature functional cells. For example, in normal resting lymphocytes the myc gene is not expressed or is expressed at very low levels. Shortly after stimulation of the cells with either antigen or mitogen, however, there is a transient rise in the level of myc mRNA and protein which precedes the entry of the cell into DNA synthesis (Kelly et al, 1983). These experiments suggest that myc and related proteins play a role in controlling the proliferative capacity of a cell.

In normal cells the expression of myc and other nuclear proteins appears to be tightly controlled, but in transformed cells the expression of such proteins is less closely regulated (Hann and Eisenman, 1984). Two examples of this are HL-60, in which there is overproduction of myc mRNA, and Burkitt's lymphoma cells, in which myc mRNA is always produced.

5.5 SUMMARY

All mammalian cells contain genes, known as proto-oncogenes, which when activated may contribute to the development of malignancy. Many of these genes are homologous to the viral oncogenes first detected in RNA viruses. Activated forms of the proto-oncogenes have been detected in malignant cells of human origin by their ability to transform normal cells after transfection of DNA, and by using labeled DNA probes that are complementary to known viral oncogenes. Protooncogenes in normal cells may be activated by mutation, by amplification or by rearrangements such as chromosome translocation. Development of the malignant phenotype probably involves activation of more than one oncogene.

The normal function of proto-oncogenes is under investigation. Some (eg, c-myc) code for nuclear proteins which seem to be involved in the control of cell proliferation and differentiation. Others (eg, ras) code for cytoplasmic GTP-binding proteins or (eg, src) for proteins with specific phosphokinase (tyrosine kinase) activity; still others (eg, sis) appear to produce products which influence cellular behavior through pathways similar to those of growth factors.

The role of activated oncogenes in the generation of human cancer is unknown. Oncogenes which can transform cells in a transfection assay have been detected only in about 10% of primary human tumors. Whether this represents a limitation of the assay remains to be determined. Further elucidation of the mechanisms by which oncogene products cause malignancy in selected cells will undoubtedly improve our understanding of the processes that control cellular proliferation and differentiation.

REFERENCES

Bishop JM: Cellular oncogenes and retroviruses. *Ann Rev Biochem* 1983; 52:301–354.

Capon DJ, Seeburg PH, McGrath JP et al: Activation of Ki-ras2 gene in human colon and lung carcinomas by two different point mutations. *Nature* 1983; 304:507–513.

Chang EH, Furth ME, Scolnick EM, Lowy DR: Tumorigenic transformation of mammalian cells induced by a normal human gene homologous to the oncogene of Harvey murine sarcoma virus. *Nature* 1982; 297:479–483.

Collins S, Groudine M: Amplification of endogenous myc-related DNA sequences in a human myeloid leukaemia cell line. *Nature* 1982; 298:679–681.

Copeland NG, Zelenetz AD, Cooper GM: Transformation of NIH/3T3 mouse cells by DNA of Rous sarcoma virus. *Cell* 1979; 17:993–1002.

Craig RW, Bloch A: Early decline in c-myb oncogene expression in the differentiation of human myeloblastic leukemia (ML-1) cells induced with 12-O-Tetradecanoylphorbol-13-acetate. *Cancer Res* 1984; 44:442–446.

Defeo-Jones D, Tatchell K, Robinson LC et al: Mammalian and yeast ras gene products: biological function in their heterologous systems. *Science* 1985; 228:179–184.

Downward J, Yarden Y, Mayes E et al: Close similarity of epidermal growth factor receptor and v-erb-B oncogene protein sequences. *Nature* 1984; 307:521–527.

Eva A, Tronick SR, Gol RA et al: Transforming genes of human hematopoietic tumors: frequent detection of ras-related oncogenes whose activation appears to be independent of tumor phenotype. *Proc Natl Acad Sci USA*, 1983; 80:4926–4930.

Feo S, ar-Rushdi A, Huebner K et al: Suppression of the normal mouse c-myc oncogene in human lymphoma cells. *Nature* 1985; 313:493–495.

Filmus J, Buick RN: Relationship of c-myc expression to differentiation and proliferation of HL-60 cells. *Cancer Res* 1985; 45:822–825.

Gibbs JB, Sigal IS, Poe M, Scolnick EM: Intrinsic GTPase activity distinguishes normal and oncogenic ras p21 molecules. *Proc Natl Acad Sci USA* 1984; 81:5704–5708.

Groffen J, Stephenson JR, Heisterkamp N et al: Philadelphia chromosomal breakpoints are clustered within a limited region bcr on chromosome 22. *Cell* 1984; 36:93–99.

Gusella JF, Keys C, Varsanyibreiner A et al: Isolation and localization of DNA segments from specific human chromosomes. *Proc Natl Acad Sci USA* 1980; 77:2829–2833.

Hann SR, Eisenman RN: Proteins encoded by the human c-myc oncogene: differential expression in neoplastic cells. *Mol Cell Biol* 1984; 14:2486–2497.

Huebner RJ, Todaro GJ: Oncogenes of RNA tumor viruses as determinants of cancer. *Proc Natl Acad Sci USA* 1969; 64:1087–1094.

Hunter T, Cooper JA: Protein–tyrosine kinases. *Ann Rev Biochem* 1985; 54:897–930.

Kataoka T, Powers S, Cameron S et al: Functional homology of mammalian and yeast ras genes. 1985; *Cell* 40:19–26.

Kelly K, Cochran BH, Stiles CD, Leder P: Cell-specific regulation of the c-myc gene by lymphocyte mitogens and platelet-derived growth factor. *Cell* 1983; 35:603–610.

Klein G: The role of gene dosage and genetic transpositions in carcinogenesis. *Nature* 1981; 294:313–318.

Konopka JB, Watanabe SM, Singer JW et al: Cell lines and clinical isolates derived from Ph[1]-positive chronic myelogenous leukemia patients express c-abl proteins with a common structural alteration. *Proc Natl Acad Sci USA* 1985; 82:1810–1814.

Konopka JB, Watanabe SM, Witte ON: An alteration of the human c-abl protein in K562 leukemia cells unmasks associated tyrosine kinase activity. *Cell* 1984; 37:1035–1042.

Land H, Parada LF, Weinberg RA: Tumorigenic conversion of primary embryo fibroblasts requires at least two cooperating oncogenes. *Nature* 1983; 304:596–602.

Little CD, Nau MM, Carney DN et al: Amplification and expression of the c-myc oncogene in human lung cancer cell lines. *Nature* 1983; 306:194–196.

Parada LF, Tabin CJ, Shih C, Weinberg RA: Human EJ bladder carcinoma oncogene is homologue of Harvey sarcoma virus ras gene. *Nature* 1982; 297:474–478.

Rapp UR, Reynolds FH, Stephenson JR: New mammalian transforming retrovirus: demonstration of a polyprotein gene product. *J. Virology* 1983; 45:914–924.

Reddy EP, Reynolds RK, Santos E, Barbacid M: A point mutation is responsible for the acquisition of transforming properties by the T24 human bladder carcinoma oncogene. *Nature* 1982; 300:149–152.

Rous P: A sarcoma of the fowl transmissable by an agent separable from the tumor cells. *J Exp Med* 1911; 13:397–411.

Rowley JD: Biological implications of consistent chromosome rearrangements in leukemia and lymphoma. *Cancer Res* 1984; 44:3159–3168.

Santos E, Martin-Zanca D, Reddy EP et al: Malignant activation of a K-ras oncogene in lung carcinoma but not in normal tissue of the same patient. *Science* 1984; 223:661–664.

Schimke RT, Brown PC; Kaufman RJ et al: Chromosomal and extrachromosomal localization of amplified dihydrofolate reductase genes in cultured mammalian cells. *Cold Spring Harbor Symp Quant Biol* 1980; 45:785–797.

Schwab M, Alitalo K, Klempnauer K-H et al: Amplified DNA with limited homology to myc cellular oncogene is shared by human neuroblastoma cell lines and a neuroblastoma tumour. *Nature* 1983; 305:245–248.

Shalloway D, Coussens PM, Yaciuk P: Overexpression of the c-src protein does not induce transformation of NIH 3T3 cells. *Proc Natl Acad Sci USA* 1984; 81:7071–7075.

Sherr CJ, Rettenmier CW, Sacca R et al: The c-fms proto-oncogene product is related to the receptor for the mononuclear phagocyte growth factor, CSF-1. *Cell* 1985; 41: 665–676.

Shih C, Shilo BZ, Goldfarb MP et al: Passage of phenotypes of chemically transformed cells via transfection of DNA and chromatin. *Proc Natl Acad Sci USA* 1979; 76:5714–5718.

Shih C, Weinberg RA: Isolation of a transforming sequence from a human bladder carcinoma cell line. *Cell* 1982; 29: 161–169.

Shtivelman E, Lifshitz B, Gale RP, Canaani E: Fused transcript of abl and bcr genes in chronic myelogenous leukemia. *Nature* 1985; 315:550–554.

Tabin CJ, Bradley SM, Bargmann CI et al: Mechanism of activation of a human oncogene. *Nature* 1982; 300:143–149.

Taparowsky E, Shimizu K, Goldfarb M, Wigler M: Structure and activation of the human N-ras gene. *Cell* 1983; 34:581–586.

Varmus HE: The molecular genetics of cellular oncogenes. *Ann Rev Genet* 1984; 18:553–612.

Waterfield MD, Scrace GT, Whittle N et al: Platelet-derived growth factor is structurally related to putative transforming protein p28[sis] of simian sarcoma virus. *Nature* 1983; 304:35–39.

Westin EH, Wong-Staal F, Gelmann EP et al: Expression of cellular homologues of retroviral onc genes in human hematopoietic cells. *Proc Natl Acad Sci USA* 1982; 73: 2490–2494.

Zarbl H, Sukumar S, Arthur A et al: Direct mutagenesis of Ha-ras-1 oncogenes by N-nitroso-N-methylurea during initiation of mammary carcinogenesis in rats. *Nature* 1985; 315:382–385.

BIBLIOGRAPHY

Bishop JM: Cellular oncogenes and retroviruses. *Ann Rev Biochem* 1983; 52:301–354.

Hunter T, Cooper JA: Protein-tyrosine kinases. *Ann Rev Biochem* 1985; 54:897–930.

Klein G, Klein E: Evolution of tumours and the impact of molecular oncology. *Nature* 1985; 315:190–195.

Varmus HE: The molecular genetics of cellular oncogenes. *Ann Rev Genet* 1984; 18:553–612.

6

Chemical Carcinogenesis

Michael C. Archer

6.1 INTRODUCTION

The English physician Percival Pott recognized over 200 years ago that the occurrence of scrotal cancer in chimney sweeps correlated with their exposure over many years to soot and tar. Subsequent research in the early part of the 20th century showed that coal tar applied to the ears of rabbits yielded cancer at the site of application. Ultimately polycyclic aromatic hydrocarbons such as benzo(a)pyrene (Fig 6.1) were isolated from these combustion products and shown to be carcinogenic. In the late 19th century, the German physician Rehn observed an association between the occurrence of cancer of the urinary bladder and exposure of workers to aromatic amines (eg, benzidine, Fig 6.1) and azo compounds in the dye industry. In the 1930s several aromatic amines were shown to induce bladder cancer in experimental animals.

Since these early studies, many other chemicals have been shown to be carcinogenic. Such compounds have been identified from studies in cancer epidemiology (eg, vinyl chloride in the workplace), from routine bioassays (eg, nitrosodimethylamine and other nitrosamines) and from investigations into the etiology of other diseases in man (eg, cycasin) and animals (eg, aflatoxin B_1) (see Fig 6.1 for structures). It has recently become clear from extensive studies in cancer epidemiology that many common types of cancer are probably caused by widely distributed environmental agents, both man-made and naturally occurring (chapter 2).

In addition to those illustrated in Figure 6.1, there are several other major groups of chemical carcinogens.

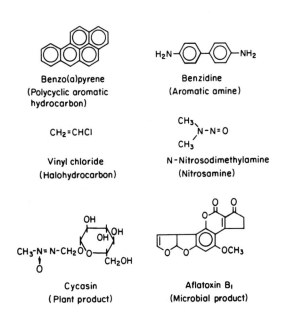

Figure 6.1. Structures of carcinogens in various chemical groups.

These include hydrazines, triazines, chlorocarbons, a relatively large, diverse selection of reactive alkylating agents, and a smaller group of reactive acylating agents. There are a variety of naturally occurring carcinogenic compounds of both microbial and plant origin that have complex structures. Several inorganic carcinogens are also known, such as compounds of beryllium, cobalt, cadmium, chromium and nickel.

Each of the major groups of chemical carcinogens comprises numerous compounds that have similar structural features. However, there are no obvious common structural features shared by the major groups or any of the other chemical carcinogens to which one might ascribe their carcinogenic activity. There is, however, a common mode of action for these agents which will be explained in section 6.3.

In addition to the obvious importance of chemical carcinogens for understanding the origins of human cancer and ways the disease may be prevented, they offer the scientist a valuable tool with which to study the mechanism of the carcinogenic process.

6.2 BIOLOGICAL CHARACTERISTICS OF CHEMICAL CARCINOGENESIS

6.2.1 DOSE–RESPONSE RELATIONSHIPS

Chemical carcinogens usually require repeated administration to the test animal in order to produce tumors. One of the characteristic features of carcinogenesis, whether induced by chemical, physical or biological agents, is the extended period of time (latency period) between the first application of the agent and the eventual development of a tumor. This latency period is dose dependent. A systematic dose–response study was performed by Druckrey (1943) with dimethyl-4-aminoazobenzene in a daily dose range of 3–30 mg per rat. At the highest dose, liver tumors were obtained after about a month, whereas at the lowest daily dose, about a year was required for tumor induction. The latency period was inversely proportional to the daily dose and the total dose of carcinogen required to induce liver tumors was about a gram in each case. A double-logarithmic plot of the daily dose against induction time gives a straight line with a slope of 1 (Fig 6.2). These results suggest that the effects of all the individual doses are additive over the life span of the animals.

When a similar dose–response experiment was carried out with nitrosodiethylamine, Druckrey et al (1963) showed that the log–log plot of daily dose against median induction time again gave a straight line (Fig 6.2), but in this case the slope was 2.3 — there was a reduction in total dose required to produce tumors at

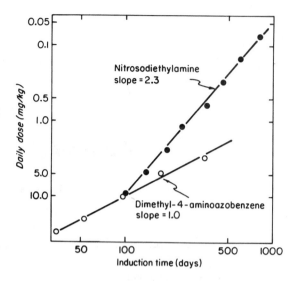

Figure 6.2. Linear dependency of tumor induction time on daily dose (double-logarithmic plot) for nitrosodiethylamine and dimethyl-4-aminoazobenzene. (Adapted from Druckrey, 1943, and Druckrey et al, 1963.)

the lower daily doses. Thus the daily doses are not simply additive, but rather carcinogenesis seems to be an "accelerated" process. Druckrey proposed that the appearance of tumors could be described by the relationship $dt^n = \text{const}$, where d = daily dose, t = induction time, and $n > 1$. We have seen that nitrosodiethylamine has an n value of 2.3. Some other carcinogens have been shown to have higher n values. Benzo(a)pyrene, for example, has an n of 4.0 for induction of mouse skin tumors.

Epidemiological findings with human tumors also support Druckrey's relationship. Incidence of lung cancer in smokers, for example, increases with about the

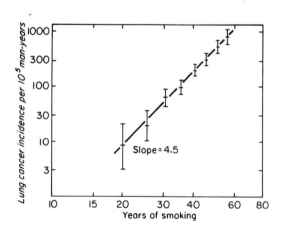

Figure 6.3. Age-specific rates of lung cancer in cigarette smokers, standardized for dose. (Adapted from Doll and Peto, 1978.)

fourth or fifth power of time (Doll and Peto, 1978; see Fig 6.3).

Some carcinogens produce tumors after a single administration. Dose–response curves for single subcutaneous injections of two different polycyclic aromatic hydrocarbons in male C3H mice are shown in Figure 6.4. It is clear that 3-methylcholanthrene is about 10 times more potent than benzo(a)pyrene in producing sarcomas at the site of injection. There is an overall variation in carcinogenic potency of about 10^7 for different chemicals administered either as single or multiple doses (Gold et al, 1984).

The carcinogenic potency of a chemical can be affected by numerous factors. There can be large differences in activities between animal species. Liver tumors, for example, are induced in rats by continuous feeding of aflatoxin B_1 in the µg/kg range, whereas there is usually no response in mice during continuous exposure to mg/kg levels. There can also be major variations in target-organ specificity between species, exemplified by 2-acetylaminofluorene as shown in Table 6.1. Even differences in the strain of animal within the same species can cause variation in cancer incidence. Table 6.2 shows that the Holtzman rat is considerably more resistant than the Carworth Farms Wistar strain to the hepatocarcinogenic effects of ethionine. This table also illustrates that there can be differences in susceptibility between males and females of the same strain. Age of the animals at the time of carcinogen administration is another important factor; newborn mice or rats are often exquisitely sensitive to the action of chemical carcinogens.

6.2.2 THE MULTISTEP NATURE OF CANCER DEVELOPMENT

Figure 6.5 illustrates a general scheme describing carcinogenesis by chemicals which will be discussed in detail in this chapter.

The time between administration of a carcinogen and the appearance of tumors may be divided into distinct periods. The first stage results directly from administration of the chemical carcinogen and is called "initiation." Initiation is an irreversible, normally rapid process, whereby the chemical produces permanent changes in the DNA of target cells.

The second stage of carcinogenesis is the process whereby tumor formation is stimulated in tissues that have been exposed to an initiating agent, and is called "promotion." In contrast to initiation, promotion involves a series of usually reversible tissue and cellu-

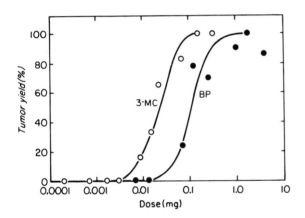

Figure 6.4. Dose–response curves for 3-methylcholanthrene (3-MC) and benzo(a)pyrene (BP) in C3H male mice. The polycyclic hydrocarbons were injected subcutaneously, and sarcomas arising at the site of single injection were counted. (Adapted from Bryan and Shimkin, 1943.)

Table 6.1. Carcinogenic Activity of 2-Acetylaminofluorene in Different Species

Species	Local	Bladder	Kidney	Liver	Intestine	Ear Duct	Breast	Other
Mouse	−	+	−	+	−	−	+	−
Rat	−	+	+	+	+	+	+	various
Hamster	−	−	−	+	−	−	−	−
Guinea pig	−	−	−	−	−	−	−	−
Rabbit	−	+	−	−	−	−	−	ureter
Cat	−	−	−	+	−	−	−	lung
Dog	−	+	−	+	−	−	−	−
Monkey	−	−	−	−	−	−	−	−
Fish	−	−	−	+	−	−	−	−
Chicken	−	−	+	+	−	−	−	fallopian tube; ovary

Note: Adapted from Garner et al (1984).

Table 6.2. Strain Differences in Induction of Liver Cancer by Ethionine

Rat Strain	Sex	Duration of Feeding of Ethionine-containing Diet (Months)	Percent Incidence of Liver Cancer
Carworth Farms Wistar	M	5.0	86
Holtzman	M	5.0	0
Carworth Farms Wistar	M	7.5	100
	F	7.5	100
Holtzman	M	7.5	60
	F	7.5	25
Fischer	M	7.5	100
	F	7.5	90

Note: Adapted from Farber (1963).

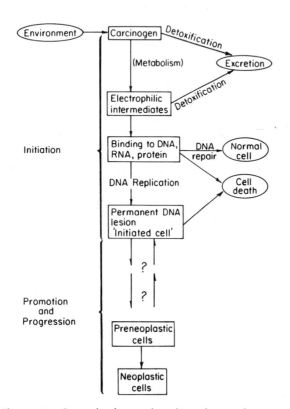

Figure 6.5. General scheme describing the mechanism of chemical carcinogenesis.

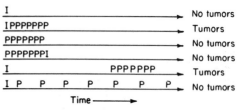

I = Application of initiator   P = Application of promotor

Figure 6.6. Experiments demonstrating the initiation and promotion phases of carcinogenesis in mouse skin.

lar changes during the long latency period before appearance of the first autonomous cancer cell. A third stage, "progression," is used to describe the stepwise evolution of cancer cells as they become progressively more malignant.

The classic experiments that allowed the initiation and promotion phases of carcinogenesis to be distinguished were performed in the 1940s using tumor induction in mouse skin as a model (eg, Berenblum and Shubik, 1947). Figure 6.6 outlines the design of such experiments and their outcome. A single, low dose of initiating agent (eg, polycyclic aromatic hydrocarbon) was chosen that produced no tumors during the life span of the animal (though at higher doses it would have produced tumors). When the low dose of initiating agent was followed by repetitive doses of a promoting agent (eg, croton seed oil), a high yield of papillomas, and ultimately carcinomas, was obtained. No tumors developed when only the promoting agent was applied or when the promoting agent was applied before the initiating agent. Tumors were obtained, however, when application of the promoting agent was delayed for many months after the application of the initiator. This result demonstrates the persistence of initiated cells. When the time between multiple applications of the promotor was sufficiently extended, no tumors were formed, demonstrating the reversible nature of promotion in mouse skin.

The stages of carcinogenesis have been demonstrated more recently in tissues other than mouse skin, and a rat liver model in which the initiation and promotion phases of carcinogenesis are distinguished will be described in section 6.4.

Chemical carcinogens are identified by their ability to act alone to cause malignant tumors after administration to animals (section 6.5.1). Such agents clearly act as both initiators and promotors and are called "complete carcinogens." The following two sections will describe the mechanisms of initiation and promotion in more detail.

6.3 THE INITIATION OF CARCINOGENESIS

6.3.1 REACTIVITY OF CHEMICAL CARCINOGENS AND THEIR CELLULAR TARGETS

The property that is common to all of the diverse types of chemical carcinogens is that they can form directly, or are metabolized to reactive electrophilic forms (Miller and Miller, 1981). These electron-deficient species can attack the many electron-rich or nucleophilic sites in molecules such as proteins and nucleic acids to form covalent adducts (addition products). The reactions, which take place principally at nitrogen, oxygen or sulfur atoms in the macromolecules, are nonenzymatic and hence nonspecific. Small molecular weight nucleophiles such as water and glutathione are also readily attacked by the electrophiles, and in some cases these reactions are catalyzed by enzymes such as glutathione-S-transferase.

The electrophilic forms of chemical carcinogens can react at numerous sites within the cell to produce damage that may be lethal. There is considerable evidence to suggest that DNA is the molecular target in the initiation process (Straus, 1981). The irreversible nature of initiation, and the persistence of initiated cells, are consistent with a change in the DNA of these cells. A nonlethal alteration in the genotype explains the permanent, heritable change that takes place in cancer cells which often exhibit chromosomal abnormalities and altered gene expression. Furthermore, some types of cancer (eg, bilateral retinoblastoma) and cancer-prone diseases (eg, familial polyposis coli) are inherited, autosomal-dominant disorders. Several other autosomal-recessive disorders known to be associated with chromosomal instability, including Bloom's syndrome, Fanconi's anemia and ataxia telangiectasia, carry a high risk for the development of certain types of cancer (see section 3.2). There is abundant evidence that carcinogens interact with DNA in vivo to produce covalent adducts (section 6.3.3), and it is now well established that most carcinogens are mutagens (Ames, 1979).

One or more carcinogens can react with virtually every nucleophilic site in the constituent bases of DNA (Fig 6.7). Phosphate residues are also targets for reaction. Adduct formation at the hydrogen-bonding sites of the base pairs can clearly cause miscoding. Miscoding may also be caused by the presence of carcinogen moieties at other sites which sufficiently distort the DNA structure to cause infidelity in DNA replication.

The intragenomic distribution of carcinogen-DNA lesions is not uniform; there is preferential binding, for example, to template-active chromatin and nucleosomal linker DNA.

Some forms of DNA damage can be repaired by cellular enzymes in processes which will be discussed more fully in section 6.3.4. Increased susceptibility to cancer in patients with certain DNA-repair-deficiency diseases also points to the importance of DNA in carcinogenesis.

6.3.2 CHEMICAL CARCINOGENS AND ONCOGENES

Strong evidence for the central role of DNA in the initiation of carcinogenesis is provided by studies which have shown that activated oncogenes (section 5.3.2) are present in cell lines transformed by chemical carcinogens (Weinberg, 1982; Sukumar et al, 1984). Furthermore, several tumors which arise in animals following administration of chemicals contain activated ras oncogenes (Sukumar et al, 1983; Balmain and Pragnell, 1983; Guerrero et al, 1984). For example, Sukumar et al (1983) induced rat mammary tumors by a single dose of nitrosomethylurea. They found that transforming H-ras genes were present in all 9 of the tumors examined. Molecular cloning of one of the isolated oncogenes showed that its mechanism of activation involved a single point mutation at the 12th codon. Interestingly, this same genetic alteration had previously been identified in ras oncogenes isolated from human tumors (section 5.3).

It is unclear from studies on genetic material isolated from malignant tumors, however, whether oncogene activation is a cause or effect in carcinogenesis. Balmain et al (1984) have shown activation and overexpression

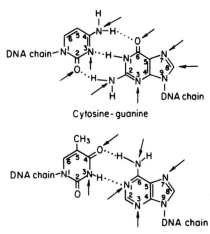

Figure 6.7. Sites of reaction of activated carcinogens with the four common bases in DNA shown by the arrows.

of H-ras in premalignant papillomas, as well as in malignant skin tumors induced by dimethylbenzanthracene. They concluded that the mutational event which induces the transforming capacity of the DNA does not take place at the transition to malignancy, but already exists in most or all of the premalignant lesions. It has recently been shown by Marshall et al (1984) that reaction in vitro of an H-ras proto-oncogene with the electrophilic form of a carcinogen (benzo(a)pyrene diol-epoxide) generates a transforming oncogene when the modified DNA is used in a transfection assay. Oncogene activation by chemical carcinogens, therefore, could be the process we have defined as initiation, though much more experimentation will be necessary to prove this hypothesis.

6.3.3 THE ACTIVATION OF CHEMICAL CARCINOGENS

As their name implies, the direct-acting alkylating and acylating carcinogens are intrinsically electrophilic, and are carcinogenic without any requirement for metabolism. Examples of such agents are shown in Figure 6.8, where $\delta+$ indicates the electrophilic atom and $\delta-$ the leaving group. Chemical carcinogens other than these alkylating and acylating agents, however, must be metabolized to their active forms. This metabolic activation of the parent or "procarcinogen" to the "ultimate" form that is actually the initiating agent may be a single-step reaction, or it may proceed by formation of one or more less reactive intermediates called "proximate" forms of the carcinogen. Metabolism may also take place to yield nonreactive forms of the procarcinogen (detoxification products) which may be excreted. The balance between metabolic activation and inactivation reactions, as well as the inherent carcinogenic activity of the ultimate electrophile, are undoubtedly important factors in determining the potency of a chemical carcinogen (Fig 6.9).

Enzymes involved in metabolism of carcinogens. The normal role of the enzymes which act on chemical carcinogens is to convert foreign, lipophilic compounds that find their way into the body into more hydrophilic forms that can readily be excreted (Jakoby, 1980). In attempting to create a hydrophilic product, the enzymes of carcinogen metabolism inadvertently form a reactive product.

Many activation reactions are two-electron oxidations that are catalyzed by cytochrome P-450–dependent mono-oxygenases. This enzyme system is located predominantly in the endoplasmic reticulum (microsomal fraction) of the cell, and to a lesser extent in the nucleus. It consists of a multiplicity of cytochromes P-450

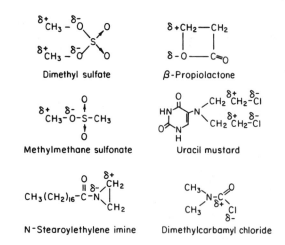

Figure 6.8. Chemical structures of direct-acting carcinogens.

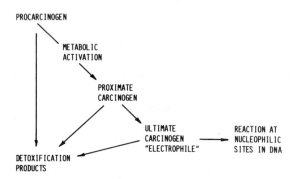

Figure 6.9. The metabolic activation and detoxification of chemical carcinogens.

(eg, ten forms so far purified to homogeneity from rat liver) with different but overlapping substrate specificities. Each enzyme is a hemoprotein with the iron atom initially in the ferric form. After binding the carcinogen, the enzyme cytochrome P-450 reductase, utilizing NADPH, reduces the iron to the ferrous form which then binds a molecule of oxygen. One atom of oxygen oxidizes the drug and one forms water, concomitantly reoxidizing the iron atom (Fig 6.10). Numerous factors can affect the activity of these oxidative enzymes, which in turn can markedly affect the potency of a chemical carcinogen (see section 6.2); these factors include the species, strain, sex, age and nutritional and hormonal status of the animal, as well as drugs and other chemicals that act as inducers or inhibitors.

Other enzymes which may be involved in the oxidation of carcinogens are the peroxidases. A peroxidative oxidation of possible physiological relevance is mediated by prostaglandin synthetase in the presence of arachidonic acid. There are other activating reactions catalyzed by nonoxidative (eg, reductive, hydrolytic)

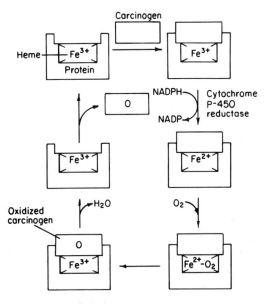

Figure 6.10. Sequence of reactions during the oxidation of carcinogens by the cytochrome P-450 system.

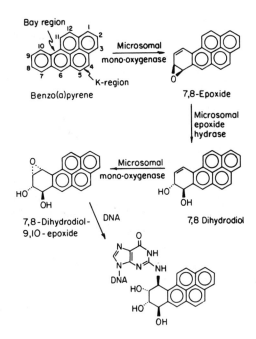

Figure 6.11. Reaction sequence for the metabolic activation of benzo(a)pyrene.

pathways that include cytosolic enzymes. Conjugation reactions (eg, addition of glucuronic acid, glutathione, glycine or sulfate) are particularly important for deactivation of carcinogens, but in some cases (eg, for aromatic amines and amides) can lead to activation.

Metabolism of carcinogens can occur in a number of tissues and organs, though the liver is quantitatively the major metabolic organ. Ability of the target organ to activate carcinogens appears in a number of cases to be a necessary, though not sufficient, condition to account for their organ specificities. The metabolic activation of important classes of carcinogens is described in the following sections and in Figures 6.11–6.14.

*Polycyclic aromatic hydrocarbons.** Since polycyclic aromatic hydrocarbons commonly induce tumors at sites of application in animals (eg, skin), they were at one time thought to be direct-acting initiating agents. They are, however, rather unreactive compounds, but are metabolized to a variety of phenols, dihydrodiols and quinones. On the basis of the formation of these metabolites, it was proposed more than 30 years ago that the primary oxidation products were epoxides. Much attention was devoted to the so-called K-region epoxides (K stands for Krebs, the German word for cancer) which are formed at a chemically reactive region of high electron density in the molecules (eg, the 4,5-position in benzo(a)pyrene, Fig 6.11). Such epoxides can react with nucleophiles and hence are candidates for being the ultimate carcinogens. K-region

----

*Reviewed by Levin et al, 1982.

epoxides proved to be mutagenic and able to transform cells in culture. Their carcinogenic potency in intact animals, however, was shown to be less than that of the parent hydrocarbons, raising doubts about their role as ultimate carcinogenic forms. When DNA adducts were characterized from cells treated with the hydrocarbons, it became clear that although epoxides are activation products, they are not those formed in the K region.

The metabolic activation of polycyclic aromatic hydrocarbons is illustrated for benzo(a)pyrene in Figure 6.11. The procarcinogen is first oxidized by the microsomal mixed-function oxidase system to the 7,8-epoxide. This epoxide is hydrolyzed by the microsomal enzyme epoxide hydrase to yield exclusively the trans 7,8-dihydrodiol. A second microsomal mono-oxygenase-dependent oxidation then takes place to form the 7,8-dihydrodiol-9,10-epoxide, which is the ultimate electrophilic form. Reaction of the 2-amino group of guanine residues in DNA with the epoxide yields the adduct shown. All of the reactions of Figure 6.11 proceed with a high degree of stereoselectivity.

Metabolic activation of other polycyclic aromatic hydrocarbons also proceeds by dihydrodiol-epoxide formation. The reactions take place in the "bay region" of the hydrocarbon that is formed by angular rings (Fig 6.11). Such bay-region epoxides have high electrophilic reactivity, are highly mutagenic, are considerably more carcinogenic than the parent hydrocarbon, and account for the major DNA adducts formed in vivo from the parent hydrocarbons.

*Aromatic amines and amides.** The activation pathway for these compounds was elucidated principally by Elizabeth and James Miller in their classic studies of the mode of action of the versatile carcinogen 2-acetylaminofluorene (AAF, Fig 6.12). Their first key observation was that N-hydroxy-AAF is a urinary metabolite in the rat. N-hydroxy-AAF is more carcinogenic than AAF in the rat and in several other rodents; moreover, it is carcinogenic in the guinea pig, whereas AAF itself does not induce tumors in this species. In keeping with this observation, the guinea pig was shown to have much less of the enzyme that oxidizes the amide nitrogen atom of AAF than the rat. AAF and N-hydroxy-AAF both produced hepatic DNA adducts in the rat, but the N-hydroxy compound does not react with DNA in vitro. These observations suggested that N-hydroxy-AAF was a proximate form, but that further metabolism was required to produce the ultimate carcinogen. It was subsequently shown that the next metabolic step is formation of the sulfate ester of N-hydroxy-AAF via a hepatic sulfotransferase enzyme that utilizes 3′-phosphoadenosine-5′-phosphosulfate as

sulfate donor. Formation of this ester weakens the nitrogen–oxygen bond which cleaves to form the highly electrophilic nitrenium ion. This in turn reacts directly with guanine residues in DNA to form an adduct at the C8 position. Alternatively, the ion can undergo rearrangement to form an adduct at the 2-amino group. The latter is the minor product, but is the persistent form in DNA, and therefore may be important in initiation (see section 6.3.5). Evidence that sulfate ester formation is a major activation pathway derives from the correlation of hepatic sulfotransferase activity with susceptibility to liver tumor formation and the observation that reduction of sulfate levels in vivo by dietary manipulation reduces the hepatotoxicity and hepatocarcinogenicity of N-hydroxy-AAF.

Formation of the sulfate ester of N-hydroxy-AAF appears to be limited to the liver, but there are other metabolic pathways that can generate electrophilic forms of AAF that may be important at extrahepatic sites (Fig 6.13). A number of tissues contain transacetylase activity that forms the electrophilic ester N-acetoxy-2-aminofluorene from N-hydroxy-AAF. Peroxidases catalyze the one-electron oxidation of N-hydroxy-AAF to yield a nitroxide-free radical. Interaction of two such radicals (dismutation) yields another reactive ester, N-acetoxy-AAF. N-hydroxy-AAF is also metabolized to an O-glucuronide, but this has only weak electrophilic activity.

*Reviewed by Miller and Miller, 1981.

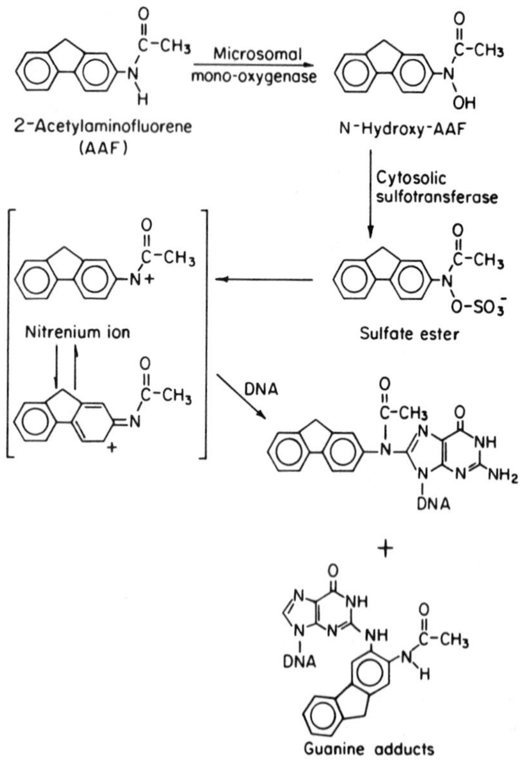

Figure 6.12. Reaction sequence for the metabolic activation of 2-acetylaminofluorene via sulfate ester formation.

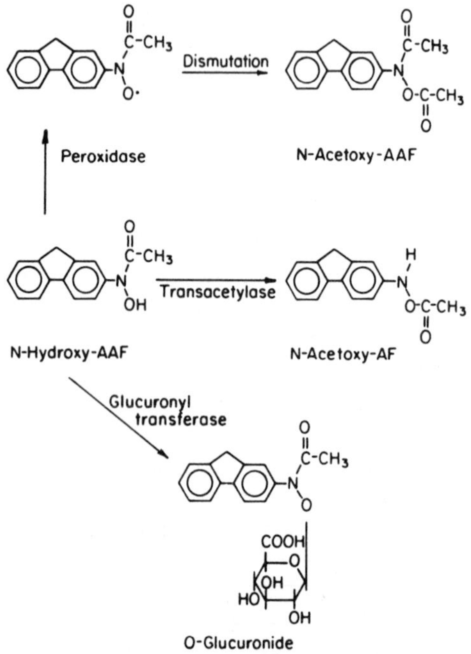

Figure 6.13. Alternate pathways for the metabolic activation of N-hydroxy-2-acetylaminofluorene.

Similar metabolic pathways involving esterification of N-hydroxy derivatives seem to be operative in the activation of other aromatic amines and amides.

*Nitrosamines.** Nitrosamides and nitrosamidines such as N-methyl-N-nitrosourea and N-methyl-N-nitro-N-nitrosoguanidine are transformed directly into electrophilic alkylating species by chemical reaction at physiological pH with nucleophiles such as water or thiols. These N-nitroso compounds induce tumors in a wide variety of tissues including the site of administration, and most species are susceptible to their carcinogenic action. Nitrosamines are also versatile carcinogens, but less so than the nitrosamides; they do not usually induce tumors at the site of administration. The tissue specificity of nitrosamines, although affected somewhat by the dose, is not usually influenced by the route of administration. The susceptible tissue depends to a large extent on the chemical structure of the nitrosamine. The mechanism for this organotropic effect is not understood, but is in part related to the necessity for the enzymatic activation of nitrosamines in the target tissue.

Early work on the metabolism of the hepatocarcinogen nitrosodimethylamine showed that carbon dioxide was the principal metabolite in the rat, from which it was concluded that demethylation takes place. Formaldehyde was identified as a major product of nitrosodimethylamine metabolism in vitro with hepatic microsomes. Subsequently DNA and RNA from the liver of rats administered radioactive nitrosodimethylamine were shown to be highly labeled, and 7-methylguanine was identified as the principal product.

As a result of these and other observations, the reaction sequence shown in Figure 6.14 was formulated to describe the metabolic activation of nitrosamines. The crucial initial step is a microsomal oxidation reaction in which a carbon atom adjacent to the N-nitroso group is hydroxylated. The α-hydroxynitrosamine so formed spontaneously cleaves to yield an aldehyde fragment and an alkyldiazohydroxide. This diazohydroxide may then produce the highly electrophilic diazonium ion and carbocation. Which of these species acts as the ultimate alkylating agent is unknown, but the cationic products are far too reactive to survive intracellular diffusion from the site of metabolic activation (the endoplasmic reticulum) to the site of reaction with DNA (the nucleus). Recently α-hydroxynitrosamines have been prepared chemically in carefully dried solvents. They have half-lives of a few seconds at physiological pH, and so

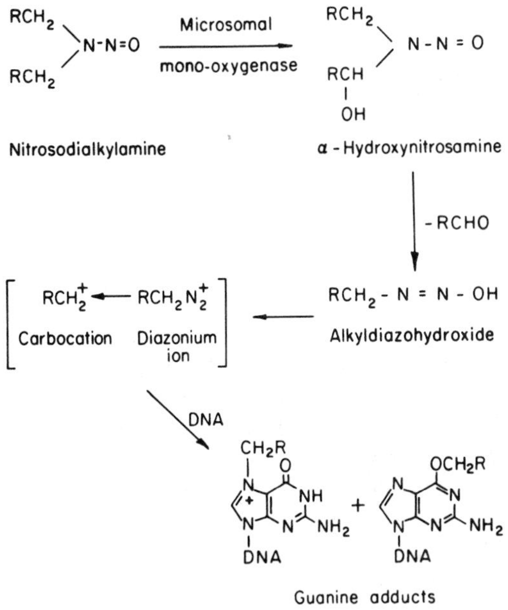

---

*Reviewed by Archer, 1985.

Figure 6.14. Reaction sequence for the metabolic activation of N-nitrosodialkylamines.

probably represent the transportable form of the activated nitrosamine.

Nitrosamines with three or more carbon atoms in the side chains can also undergo other metabolic oxidation reactions that may lead to detoxification products, or the oxidized metabolites may be involved in more complex activation pathways.

7-Alkylguanine (66.8%) is the most abundant modified base in DNA produced by nitrosodialkylamines, but a variety of other products have been identified including alkylphosphate triesters (12%), 1-, 3- and 7-alkyladenine (0.9%, 2.3%, 0.7%), 3- and O^6-alkylguanine (0.9%, 6.1%), 3-alkylcytosine (0.6%), O^4-alkylthymine (trace) and unidentified products (10%) (the numbers in parentheses are the relative proportions of the products as a percentage of the total products for in vivo methylation of DNA by nitrosodimethylamine reported by O'Connor et al, 1979). The extent of alkylation at the 7 position of guanine shows no correlation with carcinogenic activity, but several striking correlations have been obtained between tissue susceptibility to tumor induction by nitroso compounds and the initial extent of formation and subsequent persistence of O^6-alkylguanine.

There are many other examples of the activation of chemical carcinogens to reactive electrophilic forms, and the reader is referred to reviews such as Miller and Miller (1981), Searle (1984) and Anders (1985). Some chemical carcinogens, for example, carbon tetrachloride, are metabolized to free radicals which are also reactive electron-deficient species. Little is known about carcinogenesis by metal ions, but they are electrophilic, and can bind to cellular macromolecules. There is some evidence that carcinogenic metal ions result in miscoding and infidelity in DNA replication.

6.3.4 DNA REPAIR

Some forms of DNA damage can be repaired by one of several processes which play an important role in protecting cells from the effects of chemical carcinogens (reviewed by Maher and McCormick, 1979).

Prereplication excision repair and postreplication repair are reviewed in section 7.4. DNA damage produced by acetylaminofluorene, for example, is repaired by the excision mechanism, while postreplication repair has been postulated to occur in mammalian cells damaged by benzo(a)pyrene.

Formation of apurinic or apyrimidinic sites can occur by either spontaneous loss of the altered base (eg, 7-methylguanine) or by base excision by an N-glycosylase. The resulting gaps are then filled by DNA replicative processes. Direct enzymatic removal of an altered purine without breakage of a phosphodiester bond, followed by insertion of the correct base, has also been described. Guanine alkylated at the O^6 position is repaired in an unusual manner. The alkyl group is actually transferred directly from the base to a cysteine residue in the repair enzyme. For each molecule of the base repaired, a molecule of repair enzyme is irreversibly inactivated by the process.

Several rare, heritable human diseases are associated with defects in DNA repair (Setlow, 1978). The human autosomal-recessive disorder xeroderma pigmentosum (XP) is characterized by a deficiency in excision repair of DNA containing thymidine dimers caused by ultraviolet light (section 7.4). Such patients have a high risk for skin cancer. Cultures of fibroblasts from XP patients are highly sensitive to UV light and also to some chemical carcinogens (eg, acetylaminofluorene). Other diseases including ataxia telangiectasia and Fanconi's anaemia are also characterized by deficiencies in DNA repair as well as by increased risk for cancer.

There are correlations in some animal models between the persistence of DNA lesions caused by carcinogens and their target organ specificity: the target organ is less effective in removing such lesions than nontarget organs. For example, O^6-ethylguanine, formed by exposure of rats to ethylnitrosourea, persists in brain (the target tissue) much longer than in liver, which is not a target tissue. Similarly, adducts formed by some polycyclic aromatic hydrocarbons persist longer in the target lung tissue of susceptible mouse strains than in that of resistant strains.

6.3.5 THE INITIATED CELL

Chemical carcinogens usually interact with DNA in target tissues to produce covalent adducts, but this process alone does not produce initiated cells since DNA damage produced by the carcinogen may be repaired. Heritable changes are produced if the damaged DNA template is replicated before it is repaired. Initiation therefore requires that carcinogen-altered cells undergo one cycle of proliferation so that repairable DNA lesions become permanent (Fig 6.15; Farber, 1982). The mitogenic stimulus can be provided in a non-proliferating tissue (eg, liver, brain) by cellular necrosis induced by the carcinogen itself, since carcinogens are normally toxic towards the cells of the tissue in which they induce cancer. Cell proliferation may also be induced by other toxic chemicals, biological agents such as viruses or parasites, dietary deficiencies, hormones or experimental procedures such as partial hepatectomy. In a proliferating tissue (eg, bone marrow, epithelial lining of the gastrointestinal tract) cells that are already replicating in the absence of any external mitogenic stimulus may be the targets for initiation.

It should be emphasized that initiated cells are not tumor cells; they have acquired no autonomy of growth. Initiated cells cannot be distinguished from other cells that make up the target organ, and nothing is known about their genotypic or phenotypic properties except that they can be stimulated by promotors to develop focally into discrete preneoplastic lesions and ultimately cancer.

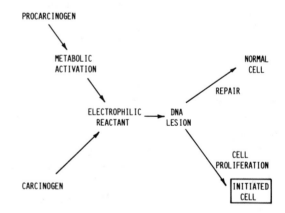

Figure 6.15. General scheme describing the initiation phase of chemical carcinogenesis.

6.4 THE PROMOTION AND PROGRESSION OF CARCINOGENESIS

Promotion may be defined as the process whereby initiated cells develop into tumor cells under the stimulus of an agent that itself may be incapable of inducing neoplastic transformation. Whereas initiation is a rapid and irreversible process, promotion usually takes place over a prolonged period of time and is reversible up to the development of the first autonomous tumor cell (Fig 6.5). Examples of promoting agents are shown in Figure 6.16. The diterpene phorbol ester, 12-O-tetradecanoylphorbol-13-acetate (TPA), the active component of croton oil, is a potent promoting agent for mouse skin carcinogenesis. Phenobarbital and certain chlorinated hydrocarbons such as 2,3,7,8-tetrachloro-dibenzo-p-dioxin (TCCD) are promotors for liver carcinogenesis, while saccharin appears to promote the formation of bladder tumors.

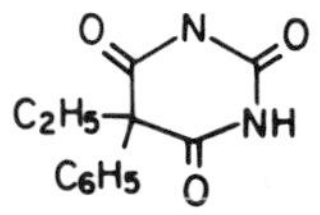

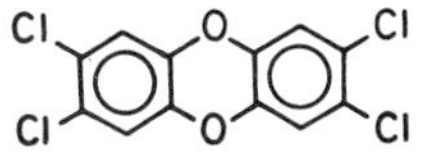

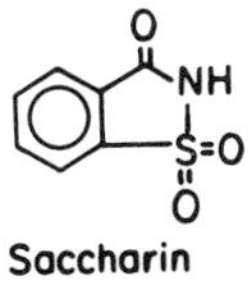

In contrast to initiators, most of the known promotors are not active via formation of electrophilic species. This is not surprising since tumor promotion is reversible and therefore it is unlikely that the critical event(s) will involve nonlethal DNA binding to produce an altered genotype. There is yet no unifying principle to explain the activity of the diverse promoting agents (reviewed by Diamond et al, 1980). The phorbol esters and related compounds are the most studied, and have been found to produce pleiotropic effects in both cultured cells and epidermal cells in vivo. These effects include changes in phospholipid synthesis, DNA and RNA synthesis, enzyme induction, polyamine synthesis and prostaglandin release, with concomitant changes in cellular morphology, mitotic rate and degrees of ter-

minal differentiation. None of these various responses can, at present, be identified as the one critical for tumor promotion.

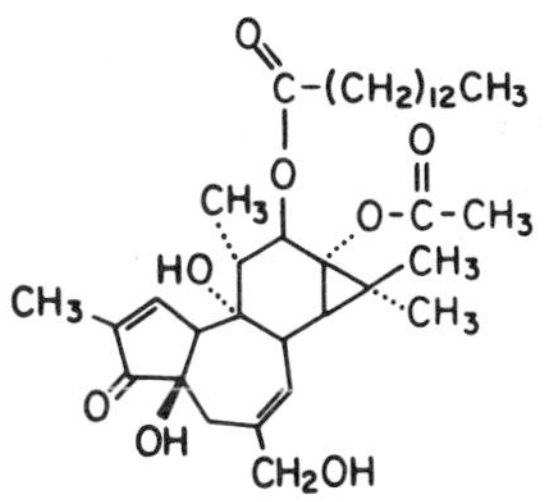

Although the mechanism of action of tumor promotors is poorly understood, several potentially important biochemical properties of phorbol esters have recently been discovered (reviewed by Weinstein et al, 1984). There is evidence that the primary target of these agents is the cell membrane. Indeed, avian, rodent and primate cells in culture have been shown to contain a high-affinity saturable receptor for phorbol dibutyrate. The natural substrate of the receptor is unknown. The abilities of a number of phorbol esters to compete with phorbol dibutyrate for receptor binding correlates well with their activities as tumor promotors on mouse skin. Receptors may therefore mediate the biologic action of the phorbol esters. Recent studies indicate that the pleiotropic cellular effects of TPA may be caused by stimulation of the activity of a calcium- and phospholipid-dependent protein kinase that phosphorylates serine and threonine residues (protein kinase C). Furthermore, TPA can stimulate the activity of a tyrosine-specific protein kinase. The critical protein targets for these kinases are unknown, although it is known that treatment of cells with TPA can alter the state of phosphorylation of receptors for epidermal growth factor, insulin and somatomedin C, with concomitant inhibition of receptor binding.

Another area of research on tumor promotors has provided evidence that phorbol esters can produce tissue damage via activated forms of oxygen (reviewed by Troll and Wiesner, 1985). Tumor promotors have also been shown to enhance the transformation of mouse fibroblasts when these cells were transfected with a cloned human oncogene (Hsiao et al, 1984). These experiments suggest that during multistage carcinogenesis promotors may enhance the outgrowth of altered cells or the expression of other cellular genes that complement the function of the activated oncogene.

Recent research suggests a model for promotion in which the promoting agent produces a differential effect on the initiated cells compared to the surrounding, unaltered cells, causing a focal proliferation of initiated cells. Cells comprising such foci continue to proliferate under the influence of the promotor to produce putative precancerous lesions such as papillomas, nodules or polyps. Many of these lesions undergo regression to yield normally differentiated cells, but a few may progress to produce malignant neoplasms.

Evidence for this model has come principally from the sequential analysis of cancer development in mouse skin and more recently in rat liver. Protocols developed by Tsuda et al (1980) and Pitot et at (1978) for rat liver

Figure 6.16. Chemical structures of promoting agents.

utilize a single low dose of an initiator administered shortly after partial hepatectomy. The carcinogen then produces DNA damage in the hepatocytes at a time when they are rapidly proliferating so that the lesions are more likely to be made permanent than to be repaired. After a recovery period, followed by a short period of exposure to a promoting agent, focal proliferation of cells that abnormally express one of a number of different enzyme activities (eg, γ-glutamyl-transpeptidase) can be detected histochemically. Such foci probably represent clonal progeny of the initiated hepatocytes. Continued administration of the promotors leads to the formation of hyperplastic nodules (Fig 6.17). Many of the nodules undergo regression or "remodeling" towards normal-appearing liver. A small number of nodules do not remodel, but persist and ultimately are sites where malignant hepatocellular carcinoma appears. Neither preneoplastic lesions nor tumors are produced in these assays unless both an initiator and a promotor are administered, clearly demonstrating the multistep nature of the process.

As mentioned previously, carcinogens are usually identified by their ability to act alone to produce tumors in animals. It is possible that for some carcinogens in some tissues, tumor development is simply a spontaneous, stochastic process after production of initiated cells, requiring no other stimulus. Alternatively, there may be endogenous promoting agents that act on target tissues or unknown promotors of dietary origin. In most cases, however, it is likely that the carcinogen acts to promote the cells it has initiated. Thus, continuous or intermittent exposure to the carcinogen itself creates the differential growth environment in which initiated cells are selectively stimulated to proliferate.

It is not clear whether stimulation of the selective proliferation of initiated cells is the only effect of pro-

motors, or whether other cellular changes are also produced. It is clear, however, that continuous administration of a promoting agent is not necessary for cancer development. All that is required is induction by a promoting agent of a persistent lesion containing cells with autonomy of growth. Subsequent expansion of this population of cells to yield a clinically evident tumor is then spontaneous and irreversible. It has been proposed that tumor progression results from acquired genetic variability within the original clone of tumor cells, allowing sequential selection of more aggressive (eg, invasive, metastatic, drug-resistant) sublines (Nowell, 1976).

6.5 ASSAY METHODS FOR CHEMICAL CARCINOGENS

6.5.1 LONG-TERM BIOASSAYS IN ANIMALS

Experiments to assess the carcinogenicity of a substance are complex in design and expensive and time-consuming to perform. Results may have political and social as well as scientific implications, and are often misinterpreted by scientists and lay people alike because of a lack of appreciation for how the tests must be performed to obtain meaningful results. For a detailed review of this important area, the reader is referred to several articles written by groups of experts describing a consensus of opinion on the design and conduct of such tests (L Goldberg, 1974; Scientific Committee of the Food Safety Council, 1978; Interagency Regulatory Liaison Group, 1979; Interdisciplinary Panel on Carcinogenicity, 1984).

An adequately designed long-term bioassay usually includes both sexes of two species. Rats and mice are most often used since they are sensitive to many carcinogenic agents and are relatively short-lived. Long latency periods for tumor induction require that both exposure and observation last through most of the life span of the test animals. Treatment is usually started after weaning, though it may be started in the neonatal period or even during fetal development. The route of exposure should either be the same as that in humans, if a potential human hazard is being evaluated, or should be one that leads to adequate absorption and distribution of the test substance in the animal. Usually the test substance is either a highly purified chemical or an actual product to which humans are exposed, including the impurities.

Each group of animals should provide enough survivors at the termination of the experiment to permit pathological and statistical evaluation. Resources normally limit the number of animals that can be used, but a small number (often 25–50 of each sex) can yield posi-

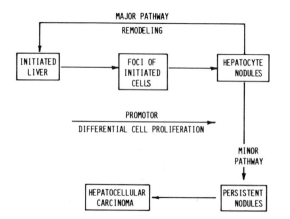

Figure 6.17. General scheme showing the sequential development of liver cancer.

tive results if the tumor incidence in controls is low. When the incidence of a neoplasm observed in the test group is also high in the controls, rigorous statistical evaluation is required, and retesting may be necessary using a larger number of animals. If the same tumor appears in both control and test groups, then the chemical may not be a carcinogen per se, but merely potentiate the carcinogenic process. The significance of rare tumors can often be assessed by comparing the incidence in experimental groups with that in colonies of untreated control animals observed in experiments over a number of years under the same maintenance conditions (historical controls).

Two or three dose levels of the test substance are usually used to establish a dose-response relationship. The highest dose should be tolerated without toxicity. The "maximum tolerated dose" is determined by prior experimentation and, among other criteria, should not inhibit normal weight gain by more than 10%.

Testing for carcinogenicity of chemicals is often criticized because large doses of test substances are administered. Dose levels and experimental conditions, however, normally need to be chosen to maximize the signal (induced-tumor incidence) to noise (spontaneous-tumor incidence) ratio. Using such animal models, tumor incidences of 5–10% can often be detected. To deal with cancer risks for the human population, however, exposure to a carcinogen that would increase the risk by even 1% is clearly totally unacceptable. Exposure to levels of agents that may produce cancer incidences in the range of 1 in 10^6 to 1 in 10^8 are perhaps acceptable. In order to assess the dose of a carcinogen

that produces this tumor incidence, dose-response curves must be extrapolated to levels well below those determined experimentally. A number of mathematical procedures have been developed for making such extrapolations (Scientific Committee for the Food Safety Council, 1978; Interagency Regulatory Liaison Group, 1979), but enormous differences in risk may be obtained depending on the slope of the extrapolation curve. This problem is illustrated in Figure 6.18 for the dose-response curve of nitrosopyrrolidine, a carcinogen that occurs in low levels in foods (section 6.6). It is clear that three commonly used extrapolation methods give very different values for the dose to produce 1 tumor in 10^8 or even 10^6 rats. The regulatory agencies are constantly faced with this problem in risk assessment of carcinogens. Furthermore, additional assumptions must be made concerning the sensitivity of man to carcinogens compared to experimental animals.

6.5.2 SHORT-TERM TESTS

In view of the complexities, duration, and cost of chronic bioassays to investigate the carcinogenic potential of chemicals in rodents, numerous short-term tests have been developed that attempt to identify initiators of carcinogenesis (Hollstein et al, 1979; International Commission for Protection Against Environmental Mutagens and Carcinogens, 1982; as well as references cited in section 6.5.1). A large group of tests have been developed from the concept that carcinogenesis is initiated by genetic alterations in somatic cells. Organisms used in these tests include bacteria, fungi, cultured

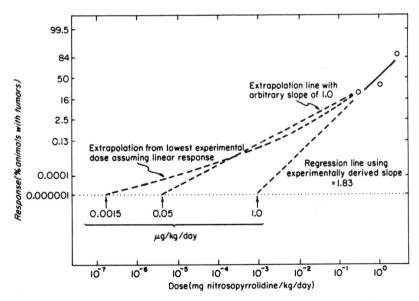

Figure 6.18. Extrapolation of the dose-response data of Preussmann et al (1977) for nitrosopyrrolidine (Courtesy of L Green and SR Tannenbaum).

mammalian cells, insects and rodents. Biological end-points include tests for DNA damage (eg, adduct formation, strand breakage, repair), mutation, and chromosome damage (eg, aberrations, sister chromatid exchange, micronucleus formation). Since many carcinogens require metabolic activation before they can damage cellular constituents, and since many of the test organisms lack the appropriate enzymes, preparations from mammalian liver (eg, the 9000 × g supernatant or S9 fraction of rat liver) are commonly used in conjunction with the assay to provide this activity. If target organ-specific metabolism is suspected, target organ enzyme preparations can be used in place of hepatic S9. "Host-mediated" assays are sometimes employed in which bacteria or fungi are injected into an animal which has been exposed to the test compound. After a period of time, the organism is recovered and assayed for mutations.

Perhaps the most widely used short-term test is the mutagenicity assay developed by Bruce Ames using *Salmonella typhimurium* (Fig 6.19, reviewed by Hollstein et al, 1979). Ames produced mutant strains of *Salmonella* which are unable to synthesize the essential amino acid histidine, and hence are unable to grow into colonies in the absence of histidine in the growth medium. Mutagens can convert these bacteria to histidine independence so that the revertants are able to grow into viable colonies. Rat liver preparations can be readily added to the bacteria to provide metabolic activation.

Performance of short-term tests based on genetic alterations to predict carcinogenicity varies widely depending on the particular test, chemical class, and laboratory. A recent estimate suggests that the success rate in detecting compounds known to be carcinogenic from chronic bioassays in animals is in the range 50–70% (Interdisciplinary Panel on Carcinogenicity, 1984).

A number of methods have been developed to detect the ability of chemicals to transform mammalian cells in culture (Heidelberger et al, 1983). Perhaps the most widely used systems involve hamster embryo cells and mouse embryo fibroblasts. Again, enzymes for metabolic activation can be used with these cells, although some cells in culture retain their intrinsic metabolic capacity. Criteria of transformation include ability of cells to form colonies or foci, growth of cells in soft agar, changes in cellular morphology, and ability of cells to form malignant tumors when transplanted into animals (section 8.4.2). Although transformation of human fibroblasts and rodent epithelial cells has been reported, these systems are technically difficult to manipulate, and cannot be used on a routine basis.

Another approach for the rapid identification of carcinogenic activity is to make use of early markers of neoplasia in the whole animal such as those described for rat liver in section 6.4. These relatively short-term tests in the whole animal hold considerable promise and need to be more widely validated.

To minimize false-negative and false-positive results in short-term assays of carcinogenic potential, use of a battery of tests is usually recommended. The results of such tests are usually interpreted with caution. Positive responses are considered only to be suggestive of carcinogenic activity, and are used to select substances for more extensive testing in long-term animal bioassays. Negative results in short-term tests do not establish safety.

6.6 CHEMICAL CARCINOGENS IN HUMAN CANCER CAUSATION

Epidemiological evidence that environmental factors play a major role in human cancer causation has been reviewed in chapter 2. The best evidence that specific chemicals are carcinogenic in humans comes from exposures in the workplace that are correlated with increased risk for a specific type of cancer. Several occupational cancer hazards were already mentioned in the Introduction and a number more are listed in Table 6.3.

Increased risk of cancer is associated with the use of certain drugs for medical purposes. One of the best-documented examples is the occurrence of vaginal cancer in the daughters of women who were exposed during pregnancy to the estrogen analog diethylstilbestrol. A number of drugs used to treat cancer are also carcinogenic and may give rise to lymphomas or leukemias some years following the original chemotherapy (section 17.5.4).

Cigarette smoking is a major causative factor for cancer of the lung, upper alimentary tract, urinary bladder and possibly pancreas (reviewed by Wynder and Hoffmann, 1979). Alcohol consumption and smoking

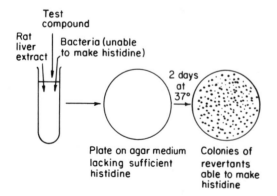

Figure 6.19. Method of detecting mutagenic compounds using *Salmonella typhimurium* (Ames test).

Table 6.3. Examples of Occupational Carcinogens

Agents	Sites of Tumor Formation
2-Naphthylamine	Urinary bladder
Benzidine	Urinary bladder
4-Aminobiphenyl	Urinary bladder
Bis(chloromethyl)ether	Lungs
Bis(2-chloroethyl)sulfide (mustard gas)	Respiratory tract
Vinyl chloride	Liver mesenchyme
Tars, soots, and oils	Skin, lungs
Chromium compounds	Lungs
Nickel compounds	Lungs
Asbestos	Pleura, peritoneum (lungs when combined with cigarette smoking)
Benzene	Lymphoid tissue

appear to act synergistically in the causation of cancer of the mouth and esophagus. Cigarette smoking and asbestos exposure act synergistically in the induction of lung cancer.

Tobacco smoke contains about 4000 compounds, including many known carcinogens. The gas phase of cigarette smoke contains a number of volatile nitrosamines including nitrosodimethylamine, nitrosodiethylamine and nitrosopyrrolidine. The particulate matter of cigarette smoke contains polycyclic aromatic hydrocarbons such as benzo(a)pyrene and benz(a)anthracene as well as nitrosamines derived from the tobacco alkaloids nicotine, nornicotine, anabasine and anatibine (Fig 6.20). The latter compounds are also found in high levels in chewing tobacco and snuff, and may be responsible for cancer of the oral cavity that is associated with the use of these products. In some parts of the world (eg, India) chewing of betel nuts plays a major role in the causation of cancer of the mouth, pharynx and esophagus; again, a nitrosamine may be involved.

Much attention has been devoted recently to determining whether dietary chemicals cause certain types of cancer. The use of well-designed bioassay procedures should make it possible to avoid using food additives that are carcinogenic. A number of chemicals enter the food supply unintentionally, however, such as pesticides and herbicides, drugs given to livestock, chemicals used in food processing, packaging materials, and lubricants and other chemicals associated with food-processing equipment. So far, no association has been made between exposure to any of these agents and cancer. Cooking of foods in which the organic material is pyrolyzed (eg, barbecuing of meat) can produce polycyclic aromatic hydrocarbons and other carcinogenic compounds, though there is no evidence that ingestion of small quantities of these agents causes human cancer. Some foods stored under warm, moist conditions can become contaminated with microorganisms which produce carcinogenic secondary metabolites. An important example, first discovered in moldy peanuts, is the fungus *Aspergillus flavus* which produces alfatoxin B_1. Correlations have been reported between consumption of this mycotoxin and the incidence of liver cancer in parts of Africa and the Far East, though there may also be an involvement of hepatitis B virus in the etiology of this disease (see section 4.3.4).

A number of nitrosamines have been shown to form in foods preserved with sodium nitrite (eg, nitrosopyrrolidine in cooked bacon), though in most cases their formation can be blocked when agents such as ascorbic acid or α-tocopherol are added to the foods. Of potential greater importance is the formation of N-nitroso compounds from precursors in the body itself, particularly the stomach, where acidic conditions catalyze their formation. It is possible that direct-acting N-nitroso compounds formed in this way initiate stomach cancer.

There is a strong correlation between consumption of high levels of dietary fat and the incidence of breast and colon cancer. The same correlations may be made

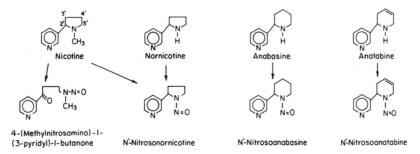

Figure 6.20. Tobacco alkaloids and the nitrosamines formed from them which are present in tobacco and tobacco smoke.

between cancer incidence and the lack of fiber in the diet, and the mechanisms involved are not understood.

In addition to a wide variety of carcinogens, the environment, including diet, also contains substances capable of inhibiting chemical carcinogenesis. Some of these inhibitors are active at the stage of tumor initiation; others modify the effect of tumor promotors (Slaga and Digiovanni, 1984). Continued characterization of both carcinogens and their antagonists and elucidation of their mechanisms of action will hopefully lead to rational approaches for the prevention of human cancer.

6.7 SUMMARY

The model developed in this chapter to explain the chemical induction of cancer is summarized in Figure 6.5. After exposure, the environmental carcinogen is distributed to various sites in the body and may then either be excreted directly or following detoxification. A reactive electrophilic form of the carcinogen, produced by chemical or metabolic activation, reacts with a variety of cellular nucleophilic targets. Reaction at some sites may cause cell death. Damaged DNA may be repaired leading to a normal cell. If DNA replication takes place prior to repair, however, an oncogenic lesion may become permanent, producing an initiated cell. Clonal expansion of these initiated cells to produce preneoplastic lesions is caused by promoting agents, possibly including the carcinogen itself. Most of these lesions regress, but rarely progressive development leads to the appearance of neoplastic cells.

REFERENCES

Ames BN: Identifying environmental chemicals causing mutations and cancer. *Science* 1979; 204:587–593.

Anders MW (ed): *Bioactivation of Foreign Compounds.* Academic Press Inc., San Diego, CA, 1985.

Archer MC: Nitrosamines, in Anders MW (ed), *Bioactivation of Foreign Compounds.* Academic Press Inc., San Diego, CA, 1985.

Balmain A, Pragnall IB: Mouse skin carcinomas induced in vivo by chemical carcinogens have a transforming Harvey-ras oncogene. *Nature* 1983; 303:72–74.

Balmain A, Ramsden M, Bowden GT, Smith J: Activation of the mouse cellular Harvey-ras gene in chemically induced benign skin papillomas. *Nature* 1984; 307:658–660.

Berenblum I, Shubik P: A new quantitative approach to the study of the stages of chemical carcinogenesis in the mouse's skin. *Br J Cancer* 1947; 1:383–391.

Bryan WR, Shimkin MB: Quantitative analysis of dose–response data obtained with three carcinogenic hydrocarbons in strain C3H male mice. *J Natl Cancer Inst* 1943; 3:503–531.

Diamond L, O'Brien TG, Baird WM: Tumor promoters and the mechanism of tumor promotion. *Adv Cancer Res* 1980; 32:1–74.

Doll R, Peto R: Cigarette smoking and bronchial carcinoma: dose and time relationships among regular smokers and life-long non-smokers. *J Epidemiol Community Health* 1978; 32:303–313.

Druckrey H: Quantitative Grundlagen der Krebserzeugung. *Klin Wchnschr* 1943; 22:532.

Druckrey H, Schildbach A, Schmahl D, Preussmann R, Ivankovic S: Quantitative analyse der carcinogenen Wirkung von Diathylnitrosamin. *Arzneimittel-Forsch* 1963; 13:841–851.

Farber E: Ethionine carcinogenesis. *Adv Cancer Res* 1963; 2:383–474.

Farber E. Chemical carcinogenesis. A biologic perspective. *Am J Path* 1982; 106:269–296.

Garner RC, Martin CN, Clayson DB: Carcinogenic aromatic amines and related compounds, in Searle CE (ed), *Chemical Carcinogens*, ed 2, *ACS Monograph* 182. American Chemical Society, Washington, DC, 1984, pp 175–276.

Gold LS, Sawyer CB, Magaw R, Backman GM, De Veciana M, Levison R, Hooper NK, Havender NR, Bernstein L, Peto R, Pike MC, Ames BN: A carcinogenic potency database of the standardized results of animal bioassays. *Envir Health Perspect* 1984; 58:9–319.

Goldberg L (ed): *Carcinogenesis Testing of Chemicals.* CRC Press, Cleveland, OH, 1974.

Guerrero I, Calzada P, Mayer A, Pellicar A: A molecular approach to leukemogenesis: mouse lymphomas contain an activated c-ras oncogene. *Proc Natl Acad Sci USA* 1984; 81:202–205.

Heidelberger C, Freeman AE, Pienta RJ et al: Cell transformation by chemical agents—a review and analysis of the literature. *Mutation Res* 1983; 114:283–385.

Hollstein M, McCann J, Angelosanto F, Nichols WW: Short-term tests for carcinogens and mutagens. *Mutation Res* 1979; 65:133–226.

Hsiao W-LW, Gattoni-Celli S, Weinstein IB: Oncogene-induced transformation of C3H 10T 1/2 cells is enhanced by tumor promoters. *Science* 1984; 226:552–555.

Interagency Regulatory Liaison Group: Scientific bases for identification of potential carcinogens and estimation of risks. *J Natl Cancer Inst* 1979; 63:241–268.

Interdisciplinary Panel on Carcinogenicity: Criteria for evidence of chemical carcinogenicity. *Science* 1984; 225:682–687.

International Commission for Protection Against Environmental Mutagens and Carcinogens: Mutagenesis testing as an approach to carcinogenesis. *Mutation Res* 1982; 99:73–91.

Jakoby WB (ed): *Enzymatic Basis of Detoxication.* Academic Press, New York, NY, 1980, Vols I, II.

Levin W, Wood A, Chang R et al: Oxidative metabolism of polycyclic aromatic hydrocarbons to ultimate carcinogens. *Drug Meta Rev* 1982; 13:555–580.

Maher VM, McCormick JJ: DNA repair and carcinogenesis, in Grover PL (ed), *Chemical Carcinogens and DNA.* CRC Press, Boca Raton, FL, 1979, Vol II, pp 133–158.

Marshall CJ, Vousden KH, Phillips DH: Activation of c-Ha-ras-1 proto-oncogene by *in vitro* modification with a chemical carcinogen, benzo(a)pyrene diol-epoxide. *Nature* 1984; 310:586–589.

Miller EC, Miller JA: Searches for ultimate chemical carcinogens and their reactions with cellular macromolecules. *Cancer* 1981; 47:2327–2345.

Nowell PC: The clonal evolution of tumor cell populations. *Science* 1976; 194:23–28.

O'Connor PJ, Saffhill R, Margison GP: N-Nitroso compounds: biochemical mechanisms of action, in Emmelot P, Kriek E (eds), *Environmental Carcinogenesis*. Elsevier/North-Holland Biomedical Press, Amsterdam, 1979, pp 73–96.

Pitot HC, Barsness L, Goldsworthy T, Kitagawa T: Biochemical characterization of stages of hepatocarcinogenesis after a single dose of diethylnitrosamine. *Nature* 1978; 271:456–458.

Preussmann R, Schmahl D, Eisenbrand G: Carcinogenicity of N-nitrosopyrrolidine: dose–response study in rats. *Z Krebsforsch* 1977; 90:161–166.

Scientific Committee of the Food Safety Council: Proposed system for food safety assessment. *Food Cosmet Toxicol* 1978; 16(suppl 2).

Searle CE (ed): *Chemical Carcinogens*, ed 2, *ACS Monograph* 182. American Chemical Society, Washington, DC, 1984.

Setlow RB: Repair deficient human disorders and cancer. *Nature* 1978; 271:713–717.

Slaga TJ, Digiovanni J: Inhibition of chemical carcinogenesis, in Searle CE (ed), *Chemical Carcinogens*, ed 2, *ACS Monograph 182*. American Chemical Society, Washington, DC, 1984, pp 1279–1321.

Straus DS: Somatic mutation, cellular differentiation, and cancer causation. *J Natl Cancer Inst* 1981; 67:233–241.

Sukumar S, Notario V, Martin-Zanca D, Barbacid M: Induction of mammary carcinomas in rats by nitrosomethylurea involves malignant activation of H-ras-1 locus by single point mutations. *Nature* 1983; 306:658–661.

Sukumar S, Pulciani S, Doniger J, DiPaolo JA, Evans CH, Zbar B, Barbacid M: A transforming ras gene in tumorigenic Guinea pig cell lines initiated by diverse chemical carcinogens. *Science* 1984; 223:1197–1199.

Troll W, Wiesner R: The role of oxygen radicals as a possible mechanism of tumor promotion. *Ann Rev Pharmacol Toxicol* 1985; 25:509–529.

Tsuda H, Lee G, Farber E: Induction of resistant hepatocytes as a new principle for a possible short-term *in vivo* test for carcinogens. *Cancer Res* 1980; 40:1157–1164.

Weinberg RA: Oncogenes of spontaneous and chemically induced tumors. *Adv Cancer Res* 1982; 36:149–163.

Weinstein IB, Gattoni-Celli S, Kirschmeier P et al: Multistage carcinogenesis involves multiple genes and multiple mechanisms. *J Cellular Physiol Suppl* 1984; 3:127–137.

Wynder EL, Hoffmann D: Tobacco and health: a societal challenge. *N Engl J Med* 1979; 300:894–903.

7

Radiation Carcinogenesis

A. Michael Rauth

7.1 INTRODUCTION

Radiation, both ionizing and ultraviolet (UV), is a normal component of our environment. Low levels of background radiation originate from the earth and outer space, while long-wavelength UV radiation reaches us from the sun. The use of ionizing radiation or UV radiation for diagnostic and/or therapeutic purposes, as well as the increased use of nuclear energy and the testing and use of nuclear weapons, has increased concern about both their short- and long-term effects. Long-term effects include the induction of cancer and increases in the mutation rate, leading to genetic damage which can be passed on to future generations.

In this chapter, the basic physical interactions of radiation with biological material, primarily DNA, will be considered. Next, the effects of radiation on cells, both in vitro and in vivo, will be discussed in terms of

the carcinogenic process. Finally, data on the carcinogenic effects of radiation in humans will be reviewed and current mechanisms for carcinogenesis presented.

7.2 THE ABSORPTION OF RADIATION BY BIOLOGICAL MATERIALS

7.2.1 IONIZING RADIATION

X-rays are part of the spectrum of electromagnetic radiations which include ultraviolet radiation as well as visible light, infrared, radio and electrical waves, as shown in Figure 7.1. These radiations can be considered to consist of photons, discrete bundles of energy which travel with the speed of light and have wave properties. However, in many interactions they behave as particles. There is a constant relationship between the wavelength of a photon (λ), its frequency (ν) and energy (E) given by the equations

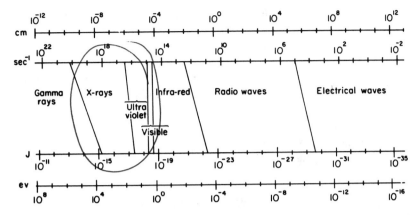

Figure 7.1. Electromagnetic spectrum showing the relationship of photon wavelength in centimeters (cm) to its frequency in inverse seconds (s^{-1}) to its energy in joules (J) and electron volts (eV). The various bands in the spectrum are indicated. Slanted lines between bands indicate the degree of overlap in the definition of the various bands. (Adapted from Upton, 1982b.)

$$c = \lambda \nu \ , \qquad (7.1)$$

where c is the speed of light, 2.988×10^8 m/s, and

$$E = h\nu \ , \qquad (7.2)$$

where h is Planck's constant (6.625×10^{-34} J-s). When the energy per photon is greater than the binding energies of electrons in the target, the interaction of the photon and the target atom can result in ejection of an electron from its atomic orbit and ionization occurs. Typical binding energies for electrons in biological material are in the neighborhood of 10 eV. Thus photons with energies greater than 10 eV are considered to be ionizing radiation, while photons with energies of 2–10 eV are in the ultraviolet range and are nonionizing. Electromagnetic radiations with successively lower energies than 2 eV are visible light, infrared, radio and electrical waves respectively (Upton, 1982b). Since only UV and ionizing radiation, in the electromagnetic spectrum, are known to be carcinogenic, the rest of this chapter will focus on these radiations.

7.2.2 ENERGY-LOSS PROCESSES

Mechanisms by which photons of energy sufficient to ionize atoms interact with matter and lose their energy can be divided into three types (Johns and Cunningham, 1983), as illustrated in Figure 7.2 (a–c). In the low-energy range (10–100 keV), energy loss in biological materials is primarily by the photoelectric effect in which all the energy of the photon is transferred to the target electron, usually an inner-shell electron at higher photon energies. In the range of 100 keV to 3 meV, photons lose energy primarily by Compton scattering, where a fraction of the photon energy is lost in each

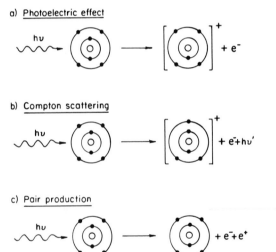

Figure 7.2. Modes of energy loss by high-energy photons. *a, Photoelectric effect.* All the incident energy of the photon, $h\nu$, is transferred to an inner shell electron of an atom, e^-, whose energy is equal to the photon energy less the binding energy of the electron. *b, Compton scattering.* Part of the incident energy of the photon, $h\nu$, is transferred to an outer shell electron, e^-. The scattered photon is of reduced energy $h\nu'$. The energy of the electron is equal to the energy loss of the incident photon less the binding energy of the electron. *c, Pair production.* The incident photon of energy, $h\nu$, greater than 1.02 MeV, interacts with the nucleus to yield an electron, e^-, and a positron, e^+, whose total energy is that of the incident photon less the energy required to create them, 1.02 MeV.

interaction; the energy is transferred to outer orbital electrons, thus setting them into motion. At photon energies higher than 1.02 MeV, pair production can occur, wherein the photon interacts with the nucleus of a target atom and is converted to an electron and a positron. Thus, all ionizing photon interactions result in the production of energetic electrons which in turn lose energy by exciting and ionizing target atoms and molecules, and setting more electrons in motion (Fig 7.3a).

Accelerators and radioactive isotopes can act as direct sources of high-energy charged particles such as electrons, protons and other heavier charged particles. These particles lose energy along their track as they traverse the target. The particle's energy loss, $-dE$, along a portion of this track, dx, is dependent on its velocity v, charge Z, and the electron density of the target, ρ, as indicated by the equation

$$-\frac{dE}{dx} \propto \frac{Z^2 \rho}{v^2} \ . \tag{7.3}$$

Thus the rate of energy loss in biological materials can vary greatly along the track of the particle depending upon its velocity and charge, increasing at lower velocity and higher charge.

A second type of particle of importance in radiation effects is the neutron produced in nuclear reactors, particle accelerators and neutron generators. Because they lack a charge, neutrons do not displace electrons but instead interact with nuclei, primarily hydrogen; they undergo elastic scattering, setting protons in motion, which are called recoil protons (Fig 7.3b). The neutrons can also be captured by nuclei such as oxygen and nitrogen, resulting in unstable nuclei which decay, producing additional energetic charged particles and sometimes photons (Fig 7.3c). These charged particles and photons lose energy via the mechanisms discussed above.

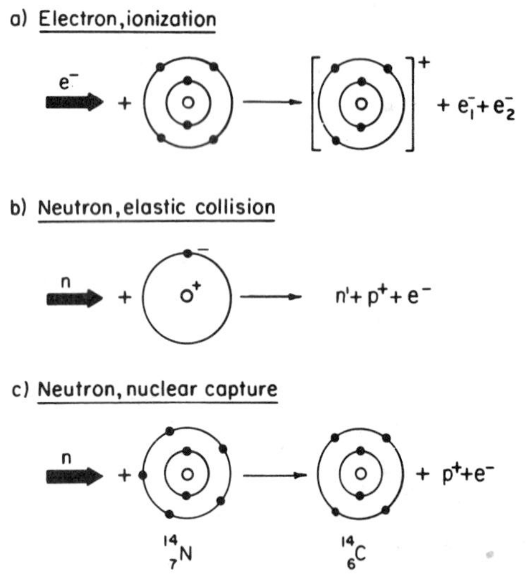

7.2.3 CONCEPT OF LINEAR ENERGY TRANSFER

The efficiency with which different types of ionizing radiation cause biological damage varies, even though photons, charged particles and neutrons ultimately all set electrons in motion (Figs 7.2 and 7.3). The important difference between different types of radiation is the average density of energy loss *along* the path of the particle. This is referred to as the linear energy transfer (LET) of the radiation (Hall, 1978). The units of LET are given in terms of energy lost per unit pathlength, eg, keV/μm. Some representative values of LET for different particles are given in Table 7.1. From eq (7.3), it can be seen that as a particle loses energy and slows down, its effective LET increases. The greater the LET of a particle of a given energy, the shorter its range, that is, the distance it travels in tissue.

The concept of LET does not address the size of the individual energy-loss events which occur along the track of a particle. Since all radiations set electrons in motion, energy loss by this particle will be briefly considered. The amount of energy lost per collision of a 20-keV electron with target molecules has a distribution

a) Electron, ionization

b) Neutron, elastic collision

c) Neutron, nuclear capture

Figure 7.3. Processes by which energetic particles lose energy. *a*, An electron, e^-, ionizes an orbital electron of a carbon atom to yield a positively charged carbon ion, the incident electron of reduced energy, e_1^-, and a new electron, e_2^-, to which the incident electron has transferred part of its energy. *b*, A neutron n interacts with a hydrogen atom nucleus in an elastic collision to yield a neutron of reduced energy n', a proton p^+ to which it has transferred part of its energy, and an electron e^-. *c*, A neutron n is captured by a nitrogen atom N of atomic mass 14 and atomic number 7. A nuclear decay occurs yielding a radioactive carbon atom of atomic mass 14 and atomic number 6, a proton p^+ of energy 660 keV and an electron e^-.

Table 7.1. Linear Energy Transfer (LET) of Various Radiations

Radiation	LET (keV/μm)
Photons	
^{60}Co (~1.2 MeV)	0.3
200-keV X-ray	2.5
Electrons	
1 MeV	0.2
100 keV	0.5
10 keV	2
1 keV	10
Charged particles	
proton 2 MeV	17
alpha 5 MeV	90
carbon 100 MeV	160
Neutrons	
2.5 MeV	15–80
14.1 MeV	3–30

as shown in Figure 7.4. The discrete energy-loss events (mode approximately 20 eV) are large relative to the energy required to break chemical bonds. Using the value 60 eV for the average energy lost per inelastic scattering event the number of such events per unit path length can be calculated.

The density of these discrete energy-loss events along the particle track increases with LET (Fig 7.5). When the dimensions of the target for radiation action are small, the LET is high and the overall dose is low, the highly localized nature of the energy-loss events along the particle track becomes important (Fig 7.5b; Kellerer and Rossi, 1982). It is possible under these circumstances to have a condition where some targets will be crossed by a particle track and destroyed while others will not be crossed by the particle track and will remain intact. This is important in the consideration of the carcinogenic effectiveness of radiation as a function of dose rate and LET.

7.2.4 UNITS OF DOSE FOR IONIZING RADIATION

Historically the unit of radiation exposure (the roentgen) was based on measuring the amount of ionization produced in a given volume of air at standard temperature and pressure. The exposure dose does not, however, indicate the amount of energy absorbed in matter. The unit of absorbed dose, the rad, is that dose of radiation resulting in an energy deposition of 100 ergs per gram. The measurement of absorbed dose can be carried out by a number of means including calorimetry and chemical dosimetry (Johns and Cunningham, 1983). The new SI unit is the gray (Gy), 1 joule per kg, which is equivalent to 100 rads.

Since different types of radiation have different biological effectiveness depending on their LET values, another unit referred to as the dose equivalent has been defined. The dose equivalent is calculated by multiplying the absorbed dose by a quality factor which takes into account the greater effectiveness of high-LET radiation in causing biological damage. The original unit of dose equivalent was the rem, which was the dose in rads times the quality factor. In the SI system of units, it is the dose in grays times the quality factor and is called the sievert. One hundred rems equals 1 sievert. For low-LET radiation the quality factor is unity, so for this type of radiation sieverts are equivalent to grays. For high LET radiation quality factors can be as high as 10.

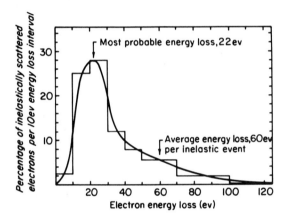

Figure 7.4. The distribution of "first-collision" energy loss for 20-keV electrons passing through a "biologically equivalent" solid. (Adapted from Rauth and Simpson, 1964.)

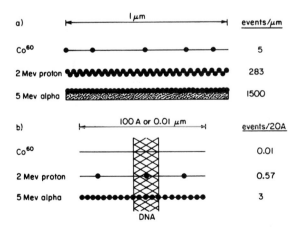

Figure 7.5. The frequency of primary energy-loss events along the tracks of various radiations of widely differing LETs. *a*, Schematic diagram of primary energy-loss events over a distance of 1 μm. *b*, The pattern of primary energy-loss events over a distance of 0.01 μm or 100 Å. The cross-hatched region represents the dimensions of a DNA double helix.

7.2.5 INTERACTION OF IONIZING RADIATION WITH TARGET MOLECULES

When particles lose energy, chemical bonds can be broken. Direct effects of radiation can lead to disruption of bonds in target molecules. Cells are 80% water, however, so that the majority of the energy-loss events occur in water. These events produce ionization and resultant fragmentation of the water, yielding three major species of reactive radicals. These species are the hydroxyl radical $OH\cdot$, the solvated electron e_{aq}^-, and the hydrogen radical $H\cdot$ (Fig 7.6). These water radicals are short lived but can diffuse up to 30 nm for an $OH\cdot$ radical and further for e_{aq}^- and react with targets giving rise to indirect damage.

Much radiobiological data indicates that DNA is the important target for many of the biological effects of radiation. Both direct and indirect damage to DNA can

Ionization of water by radiation, hυ,

$$H_2O \xrightarrow{h\upsilon} H_2O^+ + e^-$$

a) Reaction of H_2O^+ to form a hydronium ion plus a hydroxyl radical

$$H_2O^+ + H_2O \longrightarrow H_3O^+ + \boxed{OH^\cdot}$$

b) Solvation of free electron in a cage of water molecules

$$e^- + \left[H_2O\right]_n \longrightarrow \boxed{e^-_{aq}}$$

c) Reaction of e^-_{aq} with water to form a hydrogen radical

$$e^-_{aq} + H_2O \longrightarrow OH^- + \boxed{H^\cdot}$$

Figure 7.6. The formation of the three major water radical species (square boxes) by the action of ionizing radiation.

result in damage to bases and to strand breaks in the sugar–phosphate backbone (Fig 7.7). Damage to bases can result in their alteration or loss, leaving depyrimidinated or depurinated sites, while attack on the sugar–phosphate backbone can result in single- and (more rarely) double-strand breaks.

7.2.6 UV RADIATION

In contrast to ionizing radiation, ultraviolet radiation (wavelength 200–400 nm) deposits energy in the range 3–10 eV in absorbing chromophores (Rauth, 1986). This is not enough energy to ionize these molecules, but it is enough to put them in a short-lived excited

state and make them chemically reactive. In DNA in aqueous solution, absorption of photons with a wavelength in the range 200–300 nm results in the excitation of pyrimidine bases (thymine or cytosine) which can react with water to form pyrimidine hydrates or with a neighboring pyrimidine to give rise to pyrimidine dimers of the cyclobutane type (thymine–thymine, cytosine–thymine, or cytosine–cytosine), as well as other linkages (Fig 7.8). Dimers formed in DNA are chemically stable, but the pyrimidine hydrates are unstable and can dehydrate, resulting in the restoration of the original pyrimidine or, in the case of cytosine, a deaminated derivative. Reaction of excited pyrimidines with other molecules such as amino acids can occur and evidence for DNA–protein cross-links in cells has been obtained. Because of its chemical stability, the lesion that has been most extensively monitored in biological systems is the cyclobutane pyrimidine dimer.

The measurement of UV dose is based on the exposure dose expressed as incident energy per unit area. Originally the units were erg/mm^2 but the SI units are expressed as J/m^2. One J/m^2 is equal to 10 erg/mm^2.

The initial lesions formed in biological material by ionizing and by UV radiation are quite different in their type and distribution throughout the cell. These differences are reflected in differences in the cellular

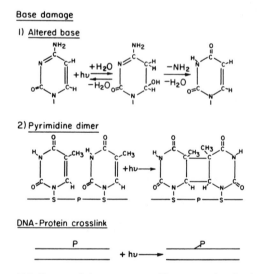

Figure 7.8. Types of damage caused by a UV photon, $h\upsilon$. (1) UV radiation can cause alteration of bases due to the addition of a water molecule across the 5, 6 double bond of an excited pyrimidine base. This can spontaneously dehydrate forming the original base or may, in the case of cytosine as shown, deaminate and dehydrate forming uracil. (2) An excited pyrimidine may also interact chemically with a neighbouring pyrimidine to form a cyclobutane linkage and thus dimerize the two bases. This is shown for two thymine bases (thymine dimer). An excited base can also interact with a protein, P, to form a covalent DNA–protein cross-link.

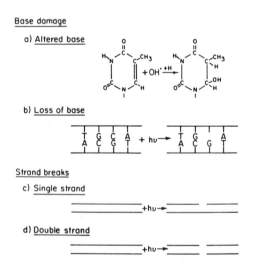

Figure 7.7. Types of damage caused by an ionizing photon, $h\upsilon$, in DNA include: a, base damage, in which the hydroxyl radical produced by $h\upsilon$ in water attacks thymine forming a hydroxyl radical adduct or an altered base; b, breakage of a glycosidic bond, leading to the loss of a pyrimidine base; c, single-strand breaks of the sugar–phosphate backbone; and d, double-strand breaks of the sugar–phosphate backbone.

and molecular behaviour of cells exposed to these radiations.

7.3 RADIATION DAMAGE IN MAMMALIAN CELLS

7.3.1 LOW LET RADIATION AND CELL SURVIVAL

Exposure of cells to ionizing radiation results in molecular damage which can be expressed at the cellular, metabolic or chromosomal level. The most extensively studied radiation effect is that of cell survival, assayed by determining the proportion of cells that can give rise to colonies. A colony is defined usually as 50 or more progeny cells in the in vitro colony-forming assays (see section 15.4.1). A typical survival curve for an asynchronous population of mammalian cells treated with a low-LET ionizing radiation is shown in Figure 7.9a, where percent survival of colony-forming ability is plotted (on a logarithmic scale) as a function of dose (on a linear scale). The survival curve has a shoulder region at low doses (0–5 Gy) and an approximately linear part at higher doses. There are a variety of mathematical expressions that can be used to fit such curves

(see section 15.5). One of them is the linear-quadratic model, which can be written $S = \exp[-(\alpha D + \beta D^2)]$, where S is fractional survival, D is the dose of radiation and α and β are constants. At low doses of radiation, the linear term predominates and at higher doses the quadratic term dominates. The radiation sensitivity of a cell varies as a function of the position of the cell in the cell cycle. This cell-cycle variation in radiation sensitivity can differ from one cell line to another (see section 15.6.2).

The presence of a shoulder on survival curves appears to be due to the accumulation of sublethal and repairable damage (Elkind, 1984). This can be demonstrated by fractionating the dose of radiation so that several hours elapse between treatments. When the second fraction of radiation is given, the surviving cells respond as if they had not seen the first dose of radiation (Fig 7.9b). The exact nature of the molecular lesion that is repaired is unknown, although repair of most DNA single-strand breaks and some DNA double-strand breaks can occur during the fractionation interval.

A second class of repair of radiation damage that can occur in mammalian cells is repair of potentially lethal

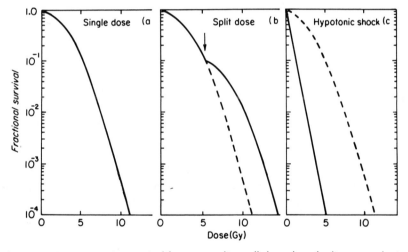

Figure 7.9. Representative survival for mammalian cells based on the linear-quadratic model with $\alpha = 1.6 \times 10^{-1}$ Gy^{-1} and $\beta = 6.2 \times 10^{-2}$ Gy^{-2}. a, Survival of cell colony-forming ability after single doses of low-LET radiation at a dose rate of the order of 1.0 Gy/min. At low doses a shoulder is present on the survival curve but the rate of cell killing increases with dose. b, Survival curve in which the first 5 Gy were given and cells were then left for several hours and irradiation was subsequently continued. The cells surviving the first dose of radiation respond to the second dose of radiation, solid line, as if they had not been previously irradiated. The dotted line is the curve from a. Return of the "shoulder" is due to the repair of sublethal damage. c, Cells are irradiated as in a but immediately after radiation are exposed to hypotonic medium for 30 min before being assayed for their survival, solid line. The increased cell killing indicates the presence of potentially lethal damage uncovered by the hypotonic treatment. The dotted line reproduces the survival curve from a. If cells are left for several hours after irradiation in normal medium before being exposed to hypotonic medium no increase in cell killing is seen.

damage which is dependent on the cellular environment after irradiation (Fig 7.9c). For example, if irradiated cells are exposed to hypertonic or hypotonic conditions for 30–60 min immediately after irradiation and then plated, their survival will be decreased relative to that observed when the hypertonic or hypotonic exposure is delayed (Elkind, 1984). The molecular nature of the repairable lesion and the degree to which it overlaps with sublethal damage is not known, although it, like sublethal damage, is thought to involve DNA and/or chromatin. Current data indicate that double-strand breaks may be lesions responsible for potentially lethal damage.

The importance of repair processes is that the effect of a given dose of radiation becomes a function of the temporal sequence in which the radiation is given. Thus acute doses, fractionated doses and continuous low-dose-rate treatment will lead to varying biological effects, even though the total dose may be the same.

7.3.2 HIGH LET RADIATION AND CELL SURVIVAL

As the LET of radiation increases, the effectiveness of the radiation per unit dose increases. This is reflected by a decrease in the shoulder and an increase in the slope of the survival curve (Fig 7.10). At very high LETs (>100 keV/μm) the survival curve becomes strictly exponential (ie, no shoulder), and there is no evidence for accumulation or repair of sublethal or potentially lethal damage. Simplistically, this lack of repair can be explained on a molecular basis by the high density of energy-loss events along individual particle tracks producing damage to DNA that is so extensive that it is not repairable.

The relative biological effectiveness (RBE) of different types of radiation is defined as the ratio of the dose of a standard low LET radiation, typically X-rays or γ-rays, to the dose of the test radiation which gives the same biological effect. RBE depends on the biological endpoint as well as dose, dose rate and LET. Thus, in Figure 7.10 the RBE for killing cells to a survival level of 10^{-3} would be 2.2 for neutrons (9.3 Gy/4.2 Gy) and 5.5 for alpha particles (9.3 Gy/1.7 Gy) relative to γ-rays as a standard radiation. Use of these same survival curves to determine the RBE for killing cells to a survival of 10^{-1} gives values of RBE equal to 3.1 for neutrons and 8.3 for alpha particles. This example illustrates that values of RBE are often greater at low doses of radiation than at high doses (Kellerer and Rossi, 1982; see also section 15.6.1).

7.3.3 UV RADIATION AND CELL SURVIVAL

When asynchronous populations of mammalian cells are exposed to UV irradiation and the survival of their colony-forming ability determined, a survival curve that is qualitatively similar to curves seen for ionizing radiation is obtained. When survival is determined for synchronized cell populations, a substantial degree of variation can occur throughout the cell cycle (Rauth, 1986). For many, but not all, cell lines late S-phase cells are most resistant to UV radiation and there is increasing sensitivity through G_2, M and G_1 to early S phase. This pattern differs from that seen with ionizing radiation (section 15.6.2).

Pyrimidine dimers can be directly measured in mammalian cells by a variety of techniques and at doses of biological interest their production is linear with dose. At high doses an equilibrium is established between dimer formation and reversal which is dependent on wavelength. Dimers appear to be formed at equal rates in cells in all phases of the cell cycle.

The relative effectiveness of different wavelengths of UV light to inactivate cell colony-forming ability has a close correspondence to the absorption spectrum of DNA. This spectrum is identical to the action spectrum for dimer formation. Lethal damage probably arises from an initial excitation of pyrimidine bases with sub-

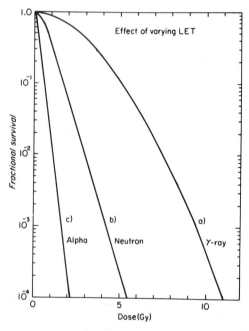

Figure 7.10. Typical mammalian cell survival curves for radiations varying in their linear energy transfer: *a*, Co^{60} γ-rays—0.3 keV/μm; *b*, neutrons—15–80 keV/μm; *c*, 5-MeV alpha particles—90 keV/μm. Note that the ratio of doses for the same level of killing (RBE) is not constant but is greater at low than at high doses.

sequent formation of dimers. However, the reaction of excited bases with other cellular components such as proteins might also explain the lethal effects of radiation.

Evidence for the production of sublethal or potentially lethal damage is not as clear for UV radiation as for ionizing radiation. The response of a cell to fractionated UV radiation depends on the passage of the cell through its DNA synthetic phase between fractions. Surviving cells respond to a second dose of UV radiation as if they had not seen the first dose if they are allowed to progress through their DNA synthesis phase between the doses of fractionated radiation (Rauth, 1986). Presumably, damage is repaired during the period of DNA synthesis.

7.3.4 MUTATION AND CHROMOSOME ABERRATIONS

The presence of damage in DNA can lead to mutations and/or chromosomal abnormalities. Mutations can take a variety of forms including base alterations, frame-shift mutations and deletions. Both ionizing radiation and UV irradiation can increase the frequency of specific mutations as well as chromosome abnormalities (Bender, 1969). Breakage and rearrangement of chromosomes can occur by direct or indirect effects or may occur during DNA replication and/or repair of radiation damage (eg, by error-prone or postreplication repair of pyrimidine dimers as discussed in section 7.4). When two chromosome breaks are near one another, the end from one break may rejoin with an end from the other, resulting in chromosomal rearrangement (Fig 7.11).

For ionizing radiation the number of chromosomal aberrations is found to increase as a function of dose with no evidence of a threshold at lower doses of radiation. The slope of this relationship increases with dose rate for low LET radiations. In contrast, high LET radiation has a steeper slope initially and is not very dependent on dose rate. From such dose–effect relationships, it can be concluded that a chromosome aberration requires that two or more radiation breaks arise in a given region in the DNA close in space and time to one another, so that they can interact. For high LET radiation, the probability of lesions per unit path length is high and thus the spatial and time requirements for lesion interaction are satisfied by one particle track, whereas for low-LET radiation two independent tracks are required. In this way the efficiency of chromosome damage can increase per unit dose for high LET compared to low LET ionizing radiation. Available evidence suggests that double-strand breaks produced directly by ionizing radiation or through mis-

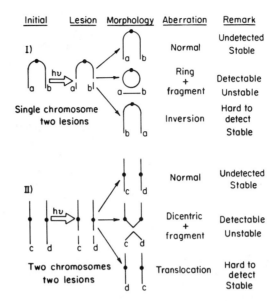

Figure 7.11. Some types of chromosome damage produced by ionizing radiation. (I) Single chromosome exposed to radiation (*hν*), resulting in two lesions, one in each arm. (II) Two separate chromosomes with a lesion in one arm of each chromosome. If lesions are not close in space and time they may be joined by a repair process, resulting in a normal chromosome. If two lesions are close to one another in space and time, they may be misrepaired and joined to form aberrant chromosomes. The stability of these abnormal forms and their ease of detection can vary. (Adapted from Upton, 1982a.)

repair are crucial lesions for inducing chromosome rearrangements.

7.4 DNA REPAIR IN MAMMALIAN CELLS

7.4.1 REPAIR-DEFICIENT MUTANTS

Mutant cells which are deficient in one or more steps in DNA repair processes, and are thus radiation sensitive, have played a major role in developing an understanding of the details of repair processes (Paterson et al, 1984). This is especially true for UV radiation since the initial discovery of the excision-repair process was made using mutant bacteria that were unable to remove pyrimidine dimers from their DNA at normal rates. Similarly, a human genetic disease, xeroderma pigmentosum, which is autosomal recessive, involves a repair defect that results in cells from such patients being unable to remove pyrimidine dimers from their DNA efficiently. Such patients have a high frequency of skin tumors when exposed to sunlight. Subsequently other human genetic diseases have been discovered that have defects in repair of DNA as part of their mutant phenotype (Table 7.2). Mutants have also been isolated from established mammalian cell lines which are sensitive to

Table 7.2. Some Radiation-Sensitive Mammalian Cells Used in Studies of DNA Repair

Source	Characteristics
Human genetic diseases	
Xeroderma pigmentosum	• autosomal recessive • sensitive to UV • cells deficient in ability to excise dimers • 9 complementation groups
Ataxia telangiectasia	• autosomal recessive • sensitive to ionizing radiation • repair deficiency not clear • at least 5 complementation groups
Chinese hamster cell lines	
Chinese hamster ovary cells derived from CHO AA8-4 by mutation and selection	• autosomal recessive • sensitive to UV and a variety of chemicals • some lines deficient in ability to excise dimers • at least 6 complementation groups

Note: Data adapted from Paterson et al, 1984, and Thompson et al, 1981.

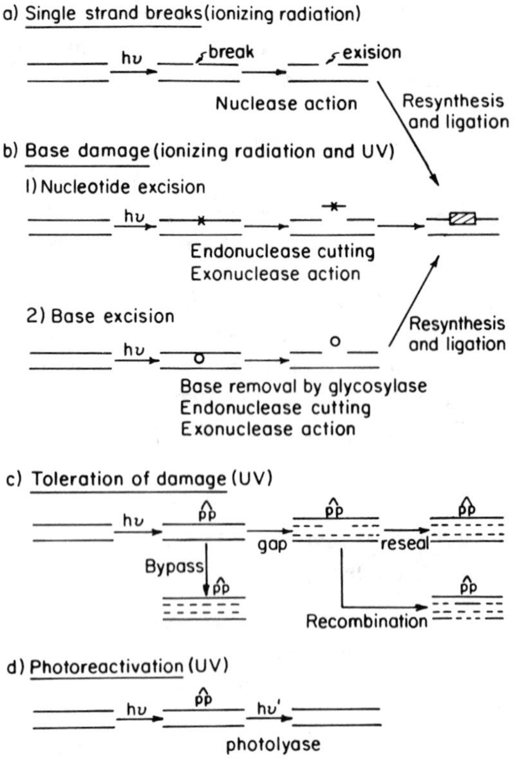

Figure 7.12. DNA repair processes that may occur in mammalian cells. *a,* Single-strand breaks produced by both direct and indirect effects of ionizing radiation are acted on by an exonuclease which may remove 3–10 nucleotides in the vicinity of the initial break. New DNA is resynthesized by a DNA polymerase using the intact strand as a template and the strands are joined by DNA ligase. *b,* Base damage can be (1) excised by an endonuclease which cuts on either side of the lesion, removing 10–15 nucleotides, or (2) the damaged base can be removed by a glycosylase leaving an apurinic or apyrimidinic (AP) site, which is acted on by an AP endonuclease and exonuclease. *c,* After UV radiation pyrimidine dimer (p̂p) damage may be bypassed by continuous synthesis of new DNA (dotted lines) or a gap may be left. Gaps may be resealed by subsequent synthesis past the lesion, or a recombination process can occur where original parental DNA is used to fill the gap and resynthesis and ligation fill in the resulting gap in the parental strand. *d,* UV-induced pyrimidine dimers can also be repaired by a photoreactivation enzyme (photolyase) which binds to the dimer and when exposed to long-wavelength UV light (*hν'*) catalyses the uncoupling of the dimer, restoring the pyrimidines to their original state.

UV or ionizing radiation, as well as to a variety of chemical agents. Study of these cells has led to the following models for DNA repair processes in mammalian cells.

7.4.2 REPAIR OF DNA STRAND BREAKS

The number of single-strand breaks in DNA diminishes as a function of time after ionizing radiation (Elkind, 1984). This information has been obtained by a variety of techniques including alkaline sucrose gradients and alkaline elution assays, which measure both existing breaks and DNA damage that can be converted to a break by the high pH used in the assays (Kohn et al, 1981). This repair can occur on a time scale of minutes to hours and is complex, since it involves more than one type of damage. The repair process appears to involve the enzymatic removal of three to ten nucleotides followed by resynthesis, probably using the opposite intact strand as a template. A ligase then allows closure of the interrupted strand (Fig 7.12a).

Evidence exists that double-strand breaks can also be repaired but probably at a lower rate than single-strand breaks. The steps in this process are uncertain since the opposite strand is not available as an intact template for the repair process. It is thought that homologous chromosomes may be involved in supplying the missing information for this type of repair.

7.4.3 BASE DAMAGE: EXCISION REPAIR

Segments of DNA containing an altered base (due to UV or ionizing radiation) can be recognized by specific enzymes which remove the damaged base and replace it with a normal nucleotide using the intact complementary strand as a template (Paterson et al, 1984). At least two modes of repair are currently known (Fig 7.12b). The first is nucleotide excision, which involves the removal of a section of DNA containing the lesion, and then repair synthesis using the intact DNA strand as a template for restoring the gap. At least four enzyme activities are required: (a) a specific endonuclease to cut the DNA strand close to the lesion; (b) an exonuclease to remove the damage; (c) a polymerase to synthesize DNA in the gap; and (d) a ligase to restore the continuity of the DNA strand. This process should result in error-free repair. These enzymes have not been as well characterized in mammalian cells as in bacteria. In addition, the organization of the DNA in mammalian cells into nucleosomes involves DNA–protein interactions not present in bacteria, as well as extensive higher-order folding and organization. The role that such tightly bound protein plays in limiting the accessibility of chromatin to repair enzymes is a subject of current study.

In the other mode of repair, base excision, the abnormal base is enzymatically removed by a specific DNA glycosylase. The resulting apurinic/apyrimidine (AP) site can be restored by the action of an AP endonuclease and exonuclease and the gap closed by repair synthesis and ligation (Fig 7.12b). These two modes of repair can be distinguished because nucleotide excision repair acts on "bulky lesions" (eg, pyrimidine dimers), makes repair patches 10–30 nucleotides long and requires up to 24 hr for completion, while base excision acts on small lesions (eg, deaminated cytosine); its repair patches consist of at most several nucleotides and repair is complete within an hour.

7.4.4 OTHER FORMS OF DNA REPAIR

Two other forms of repair can operate on pyrimidine dimers, although in some cases repair may be a misnomer in that damage is not being eliminated but is being bypassed or tolerated. If a dimer is present in the DNA when it is to be replicated during normal synthesis, postreplication repair can occur (Fig 7.12c; Rauth, 1986). Synthesis of new DNA may stop at the dimer and then start downstream, leaving a gap. This gap may be closed at a later time by new DNA synthesis in a process that is prone to error since this new DNA is not synthesized on a normal template. Alternatively, the gap may be eliminated by repair in which recombination occurs, with a 50% probability of transferring the dimer to the newly synthesized strand or of it remaining in the parent strand. A second possibility is that when new DNA synthesis reaches a dimer, it slows down but bypasses the dimer in a continuous fashion. These mechanisms are susceptible to error since the normal template is lacking. Thus, in comparison to the excision repair mechanism, the postreplication repair

mechanisms are much more likely to give rise to mutations.

Another mechanism for repair of dimers is photoreactivation in which a photoreactivating enzyme, photolyase, binds to the dimer; in the presence of visible light the enzyme uncouples the dimer and converts the pyrimidines to their original state (Fig 7.12d). Placental mammals have low levels of this enzyme in comparison to more primitive cells.

7.5 CELL TRANSFORMATION

7.5.1 TRANSFORMATION ASSAYS

It is possible with a variety of fresh explants of cells (Borek, 1979) and established cell lines (Hall and Hei, 1985; Little, 1977) to assay cell transformation in vitro. Two cell lines have been widely used for such studies: a line originally isolated from C$_3$H mouse embryos called 10T1/2 and a line isolated from Balb/C mouse embryos called 3T3. These cell lines are not normal because they are aneuploid and immortal, ie, they will grow indefinitely if subcultured under appropriate conditions and do not senesce as normal cell lines do (see also section 8.4). The cells are not considered to be malignant since they do not form tumors when reinjected into their original host.

Both cell lines, when grown in Petri dishes, undergo contact inhibition, ie, when cells come in close proximity to one another, they stop dividing but remain viable. Occasionally a spontaneous change (transformation) occurs whereby the cell loses its contact inhibition and continues growing by spreading over adjacent cells and piling up. Such transformed cells form colonies or foci of transformed cells which can be distinguished and counted upon staining. When cells in such foci are isolated, cloned, expanded and reinjected back into their host of origin, they often form tumors. For further discussion of the properties of transformed cells see section 8.4.2.

Transformed foci can be induced by radiation treatment of the cells. A general procedure for studying cell transformation in vitro is illustrated in Figure 7.13. Cells are plated at low cell density to measure cell killing by the radiation and at higher density so that approximately 400 cells will survive the treatment. These latter cells are then left to grow to confluency, which requires 11–13 divisions. At this time no foci are seen but if the dishes are held with appropriate media changes for 4–6 weeks after confluency is obtained, discrete foci of transformed cells can be counted after appropriate staining of the dishes. These foci are identified by their dense, multilayered structure, basophilic staining, and the random orientation of the spindle-

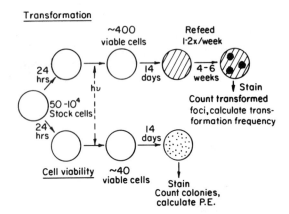

Figure 7.13. A general procedure for studying cell transformation in vitro. Cells from a carefully controlled stock supply are seeded into a number of Petri dishes at a variety of cell densities and left for 24 hr. The dishes are exposed to various doses of radiation, choosing appropriate cell densities to yield 400 viable cells per dish for a transformation assay, or 40 viable cells per dish for a cell viability assay. Dishes are left for 14 days. At this time the former assay dishes have formed a contact-inhibited monolayer and no foci are visible; the latter dishes have formed discrete colonies. At this time dishes used to assess cell viability are stained, colonies counted and the plating efficiency (PE), defined as the number of colonies per initial cell plated, can be determined. The dishes used to assess transformation are left for a further 4–6 weeks, with media changes weekly, and then stained. Transformed foci are counted. By combining the data for cell viability with that for focus formation, a transformation frequency per viable cell can be determined.

shaped cells. The number of foci can be expressed as the number of foci per irradiated cell or number of foci per surviving cell.

A number of experiments have shown that cell multiplication is important for both fixation of the initial damage and expression of the transformed phenotype. The period from 0 to 48 hr after exposure to radiation is referred to as the period of damage fixation in which unrepaired or misrepaired damage in DNA is replicated and permanently "fixed" in the cell genome. The subsequent period of growth is referred to as the period of expression of the initiated cell leading to the transformed phenotype.

The frequency of transformation can be increased by known tumor promoters such as "croton oil" or phorbol esters (see section 6.4) and inhibited by protease inhibitors or by vitamins C or E (Little, 1981). The importance of the in vitro transformation assay is that it allows aspects of the carcinogenic process to be studied in a single type of cell under controlled conditions. However, unequivocal in vitro focus assays have not yet been established for human cell lines. The reason for this is not known.

7.5.2 TRANSFORMATION BY IONIZING RADIATION

Spontaneous transformation frequencies in 10T1/2 or 3T3 cells are 10^{-4} to 10^{-5} per viable cell or lower. When such cells are irradiated with low LET radiation, plated, and their survival and transformation frequencies measured, results as seen in Figure 7.14 are obtained. The number of transformants per irradiated cell increases with dose initially, over the range where little cell killing occurs (ie, the shoulder of the cell-survival curve). At higher doses, as cell killing increases, the observed number of transformed foci decreases. Thus there is an optimum dose for maximal transformation (as has been seen for tumor induction in animals and man—sections 7.6 and 7.7). Plotting transformants per surviving cell, as in Figure 7.14, indicates that the number of transformants increases for doses up to about 4 Gy and then plateaus, remaining constant up to about 12 Gy.

When high LET radiation is used (eg, neutrons) the transformation frequencies appear to parallel qualita-

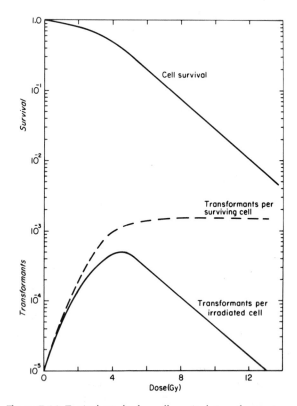

Figure 7.14. Typical results for cell survival, transformants per irradiated cell and transformants per surviving cell for 10T1/2 cells exposed to low LET ionizing radiation. When corrected for cell killing, the transformation frequency increases from a spontaneous level of 10^{-5} to a plateau value at 4–5 Gy of greater than 10^{-3}. (Adapted from Little, 1977.)

tively the cell-survival data. The cells are more efficiently killed and are more efficiently transformed (Elkind, 1984); thus the RBE for transformation is also greater than unity. Also, as is seen for cell survival, the RBE for cell transformation by high LET radiation increases as dose decreases.

Fractionation of doses of low LET radiation increases cell survival compared to equivalent single doses due to the repair of sublethal damage (see sections 7.3.1 and 15.6.3). For cell transformation the results are more complex (Hall and Miller, 1981). At doses less than 1 Gy fractionation of the radiation dose increases the number of transformants per irradiated cell, while at doses above 1 Gy it diminishes transformation relative to the same single dose of radiation. Thus, it has been suggested that the type of damage which leads to transformation (or the mechanism of its repair) may differ from that involved in cell survival. Fractionation or protraction of high LET radiation does not decrease its ability to transform cells. In fact, some data indicate that fractionation of neutron exposures enhances their transforming ability compared to acute single exposures of the same dose. Thus, as for low LET radiation at lower doses, cell survival after fractionated high LET radiation does not necessarily parallel transformation of the same cells. Whether or not this is a general feature of the transformation process remains to be shown. It is important to note that low doses are of the greatest interest in relation to setting guidelines for radiation exposure to man.

7.5.3 TRANSFORMATION BY UV RADIATION

UV irradiation also causes transformation of cells. Data similar to that in Figure 7.14 is obtained for UV irradiation although the maximal levels of transformation appear to be lower by a factor of approximately 3 (Little, 1977). The action spectra for mammalian cell transformation are similar to the action spectra for pyrimidine dimer production (Rauth, 1986). This result strongly implicates initial damage to DNA as being a major factor in UV-induced mammalian cell transformation. Detailed studies of dose fractionation or dose-rate effects have not been carried out with UV irradiation but would be of interest for comparison with the effects obtained with ionizing radiation.

7.5.4 TRANSFORMATION, CELL SURVIVAL AND MUTATION

It is instructive to compare the relative sensitivity of cells to killing, transformation or mutation by ionizing radiation as a function of the LET or track structure of

the radiation used. This can be done by calculating a cross section for each of these endpoints (Goodhead, 1984). This cross section is a hypothetical geometric area in a cell through which a particle track must pass to produce a lesion, which results in the particular biological effect being studied, multiplied by the probability that the track will produce an effective lesion. The cross sections at low LET are small due to the low probability of individual tracks causing damage and the fact that the damage has a high probability of repair. At high LET the cross sections increase due to the high probability that the individual track will cause damage in the target and the fact that the damage has a low probability of repair. The relationship between the cross sections and the LET of the radiation is shown in Figure 7.15. The ratio of the cell-killing cross section to the cell-transformation cross section to the mutation cross section is approximately $1/10^{-2}/10^{-4}$ for radiations with LET values of 2–10 keV/μm and $1/10^{-1}/10^{-4}$ for high LET radiations. Since the cross section for transformation is higher than that for point mutations it has been suggested that the target for transformation is larger than a single gene and smaller than a

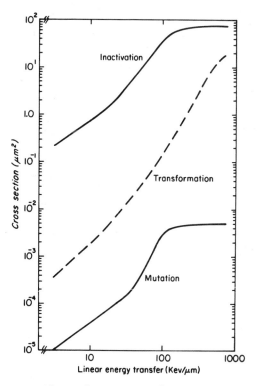

Figure 7.15. Observed cross sections for mammalian cell inactivation, transformation and mutation as a function of the LET of the radiation to which they are exposed. The solid lines are approximate fits to the data as presented by Goodhead (1984). The dotted line for transformation has greater uncertainty since it is based on more limited data. (Adapted from Goodhead, 1984.)

chromosome, involving more than one gene on one or more chromosomes.

Thus direct activation of a transforming or oncogene may not be occurring. Rather it may be that there are a variety of genes that control the stability of DNA and/or the fidelity of DNA replication and that when any one of these genes is damaged by radiation, an increased probability of errors in DNA replication occurs in subsequent cell cycles. Thus the likelihood of a second step leading to expression or activation of an oncogene increases.

7.6 RADIATION CARCINOGENESIS IN ANIMALS

7.6.1 TISSUE SENSITIVITY TO IONIZING RADIATION

Single doses of low LET radiation in the range of 0.25–8 Gy given whole body can increase the frequency of malignant and benign tumors in irradiated animals (Fry, 1981). A variety of animals has been studied including dogs, monkeys and rats, but the most extensive studies have been done with mice. In an experiment (Storer, 1982) in which a total of 12,000 female mice were irradiated with 0.1–4 Gy of γ-rays and then followed for their lifetimes, autopsies and histological examinations indicated relative tissue sensitivities in terms of tumor induction as shown in Table 7.3. The order of sensitivities of these tissues is not the same for all animals or even all strains of mice, but the important point is that all tissues are not equally sensitive to radiation. This implies that the initial damage, which is uniformly produced at the tissue level, is subject to a number of host factors such as levels of repair enzymes, rate of cell proliferation, endocrine function and immune competence which contribute to the overall process of cancer induction. An example illustrating the potential complexity of such host factors is the induction of thymic lymphomas in C57Bl mice by small whole-body doses of radiation (1.75 Gy) given weekly for four weeks. In this system evidence for the activation of a unique leukemia virus, Rad LV, which interacts with target cells in the thymic environment has been obtained (Weissman, 1985). Induction of tumor viruses does not appear to be a general mechanism of radiation carcinogenesis. In fact, it appears to be the exception rather than the rule but it may have a role to play in selected systems.

7.6.2 DOSE DEPENDENCE OF TUMOR INDUCTION BY IONIZING RADIATION

Since there are differences in tissue susceptibility to carcinogenesis, it is not surprising that the dose dependence for the carcinogenic process can differ for different tumors. Nevertheless, there are certain general principles which are illustrated schematically in Figure 7.16, curve A, for single acute doses of low LET ionizing radiation given to the whole body. In general, the relationship between tumor induction and dose appears sigmoid. At low doses there is little induction but as the dose increases there is a steep increase in the number of tumors followed by a saturation or even a decrease at high doses. Factors to be noted in relation to curve A follow:

1. Many strains of mice have a significant spontaneous level of occurrence of the specific tumor under study (in this hypothetical example 10%) even in the absence of radiation. Spontaneous tumors may complicate the assessment of tumor induction at low doses of radiation. There is nothing unique about radiation-induced tumors and they cannot be differentiated from spontaneous tumors.
2. The induction curve for a specific tumor might have a very short initial threshold portion so the rate of tumor production could appear to be linear with dose.
3. As the dose of radiation increases, a maximal induction is reached and incidence decreases. This may be due to killing of induced cells as is observed in the in vitro transformation assays.
4. There is a latent period between the radiation treatment and tumor detection. Thus an increase in the frequency of tumors at a certain time after radiation may represent an effect on the absolute level of tumor incidence or an earlier occurrence of tumors or both.

Tumor induction for a single dose of high LET radiation given whole body is in general more efficient than

Table 7.3. Relative Tissue Sensitivities of RFM Female Mice to the Induction of Cancer by Radiation*

High Sensitivity	Moderate Sensitivity	Low Sensitivity
thymus	pituitary	bone
ovary	uterus	skin
	breast	stomach
	myelopoietic tissue (myeloid leukemia)	liver
	lung	
	Haderian gland	GI tract

*Twelve thousand mice were irradiated at 10 weeks of age and followed for their lifetimes. High, moderate or low sensitivity was defined as significant induction of tumors over controls at 0.25, 0.5–1.5, or greater than 1.5 Gy respectively. Data is from Storer, 1982.

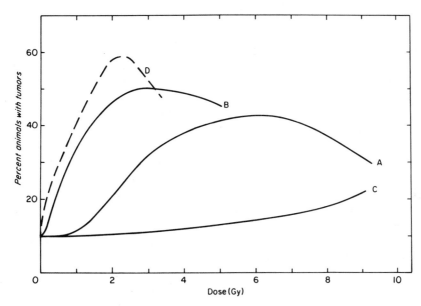

Figure 7.16. Schematic diagram of induction of a specific tumor type in mice exposed to various doses of ionizing radiation given to the whole body based on a review of a number of different in vivo results. *Curve A*: Tumors induced by single acute doses of low LET ionizing radiation. *Curve B*: Tumors induced by single acute doses of high LET radiation. *Curve C*: Tumors induced by fractionated doses (eg, 1 Gy/day), of low LET radiation. *Curve D*: Tumors induced by fractionated doses (eg, 0.5 Gy/day), of high LET radiation.

for low LET radiation. This is illustrated in Figure 7.16 by the schematic curve B. Most of the studies in mice with external-beam irradiation have used neutrons because of the difficulty in delivering uniform doses of other high LET radiations (eg, charged heavy particles). Curve B is drawn with a small low-dose "threshold" portion so tumor induction appears initially to be almost linear with dose. The curve continues to a maximum, which indicates that a higher incidence of tumors occurs at a lower dose than for low LET radiation and then decreases. In Figure 7.16, 3.3 Gy of low LET radiation gives 35% tumor induction, while a single dose of 1.1 Gy of neutrons gives the same effect. Therefore the RBE of neutrons relative to the low LET radiation would be approximately 3.0. It is important to recognize that the RBE for neutrons, although increased, is very dependent on the biological effect being studied as well as the precise endpoint. The RBE for 15% tumor induction is 6.0, quite different from that for 35% tumor induction. This increase in RBE for tumor formation at low doses of radiation is important for assessment of radiation risk (Kellerer and Rossi, 1982).

Special problems arise in trying to assess the effect of radiation dose delivered in animals or humans by internally deposited radioisotopes (Walburg, 1974). The major problem is to determine the dose delivered to the susceptible cell population. Different isotopes localize in different tissues as a function of their mode of administration and a variety of physiological and environmental variables. The deposited isotope may be subject to metabolism or replacement which is tissue and host dependent. Thus the dose to the tissue of interest will be a function of the physical half-life of the isotope and its physiological behavior. It appears in general, however, when dose patterns are comparable to those for external radiation that internal emitters produce similar results.

7.6.3 EFFECTS OF DOSE FRACTIONATION AND LOW DOSE RATES OF IONIZING RADIATION

Other than exposures due to accidents and nuclear explosions, most radiation exposures of concern to man involve fractionated or low-dose-rate irradiation. The effectiveness of fractionated or low-dose-rate irradiation in causing tumors is quite different for low LET and high LET radiation. Most tests of fractionated low LET radiation have resulted in a reduction of tumor incidence for a given total dose as illustrated by curve C of Figure 7.16. Fractionation of radiation allows for extensive repair of sublethal radiation damage and also results in reduced carcinogenic effect. Continuous radiation at a low dose rate gives a curve similar to curve C.

In contrast, fractionating high LET radiation or exposure at low dose rates has little effect on tumor induction, giving the same results as for single acute doses (curve B, Figure 7.16) or, in some recently reported cases, proving significantly more efficient in causing tumor induction (curve D, Figure 7.16). Lack of repair of damage after high LET radiation means that fractionation or prolonging the time for radiation delivery is of little benefit in reducing the probability of tumor induction.

In summary, radiation induces tumors in different tissues with different efficiencies, implying the existence of a variety of host factors. Low LET radiation induces tumors giving a dose–tumor induction curve of sigmoid shape and there is less tumor induction with dose fractionation or low dose rates, implying that repair of carcinogenic damage is occurring. High LET radiation is more efficient in causing tumors, resulting in an RBE that is higher at low doses. The effectiveness of high LET radiation is not diminished and may be increased by dose fractionation or protraction.

7.6.4 UV CARCINOGENESIS

Because of the limited penetration of UV light through tissue, studies of the carcinogenic effect of UV radiation in animals have been limited in the main to induction of tumors in skin (Fry and Ley, 1983). Studies of UV carcinogenesis have focussed on three ranges of wavelength: UV-C, UV-B, and UV-A, corresponding to 200–290 nm, 290–320 nm and >320 nm, respectively. Because of filtering of UV light by the ozone layer, wavelengths shorter than 290 nm (UV-C) are believed to play little role in the exposure of the human population to solar radiation. UV-B is the most effective range of wavelength for skin carcinogenesis.

Early studies on the UV induction of skin tumors were carried out on the ears of albino rats and mice. The induced tumors were a mixture of fibrosarcomas and squamous-cell carcinomas. More recent experiments using hairless mice and lower doses produced mainly squamous-cell carcinomas. Attempts to determine the efficiencies of different wavelengths of UV light in causing cancer induction (ie, the action spectra for carcinogenesis) are complicated, largely because of the problem of relating exposure dose in J/m^2 to the dose produced at some depth in the basal-cell layer of the skin, the presumptive site of the target cells.

It has been difficult to obtain tumors with single doses of UV radiation, and multiple exposures to UV are required for reproducible results (Fry and Ley, 1983). Typically, low daily doses of UV are given over weeks to months. In the older literature, plots were made of the percentage of mice with tumors as a function of time after starting daily exposures. Results indicated that as the daily dose decreased and dose rate decreased, the time for initial tumor appearance increased and the rate of tumor induction decreased. However, other experiments have indicated that a given total dose of UV radiation appears to be more effective as a carcinogen administered at a lower exposure rate or as a fractionated course. This is a different result than that seen for low LET ionizing radiation.

UV is a complete carcinogen in that it can induce tumors by itself, as does ionizing radiation. In experiments where multiple UV doses were given that induced a known number of pyrimidine dimers in the target basal-cell layer of skin, a clear dose–effect relationship was obtained (Fry and Ley, 1983). In these experiments there was an appreciable dose range where no tumors were induced, followed by a significant increase with UV dose to the basal layer. Treatment of UV-irradiated animals with the tumor promoter 12-0-tetradecanoylphorbol-13 acetate (TPA) converted this curvilinear response to an apparent linear no-threshold-type response. Thus the ability of UV radiation to transform cells could be enhanced by the addition of a known tumor promoter.

Sarcomas induced by UV radiation tend to be strongly immunogenic. Recent experiments have indicated that repeated UV irradiation of mice induces not only sarcomas, but also an immunological change which inhibits the ability of an irradiated mouse to reject transplanted syngeneic tumors that were induced by UV radiation (Kripke, 1981). Thus the dose–response relationships for UV induction of tumors may be complex because the dose–response relationships for cancer induction and immune suppression may not be the same, and the appearance of tumors will be mediated by both effects. This effect of UV irradiation on immune responses is currently under intensive study and promises to supply valuable information on the relative contribution of processes of initiation and promotion in UV carcinogenesis.

In summary, most studies of UV carcinogenesis in rodents have involved multiple doses of UV irradiation. Tumor induction increases with total dose, but the dependence on time–dose fractionation is not well understood. Both fibrosarcomas and squamous-cell carcinomas can be induced. Besides its effect in initiating carcinogenesis, UV can alter an animal's ability to reject UV-induced tumors which are immunogenic. This effect of UV on antitumor immunity does not appear to have a parallel in carcinogenesis by ionizing radiation.

7.7 HUMAN DATA ON RADIATION CARCINOGENESIS

7.7.1 TISSUE SENSITIVITY TO IONIZING RADIATION

The effects of ionizing radiation in man are based upon

1. occupational exposures (eg, radiologists and uranium miners);
2. therapeutic exposures (eg, unavoidable treatment of normal tissues in cancer therapy, or treatment of ankylosing spondylitis);
3. accidental exposures;
4. diagnostic exposures; and
5. atomic bomb exposures.

As in animals, there is a wide range of tissue sensitivities or susceptibilities to cancer induction. A general ranking of human tissues in terms of their radiation sensitivities is given in Table 7.4 (Storer, 1982). There are some differences in tissue sensitivities as compared to mice (see Table 7.3).

The most extensive data on the carcinogenic effects of ionizing radiation comes from detailed follow-up of the approximately 109,000 survivors and controls of the atomic bombs dropped on Nagasaki and Hiroshima in 1945 (Kohn and Fry, 1984). The average dose of radiation received by these individuals has been estimated as 0.27 Gy, and at present the detailed analysis of data represents a follow-up period of over 30 years. The dosimetry of these exposures has undergone reevaluation, and currently the γ-ray and neutron components of the radiation doses have been recalculated. This has required some reassessment of the data since, in trying to estimate risks, weighting factors are required to account for the greater RBE of high LET radiation components.

Table 7.4. Relative Sensitivities of Various Human Tissues to the Induction of Radiogenic Cancer

High Sensitivity	Moderate Sensitivity	Low Sensitivity
Myelopoietic tissue (acute and myeloid leukemia)	Breast Lung	Skin Bone
Thyroid	Salivary gland	Stomach Other tissues

Note: Adapted from Storer (1982).

The late effect that first appeared in the irradiated populations was an increase in the incidence of leukemias; this was due primarily to the short latent period for this malignancy. Subsequently, cancers of almost all other organs (which have longer latent periods) have been found to be increased significantly. Thus there appears to be an increase in risk due to radiation rather than just a shortening of the latent period.

7.7.2 DOSE DEPENDENCE OF CANCER INDUCTION BY IONIZING RADIATION

There are many problems in utilizing data from humans to estimate carcinogenic risk at low doses (Storer, 1982; Kohn and Fry, 1984). The nature of some of these problems is illustrated schematically in Figure 7.17, where increase in tumor incidence is plotted as a function of an acute single dose of radiation. Data is only available at higher doses of radiation so that an extrapolation is required to predict risk at low doses. The problem is how to make this extrapolation; a linear fit to the data, curve A, a linear-quadratic curve, curve B, or a threshold linear curve, curve C, are three possibilities. The linear curve A is a conservative approach. It assures that hazards are not under-

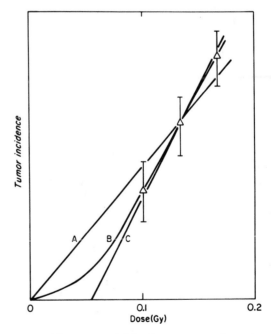

Figure 7.17. Illustration of difficulties in extrapolating limited data at high doses in humans to a low-dose region where no data exists. Hypothetical data for tumor incidence versus dose are shown by the triangles with error bars. Curve A is the best linear fit. Curve B is a linear-quadratic fit to the data. Curve C is a threshold-linear fit to the data.

estimated (unless fractionation increases tumor induction rate) and it has been used by those concerned with health protection. It assumes that any dose of radiation has the potential to induce cancer and that the risk of cancer induction is directly proportional to dose. This extrapolation implies that the increase in tumor number is the same for 100,000 persons each receiving 0.01 Gy of radiation as for 10,000 people receiving 0.1 Gy each. This may not be a valid assumption. Extrapolation curves B and C of Figure 7.17 are more consistent with data from animals, but the exact shape of the low-dose portion of the curve varies from one experimental system to another; thus it is probably wrong to assume a generalized slope for such curves. No human data exists for proven carcinogenic effects of radiation below 0.1 Gy.

Radiation risk is defined as the increase in the number of cancer deaths over that expected for an unirradiated population. It is expressed in units of per person exposed per gray of radiation. Estimates based on linear extrapolation (Figure 7.17, curve A) of the atomic bomb data and on other more limited data from pooled results of various partial body exposures give total cancer mortality risks for a general population exposed to whole-body radiation of 1–4×10^{-2} per person-Gy (Kohn and Fry, 1984). It is important to note that this estimate is dominated by the atomic bomb data and, within this data, by the 13% of the population which received 0.50 Gy or more. Furthermore, after 30 years 60% of the study population is still alive; thus, because cancer frequencies increase with age, the number of excess cases will certainly increase with further follow-up. Currently, the increase in total tumor incidence for the atomic bomb victims over the control group, 5–30 years after radiation, is about 5% or 2 per 1000 persons at risk.

Each atomic bomb gave effectively a single acute radiation exposure, and the estimate given above was made using a linear extrapolation of the high-dose data assuming no effect of fractionation. The guide for allowable radiation exposure for the general population is 0.0017 Gy/yr with a maximum of 0.05 Gy in 30 years. Using the above estimates of cancer risk, a person receiving this maximum dose will have an increased risk of cancer of 0.05–0.2% over a lifetime. Since currently 1 in 4 people in North America die of cancer, this represents a small increase in total risk. However, appropriate guidelines for allowable exposures at low doses are still controversial. In particular, there is concern about the low-dose effects of high LET radiation since, in experimental systems, RBE increases as dose decreases, and recent data suggest the possibility of an increased risk at low dose rate (see section 7.6.3).

In summary, the risk of cancer may increase in humans exposed to moderate doses of radiation (0.1–1 Gy). Most tissues are affected but their relative sensitivities vary. Estimates of risk for low doses of radiation spread over long periods of time are made by a linear extrapolation of acute-dose data assuming no effects of dose rate on risk. Currently these estimates appear to be conservative and may overestimate true risk.

7.7.3 UV RADIATION

There is a correlation between latitude (average sun exposure) and malignant tumors of the skin (Urbach, 1978) with tumors tending to occur on sun-exposed areas, such as the face. Genetic background can also be a determining factor, especially low skin pigmentation (Celts, Scottish, Welsh), since this can contribute to a possible increase in the effective dose delivered to the cells in the basal layer of the epidermis that are at risk. There appears to be a requirement for chronic exposure to sunlight for carcinogenesis, suggesting the requirement for a number of interactions of UV radiation with target cells spread out over time. The same behavior was noted for the induction of skin tumors in rodents (section 7.6.4). A proposed relationship between dose D and incidence I of nonmelanoma skin cancer is $I \propto D^2$: in other words, the incidence curve is curvilinear with an apparent nonzero threshold (Fry and Ley, 1983).

In animal studies, it was noted that multiple doses of UV could effectively reduce a normal immune response against UV-induced tumors. In this regard recent data have indicated that Australians (who have a high average sun exposure) undergoing immunosuppressive therapy for renal transplants have a higher frequency of squamous-cell tumors than those in the general population. Immunosuppression may allow previously initiated cells to express their malignant phenotype, as appears to happen in animals.

7.8 SUMMARY—MECHANISMS OF RADIATION CARCINOGENESIS

Ionizing radiation and ultraviolet radiation produce a number of different lesions in the DNA of cells. Both types of radiation give rise to tumors, suggesting that a number of quite different DNA lesions may initiate the process of carcinogenesis. Mutation of one specific gene does not appear to be the cause of the carcinogenic process since target-theory calculations indicate that the size of a target for transformation in vitro is 30–100 times the size of a gene (Goodhead, 1984).

Chromosome breakage, faulty repair and/or translocation are possible mechanisms that would allow oncogenic activation of normal genes by changing their chromosomal position or by allowing the insertion of activating genes near to them. Recent studies have identified a number of oncogenes whose expression may have a role in the development of some tumors (see chapter 5). The inappropriate expression of these oncogenes can be related to point mutations in these genes or in genes regulating their expression. Recent experiments in mice have shown that a particular oncogene (K-ras, see section 5.3) is activated in mouse lymphomas that were induced by gamma radiation (Guerrero et al, 1984). A single base change was detected in the DNA sequence of the gene in the tumor, suggesting that gamma radiation was acting as a source of point mutations. Whether such oncogene mutations are an early primary event in radiation carcinogenesis or a late step in the oncogenic process is not clear.

Cancer induction is a multistage process. Both ionizing and UV radiation act as complete carcinogens, but initiated cells may lie dormant until stimulated to grow by a tissue or systemic factor(s). The role of ultraviolet irradiation in suppressing the immune system is an example of a potential promoting effect of this radiation for initiated cells. Similarly, chemical promoters such as phorbol esters have been shown to increase the incidence and shorten the time of appearance of tumors initiated by both UV and ionizing radiation in in vivo model systems.

Although initial stages of radiation carcinogenesis may depend on specific lesions in DNA, and their lack of repair or misrepair that leads to mutations or chromosomal rearrangement, subsequent steps in the carcinogenic process will most likely be more tissue specific. Interaction of the basic process of initiation with the subsequent processes of progression and tumor development will have to be unravelled before a complete understanding of the mechanism of radiation carcinogenesis will be obtained.

REFERENCES

Bender MA: Human radiation cytogenetics, in Augenstein LG, Mason R, Zelle M (eds), *Advances in Radiation Biology*. Academic Press, New York, 1969, vol 3, pp 215–276.

Borek C: Malignant transformation in vitro: criteria, biological markers, and application in environmental screening of carcinogens. *Radiat Res* 1979; 79:209–232.

Elkind MM: Repair processes in radiation biology. *Radiat Res*, 1984; 100:425–449.

Fry RJM: Experimental radiation carcinogenesis: what have we learned? *Radiat Res* 1981; 87:224–239.

Fry RJM, Ley RD: Ultraviolet radiation carcinogenesis, in Slaga TJ (ed): *Mechanisms of Tumor Promotion*. CRC Press,

Boca Raton, FL, 1983, vol II: *Tumor promotion and skin carcinogenesis*, pp 73–96.

Goodhead DT: Deductions from cellular studies of inactivation, mutagenesis and transformation, Boice JD Jr, Fraumeni JF, Jr (eds): *Radiation Carcinogenesis: Epidemiology and Biological Significance*. Raven Press, New York, 1984, pp 369–385.

Guerrero I, Villasante A, Corces V, Pellicer A: Activation of a c-K-ras oncogene by somatic mutation in mouse lymphomas induced by gamma radiation. *Science* 1984; 225: 1159–1169.

Hall EJ: *Radiobiology for the Radiologist*, ed 2. Harper and Row, Hagerstown, MD, 1978.

Hall EJ, Hei TK: Oncogenic transformation with radiation and chemicals. *Int J Radiat Biol* 1985; 48:1–18.

Hall EJ, Miller RC: The how and why of in vitro oncogenic transformation. *Radiat Res* 1981; 87:208–223.

Johns HE, Cunningham JR: *The Physics of Radiology*, ed 4. Charles C Thomas, Springfield, IL, 1983.

Kellerer AM, Rossi HH: Biophysical aspects of radiation carcinogenesis, in Becker FF (ed): *Cancer—A Comprehensive Treatise*, ed 2. Plenum Press, New York, 1982, vol I, pp 569–616.

Kohn HI, Fry RJM: Radiation carcinogenesis. *N Engl J Med* 1984; 310:504–511.

Kohn KW, Ewig RAC, Erickson LC, Zwelling LA: Measurement of strand breaks and cross-links by alkaline elution, in Friedberg EC, Hanawalt PC (eds): *DNA Repair, A Laboratory Manual of Research Procedures*. New York, Marcel Dekker, 1981, pp 379–401.

Kripke ML: Immunologic mechanisms in UV radiation carcinogenesis, in: Klein G, Weinhouse S (eds): *Adv Cancer Res*. 1981; 34:69–106.

Little JB: Radiation carcinogenesis in vitro: implications for mechanisms, in Hiatt HH, Watson JD, Winston JA (eds): *Origins of Human Cancer, Book B, Mechanisms of Carcinogenesis*. Cold Spring Harbor Laboratory, Cold Spring Harbor, NY, 1977, pp 923–939.

Little JB: Influence of noncarcinogenic secondary factors on radiation carcinogenesis. *Radiat Res* 1981; 87:240–250.

Paterson MC, Gentner NE, Middlestadt MV, Weinfeld M: Cancer predisposition, carcinogen hypersensitivity and aberrant DNA metabolism. *J Cell Physiol Suppl* 1984; 3:45–62.

Rauth AM: The induction and repair of ultraviolet light damage in mammalian cells, in Burns FJ, Upton AC, Silini G (eds): *Radiation Carcinogenesis and DNA Alterations*. Plenum Press, 1986, pp. 212–226.

Rauth AM, Simpson JA: The energy loss of electrons in solids. *Radiat Res* 1964; 22:643–661.

Storer JB: Radiation carcinogenesis, in Becker FF (ed): *Cancer: a Comprehensive Treatise*, ed 2. Plenum Press, New York, 1982, vol 1, pp 629–659.

Thompson LH, Busch DB, Brookman K et al: Genetic diversity of UV-sensitive DNA repair mutants of Chinese hamster ovary cells. *Proc Natl Acad Sci USA* 1981; 78:3734–3737.

Upton AC: The biological effects of low-level ionizing radiation. *Sci Amer* 1982a 246:41–49.

Upton AC: Physical carcinogenesis: radiation—history and

sources, in Becker FF (ed): *Cancer: A Comprehensive Treatise*, ed 2. Plenum Press, New York, 1982b; pp 551–567.

Urbach F: Evidence and epidemiology of ultraviolet-induced cancers in man, in Kripke ML, Sass ER (eds): *International Conference on Ultraviolet Carcinogenesis*. National Cancer Institute, DHEW Publication, 1978, monograph 50, pp 5–10.

Walburg HE Jr: Experimental radiation carcinogenesis, in Lett JT, Adler H, Zelle M (eds): *Adv in Radiat Biol* 1974; 4:209–254.

Weissman IL: Thymic lymphocyte differentiation and thymic leukemogenesis. *Int J Radiat Oncol Biol Phys* 1985; 11:57–64.

BIBLIOGRAPHY

Boice JD Jr, Fraumeni: JF, Jr (eds): *Radiation Carcinogenesis: Epidemiology and Biological Significance*. Raven Press, New York, 1984.

Hall EJ: *Radiobiology for the Radiologist*, ed. 2. Harper and Row, Hagerstown, MD, 1978.

Johns HE, Cunningham JR: *The Physics of Radiology*, ed 4. Charles Thomas, Springfield, IL, 1983.

PART 2

CANCER BIOLOGY

8

Properties of Malignant Cells

Ronald N. Buick and Ian F. Tannock

8.1 INTRODUCTION

Human tumors vary greatly in their properties. They arise in different tissues and vary with respect to their retention of normal patterns of differentiation (tumor grade) and in their degree of invasion of surrounding tissue and metastasis to distant sites (tumor stage). The studies of cancer causation described in preceding chapters suggest strongly that carcinogenesis involves genetic alterations in cells whose progeny constitute the tumor mass. These genetic events lead to biological properties that collectively constitute the malignant phenotype. Many of these properties lead only to subtle differences from the normal cells of the tissue of origin, and the lack of specific distinguishing features between malignant and normal cells has been a major barrier to the development of tumor-specific therapy.

Information pertinent to the biology of the cancer cell has been derived from a variety of experimental systems. Broadly, these fall into three classes: spontaneous human tumors, transplanted or induced tumors in laboratory animals, and in vitro systems relying on tissue culture. Concepts that have been derived from study of these diverse systems are summarized in the present chapter.

8.2 THE STEM CELL CONCEPT APPLIED TO TUMORS

8.2.1 CELL RENEWAL IN NORMAL TISSUE

Studies of cellular proliferation in animals including man (section 9.5) have shown that normal tissues may be classified into those that are constantly renewing their population (eg, bone marrow and intestine), those that proliferate slowly but may renew their population in response to injury (eg, lung and liver), and those that are static (eg, nerve and muscle). Most human tumors arise in renewing cell populations, while others which originate in tissues with a slower rate of proliferation are often preceded by tissue injury that induces cell proliferation (eg, irritants such as cigarette smoke in lung, or hepatitis B infection in liver).

Renewal tissues represent a hierarchy of cells produced by differentiation and cell division from a small number of stem cells (Fig 8.1). Stem cells have a high capacity for cell proliferation, but their actual rate of cell division is usually quite low in the absence of tissue injury or demand. Various signals may operate on stem cells or their immediate progeny to indicate a need for more rapid proliferation. Slightly more mature cells

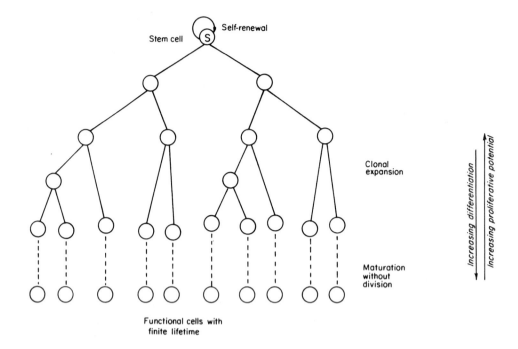

Figure 8.1. The hierarchy of cells in a renewal tissue. The population is maintained by clonal expansion from a small number of stem cells, which must undergo self-renewal to avoid depletion. It is not known whether the number of cell divisions is constant during clonal expansion. The more mature cells may continue to differentiate without proliferating and are ultimately lost from the population. Homeostatic mechanisms maintain a balance between cell production and cell loss. There is an inverse relationship between cellular differentiation and proliferative potential.

in the hierarchy proliferate rapidly, leading to a large degree of clonal expansion and production of numerous differentiated cells. Examples are the myeloblasts and myelocytes in bone marrow, and cells in the crypts of the small intestine (section 9.5). The potential for clonal growth of a cell appears to be related inversely to its state of differentiation, and there may be continued differentiation of mature cells after they have lost the capacity for proliferation. Thus, in bone marrow, metamyelocytes mature into functional polymorphonuclear leukocytes and reticulocytes synthesize hemoglobin and mature into erythrocytes. The cell-renewal system is under fine control so that loss of mature functional cells is balanced by production of new cells.

Stem cells have two critical functions (Fig 8.1). First, they can generate a large family of descendants which will perform the function of the tissue. Second, stem cells must demonstrate the property of self-renewal so that their numbers are not reduced by the process of differentiation. The molecular mechanisms which underlie this tight control are thought to be based on hormonal modulators that act through receptor mechanisms in a tissue-specific fashion. Knowledge of such mechanisms is most advanced in the study of hemo-

poietic tissue, where numerous regulatory molecules have been identified and purified (Burgess and Nicola, 1983).

8.2.2 MALIGNANCY AS ABERRANT CELL RENEWAL

Tissues with cell-renewal capacity may undergo expansion either with (metaplasia) or without (hyperplasia) changes in the proportion of differentiated cells. Examples are the cyclical changes in endometrial epithelium in response to hormonal changes during the normal menstrual cycle, and the accumulation of epidermal cells in the benign skin condition known as psoriasis.

The reversibility of the proliferative response in hyperplasia and metaplasia distinguishes such proliferation from neoplastic growth, in which the response is permanent and inherited by subsequent generations of cells. Tumor growth is therefore related to heritable changes in the control of cell proliferation and differentiation. Several features of the tissue of origin may remain, and the rate of cell production may show only a small increase over the rate of cell loss (section 9.6).

Tumors have been described as "caricatures" of normal tissue renewal (Pierce et al, 1978).

8.2.3 MONOCLONAL ORIGIN OF HUMAN TUMORS

Human tumors appear to be monoclonal, suggesting that they arise from a single transformed cell. This concept has gained support from two lines of evidence. First, common clonal markers can be found in all the cells of some types of tumors. An example can be seen in some B-cell tumors. Immunoglobulins and their component heavy or light chains are produced and secreted by malignant plasma cells in multiple myeloma; they are produced also by malignant cells of B-cell lymphomas and are then expressed usually as antigens on the surface of the cell. Extensive studies have shown that the immunoglobulin products of each B-cell tumor are unique, indicating clonal expansion from a single aberrant immunoglobulin-producing cell. Recent studies of rearrangements of the T-cell receptor in human T-cell malignancies provide similar evidence for a single clone of malignant cells (Minden et al, 1985).

The second line of evidence derives from work by Fialkow and his colleagues, who studied isoenzymes of glucose-6-phosphate dehydrogenase (G6PD) in malignant cells of heterozygous black females. The G6PD gene lies on the X chromosome. Since one of the X chromosomes becomes inactivated at random in all cells of females during early life, the normal tissues of heterozygous females contain approximately equal numbers of cells which produce one or the other isoenzyme but not both (Fig 8.2). However, tumors arising in such individuals usually express only a single isoenzyme of G6PD, suggesting that the tumor has arisen from a single cell. Much of the data obtained using this technique relate to hemopoietic tumors in which it is relatively easy to obtain a pure population of tumor cells. For solid tumors the data are somewhat more equivocal due to the difficulty of obtaining tumor tissue in the absence of normal tissue contamination. Nevertheless, a variety of solid tumors have been shown to be monoclonal by this technique (Table 8.1). Potentially, the above method can be adapted to the study of a tumor in any female who is heterozygous for any property determined by the X chromosome. Thus, recent analysis of restriction-fragment-length polymorphisms for an X-linked gene has provided evidence of monoclonality for three human tumors (Vogelstein et al, 1985).

Although the most likely explanation for the above results is that tumors originate in a single cell, they prove only that the tumor cells present at the time of

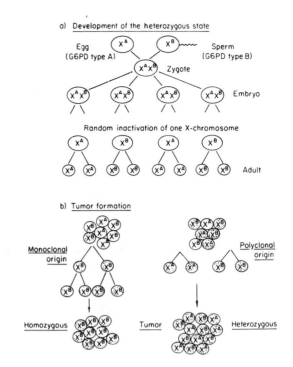

Figure 8.2. The use of X-linked enzymes to study clonality in tumors. *a,* Females have random inactivation of an X chromosome during development, and the cells then breed true. Subjects who are heterozygous for an X-linked enzyme (eg, G6PD) have normal tissues that are heterozygous for production of the isoenzymes. *b,* A tumor originating in a single cell will produce only one isoenzyme, whereas a tumor of multicellular origin will produce both types.

observation had a common antecedent cell; this could occur in a tumor that arose in multiple cells if one of their progeny developed a sufficient growth advantage that its descendants became dominant in the tumor (see section 8.3.1).

8.2.4 EVIDENCE FOR STEM CELLS IN HUMAN TUMORS

Two general theories have been proposed about the original transformed cell that initiates a tumor. First, a carcinogenic event might occur in a differentiated cell of a particular tissue, rendering that cell proliferative, although retaining its ability to organize tissue-specific differentiation. The acquisition of proliferative features in a differentiated cell necessitates the concept of "dedifferentiation" and there is no convincing evidence that this may occur. The alternative theory proposes that tumors arise from carcinogenic events occurring in the stem cells of a particular tissue. The properties of stem cells are such that it is not necessary to assume "dedifferentiation" as a mechanism of tumor induction.

Table 8.1. Evidence for Monoclonal Origin of Human Tumors*

Malignancy	Number Studied**	Evidence for monoclonal origin
Multiple myeloma	Numerous	Synthesize unique immunoglobulin molecule
Chronic lymphogenous leukemia	>160(2)	Unique cell-surface-associated immunoglobulin markers
Burkitt's lymphoma	93(1)	
Other non-Hodgkin lymphomas	>20(3)	Unique idiotypes on tumor cells (two clones of cells were present in 3 patients)
T-cell lymphoma/leukemia	14	Unique rearrangements of T-cell receptor gene
Chronic myelogenous leukemia	12	
Solid tumors		
bladder	1	
nasopharynx	2	Single isoenzyme of G6PD in heterozygous females
thyroid	5	
palate	3	
cervix	15(2)	
melanoma	2	
Acute myelogenous leukemia	1	Unique restriction fragments coding for
leiomyoma	1	X-linked enzymes in heterozygous females
Wilms' tumor	1	

*Includes data reviewed by Fialkow (1974), Sklar et al (1984), Minden et al (1985) and Vogelstein et al (1985).

**Number in parentheses indicates tumors where there is evidence for more than one clone.

Rather, it is proposed that the changes associated with the carcinogenic insult cause a defect in the control of the normal stem-cell functions, self-renewal and differentiation.

The following evidence supports the validity of stem cell mechanisms in the growth of human tumors (Selby et al, 1983).

1. The monoclonal origin of tumors which contain cells from multiple lineages of differentiation (eg, CML) is consistent with the cell of origin being a stem cell.

2. Tissue-specific differentiation is a distinguishing feature of many human tumors, and evidence exists to support the ability of human tumor cells to differentiate in vivo and in vitro (section 8.4.4). In many tumors an inverse relationship has been observed between indices of cell proliferation and differentiation. Sequential studies of animal tumors following thymidine labeling have shown that differentiated cells (which cannot generate a tumor on transplantation) are derived from undifferentiated cells which can generate tumors when transplanted into new hosts (Pierce and Wallace, 1971). This relationship is similar to that which is observed in normal renewing tissues (Fig 8.1).

3. Experience with radiation therapy suggests that in many human tumors only a small proportion of tumor cells have regenerative capacity. These conclusions are based on the knowledge of radiation sensitivity of human cells, and the fact that relatively small doses of radiation can achieve permanent local control of large skin, breast, and cervical tumors (Bush and Hill, 1975). These results would be expected if the proportion of stem cells in such tumors was approximately 1 in 1000, since only stem cells would need to be sterilized to achieve cure.

4. A large degree of heterogeneity has been observed when properties of individual cells have been studied (section 8.3). In some tumors it has been shown that proliferative potential and expression of differentiated phenotypes are restricted to separate subpopulations of cells (Mackillop et al, 1982). Also, studies of cell kinetics (chapter 9) show clearly that tumor cells are not radically different from normal cells with respect to cell-cycle parameters. Rather, the major difference between normal and malignant tissue appears to be the failure of tumor stem cells to respond to the controlling signals that maintain normal homeostasis.

The stem-cell model has major implications for the treatment of human tumors. When the aim of treatment is cure or long-term control, then therapy must be directed toward eradication of stem cells, since only these cells maintain the potential to regenerate the tumor population (Fig 8.3). If stem cells represent a small subpopulation of the total cells in some tumors, as suggested by the results of treatment with radiother-

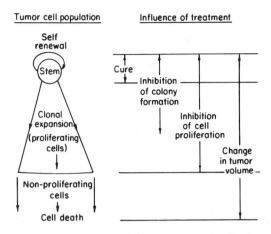

Figure 8.3. The stem-cell model has important implications for cancer treatment. Curative treatment requires eradication of stem cells, whereas changes in cell proliferation or in tumor volume depend respectively on many or all of the cells in the tumor. Assessment of the effects of treatment against stem cells requires the use of a colony-forming assay, but nonstem cells may form colonies of limited size.

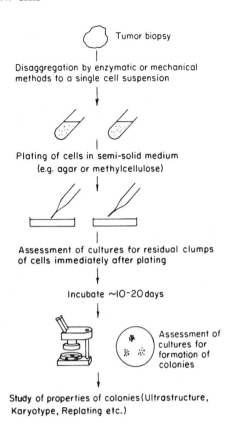

Figure 8.4. Major steps in assays used to assess stem-cell function of human tumors by colony formation in semisolid medium.

apy, then short-term changes in tumor volume may not reflect the effects of treatment on stem cells. Rather, stem-cell effects must be evaluated by placing the cells in an environment where they may express their potential to generate a large number of progeny, that is, a colony-forming assay.

8.2.5 PROPERTIES OF TUMOR STEM CELLS

Unlike animal tumors, where transplantation assays can be used to quantitate cells with high growth potential, more indirect means must be applied to human tumors. One of the most valuable and versatile approaches has been the assessment of colony formation by tumor cells in semisolid medium (Hamburger and Salmon, 1977; Courtenay et al, 1978). Such methods have drawn heavily on experience gained through study of colony-forming normal and malignant stem cells in human bone marrow, and from experimental tumors in animals. Figure 8.4 summarizes the essential features of some of these assays.

Formation of colonies in semisolid medium from stem cells in human bone marrow requires the addition of stimulating factors in the form of conditioned medium (ie, medium that has been exposed previously to leukocytes or other cells), as well as the presence of serum. Although such additional factors are unnecessary for growth of colonies from most solid tumors, there are some reports of improved growth when hormones or growth factors are added to the medium. These data suggest that stem cells in tumors may re-

spond to some types of mitogenic stimuli, and that they may possess receptors for hormones or growth factors which are known to control the proliferation of cells in normal tissues (section 8.4.5). Cloning efficiency of cells from solid tumors has been found to vary widely with culture conditions, but is usually in the range 0.001–1.0%. While these values are consistent with the presence of a small proportion of stem cells in human tumors, colony formation depends critically on the culture environment. Thus estimates of plating efficiency should not be regarded as estimates of the proportion of stem cells that existed in vivo.

Cells from human tumors may be separated into different fractions on the basis of size or density by using centrifugation techniques, prior to cloning in semisolid medium (eg, Mackillop et al, 1982). These studies have shown enrichment of clonogenic cells in some fractions. The cells within these different fractions were studied for various properties including markers of differentiation, receptors for hormones or growth factors, or proliferative rate as measured by susceptibility to high-specific-activity tritiated thymidine (see section 9.3.5). The results suggested a rapid rate of proliferation of colony-forming cells in several human tumors, and indicated that overt markers of differentiation tend to be associated with cells that do not form colonies.

The study of properties of clonogenic cells in tissue culture suffers from the selection of clonogenic cells in human tumors, whose properties allow a high probability of growth in culture. Despite this limitation, improvements in culture methods and the continued study of stem-cell properties is likely to lead to an improved understanding of the biological properties of human tumors.

8.2.6 ENVIRONMENTAL EFFECTS

Studies of teratocarcinomas which may be induced in the mouse have provided important information about the relationship between malignancy, stem-cell concepts, and differentiation. These embryonal cell tumors were induced by the implantation of mouse neural crest embryo cells into the testes, demonstrating that these normal cells with high proliferative potential may become malignant under the influence of an abnormal environment (Stevens, 1967). The teratocarcinomas have the potential for multiple pathways of cellular differentiation. Similar properties can also be observed in spontaneous human testicular tumors, which may differentiate in different regions to form apparently mature cells such as cartilage or muscle. Detailed studies by Pierce and his collaborators (1978) have established that transplantability of the murine teratocarcinoma is a function of primitive stem cells, whereas a variety of differentiated cells are unable to generate tumors on transplantation. On the basis of this model, he proposed a central role for abnormalities in stem-cell differentiation in human cancer.

Other experiments with teratocarcinoma cells have had an important impact in the field of carcinogenesis. When teratocarcinoma cells were incorporated into a very early embryo (blastocyst), intriguing and unexpected results were obtained (Brinster, 1975; Mintz and Fleischman, 1981). When grown to maturity, the blastocyst was sometimes found to produce a normal mouse, and the tissues of these mice had recognizable genetic markers which showed that they were derived both from teratocarcinoma cells and from the normal blastocyst (Fig 8.5). Some of the tumor cells retained full potential for normal differentiation even after multiple transplantation between animals as a tumor cell line.

The murine teratocarcinoma model demonstrates that one particular type of stem cell may express either normal proliferation and differentiation, or may produce a malignant clone depending upon its environment. The model emphasizes the close relationship

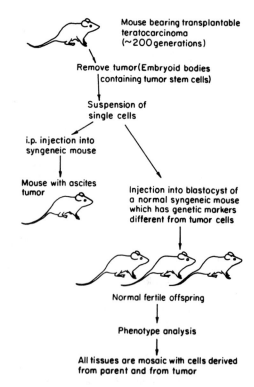

Figure 8.5. Schematic illustration of experiments performed by Mintz and others (eg, Mintz and Fleischman, 1981). These experiments demonstrate that stem cells of a transplantable murine teratocarcinoma could contribute to the development of a phenotypically normal but mosaic mouse when injected into the blastocyst. Genetically determined markers used to demonstrate mosaicism in adult tissues have included coat color, isoenzymes of glucose phosphate isomerase, immunoglobulins, hemoglobin, liver proteins and melanin.

between properties of normal and malignant stem cells. However, it differs from many other types of malignancy where there is strong evidence for genetic mutation; this evidence has been reviewed in chapter 3. In contrast, the high incidence of tumors in some strains of mice when embryo cells are implanted to the testis, and the retained potential of some teratocarcinoma cells to generate normal tissues when implanted into the blastocyst, is evidence against mutation as a cause of malignancy in this model. Environmental influences on the expression of genes appear sufficient to produce malignancy in these primitive embryonic cells.

8.3 TUMOR PROGRESSION AND HETEROGENEITY

8.3.1 TUMOR PROGRESSION

Many tumors show a tendency to increasing malignancy with time. Evidence for this tumor progression comes from a number of observations as follows:

1. In some tumors there is an orderly progression from benign tissue to noninvasive but premalignant lesions (eg, carcinoma in situ of the cervix) to frank malignancy.
2. There is a trend to increasing anaplasia and increasing chromosomal aberrations in human tumors that are studied at different phases of their life history.
3. Transplantation of spontaneous tumors into animals usually leads to an increase in growth rate and decreased differentiation in successive passages (Steel et al, 1966; Fig 8.6). It is unusual, however, to record increases in the rate of tumor growth of a human tumor in situ, perhaps because failing nutrition and increasing cell death (section 9.2) tend to counter the effects of increasing malignancy.

Nowell (1976) has provided a model for tumor progression (Fig 8.7). He suggests that tumor cells tend to be genetically unstable, and therefore subject to a high rate of random mutation during clonal expansion from a single cell of origin. Many mutations will be lethal, or will place the cell at a disadvantage with respect to its neighbors, and these subclones will disappear from the tumor population. A few of the mutations may convey greater autonomy and a selective growth advantage; these more malignant subclones will tend to become dominant in the population, leading to tumor progression.

8.3.2 HETEROGENEITY

As predicted by the Nowell model, cells within human and animal tumors demonstrate considerable heterogeneity in their properties (Heppner, 1984). This heterogeneity extends to almost any property that can be assessed and includes morphology, cell proliferation, karyotype, surface markers, biochemical products, metastatic behavior and sensitivity to therapeutic agents. At least three mechanisms contribute to the generation of this diversity as a tumor clone expands from a single cell to the time of its clinical detection: differentiation-related heterogeneity within a clone, nutritional heterogeneity, and the generation of new subclones during tumor progression.

Heterogeneity within a clone has been described in section 8.2.5. Its major manifestation is the expression of different cellular properties that are related to differentiation within the hierarchy produced by clonal expansion from a stem cell.

Nutritional heterogeneity occurs because of limited proliferation of the vascular tree in growing tumors, and its most obvious manifestation is cell death and necrosis (Tannock, 1970). Large gradients in the concentration of oxygen, glucose and many other metab-

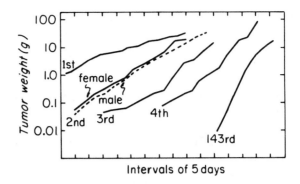

Figure 8.6. Growth curves for a rat mammary tumor obtained for its first, second, third, fourth and 143rd transplants. Note the increase in growth rate during successive transplantation. (Adapted from Steel et al, 1966.)

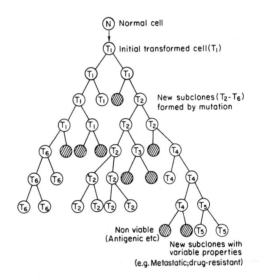

Figure 8.7. Schematic illustration showing the clonal evolution of tumors. New subclones may arise by mutation. Many of these may become extinct (indicated by shading) but others may have a growth advantage and become dominant. All of the subclones (indicated by T_2-T_6) may share common clonal markers, but many of them have new properties leading to heterogeneity. (Adapted from Nowell, 1976.)

olites exist in the environment of living cells situated at different distances from tumor blood vessels, and these gradients are likely to have a profound influence on cellular properties including metabolism, proliferative rate and response to treatment. A well-characterized example is the resistance of hypoxic cells in tumors to radiation treatment.

The development of subclones with differing properties is thought to be the major mechanism underlying tumor progression, and is illustrated in Figure 8.7. Two sources of evidence support the existence of clonal heterogeneity. First, when single human tumors are propagated in tissue culture, it is often possible to subclone the resultant cell line to derive genetically distinct homogeneous populations. These are thought to represent subclones present in the initial tumor, and frequently have diverse properties (eg, Shapiro et al, 1981). A second line of evidence derives from studies of the karyotype of biopsied human tumors. Many studies have described karyotypic diversity between individual cells of a tumor, but in many cases, a common stem line abnormality is present. The additional chromosomal abnormalities are thought to be due to clonal progression.

8.4 MALIGNANT CELLS IN TISSUE CULTURE

Although the concepts of monclonality, tumor stem cells and cellular heterogeneity have derived largely through observation of tumors growing in vivo, an understanding of the molecular mechanisms underlying the abnormal growth of tumor cells depends on the availability of versatile laboratory models of the process. For this reason, tissue-culture procedures have assumed a role of central importance and spawned the development of a new technology.

8.4.1 PROPAGATION OF CELLS IN TISSUE CULTURE

Over the last two decades conditions have been developed to perform cell culture routinely for a variety of normal and malignant cell types. Trial and error have indicated that a number of variables are important in the establishment of cultures; these include an appropriate substratum (which may necessitate a layer of "feeder cells" or cell membranes), a basic medium providing appropriate pH and nutrients, and a source of physiological factors necessary for growth derived from sources such as fetal calf serum.

Cell cultures are usually initiated by placing small pieces of tissue in a dish containing medium, followed by subculture of cells that spread out from the tissue piece. Once the culture is established, it is usually cloned to isolate a single cell type (Fig 8.8) and a cell line is obtained. Most cells that may be propagated in culture remain attached to the plastic or glass of the vessel, or to the layer of "feeder cells." Cell lines obtained in this way from tumors may often be propagated indefinitely, but cultures of normal fibroblasts tend to stop growing after about 30 generations if derived from mice, or after about 50 generations if derived from man. Some fibroblast lines may pass through this crisis period and produce permanent cell

lines which grow rapidly; such lines are immortal but do not usually lead to tumors when implanted into mice.

Culture of normal epithelium is much more difficult than normal fibroblasts, but considerable success has been achieved in the last few years, particularly with normal breast and tracheal epithelium and with epidermis (Murakami et al, 1985). Generation of continuous cell lines from carcinomas (ie, tumors of epithelial tissue) is now commonplace, and many cell lines exist which are representative of most histological types of carcinoma.

Normal hemopoietic tissue is not easily adapted to long-term tissue culture, but some success has been achieved in maintaining myelopoiesis for extended periods through the use of bone-marrow-derived feeder cell layers (see Wright and Greenberger, 1984). Hemopoietic tumors do generate cell lines with fairly high frequency; in contrast to fibroblastic and most epithelial cells, hemopoietic cell lines tend to grow in suspension, presumably reflecting the dispersed nature of their in vivo state.

8.4.2 PROPERTIES OF TRANSFORMED CELLS

Normal fibroblasts and epithelial cells in tissue culture can be treated with carcinogens to create cell lines that will form fibrosarcomas or carcinomas when inoculated into an appropriate animal. Such a process is

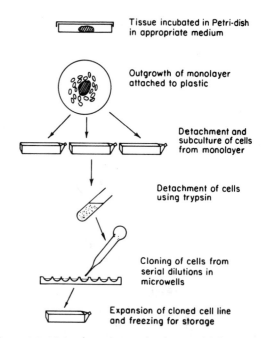

Tissue incubated in Petri-dish in appropriate medium

Outgrowth of monolayer attached to plastic

Detachment and subculture of cells from monolayer

Detachment of cells using trypsin

Cloning of cells from serial dilutions in microwells

Expansion of cloned cell line and freezing for storage

Figure 8.8. Major features involved in establishing cell lines in tissue culture. Indicated procedure is appropriate for fibroblasts and many types of transplantable tumor.

termed malignant transformation. Various agents have been used to transform rodent fibroblasts, including carcinogenic chemicals, ultraviolet light, X-rays, DNA or RNA viruses, and DNA from tumor cells.

A major characteristic of normal fibroblasts in culture is density-dependent inhibition of growth; once a group of cells grow to completely cover the dish or layer of feeder cells, so that all cells are in contact, cell division ceases. By contrast, transformed fibroblasts continue to grow after confluence has been reached, and the cells pile up and may be seen as dense colonies or foci. This property allows an assay for detection of low-frequency transformation by quantitation of foci on a monolayer of normal fibroblasts.

Another property associated with transformation of fibroblasts is the loss of requirement for attachment to the substratum (anchorage independence). This is seen as an ability of transformed, but not normal, fibroblasts to grow in suspension or in a semisolid medium such as agar or methylcellulose. Anchorage independence may be a transformation-related property only for fibroblasts; normal hemopoietic progenitor cells have the ability to form colonies in agar.

A number of other features have been noted in comparisons of normal and transformed fibroblasts (Table 8.2). In general, transformed fibroblasts require less serum than normal cells as an additive for optimal growth. This property may imply greater autonomy and a reduced requirement for growth factors. Transformed cells also show morphological changes causing cells to be rounder, with increased refractility and random orientation. Lack of organization of actin microfilaments in the cytoplasm may underlie the morphological changes seen in transformed cells. The secretion of plasminogen activator is a common but not universal feature of transformed cells; this proteolytic system allows lysis of fibrin and may be important for the development of invasive properties. Transformed cells also have subtle differences in their cell cycles as compared to normal fibroblasts. Many normal fibroblasts in culture may remain viable while arrested in a pre-DNA synthetic state commonly referred to as G_0 phase, but can be stimulated by serum and other factors to pass through the cell cycle. In contrast, transformed cells tend to die rapidly if their proliferation is inhibited by density or by lack of nutrients and are less responsive to the mechanisms which regulate passage through the cell cycle.

It has been a common research goal to determine which (if any) of the above properties of transformed cells correlates with tumor formation in a syngeneic host. Although no unique property in culture correlates with tumor formation, for fibroblast cells there is a strong association with the ability to generate colonies in soft agar (eg, Barrett et al, 1979). Other properties of transformed cells such as growth to a high population density and low dependence on serum seem to be related; thus density-dependent inhibition of growth can be overcome by increasing the content of serum in the medium. Malignant transformation probably represents a multistep process involving, in sequence, loss of a high requirement for serum, altered morphology, decreased anchorage dependence and ability to form tumors in an appropriate animal.

8.4.3 HYBRIDIZATION OF NORMAL AND MALIGNANT CELLS

Attempts have been made to identify genes associated with malignant transformation by studying somatic

Table 8.2. A Comparison of the Properties of Normal and Transformed Fibroblasts

Normal Fibroblasts	Transformed Fibroblasts
Will not form tumors in mice	Form tumors when implanted into syngeneic or immune-deprived mice
Grow attached to plastic or glass (anchorage dependent)	Grow in suspension or in semisolid media such as agar
Growth is inhibited by contact with other cells (contact inhibition)	Loss of contact inhibition allows piling up into colonies or foci
Require serum containing hormones and growth factors	Require less serum for growth
Remain viable if growth is arrested by lack of serum	Cells die if inhibited from growing
Contain well-organized actin filaments	Show disorganization of actin filaments
Do not cause fibrinolysis	May cause fibrinolysis through secretion of plasminogen activator

cell hybrids between normal and transformed cells. It is possible to fuse cells to form viable hybrid cells which contain both sets of chromosomes. Hybrid cells can be selected and studied if each fusion partner carries a different mutation that prevents their growth in a specific selective medium; the hybrid cells will grow in such a medium because recessive mutations are not expressed due to the presence of the dominant gene on the complementary chromosome from the other fusion partner (Fig 8.9). Many hybrid cells show random loss of chromosomes during passage in culture. Thus, if one fusion partner is a malignant cell and the other a normal cell, the study of hybrid cells can provide information about the relationship between their chromosome content, their in vitro properties, and the ability of such cells to form tumors when injected into animals.

Hybrid cells formed from the fusion of a malignant and a normal cell do not usually form tumors when implanted into an appropriate animal, suggesting that the malignant phenotype is recessive. An example is provided by the work of Stanbridge et al (1982), who generated hybrids between human fibroblasts and HeLa cells, a long-established human tumor cell line. These hybrid cells have a morphology intermediate between that of the epithelial HeLa cell and the normal fibroblast, and have many of the properties shared by transformed cells, such as a low requirement for serum, loss of contact inhibition, and ability to grow in soft agar. However, the hybrid cells did not form tumors in immune-suppressed mice. Hybrid cells maintained for long periods in culture lost some of their chromosomes, and some of them developed the ability to form tumors in mice. In principle, the study of these and similar hybrid cells might allow the association of tumor-forming properties with the presence or absence of specific chromosomes (see section A3.4.4), but this has varied among cell lines used as fusion partners. Also, the above experiments are open to the interpretation that a chromosome whose loss is associated with tumor formation in immune-suppressed mice contains a gene which expresses a powerful antigen sufficient to cause rejection of the xenograft, rather than a gene which might have suppressed malignant properties.

8.4.4 DIFFERENTIATION IN CULTURE

An intriguing link to the stem-cell concepts discussed in section 8.2 derives from the finding that some malignant cell lines can be rendered nonmalignant by agents which promote cell differentiation in tissue culture. Examples include the Friend erythroleukemia cell line derived from a virally induced leukemia in mice, and

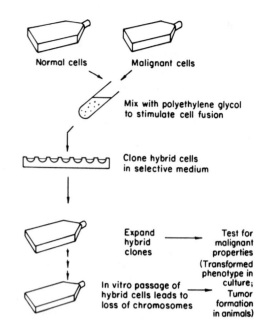

Figure 8.9. Schematic illustration of the use of hybrid cells to study malignant properties. Parent cells usually have different mutations (eg, TK-, HGPRT-) which prevent their growth in selective medium containing hypoxanthine, aminopterin and thymidine (HAT medium). Hybrids are not usually tumorigenic, but may become tumorigenic if they lose chromosomes during serial passage in culture.

teratocarcinoma cell lines described in section 8.2.6 (Mintz and Fleischman, 1981). These cultured cells can be induced to undergo terminal differentiation by the action of a variety of physiological and nonphysiological agents. Thus Friend cells may differentiate in culture to form hemoglobin-synthesizing cells, while teratocarcinoma cells may form several types of differentiated cells depending on the stimulus. Among the most potent compounds which stimulate differentiation are solvents such as dimethyl sulfoxide which are thought to act at the membrane level, possibly to alter the affinity of receptors for a regulatory molecule.

A number of cell lines derived from human malignancies have also been induced to differentiate in culture (Bloch, 1984). Common features are induction of the gene expression which would have been expected in a normal differentiated cell of the same lineage, and loss of the ability to generate tumors in immune-deficient mice. These results suggest that tumor cell lines may be viewed as selected populations of transformed stem cells which retain the potential for tissue-specific cell differentiation when given an appropriate stimulus. In principle, this is similar to the environmental control placed on the expression of malignant properties by teratocarcinoma stem cells in vivo (see section 8.2.6).

8.4.5 GROWTH FACTORS

Control of cell growth and differentiation in vivo seems to involve the production of growth factors which may stimulate proliferation of target cells. For example, the availability of tissue-culture assays has allowed the identification of a number of growth factors which stimulate proliferation of primitive myeloid cells, and these factors are probably involved in the control of hemopoiesis in vivo. Another well-characterized example is epidermal growth factor (EGF), which stimulates proliferation of a variety of cells in vivo, and in tissue culture.

Growth of cells in culture usually depends on the addition of serum to provide growth factors. Study of cell growth in defined medium in the absence of serum has indicated requirements for specific growth factors for a number of cell types. Commonly required growth factors include somatomedin C, transferrin, insulin, EGF and fibroblast growth factor. Transformed cells generally grow well in media containing less serum than that needed by nontransformed cells, and transformation of fibroblasts has been associated with a diminished requirement for EGF. These and similar results have suggested that the lack of growth regulation displayed by transformed cells might be mechanistically related to events occurring as a result of the interaction of growth factors with cellular targets.

The essential features of the interaction of growth factors with target cells are illustrated in Figure 8.10a;

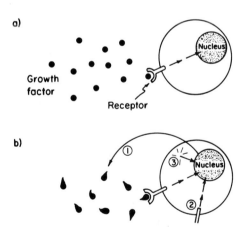

Figure 8.10. *a,* Schematic illustration of the action of growth factors to stimulate cell proliferation in normal cells. *b,* Possible perturbances in growth-factor-related pathways which might lead to malignant transformation: (1) production of transforming growth factors and autostimulation, (2) production of factors which simulate activation of the receptor, (3) constitutive activation of the intracellular regulatory mechanism. (Adapted from Heldin and Westermark, 1984.)

they involve the growth factor itself, a receptor in the membrane of the target cell, and a "second messenger" to transmit the signal from the receptor to the site of gene expression in the nucleus. Recent evidence has suggested that each of these three elements might be involved in the process of malignant transformation (Fig 8.10b). One example was provided by an investigation of the reduced EGF requirement of transformed fibroblasts in culture. Cells transformed by the Moloney murine sarcoma virus were found to produce growth factors (transforming growth factors [TGF], originally called sarcoma growth factor) which bound to EGF receptors, thereby causing a reduction in the requirement for EGF (Todaro and DeLarco, 1978). TGF and EGF have been purified; TGF has at least two protein components, known as TGF-α and TGF-β. TGF-α is homologous to EGF and binds to its receptor.

The production of factors by transformed cells which act to stimulate their own growth may represent a general mechanism in transformation, since subsequent investigations have shown that transforming growth factors are produced by a variety of malignant cells (Sporn and Roberts, 1985).

A second link between growth factors and malignancy was provided by the demonstration that platelet-derived growth factor (PDGF), which is involved in wound healing, has close homology to the transforming protein p28$_{sis}$ of simian sarcoma virus (the product of the sis oncogene; Waterfield et al, 1983). The implication from this structural homology is that the viral gene product functions as a PDGF agonist to stimulate cell replication. Homology of amino acid sequence has also been demonstrated between the transforming gene product of the avian erythroblastosis virus (the erb-B oncogene) and the intracellular part of the EGF receptor protein (Downward et al, 1984). This component of the receptor has protein kinase activity, and under normal circumstances, binding of EGF to its receptor is required for activation of the tyrosine kinase and subsequent mitogenic events. Several other oncogenes appear to encode enzymes which phosphorylate tyrosine residues in proteins (section 5.4). The implication of this relationship is that the viral gene can cause transformation by a constitutive activation (ie, in the absence of EGF) of a protein kinase activity. A high proportion of some types of human tumors (eg, breast, bladder and primary brain tumors) have abnormalities in expression of the EGF receptor gene, and this may represent a mechanism for altered growth control among these malignant cell populations. Table 8.3 lists those growth factors/receptors which have been linked to the process of malignant transformation.

The third component of the growth control system

Table 8.3. Growth Factors/Receptors Associated with Malignant Transformation*

Growth Factor	Relationship to Transformation
Epidermal growth factor (EGF)	1. The intracellular portion of the EGF receptor has homology with the product of v-erb-B oncogene from avian erythroblastosis virus 2. A high proportion of human tumors of particular types have abnormalities of the EGFR. These include glioblastomas, squamous carcinomas and breast carcinomas
Platelet-derived growth factor (PDGF and PDGF-like peptides)	1. The PDGF β-chain molecule has structural homology to the product of v-sis oncogene of simian sarcoma virus 2. A number of tumors produce PDGF-like molecules which are thought to act as autostimulators
Transforming growth factor (TGF-α)	1. Structurally related to EGF and can compete with EGF as an agonist for the EGFR 2. Produced by many tumors and acts as an autostimulator through interaction with the EGF receptor
(TGF-β)	Produced by many tumors and can act synergistically with TGF-α to promote growth
Macrophage colony-stimulating factor (CSF-1)	CSF-1 receptor shows homology to product of the c-fms proto-oncogene
Bombesin and Bombesin-like peptides	Can function as autocrine growth factors in human small-cell lung cancer.

*For further information see Heldin and Westermark (1984), Cuttitta et al (1985), and Sherr et al (1985).

(the intracellular messengers) is less well understood, although the phosphoinositide pathway (section 11.4.5) appears to be involved in transmission of signals induced by EGF and other growth factors. Recent data indicate that protein products of oncogenes (eg, c-myc and other oncogene-encoded nuclear-located proteins) are produced in response to exposure of cells to growth factors (Kelly et al, 1983). Genetically determined overproduction of these proteins might therefore lead to loss of growth control. Amplification and overexpression of the c-myc oncogene have been described in many hemopoietic tumors, and in aggressive variants of small-cell carcinoma of the lung (Little et al, 1983).

Research into properties of growth factors and their relationship with transformation and malignant properties is proceeding rapidly; such studies promise to provide a link between malignancy and mechanisms which control the growth of normal cells. Growth-factor independence and autonomous growth of transformed cells might be due to constitutive expression of any of the elements which normally control cell growth: the growth factor itself, its membrane receptor, or the intracellular signal system which leads ultimately to initiation of DNA synthesis and cell division (Fig 8.10; Heldin and Westermark, 1984).

8.5 SUMMARY

Tumors retain many characteristics of normal renewing-cell populations. Most tumors appear to arise from a single transformed cell, and to retain a limited population of stem cells which can regenerate the tumor. Other cells within the tumor may have more limited proliferative potential and may show features of differentiation. Tumor stem cells are the important targets of cancer treatment; one method of studying such cells is by a colony-forming assay, which allows them to express their proliferative potential.

Tumor cells have a high rate of mutation, and the selection of mutant subclones with a growth advantage may lead to the progression of tumors to more malignant properties. Mutation may also lead to heterogeneity of properties among the subclones, but variable properties of tumor cells may also arise through differentiation within a clone, or because of variation in the nutrient environment of tumor cells.

Normal cells (especially fibroblasts) and malignant cells may be propagated in culture. Chemical carcinogens, radiation, viruses, and DNA from tumor cells may cause malignant transformation in vitro. Features of transformed cells include loss of contact inhibition, leading to the piling up of cells in transformed foci; loss of dependence on attachment to a substrate and growth in agar; and the ability to produce tumors when injected into animals. Cells from some types of tumors (eg, teratocarcinoma) may be induced to differentiate in vivo and/or in vitro and may then lose their malignant properties.

Growth of cells in tissue culture depends on the presence of growth factors. Recent experiments have linked the properties of growth factors with those of onco-genes, and suggest a relationship between malignancy and the loss of mechanisms which control cell prolifer-ation in normal tissues.

REFERENCES

Barrett JC, Crawford BD, Mixter LO et al: Correlation of in vitro growth properties and tumorigenicity of Syrian hamster cell lines. *Cancer Res* 1979; 39:1504–1510.

Bloch A: Induced cell differentiation in cancer therapy. *Cancer Treat Rep* 1984; 68:199–205.

Brinster RL: Can teratocarcinoma cells colonize the mouse embryo?, in Sherman MI, Solter D (eds): *Teratomas and Differentiation*. New York, Academic Press, 1975, pp 51–58.

Burgess AW, Nicola NA: *Growth Factors and Stem Cells*. Academic Press, New York, 1983.

Bush RS, Hill RP: Biologic discussion augmenting radiation effects and model systems. *Laryngoscope* 1975; 85:1119–1133.

Courtenay VD, Selby PJ, Smith IE et al: Growth of human tumour cell colonies from biopsies using two soft-agar techniques. *Br J Cancer* 1978; 38:77–81.

Cuttitta F, Carney DN, Mulshine J et al: Bombesin-like peptides can function as autocrine growth factors in human small cell lung cancer. *Nature* 1985; 316:823–826.

Downward J, Yarden Y, Mayes E et al: Close similarity of epidermal growth factor receptor and v-erb-B oncogene protein sequences. *Nature* 1984; 307:521–527.

Fialkow PJ: The origin and development of human tumors studied with cell markers. *N Engl J Med* 1974; 291:26–35.

Hamburger AW, Salmon SE: Primary bioassay of human tumor stem cells. *Science* 1977; 197:461–463.

Heldin CH, Westermark B: Growth factors: Mechanism of action and relation to oncogenes. *Cell* 1984; 37:9–20.

Heppner GH: Tumor heterogeneity. *Cancer Res* 1984; 44:2259–2265.

Kelly K, Cochran BH, Stiles CD, Leder P: Cell-specific regulation of the c-myc gene by lymphocyte mitogens and platelet-derived growth factor. *Cell* 1983; 35:603–610.

Little CD, Nau MM, Carney DN, Gazdar AF, Minna JD: Amplification and expression of the c-myc oncogene in human lung cancer cell lines. *Nature* 1983; 306:194–196.

Mackillop WJ, Stewart SS, Buick RN: Density/volume analysis in the study of cellular heterogeneity in human ovarian carcinoma. *Br J Cancer* 1982; 45:812–820.

Minden MD, Toyonaga B, Ha K et al: Somatic rearrangement of T-cell antigen receptor gene in human T-cell malignancies. *Proc Natl Acad Sci USA* 1985; 82:1224–1227.

Mintz B, Fleischman RA: Teratocarcinomas and other neoplasms as developmental defects in gene expression. *Adv Cancer Res* 1981; 34:211–278.

Murakami H, Yamane I, Barnes DW et al (eds): *Growth and Differentiation of Cells in Defined Environment*. New York, Springer-Verlag, 1985.

Nowell PC: The clonal evolution of tumor cell populations. *Science* 1976; 194:23–28.

Pierce GB, Shikes R, Fink LM: *Cancer: A Problem of Developmental Biology*. Prentice-Hall, Englewood Cliffs, NJ, 1978.

Pierce GB, Wallace C: Differentiation of malignant to benign cells. *Cancer Res* 1971; 31:127–134.

Selby P, Buick RN, Tannock I: A critical appraisal of the "Human Tumor Stem-cell Assay." *N Engl J Med* 1983; 308:129–134.

Shapiro JR, Yung W-Ka, Shapiro WR: Isolation, karyotype and clonal growth of heterogeneous subpopulations of human malignant gliomas. *Cancer Res* 1981; 41:2349–2359.

Sherr CJ, Rettenmier CW, Sacca R et al: The c-fms proto-oncogene product is related to the receptor for the mononuclear phagocyte growth factor, CSF-1. *Cell* 1985; 41:665–676.

Sklar J, Cleary ML, Thieemans K et al: Biclonal B-cell lymphoma. *N Engl J Med* 1984; 311:20–27.

Sporn MB, Roberts AB: Autocrine growth factors and cancer. *Nature* 1985; 313:745–747.

Stanbridge EJ, Der CJ, Doersen C-J et al: Human cell hybrids: analysis of transformation and tumorigenicity. *Science* 1982; 215:252–259.

Steel GG, Adams K, Barrett JC: Analysis of the cell population kinetics of transplanted tumours of widely-differing growth rate. *Br J Cancer* 1966; 20:784–800.

Stevens LC: Origin of testicular teratomas from primordial germ cells in mice. *J Nat Cancer Inst* 1967; 38:549–552.

Tannock IF: Population kinetics of carcinoma cells, capillary endothelial cells, and fibroblasts in a transplanted mouse mammary tumor. *Cancer Res* 1970; 30:2470–2476.

Todaro GJ, DeLarco JE: Growth factors produced by sarcoma virus-transformed cells. *Cancer Res* 1978; 38:4147–4154.

Vogelstein B, Fearon ER, Hamilton SR, Feinberg AP: Use of restriction fragment length polymorphisms to determine the clonal origin of human tumors. *Science* 1985; 227:642–645.

Waterfield MD, Scrace GT, Whittle N et al: Platelet-derived growth factor is structurally related to the putative transforming protein $p28_{sis}$ of simian sarcoma virus. *Nature* 1983; 304:35–39.

Wright DG, Greenberger JS: *Long-term Bone Marrow Culture*. Alan R. Liss, New York, 1984.

9

Tumor Growth and Cell Kinetics

Ian F. Tannock

9.1 INTRODUCTION

Tumors grow because they contain a population of cells which is expanding as a result of cell division. They differ from normal tissues because the population of tumor cells fails to respond effectively to the homeostatic control mechanisms which maintain the appropriate number of cells in normal renewal tissues. Development of tritiated thymidine and autoradiography in the 1950s, and the more recent application of flow cytometry, have allowed a detailed analysis of tumor growth in terms of the kinetics of proliferation of their constituent cells. Proliferative rate varies widely among tumors; nonproliferating cells are common, and there is often a high rate of cell death. The proportion of tumor cells that retains the ability to regenerate the tumor (ie, the "stem cells") may be quite low. Several normal tissues, including bone marrow and intestine, contain cells with a high rate of cell proliferation, and damage to these cells may be dose limiting for chemotherapy. Concepts related to the cell cycle and the molecular events which occur during its constituent phases are therefore not only of biological interest, but are key to

understanding the interaction of drugs and radiation with tissues.

9.2 TUMOR GROWTH

9.2.1 THE CONCEPT OF EXPONENTIAL GROWTH

Tumor growth can be determined by measuring tumor volume as a function of time. Most commonly this is done by making caliper measurements of at least two orthogonal diameters, and by assuming that the tumor is ellipsoid in shape. If tumor volume (V) is then plotted against time (t) the resulting growth curve usually approximates an exponential relationship, at least during part of its growth (Fig 9.1a). It is usual to plot tumor growth curves using a logarithmic axis for volume and a linear axis for time, since the exponential relationship is then represented as a straight line (Fig 9.1b).

Exponential growth of tumors will occur if the rates of cell production and of cell loss or death are proportional to the number of cells present in the population

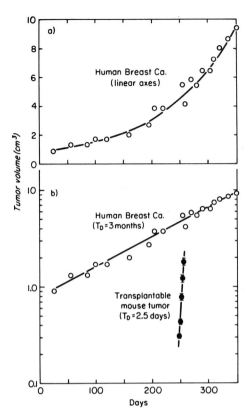

Figure 9.1. Growth curves for a lung metastasis from a human breast cancer: *a*, plotted on linear axes; *b*, same data plotted using a logarithmic scale for tumor volume. A growth curve for a rapidly growing transplantable tumor in the mouse is included in *b* for comparison. T_D = volume doubling time.

Table 9.1. Volume Doubling Time (T_D) for Representative Human Tumors

Tumor Type	Number of Tumors	Volume Doubling Time (weeks); geometric mean value
Primary lung cancer		
adenocarcinoma	64	21
squamous-cell carcinoma	85	12
anaplastic carcinoma	55	11
Breast cancer		
primary	17	14
lung metastases	44	11
soft-tissue metastases	66	3
Colorectal cancer		
primary	19	90
lung metastases	56	14
Lymphoma		
lymph node lesions	27	4
Lung metastases of:		
carcinoma of testis	80	4
childhood tumors	47	4
adult sarcomas	58	7

Note: from data reviewed by Steel (1977).

(N). The differential equation that describes tumor growth is then given by

$$\frac{dN}{dt} = (K_P - K_L)N. \qquad (9.1)$$

Here K_P and K_L are the rate constants for cell production and cell loss. Equation (9.1) can then be integrated to give

$$N = N_0 \exp[(K_P - K_L)t], \qquad (9.2)$$

where N_0 is the number of cells in the population at the initial time of observation ($t = 0$). Tumor volume (V) will also be related exponentially to time, since cell number is the principal determinant of tumor volume. Exponential growth implies that the time taken for a tumor to double its volume is constant. The volume doubling time (T_D) can be obtained by setting $N = 2N_0$ at $t = T_D$ in eq (9.2). Thus

$$T_D = \frac{\log_e 2}{(K_P - K_L)} = \frac{0.693}{(K_P - K_L)}, \qquad (9.3)$$

and the equation describing growth of the tumor may then be written

$$V = V_0 \exp(0.693t/T_D). \qquad (9.4)$$

Here V_0 is the tumor volume at time $t = 0$. During the period of exponential growth, doubling times for transplanted murine tumors are typically 1–5 days, while most human tumors grow more slowly with doubling times in the range of 1–3 months (Table 9.1).

Exponential growth often leads to the false impression that the rate of tumor growth is accelerating with time (see Fig 9.1). Increase in the size of a human tumor from a diameter of 0.5 to 1.0 cm may escape detection, whereas increase in diameter of a tumor from 5 to 10 cm is more dramatic and is likely to cause new clinical symptoms. Both require three volume doublings, and during exponential growth they will occur over the same period of time.

9.2.2 THE GROWTH OF HUMAN TUMORS

Estimates of the growth rates of untreated human tumors have been limited by the following constraints:

1. Only tumors that tend to be unresponsive to therapy can ethically be followed without treatment, although some data are available from older studies

on the growth of tumors such as lymphoma, which are now treated aggressively with drugs.

2. Accurate measurements can only be made on tumors growing in a few sites. For this reason, the majority of studies have examined lung metastases using serial X-rays. Measurements of primary tumors in tissues other than the lung have been rare, and are probably subject to substantial errors of measurement.

3. The period of observation is restricted to that between the time of detection of the tumor and either death of the host or the initiation of some form of therapy; this time interval is only a small fraction of the history of the tumor's growth.

Despite the limitations stated above, there is a large number of published estimates of the growth rate of human tumors. Many of these studies have utilized only two or three sequential measurements, so that they do not provide information about the shape of the tumor growth curve. Steel (1977) has reviewed published measurements of the rate of growth of 780 human tumors, and estimates of volume doubling time for several types of tumor are summarized in Table 9.1. A few general conclusions may be stated:

1. There is wide variation in growth rate, even among tumors of the same histological type and site of origin.

2. Representative mean doubling times for lung metastases of common tumors in man are in the range of 2–3 months.

3. There is a tendency for childhood tumors, and adult tumors that are responsive to chemotherapy (eg,

lymphoma, Ca testis), to grow more rapidly than unresponsive tumors (eg, Ca colon).

4. Adenocarcinomas tend to grow more slowly than squamous-cell carcinomas and sarcomas.

5. From the limited data available, metastases of breast and colorectal tumors tend to grow more rapidly than the primary tumor in the same patient.

9.2.3 THE LONG PRECLINICAL HISTORY OF TUMORS: DEPARTURES FROM EXPONENTIAL GROWTH

Superficial tumors may be detected clinically when they contain about 1 billion (10^9) cells; tumors of internal organs are likely to escape detection until they are considerably larger (Fig 9.2). There is indirect evidence that many tumors arise from a single cell (see section 8.2.3) and a superficial tumor of 1 g (containing about 10^9 cells) will have undergone about 30 doublings in volume prior to clinical detection. After ten further doublings in volume the tumor would weigh about 1 kg ($\sim 10^{12}$ cells), a size that may be lethal to the host. Thus the range of size over which the growth of a tumor may be studied represents a rather short and late part of its total growth history (Figs 9.2 and 9.3). The long preclinical history of the tumor may allow cells to metastasize prior to detection so that "early" clinical detection (Fig 9.2) may be expected to reduce, but not to prevent, the subsequent appearance of metastases.

The growth rate of a tumor in its preclinical phase can only be estimated indirectly. In experimental animals implantation of known numbers of tumor cells and

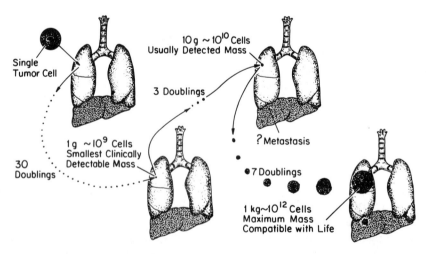

Figure 9.2. A human solid tumor must undergo about 30–33 doublings in volume from a single cell before it achieves a detectable size of 1–10 g. Metastases may have been established prior to detection of the primary tumor. Only a few further doublings of volume lead to a tumor whose size is incompatible with life. (Adapted from Tannock, 1983.)

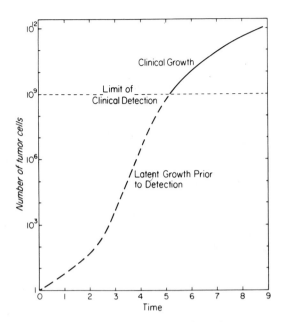

Figure 9.3. Hypothetical growth curve for a human tumor, showing the long latent period prior to detection. Tumors may show an early lag phase, and progressive slowing of growth at large size.

measurement of the time required for a tumor to grow to a predetermined size may be used to infer the rate of growth prior to detection. For some tumors, such experiments tend to support the concept of a more rapid rate of tumor growth prior to detection. Shackney et al (1978) have applied an analogous method to obtain information about the preclinical growth of human tumors. They measured the time to tumor recurrence in a group of patients who received treatment that was adequate to produce cure or local tumor control in some other members of the group. Recurrence is assumed to result from growth of a small number of cells which survived treatment. The time of appearance of tumor nodules in mastectomy scars of patients with breast cancer suggests more rapid growth of these nodules in their preclinical phase. There is, however, little evidence for deceleration of growth during the preclinical phase of rapidly progressive malignancies such as Wilms' tumor or Burkitt's lymphoma.

Deceleration of growth of large tumors is probably due to increasing cell death and decreasing cell proliferation as tumor nutrition deteriorates (see section 9.6.2). Tumor growth may also be slow at very early stages of development (Fig 9.3). The small population of tumor cells may have to overcome immunologic and other defense mechanisms of the host, and Folkman (1975) has shown that tumor populations cannot expand until they have induced proliferation of blood vessels to support them.

9.3 THYMIDINE AUTORADIOGRAPHY

9.3.1 THYMIDINE LABELING AND CONCEPTS RELATED TO THE CELL CYCLE

Present concepts of the cell cycle are based on the demonstration that a radiolabeled precursor of DNA is incorporated into a discrete population of cells (Howard and Pelc, 1951). This result indicated that DNA synthesis is not continuous from one mitosis to the next, but takes place only in a specific period of the cell cycle, the S phase.

Although ^{32}P was used initially as the isotopic precursor of DNA synthesis, ^{3}H-thymidine is now the radioactive precursor in common use. Autoradiography is used to detect the presence of radioactive thymidine in cellular DNA (Cleaver, 1967). Autoradiographs are prepared by coating thin sections of tissue on a glass microscope slide with photographic emulsion and exposing in light-tight boxes (usually for 1–4 weeks), followed by development and fixation. Because of their short range (mean ~0.5 μm) β-particles from tritium activate silver grains in the photographic emulsion immediately overlying the cell nuclei that have incorporated the isotope, thereby providing high-resolution autoradiographs in which labeled cells can be easily identified (Figs 9.4 and 9.5).

Experiments using ^{3}H-thymidine and autoradiography have led to a general model of cell proliferation shown in Figure 9.6. The gaps between mitosis (M) and S phase, and between the S phase and mitosis, are called G_1 and G_2 phase respectively; the duration of individual phases of the cell cycle may vary among cells of a population. Tumors and normal tissues both contain nonproliferating cells, and there may be a high rate of cell loss or death.

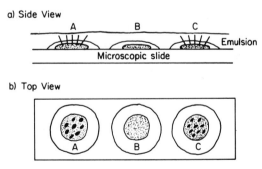

Figure 9.4. Schematic illustration of an autoradiograph. Tritium-labeled cells (A and C) and an unlabeled cell B are overlaid with a photographic emulsion. β-particles from cells A and C have short range and activate silver grains directly above their nuclei.

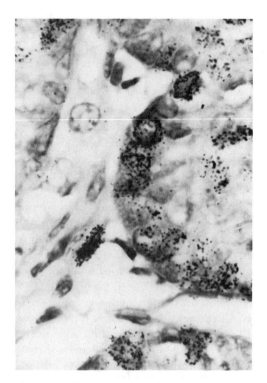

Figure 9.5. Autoradiograph showing labeled cells in a section from an experimental tumor.

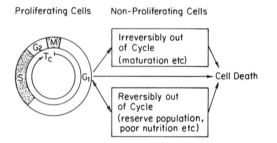

Figure 9.6. Model for a cell population indicating the relationship between proliferating and nonproliferating cells, and the process of cell death. (Adapted from Tannock, 1978.)

In normal tissues such as bone marrow or intestine there is evidence for a limited population of stem cells, which are defined by their potential for regenerating the entire cell population. There is indirect evidence that many tumors also contain a relatively small population of stem cells (see section 8.2.4). Stem cells are not always in a rapid state of proliferation, but they retain a high potential for proliferation that may be expressed following damage to normal tissues, treatment of tumors, or other stimuli.

9.3.2 ESTIMATION OF CELL-CYCLE PARAMETERS

The proportion of labeled cells in tissue at a short interval (usually one hour) after injection of ^{3}H-thymidine into an animal or patient is called the *labeling index* (LI). Since ^{3}H-thymidine is either incorporated into DNA or rapidly broken down and excreted, the LI represents the proportion of cells that were undergoing DNA synthesis at the time of injection, and is a crude measure of the overall rate of cell proliferation in a tissue. If all of the cells in a population were proliferating at a uniform rate, the LI would be related to the duration of DNA synthesis (T_s) and to cell-cycle time (T_c) by the equation

$$LI = \lambda \frac{T_s}{T_c}. \qquad (9.5)$$

Here λ is a factor whose value depends on the nature of the cell population but which is always close to 1 (Steel, 1977). It is required because each cell entering mitosis produces two daughter cells, so that there is a higher proportion of younger cells (ie, those recently produced in mitosis) in the population. Thus, the age distribution of cells in the cycle (Fig 9.7) is not rectangular (which would give $\lambda = 1$), but is bounded by a falling exponential curve.

The duration of the S phase is longer than that of mitosis, and labeled cells are more numerous and often easier to recognize than mitotic figures. Thus, it is simpler to use the labeling index than the mitotic index when comparing rates of cell proliferation among different tissues.

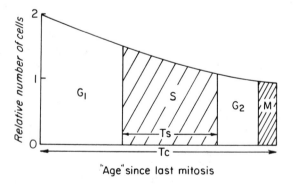

Figure 9.7. The age distribution of cells in the cycle. In an idealized cell population where all cells are proliferating, two cells are produced at mitosis from every cell that divides. Hence there is always a higher proportion of "young" cells in the population. The proportion of cells in S phase (ie, the LI) is equal to the ratio of the area indicated for S-phase cells to that of the whole diagram. (Adapted from Steel, 1977.)

Estimation of cell-cycle time T_c and of the duration of individual phases of the cell cycle requires more complex thymidine labeling studies such as the percent-labeled-mitoses (PLM) method. In the PLM method,

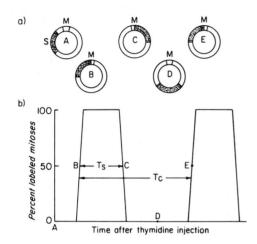

Figure 9.8. *a*, Movement of a cohort of labeled cells around the cell cycle, leading to *b*, an idealized percent-labeled-mitoses (PLM) curve for a hypothetical cell population with constant cell-cycle parameters.

serial biopsies are taken (or serial specimens from identical animals) at intervals after a single injection of ^{3}H-thymidine (Quastler and Sherman, 1959). Cells in mitosis may be recognized under the microscope, and the proportion of mitoses that is labeled is estimated from autoradiographs prepared from these biopsies. The passage of the labeled cells that were initially in S phase through the short mitotic phase leads to waves of labeled mitoses of width T_s and separation T_c (Fig 9.8). In practice, variability in phase duration leads to damping of the waves, as shown for the study of a transplantable tumor in Figure 9.9a. For human tumors the second wave of labeled mitoses may not be recognizable (Fig 9.9b), but by using computer models the mean and variance of T_c and of the constituent phases of the cell cycle (T_{G1}, T_s, T_{G2}) can be estimated.

Application of the PLM method to cytokinetic analysis of human tumors and normal tissues has provided most of the current information about cell-cycle time and duration of the individual phases. It requires, however, in vivo administration of ^{3}H-thymidine and multiple sequential biopsies from patients. It therefore tends to be limited to patients in whom it is ethical to administer a radioactive DNA precursor, and to tissues

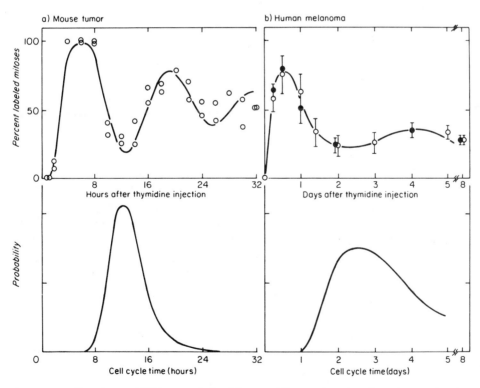

Figure 9.9. *a*, Experimental PLM curve derived for a rapidly growing transplanted tumor in mice. (Data of Tannock, 1970.) *b*, Experimental PLM curve obtained from two patients with melanoma. (Data of Shirakawa et al, 1970.) The curves were analyzed by computer methods to obtain probable distributions of cell-cycle times.

which can be biopsied easily (such as cutaneous metastases of melanoma which were biopsied to generate the PLM curve of Fig 9.9b).

Analysis of PLM curves must be interpreted with caution since the results depend not only on the experimental data (often it is difficult to discriminate between unlabeled and lightly labeled cells) but also on the assumptions of the computer model used for analysis. Necessary assumptions are that cell-cycle parameters do not change rapidly with time, and are not altered by incorporation of radiolabeled thymidine. The method tends to give information about the more rapidly proliferating cells and does not allow separation of nonproliferating cells from those with cell-cycle times much longer than the mean (Steel, 1977). This occurs because the faster-proliferating cells will pass through mitosis more frequently, and will thus constitute a higher proportion of mitotic cells than more slowly proliferating cells in any given sample.

9.3.3 GROWTH FRACTION

In many normal tissues of the adult only a small proportion of the cells is actively proliferating. Of the remaining cells, many are either differentiated and have lost the capability for cell division, or are quiescent, yet still retain the ability to proliferate in response to loss of other functional cells (Fig 9.6). Examples of the latter include stem cells in the bone marrow, which are defined as a subpopulation which has the capability to repopulate the tissue (section 9.5.1); cells in skin which participate in wound healing after damage; and cells in the liver which proliferate in response to partial hepatectomy in animals or to hepatitis in man. A reserve population of cells which is not actively proliferating but which retains the capacity to do so has been referred to as a G_0 population.

Most tumors also contain nonproliferating cells. Some of these are nonmalignant cells such as endothelial cells, fibroblasts or macrophages. Some tumor cells may have lost the capability for cell division because of differentiation or other biological change; others because of their microenvironment. Some cells may be able to return to a proliferative state if their local environment changes, as might occur after tumor treatment.

Growth fraction was defined by Mendelsohn (1960) as the proportion of cells in the tumor population that is proliferating. The PLM method allows estimation of durations of the cell-cycle phases, from which one may calculate the proportion of *proliferating* cells that is in DNA synthesis; the ratio of measured labeling index for *all* cells to this expected value for *proliferating* cells allows estimation of the growth fraction. Because the

PLM method does not distinguish nonproliferating cells from the more slowly proliferating cells of the population, such estimates of growth fraction are approximate, and depend to some extent on the model used for analysis of PLM curves. However, the estimate of growth fraction is useful in that it indicates the proportion of cells which might be sensitive to cycle-dependent chemotherapy.

An alternative method for estimation of the growth fraction (Nelson and Schiffer, 1973) is based on the hypothesis that proliferating and nonproliferating cells might be distinguished by the presence or absence of primer-available DNA-dependent DNA polymerase (PDP), an enzyme that is required by cells synthesizing DNA. An autoradiographic method has been developed to detect this enzyme in cell nuclei, and the proportion of labeled cells containing the enzyme (PDP-index) has been reported to show good correlation with other estimates of growth fraction.

9.3.4 CELL LOSS FROM TUMORS

The frequent occurrence of extensive necrosis in tumors, and the ability of tumor cells to metastasize, suggest that there may be considerable cell death or loss from tumors. In section 9.2.1, eq (9.3), tumor growth was defined in terms of rate constants for cell production (K_P) and cell loss (K_L), and the volume doubling time of the tumor was shown to be

$$T_D = \frac{\log_e 2}{(K_P - K_L)}.$$

The rate of cell loss from a tumor may be expressed as a proportion of the rate of cell production (ie, K_L/K_P), and Steel (1967) has termed this ratio the "cell-loss factor." This factor would have a value equal to 1 for a steady-state renewal tissue, and would be 0 for a tumor that did not lose cells.

In order to calculate the cell-loss factor, it is convenient to define the potential doubling time, T_{pot}, of a tumor. This parameter is defined as the doubling time that the population would have if there were no cell loss. The volume doubling time (T_D) of a tumor will usually be longer than T_{pot} because of cell loss, while mean cell-cycle time (T_c) will usually be less than T_{pot} because of the presence of nonproliferating cells. T_{pot} is related to the rate constant for cell production K_P by the relationship (cf eq 9.3)

$$T_{pot} = \frac{\log_e 2}{K_P}. \qquad (9.6)$$

From eqs (9.3) and (9.6), the cell-loss factor may be calculated as

$$\text{cell-loss factor} = \frac{K_{\text{L}}}{K_{\text{P}}} = 1 - \frac{T_{\text{pot}}}{T_{\text{D}}}. \qquad (9.7)$$

By analogy with eq (9.5), T_{pot} may be estimated from values of the labeling index and T_{s} by the relationship

$$LI = \frac{\lambda T_{\text{s}}}{T_{\text{pot}}}. \qquad (9.8)$$

Again, λ is the factor with a value close to 1 that allows for the larger proportion of younger cells in the population (Fig 9.7; Steel, 1977).

The duration of DNA synthesis (T_{s}) shows much less variability among cells of a population than the cell-cycle time T_{c} and is usually found to be relatively constant for cells in many tissues of a given species. Equations (9.7) and (9.8) therefore allow an approximate estimate of the rate of cell loss in a tumor from measurements of its labeling index and volume doubling time. It should be noted that calculation of the cell-loss factor is based on a comparison of the potential doubling time for cell number and the measured doubling time for volume. There is thus an underlying assumption that the number of cells per unit volume remains constant in the tumor.

9.3.5 THYMIDINE SUICIDE

Current methods for estimating kinetic parameters by thymidine autoradiography do not give information about the kinetics of stem cells since they cannot usually be distinguished from other cells of the population by morphological criteria. The existence of stem cells is documented through functional clonogenic assays which allow them to express their proliferative potential by forming colonies of progeny. Colony formation has been assessed on plastic or in semisolid media in tissue culture, by formation of colonies in the spleens of mice after injection of normal or malignant hemopoietic stem cells (Till and McCulloch, 1961), or by assessment of metastatic lung colonies after injection of tumor cells into mice (sections 15.4 and 17.2).

Information analogous to the labeling index may be obtained for stem cells by comparing colony formation by untreated cells, and by cells treated with high-specific-activity ^{3}H-thymidine (the "thymidine suicide method," Fig 9.10; Becker et al, 1965). Those cells that are synthesizing DNA at the time of thymidine administration will be killed by radiation damage from the high dose of tritium, leading to a reduction in the number of colonies. Experiments that are similar in concept are sometimes performed using cell-cycle phase-specific drugs instead of ^{3}H-thymidine to kill cells in the S phase.

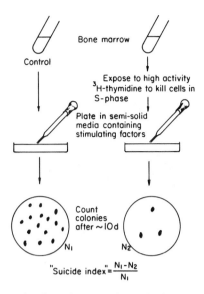

Figure 9.10. The thymidine suicide method used to estimate the proportion of clonogenic cells in bone marrow that are in S phase. Exposure of bone marrow to high-activity ^{3}H-thymidine prior to plating kills all cells in S phase. The proportion of colony-forming cells (CFU) that were synthesizing DNA ("the suicide index") may be calculated from the reduction in number of colonies as compared to control plates.

9.4 FLOW CYTOMETRY

9.4.1 PRINCIPLES OF FLOW CYTOMETRY

The study of cell kinetics has been facilitated by the use of flow cytometry, which has the advantage over autoradiography of speed and automation (Van Dilla et al, 1969; Barlogie et al, 1983). A schematic illustration of a flow cytometer is shown in Figure 9.11. A single-cell suspension is prepared and cells are stained with a fluorescent dye whose binding is proportional to DNA content. They are then directed in single file through a laser beam to excite the DNA-specific dye, and the fluorescence emission is collected and displayed as a fluorescence distribution. The technique allows enumeration of cells containing different quantities of fluorescent dye, and thus different amounts of DNA (Fig 9.12). Many instruments now incorporate a fluorescence-activated cell sorter (FACS) which allows sorting of cells with different fluorescence intensities for further biochemical and/or morphologic studies (Fig 9.11).

Several fluorescent dyes have been used to stain DNA, including ethidium bromide, propidium iodide, acridine orange, mithramycin and Hoechst 33342. Acridine orange can be used to separate and sort cells on the basis of both DNA content (green fluorescence) and RNA content (red fluorescence), and has been used to discriminate between G_1 cells and nonproliferating

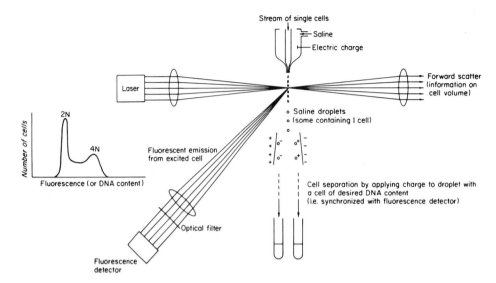

Figure 9.11. The principle of flow cytometry and cell sorting. Single cells stained with a fluorescent dye whose uptake is proportional to DNA content are directed through a laser beam. Fluorescence measurements give a distribution of DNA content, and forward light scatter gives information about cell volume. Charge may be applied to cells of different DNA content, so that they may be deflected in an electrostatic field and sorted.

subpopulations. Most dyes require fixation of cells to allow access of dye to the DNA, although selected DNA specific dyes (eg, Hoechst 33342) can enter viable cells; this stain is a prototype for vital dyes that are minimally toxic to the cells. Numerous other reagents, including fluorescence-labeled antibodies, are available which allow separation of cells by biochemical properties other than DNA content. Often, fluorescent reagents are applied sequentially to allow separation of cells on the basis of two or more criteria, and multivariate flow cytometric systems which allow simultaneous analysis of four or five variables have been described. Information about cell size may be obtained from analysis of scattered light. Multivariate analyses are particularly useful in the study of heterogeneous tissue samples.

Many tumor cells are aneuploid (see section 3.3) and DNA fluorescence histograms may therefore separate tumor cells from normal diploid cells such as fibroblasts, lymphoid cells and macrophages. This property has led to the increasing use of flow cytometry as an aid in diagnosis, and to characterize DNA content of tumors in relation to prognosis (Fig 9.12; Friedlander et al, 1984). Simultaneous measurements of DNA content, RNA content, nuclear size and other parameters may add to standard histological examination in the classification of malignancies such as leukemia and lymphoma (Barlogie et al, 1983).

The application of flow cytometry to studies of cell proliferation requires analysis of a fluorescent DNA dis-

tribution to provide an estimate of the proportions of cells with 2N DNA content (ie, G_1 and most nonproliferating cells), 4N DNA content (G_2 and mitotic cells) and intermediate DNA content (S-phase cells). DNA distributions are usually analyzed by computer and require some assumptions about the shape of the DNA distribution among cells of the population. A number of mathematical models may be used for this analysis. The results obtained depend more on the specificity of the DNA stain (some dyes may also stain cytoplasmic components), and on the sampling error in obtaining representative single-cell suspensions, than on the assumptions of the mathematical model. By using several replicate samples the technique should allow estimation of the proportion of cells in each phase of the cycle with errors of 10% or less (Dean et al, 1982). In tumors, the presence of aneuploidy, and of variable DNA content among G_1 cells, complicates analysis of DNA distributions and the estimation of cell-cycle parameters.

There is a subtle difference between the proportion of cells in a population with DNA content intermediate between that of G_1 and G_2 cells that is measured by flow cytometry (ie, a static measurement of DNA content), and the labeling index, which estimates the proportion of cells that is actively synthesizing DNA. However, most comparisons of the two methods show fair agreement between these independent estimates of the proportion of S-phase cells.

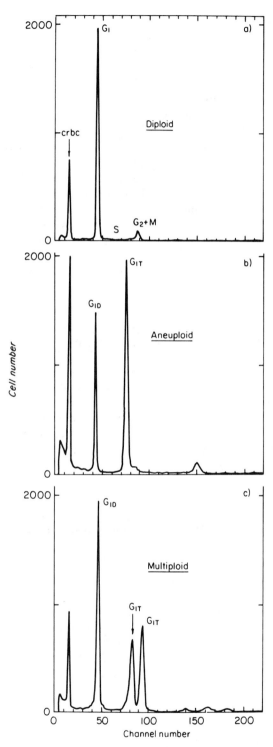

Figure 9.12. DNA histograms obtained for cells from solid human tumors. Chicken red blood cells (crbc) are used as an internal standard to identify the diploid G_1 peak (G_{1D}). Most tumors contain a diploid cell population which will include normal cells (fibroblasts, macrophages, etc) but tumor cells (G_1 peak indicated by G_{1T}) may be a, diploid, b, aneuploid, or c, multiploid. (From Friedlander et al, 1984, with permission.)

9.4.2 NEWER APPLICATIONS OF FLOW CYTOMETRY

Innovations using flow cytometry have allowed estimation of cell-cycle phase distribution, growth fraction, and kinetic properties of colony-forming cells, for cell lines maintained in tissue culture. Some of these methods are now being applied to studies of cell kinetics in vivo, although heterogeneity of cellular properties and the requirement for disaggregation of tissue into single cells add considerable complexity.

The percent-labeled mitoses (PLM) method (section 9.3.2) was based on the observation of a labeled cohort of cells as they passed through a recognizable "window" in the cell cycle (ie, mitosis). An analogous method has been adapted for flow cytometry: cells are labeled with ^{3}H-thymidine and at subsequent intervals a DNA-specific stain is applied and cells with a DNA content corresponding to mid-S phase are sorted. This short interval in mid-S phase therefore replaces mitosis as the "window" of observation, and the radioactivity per sorted cell (analogous to the proportion of labeled mitoses) is then measured by scintillation counting. The method has been shown to give similar estimates of phase duration for cultured cells as the PLM technique with autoradiography, but takes only one day instead of several weeks (Gray, 1983). The method has been applied to in vivo studies, but its application to solid tumors may be limited because the uptake of labeled precursors, and hence the radioactivity per cell, may show considerable variability among cells that are synthesizing DNA in vivo.

An alternative approach to the use of ^{3}H-thymidine is to label cells with nonradioactive 5-bromodeoxyuridine (BrdUrd), which is also incorporated into the newly synthesized DNA of S-phase cells. Cells that incorporate BrdUrd may be recognized by quenching of fluorescence after staining with the DNA-specific dye Hoechst 33258, or by the use of monoclonal antibodies which recognize BrdUrd in DNA (Dolbeare et al, 1983). Simultaneous flow-cytometric analysis of cellular DNA content and BrdUrd content is a powerful technique for cytokinetic studies. Sequential distributions obtained at different times after administration of BrdUrd give similar information to that obtained by the PLM method after pulse labeling with ^{3}H-thymidine. However, flow-cytometric analysis is faster and less subjective than autoradiography. The method has been used to estimate cell-cycle-phase duration and other cytokinetic parameters in a variety of tissues, including human leukemic bone marrow.

Another technique utilizes acridine orange staining of cellular DNA and RNA to identify cells in mitosis by flow cytometry (Darzynkiewicz et al, 1983). This method makes use of the property that the DNA of mitotic cells is more susceptible to acid denaturation (ie, separation into its single strands). Estimation of growth fraction requires the separation of nonproliferating cells with 2N DNA content from proliferating cells in G_1 phase. This can be accomplished by the BrdUrd method described above, or by flow-cytometric analysis after staining with acridine orange. Nonproliferating cells, like those in mitosis, appear to be more susceptible to denaturation of their DNA, thus offering potential for their separation by flow cytometry. Nonproliferating cells synthesize less RNA than do proliferating cells in G_1 phase; staining with acridine orange therefore gives equal green (ie, DNA) fluorescence, but greater red (ie, RNA) fluorescence, for cells in G_1 phase as compared to nonproliferating cells (Dethlefson et al, 1980).

9.4.3 FLOW-CYTOMETRIC METHODS TO STUDY CLONOGENIC CELLS

Analysis of DNA distributions does not provide information about the proliferative status of clonogenic cells. As for thymidine-labeling methods, this limitation presents a major problem in the analysis of cell kinetics after treatment with drugs or other agents where DNA distributions are complicated by the presence of lethally damaged but intact cells. Although a direct approach to analysis of clonogenic cells is not possible, several indirect methods have been developed to obtain cytokinetic information about them.

One method is to sort cells on the basis of their DNA content after staining with fluorescent nontoxic drugs, thus allowing subsequent study of their clonogenic capacity and other properties (Pallavicini et al, 1979). Unfortunately, currently available vital stains such as Hoechst 33342 sometimes show cytotoxicity, and these toxic effects depend on the cell population and may be complicated by interactions of the dye with radiation or anticancer drugs. Other problems include prolonged times required for cell sorting, and difficulty in maintaining sterility during the procedure. In spite of these problems, the development of minimally toxic DNA-specific fluorescent dyes deserves high priority.

Some information about the kinetics of clonogenic cells may be derived from using mathematical models which are then subjected to experimental test. For example, sequential DNA distributions and incorporation of ^{3}H-thymidine have been measured prior to and following treatment of an experimental tumor with cytosine arabinoside. These data were used to derive a multicompartment cell-cycle model for both clonogenic and nonclonogenic cells, and the model was then verified by its ability to predict survival of clonogenic cells

following treatment with two doses of the drug (Pallavicini et al, 1982). It seems unlikely, however, that such models could be applied with confidence to more complex systems such as human tumors, where experimental verification would be difficult.

An alternative method for studying the cell kinetics of clonogenic cells involves the combined use of flow cytometry and centrifugal elutriation. Centrifugal elutriation separates cells on the basis of size in a continuous-flow centrifuge, and since cells increase in volume as they pass through the cell cycle it can lead to separation of viable cells in different phases. Replicate samples of these separated cells can then be studied for colony formation and for DNA distribution using flow cytometry. This method has been used to study the cycle-dependent effects of drugs and radiation on clonogenic cells in experimental tumors (eg, Grdina et al, 1980).

9.5 CELL PROLIFERATION IN NORMAL TISSUES

Thymidine labeling or flow cytometry may be used to compare the overall rate of cell proliferation in a variety of normal tissues, as shown in Figure 9.13. Although this classification is based on estimates of the labeling index in mice, more limited data in man indicate that the relative rates of proliferation in different tissues are similar to the mouse, although absolute rates of cellular proliferation tend to be lower in man.

The classification of Figure 9.13 is of interest because the side effects of chemotherapy that are common to many drugs (eg, myelosuppression, mucositis, hair loss, and sterility) are observed in rapidly proliferating tissues, reflecting the greater toxicity of most anticancer

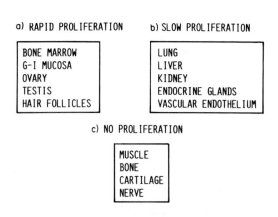

Figure 9.13. Selected normal tissues grouped under headings of *a*, rapid proliferation (labeling index > ~5% in mice); *b*, slow proliferation (labeling index ~1% in mice); *c*, no proliferation. Acute side effects of chemotherapy occur commonly in rapidly proliferating tissue.

drugs for proliferating cells (see section 17.3). Acute effects of radiation injury are also observed in these tissues. Detailed discussion of the cell kinetics of normal tissue is beyond the scope of this book (for review, see Wright and Alison, 1984) but the bone marrow and the intestine are described as examples of renewal tissues in which the pattern of cell proliferation may be an important determinant of anticancer therapy.

9.5.1 BONE MARROW

Studies of morphologically recognizable cells in bone marrow and blood have established an orderly progression of differentiation from myeloblasts to polymorphonuclear granulocytes, from pronormoblasts to red blood cells, and from megakaryocytes to platelets (Stohlman, 1962; Cronkite and Fliedner, 1964; Fig 9.14). Within these cell lineages, thymidine-labeling studies have demonstrated a high rate of cell proliferation of the recognizable immature cells with estimates of the labeling index for human myeloblasts ranging from about 30 to 75%. Estimates of cell-cycle time obtained by using the percent-labeled mitoses technique have confirmed that recognizable precursors of granulocytes and red cells are among the most rapidly proliferating cells in the human body, with estimates for T_s and T_c of about 12 hr and 24 hr respectively (Stryckmans et al, 1966; Todo, 1968). The more mature cells in each series undergo differentiation without proliferation (Fig 9.14).

The existence of bone marrow precursor cells shown in Figure 9.14 has been inferred by experiments in which human bone marrow has been cultured under defined nutrient and hormonal conditions. Colonies containing cells only of the granulocytic series occur under certain conditions in culture; while such experiments strongly suggest the existence of a granulocyte-committed colony-forming cell (CFU-C), conditions in culture might influence the progeny of a pluripotential cell to differentiate in this way. Support for the existence of committed red cell and other lineage precursors has been obtained in analogous experiments using different conditions in culture (Metcalf, 1977; Till and McCulloch, 1980). The presence of a pluripotent stem cell (ie, one that can generate all cell lineages) has been inferred by the presence of common clonal markers in red- and white-cell lineages in chronic myelogenous leukemia (Fialkow, 1974). Colonies derived from a pluripotent cell in mice (CFU-S) may be generated in the spleens of irradiated mice that receive intravenous injections of syngeneic marrow (the spleen-colony assay of Till and McCulloch, 1961; see section 17.2). More recently, colonies containing megakaryocytes and recognizable erythroid and granulocytic cells have been obtained by direct culture of human marrow (Fauser and Messner, 1979), thus providing direct evidence for the presence of a pluripotent stem cell (CFU-GEMM) in man.

The kinetic properties of the committed progenitors and pluripotent stem cells are assayed by indirect methods. The thymidine suicide method has been used to study the cell kinetics of early bone marrow precursors. Committed granulocyte precursors (CFU-C) appear to

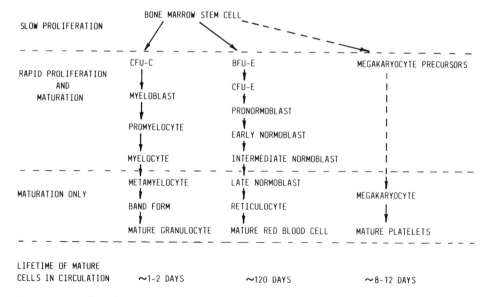

Figure 9.14. Cell proliferation and differentiation in bone marrow. The existence of bone marrow stem cells, and of the colony-forming cells CFU-C, BFU-E and CFU-E, is inferred by generation of cell colonies from them under defined conditions in culture (see text).

have a suicide index (ie, proportion of cells in S phase) of about 25% under normal conditions, a value which is less than the labeling index of myeloblasts. Spleen colony-forming cells of mice, and human pluripotent stem cells (CFU-GEMM), proliferate slowly under resting conditions and have a thymidine suicide index of only 0–10%; however, they may proliferate rapidly to restore the bone marrow population following depletion of more mature forms (eg, by cancer chemotherapy) or after bone marrow transplantation (Fauser and Messner, 1979). Thus the bone marrow is an organ with carefully controlled feedback mechanisms which are designed to restore cell number and function following stress.

9.5.2 INTESTINE

The functional part of the small intestine consists of numerous villi which project into the lumen and provide a large absorptive surface (Fig 9.15). The villi are lined by a single layer of differentiated epithelial cells which do not proliferate. There is a high rate of loss of these cells due to sloughing into the lumen, presumably because of abrasion by the intestinal contents. These cells are replaced by upward migration of cells lining the crypts of Lieberkuhn, which lie between and at the base of the villi, where there is a rapid rate of cell proliferation. Cell division also takes place in crypts in the

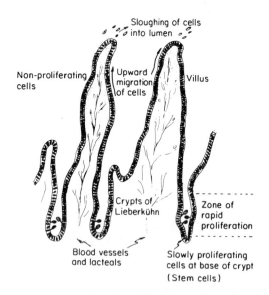

Figure 9.15. Model for cell proliferation and migration in the small intestine. Slowly proliferating cells in the base of the crypts probably act as stem cells for the entire cell population. Other cells in the lower two thirds of the crypts proliferate rapidly, with nuclei of mitotic cells visible in the lumen of the crypts. Cells migrate up the villi to replace those sloughed into the lumen.

large intestine, but here the surface is flatter and without villi.

Careful studies of the distribution of thymidine-labeled cells in rodents have established that the zone of cell proliferation extends over the lower two thirds of the crypts. During mitosis the cell nucleus moves into the lumen of the crypts although the cytoplasm remains anchored in the epithelial layer. Cell proliferation is not uniform over the zone of proliferation, but occurs more slowly at the base of the crypts (Fig 9.15). Slowly proliferating cells in this region appear to be analogous to bone marrow stem cells in that they act as precursors for the entire crypt and surrounding villi (Cairnie et al, 1965; Cheng and Leblond, 1974); they can be stimulated into cycle and induced to proliferate at an accelerated rate following perturbations. Methods to measure the cytokinetic properties of intestinal stem cells are limited by the lack of markers to identify this therapeutically relevant subpopulation. In vitro clonogenic assays to quantitate intestinal stem cells do not exist. Proliferation of stem cells after treatment may, however, be detected in mice by formation of microcolonies that can be recognized in histological section (Withers and Elkind, 1970).

In a few studies (eg, Lipkin et al, 1963) serial biopsies of human intestine have been taken through a colonoscope or peroral tube after injection of tritiated thymidine. These studies have shown values for the labeling index of crypts in the large intestine in the range of 12–18%, and have allowed the derivation of labeled-mitoses curves that suggest a short cell-cycle time of 1–2 days. Thus there is also a high rate of cell proliferation in the human intestine.

9.6 CELL PROLIFERATION IN TUMORS

9.6.1 EXPERIMENTAL TUMORS

Detailed studies of cell proliferation have been performed on tumors in rodents by using the techniques of thymidine autoradiography and flow cytometry. Most of these tumors were rapidly growing and multiply transplanted, although there have also been a few studies of early transplants from spontaneous tumors (for review, see Steel, 1977). A high proportion of cells from many of the transplanted tumors will form colonies under appropriate conditions in cell culture, and thus are stem cells. Transplantable tumors differ, therefore, from primary human tumors where the proportion of stem cells appears to be low (see section 8.2.5).

The following general conclusions may be drawn about the kinetics of cell proliferation of transplantable tumors in rodents:

1. The labeling index, or proportion of cells in S phase measured by flow cytometry, varies widely with typical mean values in the range 10–40%.
2. There is variability in labeling or mitotic indices between different parts of the same tumor.
3. Mean values for the duration of DNA synthesis and cell-cycle time in solid tumors are in the ranges 6–10 hr and 12–18 hr respectively, and are not correlated strongly with the rate of tumor growth.
4. Most tumors contain nonproliferating cells and have a high rate of cell loss.
5. Slowing of growth in solid tumors is due primarily to a decrease in growth fraction and an increase in the rate of cell loss.
6. Slowing of growth in ascites tumors is due largely to a prolongation in all phases of the cell cycle. It is of note that ascites tumors, used widely in the screening of potential anticancer drugs, have a quite different pattern of cell proliferation than do solid tumors.

9.6.2 HETEROGENEITY OF CELL PROLIFERATION WITHIN TUMORS: DEPENDENCE ON TUMOR VASCULATURE

Studies of human and animal tumors have demonstrated considerable variability in labeling and mitotic indices within different parts of the same tumor or its metastases, and PLM curves have indicated a wide range of cell-cycle times among the individual cells. One of the factors that contribute to this heterogeneity is a variable degree of differentiation which may occur within the tumor: in general, there is an inverse relationship between differentiation and proliferative rates. A second factor is the generation of variant clonal subpopulations (see section 8.3) with different proliferative capacities. A third, and perhaps dominant, factor is cell nutrition. Necrosis occurs commonly in solid tumors, and both in human and experimental tumors an orderly relationship can sometimes be observed with the edge of a necrotic region being parallel to a tumor blood vessel and separated from it by a distance that in man is commonly about 150–200 μm (Figs 9.16 and 9.17;

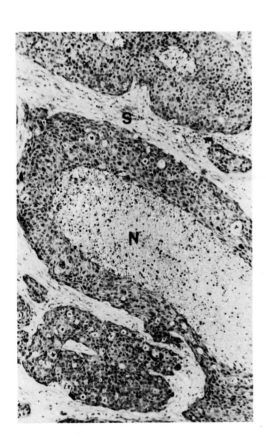

Figure 9.16. Histological section of a human lung cancer showing tumor cords between fibrous stroma (S) containing blood vessels and regions of necrosis (N). (Figure prepared by Dr R.H. Thomlinson, Mount Vernon Hospital, Northwood, England. Used with permission.)

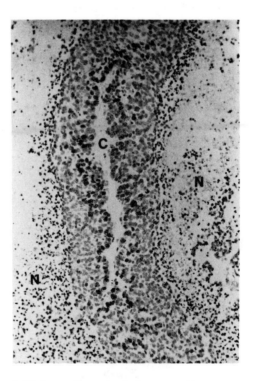

Figure 9.17. Autoradiograph of a tumor cord in a mouse mammary carcinoma. The orderly relationship between the capillary (C) and the region of necrosis (N) suggests that limited diffusion of nutrients from blood vessels contributes to mechanisms of cell death. Labeled cells are concentrated near to the blood vessel.

Thomlinson and Gray, 1955). In some tumors, this relationship may lead to the formation of either cylindrical cords of viable tissue with a central blood vessel and surrounding necrosis, or to tumor nodules with a surrounding vascular network and central necrosis. These structures suggest that necrosis may occur when the concentration of essential nutrients that diffuse from tumor blood vessels has fallen to a critically low value, and/or when toxic breakdown products of cells have reached a critically high level.

Factors which may influence cell viability and formation of necrosis in solid tumors may be studied in vivo using experimental tumors, or in vitro using tumor spheroids. Spheroids are spherical aggregates of tumor cells that grow in tissue culture, and which develop central necrosis when their diameter is above a critical value (Fig 9.18; Sutherland et al, 1971). The width of the viable rim of cells around the necrotic center remains fairly constant under standard growth conditions, but may be altered by changing metabolite concentration in the surrounding medium. Studies of rodent tumors, of spheroids, and of single cells in culture under varying nutrient conditions suggest that limited diffusion of oxygen and glucose may both contribute to loss of cell viability at the edge of a necrotic region (eg, Tannock, 1968; Freyer and Sutherland, 1986), but several other factors almost certainly contribute to this process. A better understanding of the

causes of cell death may provide insight into new approaches to cancer treatment involving the stimulation of natural processes which lead to cell death in tumors.

Studies of thymidine labeling in tumor cords and nodules and in spheroids have allowed several investigators to relate the proliferation of tumor cells to distance from their source of nutrition (ie, their nearest blood vessel). In a recent innovation it has also been possible to use the concentration gradient from diffusion of the fluorescent dye Hoechst 33342 into spheroids, or from blood vessels in experimental tumors, to separate cells in different nutrient environments by flow cytometry (Durand, 1982; Chaplin et al, 1985). Not surprisingly the rate of cell proliferation decreases rapidly with increasing distance from the surface of a spheroid or from a blood vessel in a tumor (Fig 9.17), and the ratio of labeling indices in perivascular areas of a tumor to those adjacent to a region of necrosis may be a factor of 3 or more (Tannock, 1968). In many tumors the tortuous anatomy of tumor blood vessels does not allow easy identification of tumor cords or nodules and there may be regions of high vascular density and nutrition. However, large variations in cell nutrition are probable, and provide a plausible explanation for the observed heterogeneity in the rate of cellular proliferation.

The above results suggest that cell proliferation and cell death are dependent on tumor vasculature. Work by Folkman and his colleagues (1975) has shown that tumor cells release a factor(s) (endothelial cell growth factor or tumor angiogenesis factor) that induces proliferation of vascular endothelium and penetration of blood vessels into a tumor mass. Tumor nodules (eg, those implanted into the cornea of a rabbit; see Fig 9.19) can only grow to a small and limited size (~1-mm diameter) before they develop a blood supply. After initial vascularization, tumor-cell proliferation is likely to depend on the rate at which the vascular network enlarges. Use of thymidine-labeling methods to study the rate of proliferation of vascular endothelial cells in experimental tumors has shown that their mean labeling index is often about 10% (Tannock, 1970; Denekamp and Hobson, 1982) and usually less than the labeling index of perivascular tumor cells in rapidly growing tumors. Vascular stasis and resultant necrosis have also been observed in solid tumors, and together these results imply that the functional vascular network per unit volume of tumor will decrease with tumor growth. The resulting decrease in nutrition probably leads to both slowing and variability of the rate of cellular proliferation and subsequently to cell death. These processes will lead to the decrease in growth rate that is often observed in tumors as they enlarge.

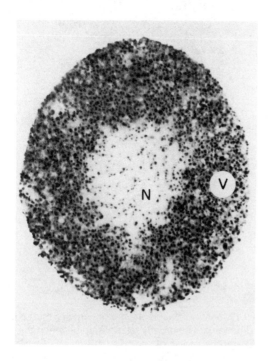

Figure 9.18. Cross section of a spheroid formed from a tumor cell line derived from human bladder cancer, showing the viable rim (V) and central necrosis (N).

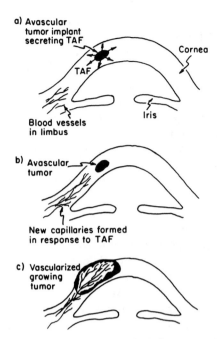

a) Avascular tumor implant secreting TAF
Cornea
TAF
Blood vessels in limbus
Iris

b) Avascular tumor
New capillaries formed in response to TAF

c) Vascularized growing tumor

Figure 9.19. Experiment to demonstrate that tumor tissue may stimulate the growth of blood vessels through secretion of tumor angiogenesis factor (TAF). A piece of tumor implanted into the avascular cornea of a rabbit's eye grows to a maximum size of ~1 mm until blood vessels are stimulated to invade it from the surrounding limbus. (Adapted from Folkman, 1975.)

9.6.3 HUMAN TUMORS

When studying human tissue, it is desirable to avoid injection of radioactive isotopes into patients. Flow cytometry provides an alternative to the use of ^{3}H-thymidine, provided that the tissue can be dissociated into single cells. The labeling index can also be estimated by preparing autoradiographs after short incubation of fresh biopsy specimens with ^{3}H-thymidine in vitro. This method may be used to estimate the proportion of cells that are synthesizing DNA in vivo provided that tissue samples are small and are incubated with adequate oxygenation (Steel, 1977). The artificial in vitro environment may influence the results, however, and few investigators have undertaken the essential step of validating their method by first comparing in vitro and in vivo estimates of the labeling index for animal tissues.

Representative values of the labeling index, estimated by in vivo and in vitro methods for several types of solid tumors and leukemia in man, are listed in Table 9.2. Cell proliferation in lymphomas is more rapid than in other types of solid tumor, for which the data of Table 9.2 indicate typical values for the labeling index in the range 2–8%. The rate of cell proliferation in human tumors is usually less than that in normal re-

newing epithelium such as the intestine (labeling index ~16%).

Values of the labeling index for human leukemia are lower than those of the granulocyte and erythroid precursors in normal bone marrow which are included in Table 9.3. Thus accumulation of cells even in acute leukemia is not due to an increased rate of cell proliferation. Instead, there is defective maturation and the population of leukemic cells increases because the rate of cell proliferation (although slower than that of normal myeloblasts) exceeds the rate of cell death or removal from the population. That leukemia is caused primarily by a defect in cell differentiation as opposed

Table 9.2. Representative Values of the Labeling Index (LI) Obtained from Studies of Human Tumors*

Type of Tumor	Number of Patients	Mean or Median LI (%)
Squamous-cell carcinoma (various sites)	68	8
Adenocarcinoma (various sites)	121	2
Sarcoma (various sites)	32	4
Lymphoma	26	30
Lung and larynx	72	8
Breast	274	2
Colon	165	3

Note: Data reviewed by Tannock (1978).

*Most estimates were obtained by incubating fresh biopsies with ^{3}H-thymidine in vitro.

Table 9.3. Published Values of the Labeling Index (LI) for Untreated Human Leukemia and for Cells in Normal Bone Marrow

Type of Leukemia	Cell Type	Range of Mean Values of LI (%)
Acute myelogenous	myeloblasts, marrow	5–11
	myeloblasts, blood	3–9
Acute lymphoblastic	lymphoblasts, marrow	4–12
	lymphoblasts, blood	2–10
Chronic myelogenous	myeloblasts	9–43
	myelocytes	8–27
	myeloblasts, blast cell crisis	6–18
Chronic lymphocytic	large lymphocytes	0–1
	small lymphocytes	0
Normal bone marrow	myeloblasts	32–75
	myelocytes	18–25

Note: Data reviewed by Tannock (1978).

to cell proliferation is further emphasized by the finding that the rate of proliferation of myeloblasts in the rapidly progressive acute myeloblastic leukemias (AMLs) is often slower than in chronic myelogenous leukemia (CML), where differentiation to more mature and partly functional cells occurs. In the aggressive preterminal phase of blast crisis in CML, differentiation is curtailed but proliferation of myeloblasts does not increase (Table 9.3).

In a few studies, serial biopsies have been taken from patients with leukemia or superficial solid tumors following injection of tritiated thymidine. These studies have allowed construction of PLM curves (eg, Fig 9.9) and estimation of the mean cell-cycle time and the duration of its constituent phases. Representative values for T_s and T_c are listed in Table 9.4. Most of these estimates were obtained directly from published PLM curves, and some of them differ from values quoted by the original authors. The curves usually had damped second waves, implying wide variability of cell-cycle time (see Fig 9.9). Mean values of T_s and T_c for acute leukemia and for solid tumors tend to be rather similar (about 20 and 60 hr respectively) despite widely different rates of growth; these values are longer than the best available estimates for granulocyte and erythroid precursors in nonleukemic marrow, or for proliferating epithelial cells in intestinal crypts.

Measured values of the labeling index for solid tumors in man are usually low, while estimates of T_s and T_c imply that a much larger proportion of prolif-

erating cells are engaged in DNA synthesis (Tables 9.2 and 9.4). It follows that most human tumors have a low growth fraction. For example, patients with malignant melanoma, whose PLM curve is shown in Figure 9.9, had a mean value for the labeling index of about 5%, consistent with a growth fraction of about 20% (Shirakawa et al, 1970). If some of the slowly or nonproliferating cells in human tumors retain the properties of a tumor stem cell (ie, they can repopulate the tumor if stimulated to divide), the low growth fraction may be a factor that contributes to the relative resistance of many slow-growing human tumors to cycle-active chemotherapy.

The data reviewed in Tables 9.1 and 9.2 have shown that volume doubling times of common human tumors are typically 2–3 months, while values of the labeling index are usually less than 10%. A tumor with a labeling index of 4% will have a potential doubling time T_{pot} of some 20 days (with the reasonable assumptions that $\lambda \sim 0.8$ and $T_s \sim 1$ day in eq 9.8). If the volume doubling time of the tumor is about 80 days, the rate of cell loss will be about 75% of the rate of cell production (eq 9.7). Even higher rates of cell loss may occur in some human tumors (Steel, 1967).

The above results have demonstrated that proliferating cells in human tumors may cycle quite rapidly, but that the rate of volume growth is fortunately much slower. The major reasons for this discrepancy are the presence of a large population of nonproliferating cells and a high rate of cell death. A model of unrestrained proliferation is inappropriate for human tumors; rather they may be compared with normal renewing epithelia, but where a defect in homeostasis has led to an imbalance in the rates of cell production and cell loss.

Table 9.4. Estimates of Mean Duration of DNA Synthesis (T_s) and of Cycle Time (T_c) Obtained for Human Tumors by Using the Percent-Labeled Mitoses Method*

Type of Tumor	Number of Studies	T_s (hr)	Mean Value T_c (days)
Melanoma	6	21	2.5
Breast	6	21	2.5
Squamous-cell Ca of head and neck	4	20	2.5
Lung and larynx	6	20	4.5
Colon and rectum	10	17	3.0
Lymphomas	7	12	2.0
Leukemias acute myelogenous	8	18	2.5
acute lymphoblastic	9	26	2.5

Note: Data reviewed by Steel (1977), and Tannock (1978).

*Duration of the cell-cycle time was found to vary widely among cells of the population and mean values of T_c have therefore been estimated to the nearest 0.5 day.

9.6.4 CLONOGENIC CELLS IN TUMORS

The concept that human tumors may contain a relatively small population of stem cells that may seed metastases or regenerate the tumor after treatment has been discussed in section 8.2. Stem cells have by definition a large proliferative potential, but this does not necessarily imply that they are proliferating rapidly (compare, for example, the bone marrow stem cell under normal conditions). Study of the cell kinetics of clonogenic cells in tumors requires a reliable assay which allows expression of colony-forming ability. Some human tumor cells may form colonies in viscous media such as dilute agar (McAllister and Reed, 1968), but the rigors of cell disaggregation and plating in this imperfect environment almost certainly allow only some of the tumor stem cells to express their colony-forming ability (see Selby et al, 1983). Although recognizing these limitations, a few investigators have sought to measure the S-phase fraction of clonogenic cells in human tumors by the thymidine suicide method (eg, Minden et al, 1978; Shimizu et al, 1982). Their results suggest a variable but often high rate of proliferation among the clonogenic cells of the few tumors that have been studied. However, these results must be interpreted with caution, since those clonogenic cells that are proliferating in vivo might be more likely to survive and to produce colonies when transferred into tissue culture, with the consequent introduction of a strong selection bias. The artificial in vitro environment might also produce erroneously high levels of thymidine suicide.

9.6.5 CELL PROLIFERATION, PROGNOSIS AND THERAPY

Several investigators have sought to define a relationship between parameters of cell proliferation in human malignancies (usually an estimate of the proportion of S-phase cells by labeling index or flow cytometry) and either prognosis or response to treatment. In general, tumors with a more rapid rate of cell proliferation tend to have a poorer prognosis, unless effective treatment is available. Thus a high initial labeling index of primary breast cancer correlates with a poor survival, and some investigators have suggested that the labeling index be incorporated into staging and used as a guide to the need for adjuvant therapy.

The relationship between proliferative parameters and response to treatment (usually with chemotherapy) is complex. Thus the pretreatment labeling index was the major predictive factor for complete remission in one group of 51 patients with acute myelogenous leukemia, whereas it was not at all predictive for a second group of 201 patients with adult leukemia (Sewell et al, 1981). Similar discrepancies are found in reports relating to solid tumors, and probably arise because of two opposing trends. Most anticancer drugs are more active against proliferating cells (see chapter 17). Thus there may be a higher chance of response to chemotherapy in some tumors with a rapid rate of cell proliferation, although intrinsic drug sensitivity of the cells is likely to be the major determinant of response. In contrast, tumors with a rapid rate of a cell proliferation will grow more rapidly in the absence of effective treatment. A further confounding factor arises because classical methods of assessing cell kinetics do not give information about proliferative rates of the clonogenic cells in tumors, which are the important targets for curative therapy. Thus pretreatment measurements of proliferative parameters presently have limited use in predicting the outcome of treatment.

Many investigators have proposed that measurement of cell kinetic parameters following initial treatment of tumors might be used as a guide to optimization of subsequent scheduling of phase-specific anticancer drugs. The labeling index and flow cytometry have been used most frequently as a guide to drug scheduling, and some authors have claimed that such methods have led to improvements in therapeutic outcome (for critical review, see Tannock, 1978). Unfortunately, such studies are again limited because they do not usually distinguish between the important surviving clonogenic cells, and a greater number of cells that were sterilized by initial treatment and which may remain intact for some time prior to their lysis.

Improved methods for studying the proliferative state of clonogenic cells are essential if cell proliferation is to be studied after cancer treatment, and used as a guide to the scheduling of phase-specific anticancer drugs.

9.7 SUMMARY

Study of the growth of human tumors is restricted to a limited period that is late in their life history, and has been constrained by the need for treatment and the feasibility of making measurements only in certain anatomical sites. Growth is often found to be exponential with mean volume doubling times of the order of 2-3 months for common types of human carcinomas. Tumors may be expected to have undergone at least 30-33 doublings from a single cell prior to detection, and will be lethal in a further 7-10 doublings; because of this long preclinical phase metastases may have occurred prior to detection.

The methods of thymidine autoradiography and flow cytometry have led to detailed studies of cell proliferation in both normal tissues and tumors, and have permitted an understanding of cellular processes that lead to tumor growth. The mean cell-cycle time in human tumors is often short (~3 days) but variable among the cells of the population. Human tumors grow quite slowly because of a low growth fraction and a high rate of cell loss and necrosis. Relatively slow proliferation of the vascular network of tumors may lead to poor and variable nutrition of tumor cells. Limited diffusion of nutrient metabolites from blood vessels, and accumulation of toxic catabolites, may be a major cause of cell death and of a variable and decreasing rate of cell proliferation in tumors.

Normal tissues which are constantly renewed by rapidly proliferating cells, such as the bone marrow and intestine, are commonly dose limiting for cancer chemotherapy. The rate of cell proliferation in human malignancies, including leukemia, is usually slower than that found for some cell populations in these normal tissues. Tumor growth occurs not because of unrestrained cell proliferation, but because cell production is greater than cell loss in tumors, whereas in normal tissues of the adult these rates are equal.

It is an axiom that human tumors, as well as normal tissues, contain a subpopulation of stem cells that can regenerate the tumor after treatment. The stem cells of bone marrow and intestine appear to have a slow rate of proliferation under unstressed conditions. Limited information about tumor stem cells suggests a more rapid rate of proliferation, but methods of assessment may be subject to artifact. Development of improved methods to identify stem-cell subpopulations and to characterize their cytokinetic properties prior to and following treatment deserves high priority.

REFERENCES

Barlogie B, Raber MN, Schumann J et al: Flow cytometry in clinical cancer research. *Cancer Res* 1983; 43:3982–3997.

Becker AJ, McCulloch EA, Siminovitch L, Till JE: The effect of differing demands for blood cell production on DNA synthesis by hemopoietic colony-forming cells of mice. *Blood* 1965; 26:296–308.

Cairnie AB, Lamerton LF, Steel GG: Cell proliferation studies in the intestinal epithelium of the rat. I. Determination of the kinetic parameters. *Exptl Cell Research* 1965; 39:528–538.

Chaplin DJ, Durand RE, Olive PL: Cell selection from a murine tumour using the fluorescent probe Hoechst 33342. *Br J Cancer* 1985; 51:569–572.

Cheng H, Leblond CP: Origin, differentiation and renewal of the four main epithelial cell types in the mouse small intestine. V. Unitarian theory of the origin of the four epithelial cell types. *Am J Anat* 1974; 141:537–561.

Cleaver JE: *Thymidine Metabolism and Cell Kinetics.* New York, Wiley, 1967.

Cronkite EP, Fliedner TM: Granulocytopoiesis. *N Engl J Med* 1964; 270:1347–1352, 1403–1408.

Darzynkiewicz Z, Traganos F, Melamed MR: Distinction between 5-Bromodeoxyuridine labeled and unlabeled mitotic cells by flow cytometry. *Cytometry* 1983; 3:345–348.

Dean PN, Gray JW, Dolbeare FA: The analysis and interpretation of DNA distributions measured by flow cytometry. *Cytometry* 1982; 3188–3195.

Denekamp J, Hobson B: Endothelial-cell proliferation in experimental tumours. *Br J Cancer* 1982; 46:711–720.

Dethlefsen LA, Bauer KD, Riley RM: Analytical cytometric approaches to heterogeneous cell populations in solid tumors: A review. *Cytometry* 1980; 1:89–108.

Dolbeare F, Gratzner H, Pallavicini MG, Gray JW: Flow cytometric measurement of total DNA content and incorporated bromodeoxyuridine. *Proc Natl Acad Sci USA* 1983; 80:5573–5577.

Durand RE: Use of Hoechst 33342 for cell selection from multicell systems. *J Histochem Cytochem* 1982; 30:117–122.

Fauser AA, Messner HA: Proliferative state of human pluripotent hemopoietic progenitors (CFU-GEMM) in normal individuals and under regenerative conditions after bone marrow transplantation. *Blood* 1979; 54:1197–1200.

Fialkow PJ: The origin and development of human tumors studied with cell markers. *N Engl J Med* 1974; 291:26–35.

Folkman J: Tumor angiogenesis: A possible control point in tumor growth. *Ann Intern Med* 1975; 82:96–100.

Freyer JP, Sutherland RM: Regulation of growth saturation and development of necrosis in EMT6/Ro multicellular spheroids by the glucose and oxygen supply. *Cancer Res* 1986; 46:3504–3512.

Friedlander ML, Hedley DW, Taylor IW: Clinical and biological significance of aneuploidy in human tumours. *J Clin Pathol* 1984; 37:961–974.

Gray JW: Quantitative cytokinetics: cellular response to cell cycle specific agents. *Pharmacol Ther* 1983; 22:163–197.

Grdina DJ, Sigdestad CP, Peters LJ: Cytotoxic effect *in vivo* of selected chemotherapeutic agents on synchronized murine fibrosarcoma cells. *Br J Cancer* 1980; 42:677–683.

Howard A, Pelc SR: Nuclear incorporation of P^{32} as demonstrated by autoradiographs. *Exptl Cell Res* 1951; 2:178–187.

Lipkin M, Bell B, Sherlock P: Cell proliferation kinetics in the gastrointestinal tract of man. I. Cell renewal in colon and rectum. *J Clin Invest* 1963; 42:767–776.

McAllister RM, Reed G: Colonial growth in agar of cells derived from neoplastic and non-neoplastic tissue of children. *Pediat Res* 1968; 2:356–360.

Mendelsohn ML: The Growth Fraction: A new concept applied to tumours. *Science* 1960; 132:1496.

Metcalf D: Hemopoietic colonies. *Recent Results Cancer Res* 1977; 61.

Minden MD, Till JE, McCulloch EA: Proliferative state of blast cell progenitors in acute myeloblastic leukemia (AML). *Blood* 1978; 52:592–600.

Nelson JS, Schiffer LM: Autoradiographic detection of DNA polymerase containing nuclei in sarcoma 180 ascites cells. *Cell Tissue Kinet* 1973; 6:45–54.

Pallavicini MG, Gray JW, Folstad LJ: Quantitative analysis of the cytokinetic response of KHT tumors *in vivo* to 1-β-D-Arabinofuranosylcytosine. *Cancer Res* 1982; 42:3125–3131.

Pallavicini MG, Lalande ME, Miller RG, Hill RP: Cell cycle distribution of chronically hypoxic cells and determination of the clonogenic potential of cells accumulated in $G_2 + M$ phases after irradiation of a solid tumor *in vivo. Cancer Res* 1979; 39:1891–1897.

Quastler H, Sherman FG: Cell population kinetics in the intestinal epithelium of the mouse. *Exptl Cell Res* 1959; 17:420–438.

Selby P, Buick RN, Tannock I: A critical appraisal of the "Human Tumor Stem Cell Assay." *N Engl J Med* 1983; 308:129–134.

Sewell RL, Lister TA, Johnson SAN, Crowther D: Lack of prognostic value of the thymidine-labelling index in adult acute leukemia. *Br J Cancer* 1981; 44:55–62.

Shackney SE, McCormack GW, Cuchural GJ Jr: Growth rate patterns of solid tumors and their relation to responsiveness to therapy. An analytical review. *Ann Intern Med* 1978; 89:107–121.

Shimizu T, Motoji T, Oshimi K, Mizoguchi H: Proliferative state and radiosensitivity of human myeloma stem cells. *Br J Cancer* 1982; 45:679–683.

Shirakawa S, Luce JK, Tannock IF, Frei E III: Cell proliferation in human melanoma. *J Clin Invest* 1970; 49:1188–1199.

Steel GG: Cell loss as a factor in the growth rate of human tumours. *Eur J Cancer* 1967; 3:381–387.

Steel GG: *Growth Kinetics of Tumours: Cell Population Kinetics in Relation to the Growth and Treatment of Cancer.* Oxford, Clarendon Press, 1977.

Stohlman F Jr: Erythropoiesis. *N Engl J Med* 1962; 267:342–348, 392–399.

Stryckmans P, Cronkite EP, Fache J et al: Deoxyribonucleic acid synthesis time of erythropoietic and granulopoietic cells in human beings. *Nature* 1966; 211:711–720.

Sutherland RM, McCredie JA, Inch WR: Growth of multicell spheroids in tissue culture as a model of nodular carcinomas. *J Natl Cancer Inst* 1971; 46:113–120.

Tannock IF: The relation between cell proliferation and the vascular system in a transplanted mouse mammary tumour. *Br J Cancer* 1968; 22:258–273.

Tannock IF: Population kinetics of carcinoma cells, capillary endothelial cells, and fibroblasts in a transplanted mouse mammary tumor. *Cancer Res* 1970; 30:2470–2476.

Tannock IF: Cell kinetics and chemotherapy: a critical review. *Cancer Treat Rep* 1978; 62:1117–1133.

Tannock IF: Biology of tumor growth. *Hosp Pract* 1983; 18:81–93.

Thomlinson RH, Gray LH: The histological structure of some human lung cancers and the possible implications for radiotherapy. *Br J Cancer* 1955; 9:539–549.

Till JE, McCulloch EA: A direct measurement of the radiation sensitivity of normal mouse bone marrow cells. *Radiat Res* 1961; 14:213–222.

Till JE, McCulloch EA: Hemopoietic stem cell differentiation. *Biochim Biophys Acta* 1980; 605:431–459.

Todo A: Proliferation and differentiation of hematopoietic cells in hematologic disorders. *In vivo* radio-autographic study of leukemia including erythroleukemia. *Acta Haemat Jap* 1968; 31:947–966.

Van Dilla MA, Trujillo TT, Mullaney PF, Coulter JR: Cell microfluorometry: A method for rapid fluorescence measurement. *Science* 1969; 163:1213–1214.

Withers HR, Elkind MM: Microcolony survival assay for cells of mouse intestinal mucosa exposed to radiation. *Int J Radiat Biol* 1970; 17:261–267.

Wright N, Alison M: *The Biology of Epithelial Cell Populations.* Clarendon Press, Oxford, 1984.

BIBLIOGRAPHY

Barlogie B, Raber MN, Schumann J et al: Flow cytometry in clinical cancer research. *Cancer Res* 1983; 43:3982–3997.

Gray JW: Quantitative cytokinetics: cellular response to cell cycle specific agents. *Pharmacol Ther* 1983; 22:163–197.

Steel GG: *Growth Kinetics of Tumours: Cell Population Kinetics in Relation to the Growth and Treatment of Cancer.* Oxford, Clarendon Press, 1977.

Tannock IF: Cell kinetics and chemotherapy: A critical review. *Cancer Treat Rep* 1978; 62:1117–1133.

10

Metastasis

Richard P. Hill

10.1 INTRODUCTION

10.1.1 THE SPREAD OF CANCER

The ability of the cells of a cancer to disseminate and form new foci of growth at noncontiguous sites (ie, to form metastases) represents its most malignant characteristic and is responsible for the majority of cancer deaths. While clinicians have been relatively successful in the development of methods to treat solid tumors which are localised, they have been much less successful in their attempts to eradicate malignant disease when it has metastasized.

Cancer cells can spread along tissue planes and into various tissues spaces and cavities, but the two major routes of metastatic spread are via lymphatic vessels or blood vessels. Indeed, for the purpose of clinical staging, metastases are subdivided into two groups: those in regional lymph nodes, which are usually regarded as having disseminated via the lymphatic circulation, and those which arise at more distant sites and organs, which have usually spread via the blood vascular system (Fig 10.1). It used to be thought that these two routes were independent options and sarcomas were regarded as most likely to spread via the blood vascu-

lar system, while carcinomas spread initially via lymphatics to lymph nodes, where the cells could be arrested before disseminating more widely. These two circulation systems are widely interconnected, however,

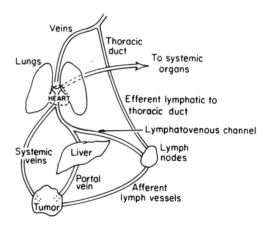

Figure 10.1. The major routes by which cancer cells can spread from a primary tumor are through the lymphatic or blood vessels. These two systems are interconnected as illustrated. (Adapted from Sugarbaker, 1981.)

such that they cannot be regarded as being independent routes of spread.

Different types of tumors have different patterns of spread. Tumors of the head and neck, for example, usually spread initially to regional lymph nodes and only when more advanced to distant sites; thus localised therapy which includes treatment of regional neck nodes can be effective if given at an early stage of disease. In contrast, tumors of the breast can spread early to distant sites. Involvement of axillary lymph nodes at the time of primary treatment is correlated with the presence of distant metastases, but about 25% of patients with no evidence of lymph node disease at the time of primary treatment are later found to have widespread metastases. Thus the lack of lymph-node metastases does not rule out the possibility that the cancer has disseminated via the blood vascular system.

10.1.2 METASTASES OF HUMAN TUMORS

Clinical observations have indicated that metastases from certain types of tumors tend to occur in specific target organs (for examples see Table 10.1). While lungs, liver, lymph nodes and brain are the most common sites of spread, the lesser, more specific sites led Paget (1889) to propose the "soil and seed" hypothesis, in which he postulated that differential tumor-cell/host-organ interactions can occur, which are more or less favourable for metastatic development. The alternate, though not mutually exclusive, hypothesis is that the so-called "organ preference" can be explained largely on the basis of hemodynamic considerations (ie, the number of metastases which develop in an organ is related to the number of cells delivered to that organ by the blood and the number that are arrested in the capillaries) (Fig 10.2).

Sugarbaker (1981) has reviewed data on the dissemination of human cancers, obtained either from autopsies or from studies of the initial development of metastatic lesions in treated patients. The extensive data from autopsies demonstrate the concept of organ specificity for metastases as noted above (Table 10.1), but sites of initial metastases tend to be the organ containing the first capillary bed encountered (first-pass organ) by the cells after release from the tumor (Fig 10.2). For tumors whose blood supply drains into the vena cava this would be the lung, while for tumors whose venous drainage is into the portal system it would be the liver. This finding is consistent with the idea that there are sites of initial metastatic development from which further metastases are spread to other (tumor-specific) organs (ie, many metastases arise as tertiary or quarternary growths). Alternatively, the observations may reflect the fact that most tumor cells are trapped in the first-pass organ and hence relatively few viable cells reach the arterial circulation in which they can be distributed to all parts of the body. Thus even if the probability that a tumor cell will survive and initiate a metastasis in the first-pass organ is very much lower than that for another (tumor-specific) organ, the large number of cells trapped could result in an overall higher chance of metastasis formation in the first-pass organ. In either case it appears likely that both hemodynamic factors and the selective growth of cells in certain organs influence the distribution of metastases from human tumors.

Recent studies in animals have allowed dissection of

Table 10.1. Clinical Metastasis to Specific Target Organs

Primary Tumor	Common Distant Secondary Sites
Clear-cell carcinoma of the kidney	lung, bone, adrenal
Prostatic carcinoma	bone
Small-cell carcinoma of the lung	brain, liver, bone marrow
Melanoma in the skin	liver, brain, bowel
Melanoma in the eye	liver
Neuroblastoma	liver, adrenal
Carcinoma of breast	bone, brain, adrenal, lung, liver
Follicular carcinoma of thyroid	bone, lung

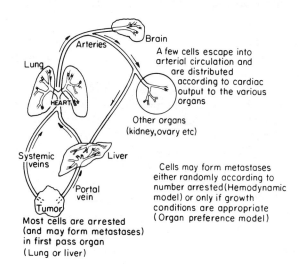

Figure 10.2. The vascular spread of tumor cells results in most of the cells being delivered initially to the lung or liver, where they are likely to be arrested in the capillary bed. If the cells traverse the capillary bed of the first-pass organ, they can be distributed to the other organs where they may be similarly trapped.

the many steps involved in the metastatic process, and a partial elucidation of the basis of metastatic distribution. The remainder of this chapter will discuss some of these studies.

10.2 THE METASTATIC PROCESS

10.2.1 METASTATIC INEFFICIENCY

The ability of tumor cells to establish metastases appears to be a very inefficient process. Blood samples taken from cancer patients, particularly during or just after surgery, often appear to contain significant numbers of tumor cells, yet the patients do not always develop metastatic disease. Such studies have been criticized on the basis that many of the cells counted may not have been tumor cells or may not have been viable, but studies with experimental animal tumors support the concept that many viable tumor cells are released into the circulation. By collecting blood samples from the sole efferent vessel of a carcinoma growing in the rat ovary, a tumor that forms very few metastases, Butler and Gullino (1975) estimated that about 1 million tumor cells were released every 24 hr. Similar results have been obtained from the shedding of cells into lymphatic vessels (Carr and Carr, 1980). Glaves (1983), who sampled blood from the right ventricle, estimated that between 10^7 and 10^8 viable cells are shed into the blood during the growth of transplantable B16 melanomas and Lewis lung tumors (approximately 20 days), but these cells give rise to less than 100 lung metastases per mouse. Furthermore, in the large number of experiments in which tumor cells have been introduced directly into the circulation of mice or rats it is rare that more than 1% of such cells form tumor nodules. More commonly the efficiency is two or more orders of magnitude lower.

All these results suggest that the initial release of tumor cells is not the limiting factor in metastatic development. Glaves (1983), however, did obtain a correlation between the number of cells released and the number of metastases observed, which is consistent with the idea that the greater the number of cells released the greater the probability that the limiting event will occur. Experimental data suggest that there are probably large differences in cell release between different tumors and that this influences metastasis formation (see, for example, Price et al, 1982).

10.2.2 THE METASTATIC CASCADE

The process which a cell must undergo to form a metastasis is complex, involving escape from the primary tumor, movement to a new location and estab-

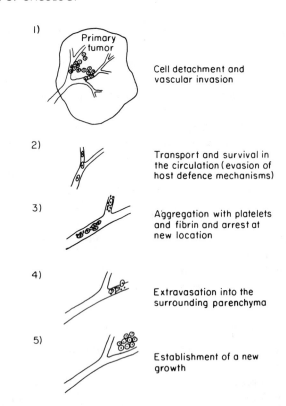

Figure 10.3. Schematic illustration of the various stages of the metastatic cascade.

lishment of growth at the new site. The various steps associated with the process, sometimes called the metastatic cascade, are essentially the same whether the cell escapes into lymphatic or blood vessels, and are illustrated in Figure 10.3. To be successful in forming a metastasis, a cell must be proficient in negotiating each of the stages depicted in Figure 10.3. It is not sufficient that it be highly capable in only one or two stages. Thus there is probably no single property of a tumor cell which is uniquely associated with the ability to form metastases.

10.2.3 DETACHMENT AND INVASION

The ability of cancer cells to invade is characteristic of malignancy. Before cells can invade they must be able to detach from their parent tumor mass and the site of initial detachment will likely influence whether the initial route of spread is via the lymphatic or venous system. In tumors in which there is ready access to the blood stream, cell detachment or shedding can occur directly into the blood vessels. This may occur as a result of prior invasion of the tumor mass into vessels or because vascular channels in some tumors can be lined with tumor cells.

A higher rate of detachment has been associated with

rapid tumor growth and the extent of necrosis in a tumor, as well as mechanical stress and increased cellular activity of various enzymes (Weiss and Ward, 1983). Decreased levels of the proteins fibronectin and laminin, which are involved in adhesion of cells to substrates, may also facilitate detachment. Transformation of cells is often associated with a reduced amount of these two proteins on the cell surface.

Histopathological studies have indicated that metastatic cells, as well as normal leukocytes, are able to transverse basement membranes. Most in vitro studies of this process have examined penetration through membranes from the endothelial cell side (ie, extravasation rather than intravasation), but it is generally assumed that similar mechanisms are involved. These mechanisms are discussed in more detail in section 10.2.5.

10.2.4 HOST DEFENSE MECHANISMS

Experimental studies in which radiolabeled tumor cells have been injected into the systemic or portal veins have demonstrated that the majority of cells are arrested initially in the lung or liver capillaries respectively (ie, the first capillary bed they encounter). Over a period of a few hours most of the cells are lost from this initial site of arrest (Fig 10.4), apparently as a result of cell death. This rapid loss of cells is not well understood but as seen in Figure 10.4, it can account

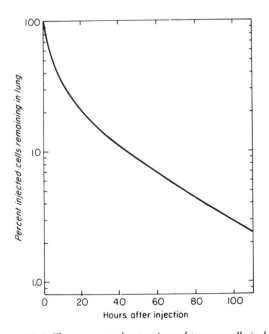

Figure 10.4. The arrest and retention of tumor cells in lung was assessed by injecting the animal intravenously with radiolabeled tumor cells and then determining the radioactivity remaining in the lungs at various times after the injection.

for 90–99% of the cells. Possible mechanisms for the death of cells include mechanical stresses in the small blood vessels, poor nutrition, toxicity due to high oxygen levels in the blood or the action of specific or nonspecific immune effector cells such as T lymphocytes, polymorphs, macrophages or natural-killer (NK) cells.

Immunological mechanisms (see section 14.4) are clearly involved in defense against metastatic development for some experimental tumors in rodents. Many experimental tumors, especially those induced by injection of chemical carcinogens or viruses or resulting from exposure to UV light, can be highly immunogenic and, although they grow locally, they rarely metastasize. It has been shown that T-lymphocyte-dependent cytotoxicity is active in preventing metastases by such tumor cells, both by establishing an inverse correlation between the degree of immunogenicity and metastatic ability and by demonstrating that a range of different immunosuppressive procedures can increase the metastatic ability of the tumor cells. These observations explain why many experimental tumors are poorly metastatic, but their relevance to human tumors or even spontaneous animal tumors is unclear, since few, if any, such tumors demonstrate significant immunogenicity in vivo (see section 14.3).

Tumor cells which are non- or only weakly immunogenic, or those which are implanted into T-cell-deficient animals (nude or immune-deprived mice or rats) also often fail to metastasize. This is particularly true of xenogeneic transplants of human tumors into nude mice. It has been suggested that NK cells, which act against malignant cells nonspecifically and are present in increased numbers in nude mice, play an important role in controlling the metastatic ability of such tumor cells. Hanna (1984) has examined this issue in detail and, by manipulating NK cell levels in the mice, has shown that there is an inverse correlation between the activity of NK cells in the host animal and the metastatic ability of injected tumor cells. NK cells appear to be most effective against circulating blood-borne tumor cells and exhibit only a limited effect against tumor cells that have already formed small metastatic foci.

10.2.5 ARREST AND EXTRAVASATION

The arrest of tumor cells in the small blood vessels of organs is often associated with thrombus formation involving the interaction of the cells with platelets and leukocytes. Thrombi have been observed around arrested tumor cells but apparently remain for only a few hours before being broken down, presumably by fibrolytic enzymes such as plasmin produced or activated by the tumor cells. Such thrombi might provide protection for the cells against mechanical trauma due to the blood flow and against host cells. Rapid fibrinolysis may be one reason why the cells are lost rapidly from the initial organ of arrest.

The importance of thrombus formation in the development of metastasis is controversial. Administration of anticoagulants can reduce the number of metastases after IV injection (experimental metastases) but has little effect on formation of spontaneous metastases (Hilgard, 1984). Aggregation of platelets may, however, be more important. Cancer cells are found associated with loose aggregates of platelets and some tumor cells have been shown to be capable of inducing platelet aggregation by releasing procoagulant activity (Gasic, 1984). Platelet adhesiveness is related to a balance of prostaglandins (prostacyclin and thromboxane), which are produced by endothelial cells and platelets respectively, and the presence of tumor cells may disrupt this balance since some tumor cells can release prostaglandins (Stringfellow, 1984).

Regions where loss of endothelial cells has occurred, either naturally or due to local trauma, might be expected to be low in prostacyclin (which inhibits platelet aggregation) synthesis. Such regions of denuded basement membrane may provide preferential sites for tumor-cell retention and this may explain the observation that trauma and inflammation apparently encourage seeding. Drugs which modify prostaglandin synthesis have been shown to affect the numbers of both experimental and spontaneous metastases formed in experimental animals (see section 19.3.2).

Recent in vitro studies of tumor cell attachment to and invasion through endothelial cell monolayers and their basement-membrane-like matrix have been reviewed by Nicolson et al (1984) and Liotta (1986), and the basic concepts are illustrated in Figure 10.5. Following attachment to the endothelial cells, the tumor cell extends pseudopodia into the endothelial cell junctions or induces endothelial cell retraction, allowing access to the basement membrane where attachment is mediated by laminin. Various proteolytic enzymes are produced which digest part of the basement membrane, permitting the tumor cell to escape into the interstitial space. Leukocytes are also capable of extravasation and migration and tumor cells have been observed apparently following leukocytes through vessel walls.

Many different proteolytic enzyme activities have been found to be produced by tumor cells growing in vitro (see Figure 10.6). For example, many tumor cells are found to produce increased levels of plasminogen activator (PA), which acts on plasminogen in the blood to release plasmin (see section 11.5.1). Some of these enzymes could act either directly or indirectly by activating other enzymes to break down major base-

ment membrane components such as type IV collagen, laminin, fibronectin and sulfated proteoglycans. Many of these enzymes are lysosomal in origin and they can probably facilitate cell detachment as well as invasion. However, there are factors in tissue and serum which can inhibit the extracellular activity of these enzymes and the role of any specific enzyme in the process of invasion in vivo has not yet been established.

10.2.6 ESTABLISHMENT OF A NEW GROWTH

As discussed earlier the extravasation of tumor cells permits them access to the tissue interstitial space, where they are partially protected and can divide and grow if conditions are appropriate, although in some cases growth can occur within the blood vessel itself. The appropriateness of the growth conditions in a *specific* organ for a *particular* tumor cell are an important aspect of Paget's "soil and seed" hypothesis to explain organ specificity of metastases. Most experimental studies have concentrated on cellular properties (the seed)

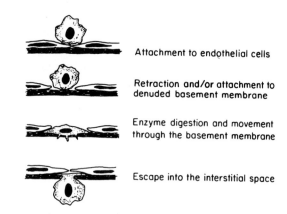

Figure 10.5. Schematic representation of the processes involved in extravasation of a tumor cell through the wall of a capillary (Adapted from Nicolson, 1982.)

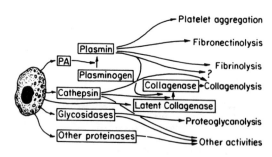

Figure 10.6. Illustration of some of the proteolytic enzymes which can be released by malignant cells and some of their possible activities. (Adapted from Nicolson, 1982.)

and specific organ properties (the soil) have received scant attention. The observations that cells require specific growth factors for proliferation and the emerging relationship between oncogenes and growth factors (see chapter 5 and section 8.4.5) have resulted in current theories about "soil" properties (Hart, 1982) being largely concerned with such factors.

Tumor cells are less dependent on growth factors than normal cells and there is evidence that the more autonomous the cells, the more capable they are of forming tumors in animals (eg, nude mice) and of metastasizing. However, most tumor cells are not entirely autonomous and the lack of appropriate growth factors and/or the presence of inhibiting factors in the tissue could prevent tumor-cell proliferation and hence formation of metastasis. Such cells may die or possibly may remain dormant in the organ until appropriate stimulation occurs. Recent studies examining the ability of individual tumor cells to grow on tissue matrix produced by the cells of different organs may provide further insight into the importance of soil properties in the development of metastases. Even if the tumor cell can proliferate in the organ, the growing tumor mass will need a blood supply if it is to become progressively larger, and it must therefore produce (or induce) angiogenesis factors (see section 9.6.2).

10.3 METASTATIC ABILITY OF TUMOR CELL POPULATIONS

10.3.1 ASSAYS FOR METASTATIC POTENTIAL

Many aspects of the metastatic cascade have been examined in vitro but in vivo studies are also necessary. A wide range of experimental models has been used for the examination of metastatic behaviour in vivo, ranging from spontaneous tumors to highly transplantable tumors. The relevance of various model systems to metastatic human tumors is often questioned but metastasis is a complex process and model systems allow examination of specific aspects of the process. The interpretation of results must, however, recognize the limitations of the chosen model.

Studies of metastatic potential have usually been performed in rodents because of the availability of a wide range of tumor systems and inbred strains of animals for testing. One exception is the use of the chorioallantoic membrane (CAM) in chicken eggs for studies of the invasive properties of tumor cells and to examine metastasis in the chick embryo itself (Fig 10.7). A small window is made in the shell of the egg and cells are introduced either onto the CAM surface or injected directly into blood vessels in the membrane. Invasion of the cells across the membrane can be observed mi-

croscopically and the formation of metastases in organs of the chick embryo can be quantitated. Because of the minimal immunological capacity of the early chick embryo this system has been used to study not only chick cells but also rodent and human cells.

In rodents most studies have examined hematogeneous spread of metastases and three basic procedures have been adopted (see Fig 10.8). Tumor cells can be injected directly into the arterial or venous blood circulation and allowed to disseminate and arrest at various sites. If the cells are radiolabeled (usually with iododeoxyuridine 125, which is incorporated into DNA in place of thymidine) then killing of the animals at various times and counting the radioactivity in different organs will give information about the initial arrest and subsequent survival of the tumor cells (see Fig 10.4). Alternatively, the cells can be allowed to form metastases and their number and distribution in the various organs may be quantitated. This latter procedure is often called a colonization or experimental metastasis assay.

In a spontaneous metastasis assay, tumor cells or pieces of tumor are implanted at a local site (eg, subcutaneously or intramuscularly) where they can form a tumor. Tumor cells can escape into the circulation and move to other sites to form metastases, which can then be quantitated after killing of the animal. To allow sufficient time for cells seeded from a local tumor to form macroscopically detectable metastases it may be necessary to remove the local tumor surgically or to ablate it with radiation. It is also possible to use a spontaneous metastasis assay to examine the ability of cells to form lymphatic metastases by implanting the cells into the hind footpad of the animal. Such primary tumors will often spread to the popliteal lymph node, which can easily be examined for tumor growth.

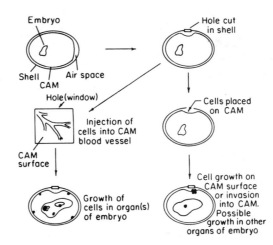

Figure 10.7. Assay for invasion and/or metastatic properties of tumor cells using the chick chorioallantoic membrane.

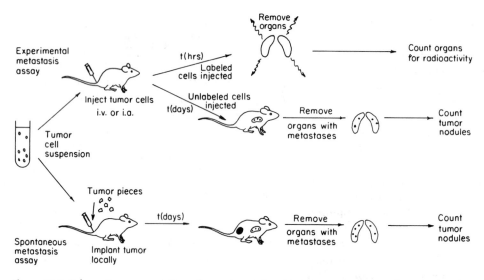

Figure 10.8. Schematic representation of experimental and spontaneous metastasis assays in mice.

These assays do not examine a single metastatic property of the cells; rather they examine the end result of a combination of properties. An experimental metastasis assay tests the ability of cells to survive in the circulation, to arrest in a target organ, to avoid host defenses, to invade a new organ and to establish a new tumor growth (ie, the latter part of the metastatic cascade). Study of spontaneous metastases tests all these properties plus the ability to initiate a tumor growth at the local site and to invade and to disseminate into blood vessels. Although a combination of properties are required for metastasis formation, one specific property may represent a "rate-limiting step," controlling the frequency of metastasis formation. It is possible that this rate-limiting property may be different for different tumors.

The experimental and spontaneous metastasis assay procedures have been compared using several different tumor cell lines with different metastatic properties. Varying degrees of correlation have been observed. Some cell populations which are effective at forming metastases after intravenous injection can be very inefficient at forming spontaneous metastases. This result may be anticipated since the experimental metastasis assay tests only part of the metastatic process. A greater efficiency at forming spontaneous metastases than expected from the results of an experimental metastasis assay may be related to tumor-cell release, as discussed earlier. A tumor which releases a very large number of cells can potentially overcome inefficiency in the latter stages of the metastatic process.

Many factors can influence formation of metastases, including the site of local tumor growth and the health, gender and age of the animals. Careful husbandry of

animals and matching of their age and sex are required for valid and reproducible experiments.

10.3.2 SELECTION OF POPULATIONS WITH SPECIFIC METASTATIC PROPERTIES

Cells with increased or decreased ability to generate metastases may be selected from experimental tumors. The now classical example of this approach is the selection of the B16F10 cell population from B16 mouse melanoma cells by Fidler (1973). The procedure (see Fig 10.9) involved serial passage of the cells through animals with selection at each stage for cells which had formed lung metastases. The cells from the lung metastases were grown in culture to expand their number before being reinjected in animals. After ten such passages a population of cells was obtained (termed B16F10 cells) which were about ten times as efficient at forming experimental lung metastases after intravenous injection as the starting B16F1 cell population. Many groups have worked with these cell populations (B16F1 and B16F10) and this difference in metastatic efficiency is usually found to be a stable property of the B16F10 cell line, although there is some variation in the numerical differences found. Other investigators have been successful, using similar approaches, in selecting cell populations from a number of experimental tumors which have enhanced metastatic ability in a variety of organs including lung, liver, ovary and brain.

A range of in vitro attributes, which are potentially related to various stages of the metastatic cascade, have also been used to select for cells which, when tested in vivo, were found to have altered metastatic ability. These procedures have included detachment from

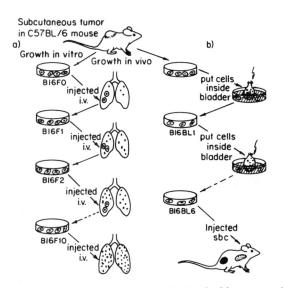

Figure 10.9. Procedures used for selecting highly metastatic cell populations from B16 melanoma cells. The B16F10 cells were selected by passaging the cells ten times through the lungs of mice, while the B16BL6 cells were selected by requiring them to invade six times through the walls of mouse bladders.

monolayers, resistance to lysis by lymphocytes, resistance to lectin-mediated toxicity, attachment to collagen and the ability to invade various tissues maintained in organ culture. In one such experiment (Hart, 1979) B16 melanoma cells were placed inside a mouse bladder suspended in semisolid agar with tissue culture medium. Cells which were capable of migrating through the bladder wall and growing in the agar were selected and the process was repeated sequentially six times (see Fig 10.9). The cell line obtained (called B16BL6) is highly invasive and more efficient at forming spontaneous metastases than unselected B16 cells. The selected cell line does not have increased ability to form experimental metastases after intravenous injection; thus its selective advantage appears to be in detachment or vascular invasion.

In a reversal of the more usual procedures Kerbel et al (1982) started with a tumor cell line that is highly metastatic in mice and attempted to select cells which had reduced metastatic ability. They isolated cells which were resistant to the lectin, wheat germ agglutinin (WGA), since lectin-resistant cells have been found to have specific changes in cell-surface carbohydrates and it was hoped to associate these with metastatic ability. Many of the WGA-resistant cells were found to be poorly metastatic, but much of this effect was due to increased immunogenicity. Detailed study of one cell line that formed tumors, some of which did metastasize, demonstrated that there was a different time course and organ distribution in the development of these metastases than that observed with the parental cells. It was found that the tumors which seeded metastases arose from hybrid cells which had formed in vivo between the tumor cells and a host cell of hemopoietic origin. The hybrid cells had lost their WGA-resistant phenotype (which is recessive) and presumably the other surface change(s) which had promoted immunogenicity. This finding raises the interesting possibility that such in vivo hybridization may be a mechanism by which tumor cells can acquire properties which enhance their ability to metastasize; for example, some types of hemopoietic cells are naturally invasive.

10.3.3 ORGAN SPECIFICITY

The concept of organ specificity of metastatic development, derived from autopsy studies (see section 10.1.2), is supported by investigations using animal tumor models. It has been found (see, for example, Tarin and Price, 1981) that cell populations which form a large number of metastatic deposits in one organ (ie, the lung following intravenous injection of the cells) are not necessarily capable of doing so in another (eg, liver following intraportal injection). Similarly, the patterns of cell arrest observed when radiolabeled cells are injected into animals, either intravenously or intraarterially, do not correlate with the development of metastases following similar injections of nonlabeled cells.

More specifically, it has been possible to obtain populations of cells which have enhanced ability to form metastases in particular organs by serially selecting cells from metastases in these organs. Furthermore, it has been shown that cells which form metastases preferentially in lung will "home" to this organ even when it is transplanted ectopically into a subcutaneous site; such cells do not form metastases nonspecifically in any organ which is transplanted ectopically (Fig 10.10). A similar result has been obtained using parabiosed animals (ie, a pair of animals in which the circulation systems have been joined so that blood flows between the two animals). Tumor cells injected into one animal will form metastases preferentially in the same organ in both animals (Fig 10.10).

The selection of cell populations with enhanced or organ-specific metastatic properties suggests either that cells can adapt to growth in a specific organ or that specific metastatic cells preexist in the tumor cell population at low frequency and that the selection procedure increases this frequency. Experiments in which cells were serially passaged by direct injection into particular organs demonstrated that growth in the organ did not, of itself, enhance the ability of cells injected intra-

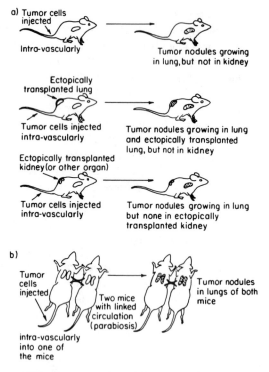

Figure 10.10. Demonstration of the organ selectivity of tumor cells. *a,* Tumor cells which are highly metastatic to lung will form metastases in ectopically transplanted lung but not other ectopically transplanted organs. *b,* If two animals have their circulation systems linked by parabiosis then cells injected intravenously into one mouse will form metastases in the same organs (eg, lung) in both mice.

venously to form metastases in that organ. The possibility of the presence of subpopulations of cells, with specific metastatic properties, within a tumor-cell population has been examined using cloning experiments and is discussed in the next section.

10.3.4 CLONAL POPULATIONS AND HETEROGENEITY

Fidler and Kripke (1977) cloned B16 melanoma cells by plating in vitro at limiting dilution, so that any growth could be expected to originate from a single cell. A number of clones were isolated, expanded in culture and their cells tested for their ability to form experimental metastases (see Fig 10.11). The number of metastases produced by any one clone was relatively constant within the group of mice injected, but the individual clones demonstrated a wide variation amongst themselves. These results indicated wide heterogeneity in metastatic ability between the different clones and limited experiments in which subclones were isolated and tested, suggested that the individual clones "bred true" in terms of metastatic ability. This result is consistent with the presence, in the original tumor cell population, of cells with different metastatic abilities.

In subsequent experiments, similar results have been described for a wide range of different tumor cell lines, including a number of newly induced tumors. Results obtained using the transplantable KHT fibrosarcoma

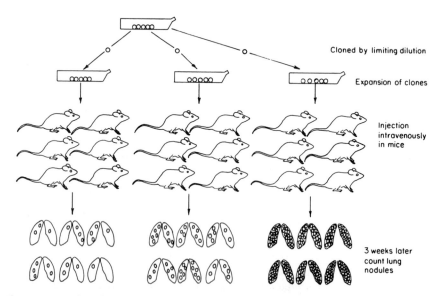

Figure 10.11. Clonal heterogeneity is demonstrated by establishing a series of clones from a tumor cell population and, after expansion, testing them for metastatic ability. Although there is some variability in the number of nodules observed in different animals injected with cells from the same clone, there is much greater variability between the clones.

are shown in Figure 10.12. These data show that wide heterogeneity is observed even if the tumor cells are cloned (by limiting dilution) in vivo and not exposed to in vitro growth. In a number of these cloning studies heterogeneity has been demonstrated both for the formation of experimental metastases and for production of spontaneous metastases.

These findings, which demonstrate wide variation between clonal populations, have been interpreted to indicate that the parental tumor population is heterogeneous and that the cloning procedure reveals this heterogeneity. This conclusion seems to be supported by the subcloning experiments which demonstrated that many of the clones appeared to breed true, and by studies in which sublines isolated from individual metastases were found to exhibit a more uniform metastatic potential. However, subsequent studies of the metastatic properties of clonally derived populations have often shown them to be relatively unstable, if they are grown continuously in culture and tested at various times. Moreover, recent results (see section 10.4.3) sug-

gest that variant cells expressing a phenotype which increases their probability of forming metastases can be generated spontaneously at a rapid rate in some cloned tumor-cell populations. Much of the heterogeneity observed between clones could thus be the result of the stochastic nature of the generation of such variants.

10.3.5 CLONAL INTERACTION

Heterogeneity within tumor-cell populations is not confined to metastatic ability, but is characteristic of many other properties such as antigenicity and response to drugs. Furthermore, interaction has been shown to occur between different cloned populations, leading to modulation of the expression of these properties in the individual clones (Heppner, 1984). Clonal interaction has also been demonstrated (Poste and Greig, 1982) to influence the metastatic behavior of cloned cell lines of the B16 melanoma (Fig 10.13). When individual clones were grown in culture for a short time (less than ten passages) and were then subcloned, the subclonal popu-

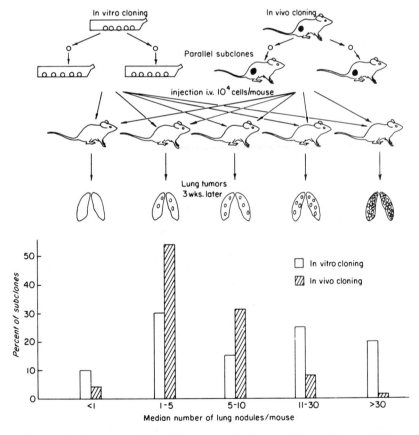

Figure 10.12. The range of clonal heterogeneity observed for subclones of KHT sarcoma cells grown either in vitro (40 subclones) or in vivo (26 subclones). (Adapted from Chambers et al, 1981.)

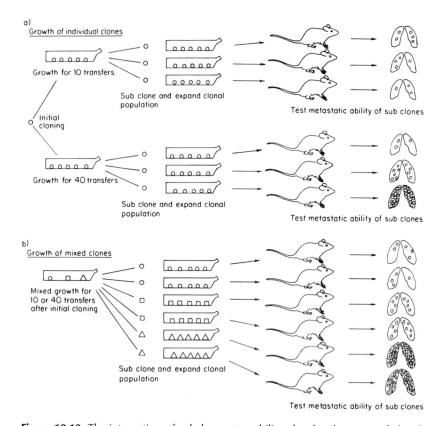

Figure 10.13. The interaction of subclones to stabilize the development of clonal heterogeneity can be demonstrated by growing clones with different metastatic abilities as a mixed population. *a,* If individual clones are grown for either 10 or 40 transfers and then subcloned, the metastatic ability of the cells in the subclones is found to be quite similar after 10 transfers but to be very heterogeneous after 40 transfers. *b,* When clones with different metastatic abilities (identifiable by drug-resistant markers) are grown as a mixed population for 10 or 40 transfers and then subcloned, the metastatic ability of the cells in the subclones is maintained and heterogeneity is not observed within each group of drug marked subclones.

lations exhibited relatively uniform metastatic ability. However, when the clones were grown for 40 passages in culture before subcloning, there was considerable variation between the subclones, consistent with the concept of clonal instability. If individual clonal populations which had different metastatic abilities (and could be identified by their resistance to certain drugs) were mixed together and then grown for 40 passages before subcloning and testing of the metastatic ability (and drug resistance), the individual clones demonstrated much less variability. Apparently the clones had interacted to stabilize each other. Further studies demonstrated that clones derived from different types of cells did not interact with each other. The generality of these interesting findings needs to be examined in other types of tumor cells, but they illustrate a new and largely unexplored area of cooperative cell biology.

10.4 PROPERTIES OF METASTATIC CELLS

10.4.1 BIOCHEMICAL PROPERTIES AND THE CELL SURFACE

It is the outer plasma membrane of a cell which interacts with the environment; thus any change in metastatic properties seems likely to involve changes at the cell surface. A number of different methods have been used to study specific properties of the cell surface which might correlate with metastatic ability. The availability of cell populations which can be selected from a tumor to have different metastatic properties, either by serial passage or by cloning, has provided populations of cells whose properties could be compared. Cells derived directly from a primary tumor or from its metastases have also been studied. Alternatively, several investigators have selected cells in vitro for specific properties such as lack of adhesiveness, ability to produce a specific enzyme, or ability to invade, or they have treated cells with agents that change cell-surface properties. They have then examined the metastatic abilities of the selected or treated cells.

The large number of studies which have tried to identify specific biochemical properties of the cell surface which may be related to metastatic behaviour have been reviewed extensively (Nicolson, 1982; Turner, 1982) and fall into a number of different categories (see Table 10.2). Many of these studies have obtained correlations between specific changes at the cell surface and metastatic behaviour for one type of cell. However, other studies, using different cell lines and experimental procedures, have often found different results. Alternatively, pairs of cell lines which are either poorly (or non-) metastatic or highly metastatic in vivo have been found to demonstrate multiple differences in their cell-surface properties. Whether any or all of such differences are responsible for the different metastatic behaviour, however, remains an open question. In the conclusion to his review Turner states, "As yet, biological and biochemical investigations of the cell surface have not discovered a *unique* property that is related to metastasis."

10.4.2 SURFACE ANTIGENS

Another approach to examining cell-surface alterations is to identify antigenic differences by developing monoclonal antibodies specific to metastatic cells. A large number of monoclonal antibodies have been developed with varying degrees of specificity against different tumor cells, and some of these have been shown to be capable of preventing or reducing the development of metastases. However, to date there are only a few reports of monoclonal antibodies which demonstrate specificity for a metastatic phenotype expressed by cells or cell populations (Shearman and Longenecker, 1981; Olsson and Forchhammer, 1984). The paucity of reports of successful isolation of monoclonal antibodies specific for metastatic cells suggests that it is exceedingly difficult to obtain them. Possible reasons are that highly metastatic cells arise as a result of the loss of antigenic determinants, or that antigenic differences are unstable or expressed only on a minority of the population. Instability of the metastatic phenotype would limit the potential of such experiments.

The importance of the expression of major histocompatibility complex (MHC) gene products (see chapter 14) on the cell surface in relation to metastases has been examined by Eisenbach et al (1984). In two different tumors the relative expression of the K and D ends of the MHC haplotype was different for subpopulations with different metastatic potential. However, it was the ratio of their expression (ie, H-2K/H-2D) which correlated with increased metastatic ability, rather than increased expression or loss of either haplotype. It seems likely that these findings relate to altered immunogenicity of the cells.

10.4.3 GENETIC BASIS OF METASTASIS

The evidence that metastatic properties of cells are heritable, at least in the short term, suggests that genetic changes may be involved. The question of

Table 10.2. Comparisons of the Properties of Highly Metastatic and Poorly or Nonmetastatic Cells

Cell Property Studied	General Comments
Membrane proteins and glycoproteins	A wide range of changes has been observed using a range of different techniques. No general relationships demonstrated
Surface carbohydrates	Many different carbohydrate side-chain modifications have been observed particularly related to sialic acid (and surface charge). No definitive relationships have been established
Glycolipids	There are currently no obvious general glycolipid changes which are associated with metastatic ability
Enzymes (proteases, glycosidases, glycosylases) released	Many different enzymes appear to be correlated with metastatic behavior in particular cell lines, but the role of any specific enzyme, eg, plasminogen activator, remains uncertain
Adhesive properties	No one adhesive component is able to explain the many complex interactions which occur during metastasis
Surface charge	There is no obvious relationship between surface charge and the malignancy of a cell

Note: Adapted from Nicolson, 1982.

whether metastatic phenotypes are dominant or recessive has been studied using cell hybrids with a variety of different fusion partners. Results of these studies (see Ling et al, 1985) have suggested that nonmetastatic cells can acquire metastatic properties by fusing with normal cells, possibly as a result of modified immunogenicity, but this is not a universal finding. Results involving fusions of tumor cells with different metastatic properties have also been equivocal.

Some recent studies have also addressed the question of whether metastatic potential can be transferred by DNA transfection. These studies (see Ling et al, 1985; Bernstein and Weinberg, 1985) demonstrate that transfection of a metastatic phenotype is possible, but further studies are required to establish the generality of the phenomenon. At present the specific genes responsible have not been identified and it is unknown whether they have any similarities in biochemical function.

The rapid changes in metastatic properties which have been observed and their relative instabilities imply that any genetic changes may also be unstable. Ling et al (1985) have described experiments in which they applied Luria–Delbruck fluctuation analysis (see section

19.2) to examine the rapid changes in metastatic properties which they had observed in cloned populations of KHT fibrosarcoma and B16F1 and B16F10 melanoma cells (see Fig 10.14). They found that metastatic variants (cells capable of forming experimental metastases) were being generated spontaneously during the growth of the cloned populations. To explain these results they postulated a "dynamic heterogeneity" model in which it was proposed that the metastatic properties of the variants are unstable (ie, they are generated and lost at a high rate), so that growing cell populations establish a dynamic equilibrium between a small subpopulation of highly metastatic (variant) cells and a majority of essentially nonmetastatic cells.

Genetic changes which occur at high rates and which are unstable in the absence of selective pressure have been associated with the development of drug resistance (see section 19.2) due, for example, to unstable gene amplification. A similar mechanism may be responsible for the development of the metastatic variants. Some highly metastatic cells have been shown to have a more rapid rate of generation of drug-resistant cells than poorly or nonmetastatic cells. An alternative pos-

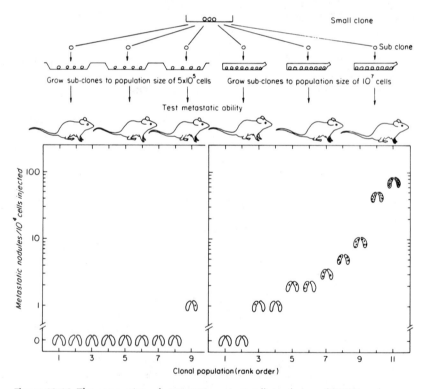

Figure 10.14. The generation of metastatic variant cells in clones of B16F1 melanoma cells. A small clone was subcloned and the subclones were grown to carefully controlled population sizes before the cells were tested for metastatic ability using an experimental metastasis assay. Although the same number of cells was injected into both groups of animals, many more metastases were observed in the mice injected with cells from the larger clones. (Adapted from Hill et al, 1984.)

sibility to specific genetic changes is that the instability of the metastatic phenotype is due to changes in gene expression. Olsson and Forchhammer (1984) have observed that treatment of tumor cells with the drug 5-azacytidine can influence their metastatic ability, although the changes observed were often unstable. Since 5-azacytidine induces hypomethylation of DNA and there is evidence that the extent of DNA methylation influences whether or not a gene is expressed, the generation and loss of metastatic properties might occur as a result of unstable alterations in the methylation of particular genes (Frost and Kerbel, 1983).

10.4.4 TUMOR PROGRESSION AND METASTASIS

Regardless of the mechanism, the concept of cells with unstable properties being generated and lost at high rates is consistent with the concept of tumor progression proposed by Nowell (1976). He suggested that the initiating event in carcinogenesis resulted in the destabilization of the genome, allowing increased random generation of variant cells. Most of such variant cells would be eliminated by the host, but occasionally one would have a growth advantage, perhaps by developing greater autonomy. As this process proceeded there would be continued selection for more autonomous cells and the tumor would progress to a more malignant state. The development of metastatic potential may thus be viewed as one of the late stages in the process of tumor progression, which results in the evolution of populations of cells which become ever more malignant.

10.5 GENERAL MODELS FOR METASTASIS

10.5.1 RANDOM OR SPECIFIC

Despite the evidence that cell populations with specific metastatic properties can be isolated, there is controversy concerning the extent to which metastasis is a specific process. There are three basic models of metastatic development (see Weiss, 1983, and Fig 10.15). In the random survival model it is postulated that all cells have equal probability of forming a metastasis, but few do so because most fail to survive the rigors of the metastatic cascade. Alternatively, in the (stable) preexisting metastatic phenotype model, it is supposed that a small subpopulation of cells with a high probability of surviving through the cascade preexist in the primary tumor. Such a subpopulation would be very small since even the most highly metastatic cell populations have a metastatic efficiency of only about 1% following intravenous injection.

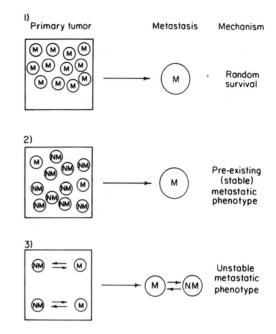

Figure 10.15. Three possible models for metastasis. Tumor cells may form metastases purely as a result of random chance (1). Alternatively, there may be specific phenotypes which increase the probability that a given cell can form a metastasis. Such phenotypes could be stable (2) or unstable (3). (Adapted from Weiss, 1983.)

Support for the random nature of the metastasis process derives from extensive studies which have failed to demonstrate that cells obtained from metastases are consistently more metastatic than cells from the parent tumor, as would be expected if such cells were expressing a stable phenotype which predisposed them to form metastases (see Chambers et al, 1984 for review). Although there are notable exceptions (such as the development of the B16F10 cell population) multiple passaging of cells from metastasis to metastasis often fails to result in the selection of a cell population which is consistently more metastatic than the original parent population. These observations seem at variance with the concept of a specific metastatic phenotype, yet as discussed earlier there is strong evidence to support this concept.

The third model in Figure 10.15 is that of an unstable metastatic phenotype. One such model is discussed in section 10.4.3 and implies that a malignant cell population is in a state of dynamic equilibrium between a small subpopulation of highly metastatic cells and a majority of essentially nonmetastatic cells. If an individual cell is isolated from such a population then as it grows to form a new cell population the dynamic equilibrium will tend to reestablish itself. Thus a metastasis arising from a highly metastatic cell may, by the time the metastatic nodule can be detected and isolated, have reached a population size at which the dynamic equilibrium is reestablished. Hence when the cell population from the metastasis is tested for its metastatic ability it will be similar to the original parent tumor, which would explain the observations mentioned in the previous paragraph.

The concept of a small subpopulation of cells expressing metastatic properties existing in dynamic equilibrium with the majority of cells not expressing these properties can also explain why the identification of specific biochemical or cellular changes associated with metastatic ability has proved so elusive (see section 10.4)—because the majority of the cells in the populations being compared are similar.

The three models outlined in Figure 10.15 are not mutually exclusive. The results discussed in this chapter indicate that both stable and unstable metastatic phenotypes, which predisposes cells to form metastases, can be expressed by tumor cells. Furthermore, there is good evidence for a random component being involved in metastatic development. It thus seems likely that different tumor-cell populations may conform to different models. Alternatively, a combination model may be appropriate. Such a model might suppose the existence of subpopulations of cells expressing stable and/or unstable metastatic phenotypes, but that such cells are still subject to random factors during the actual establishment of a metastasis. Further studies are required to establish the range of applicability of any of the models discussed above both to experimental systems and to the development of metastases in cancer patients.

10.6 SUMMARY

Metastasis is the major cause of deaths due to cancer, and occurs primarily by dissemination of tumor cells through the lymphatic and blood vessels. In humans there is evidence for organ-site specificity in the development of metastases from particular types of primary tumors, and cells which have specific organ-site preferences for metastatic development have been selected from tumors in animals. Isolation of cloned cell populations from rodent tumors has demonstrated wide heterogeneity in metastatic potential between clonal populations. The metastatic phenotype of such clonal populations has, however, usually been found to be unstable.

There are several major steps involved in the process of metastasis (the metastatic cascade), which include the ability to invade into and out of blood vessels, to survive in the circulation and to arrest and grow at a new site. Extensive studies have identified a range of prop-

erties (particularly those relating to the cell surface) which may be involved in the process of metastasis, but identification of common properties which characterize all metastatic cells has proved elusive.

Despite the evidence for specificity in metastatic development, metastasis is an inefficient process and may depend to some extent on random survival factors associated with traversing the metastatic cascade. A finding in animal tumors, that unstable metastatic properties can arise at high rates, suggests that the development of metastatic potential can be a stochastic event which is part of an ongoing process of tumor progression towards more malignant properties.

REFERENCES

Bernstein SC, Weinberg RA: Expression of the metastatic phenotype in cells transfected with human metastatic tumor DNA. *Proc Natl Acad Sci USA* 1985; 82:1726–1730.

Butler TP, Gullino PM: Quantitation of cell shedding into efferent blood of mammary adenocarcinoma. *Cancer Res* 1975; 35:512–516.

Carr I, Carr J: Experimental lymphatic invasion and metastases, in Weiss L, Gilbert HA (eds): *Lymphatic System Metastases*. Boston, G.K. Hall, 1980, pp 41–75.

Chambers AF, Harris JF, Ling V, Hill RP: Rapid phenotype variation in cells derived from lung metastases of KHT fibrosarcoma. *Invasion Metastasis* 1984; 4:225–237.

Eisenbach L, De Baetselier P, Katzav S et al: Immunogenetic control of metastatic competence of cloned tumor cell populations, in Nicolson GL, Milas L (eds): *Cancer Invasion and Metastasis: Biologic and Therapeutic Aspects*. New York, Raven Press, 1984, pp 101–121.

Fidler IJ: Selection of successive tumour lines for metastasis. *Nature New Biology* 1973; 242:148–149.

Fidler IJ, Kripke ML: Metastasis results from preexisting variant cells within a malignant tumor. *Science* 1977; 198:893–895.

Frost P, Kerbel RS: On a possible epigenetic mechanism(s) of tumor cell heterogeneity. The role of DNA methylation. *Cancer Metastasis Rev* 1983; 2:375–378.

Gasic GJ: Role of plasma, platelets and endothelial cells in tumor metastasis. *Cancer Metastasis Rev* 1984; 3:99–114.

Glaves D: Correlation between circulating cancer cells and incidence of metastases. *Br J Cancer* 1983; 48:665–673.

Hanna, N: Role of natural killer cells in host defense against cancer metastasis, in Nicolson GL, Milas L (eds): *Cancer Invasion and Metastasis: Biologic and Therapeutic Aspects*. New York, Raven Press, 1984, pp 309–319.

Hart IR: The selection and characterization of an invasive variant of the B16 melanoma. *Am J Pathol* 1979; 97:587–600.

Hart IR: "Seed and soil" revisited: Mechanisms of site-specific metastasis. *Cancer Metastasis Rev* 1982; 1:5–16.

Heppner GH: Tumor heterogeneity. *Cancer Res* 1984; 44:2259–2265.

Hilgard P: Anticoagulants and tumor growth: Pharmacological considerations, in Nicolson GL, Milas L (eds): *Cancer Invasion and Metastasis: Biologic and Therapeutic Aspects*. New York, Raven Press, 1984; pp 353–360.

Hill RP, Chambers AF, Ling V, Harris IF: Dynamic heterogeneity: Rapid generation of metastatic variants in mouse B16 melanoma cells. *Science* 1984; 224:998–1001.

Kerbel RS, Dennis JW, Lagarde AE, Frost P: Tumor progression in metastasis: An experimental approach using lectin resistant tumor variants. *Cancer Metastasis Rev* 1982; 1:99–140.

Ling V, Chambers AF, Harris JF, Hill RP: Quantitative genetic analysis of tumor progression. *Cancer Metastasis Rev* 1985; 4:173–192.

Liotta LA, Tumor invasion and metastases—Role of the extracelluar matrix. *Cancer Res* 1986; 46:1–7.

Nicolson GL: Cancer metastasis. Organ colonization and the cell-surface properties of malignant cells. *Biochim Biophys Acta* 1982; 695:113–176.

Nicolson GL, Irimura T, Nakajima M, Estrada J: Metastatic cell attachment to and invasion of vascular endothelium and its underlying basal lamina using endothelial cell monolayers, in Nicolson GL, Milas L (eds): *Cancer Invasion and Metastasis: Biologic and Therapeutic Aspects*. New York, Raven Press, 1984; pp 145–167.

Nowell PC: The clonal evolution of tumor cell populations. *Science* 1976; 194:23–28.

Olsson L, Forchhammer J: Induction of the metastatic phenotype in a mouse tumor model by 5-azacytidine, and characterization of an antigen associated with metastatic activity. *Proc Natl Acad Sci USA* 1984; 81:3389–3393.

Paget S: The distribution of secondary growths in cancer of the breast. *Lancet* 1889; 1:571–573.

Poste G, Greig R: On the genesis and regulation of cellular heterogeneity in malignant tumors. *Invasion Metastasis* 1982; 2:137–176.

Price JE, Carr D, Jones LD et al: Experimental analysis of factors affecting metastatic spread using naturally occurring tumours. *Invasion Metastasis* 1982; 2:77–112.

Shearman PJ, Longenecker BM: Clonal variation and functional correlation of organ-specific metastasis and an organ-specific metastasis-associated antigen. *Int J Cancer* 1981; 27:387–395.

Stringfellow DA: Prostaglandins and metastasis, in Nicolson GL, Milas L (eds): *Cancer Invasion and Metastasis: Biologic and Therapeutic Aspects*. New York, Raven Press, 1984, pp 123–131.

Sugarbaker EV: Patterns of metastasis in human malignancies. *Cancer Biol Rev* 1981; 2:235–278.

Tarin D, Price JE: Influence of microenvironment and vascular anatomy on "metastatic" colonization potential of mammary tumors. *Cancer Res* 1981; 41:3604–3609.

Turner GA: Surface properties of the metastatic cell. *Invasion Metastasis* 1982; 2:197–216.

Weiss L: Random and non-random processes in metastasis and metastatic inefficiency. *Invasion Metastasis* 1983; 3:193–207.

Weiss L, Ward PM: Cell detachment and metastasis. *Cancer Metastasis Rev* 1983; 2:111–127.

BIBLIOGRAPHY

Nicolson GL, Milas L (eds): *Cancer Invasion and Metastasis: Biologic and Therapeutic Aspects*. New York, Raven Press, 1984.

Poste G, Fidler IJ: The pathogenesis of cancer metastasis. *Nature* 1980; 283:139–146.

Schirrmacher V: Cancer metastasis: experimental approaches, theoretical concepts and impacts for treatment strategies. *Adv Canc Res* 1985; 43:1–73.

Weiss L: *Principles of Metastases*. Orlando, FL, Academic Press, 1985.

11

Biochemical Properties of Cancer Cells

Robert K. Murray

11.1 INTRODUCTION

11.1.1 OVERVIEW

This chapter will attempt to summarize knowledge of the major biochemical properties of cancer cells. The topics selected necessarily cover a wide range, and in a number of cases there is no evident interrelationship between them (eg, isozymes and cell-surface glycoconjugates). Also, as will become evident, the studies described cannot be said to have yet provided definitive answers as to what are the key biochemical changes responsible for the development of malignancy; thus, the overall picture provided is still quite fragmentary. Despite these considerations, it is believed that the subjects covered do reflect the principal advances made in our understanding of the biochemistry of cancer and that recent insights permit at least a cautious air of optimism concerning the future development of the field.

The classical biochemical approach to cancer includes measurements of the activities and regulation of enzymes, analyses of various cellular constituents and studies using subcellular fractionation. Enzyme profiles and general metabolic activities have been determined for various tumors, with the most detailed information originating from the study of a series of transplantable rat hepatomas, the Morris hepatomas (Morris, 1975).

Enzymes and other proteins have been identified that are synthesized and secreted by some types of tumors, and these molecules are sometimes used clinically as markers of tumor activity (see chapter 12). Studies of the metabolism of carcinogens and of their interaction with DNA (see chapter 6) have allowed an understanding of some mechanisms involved in chemical carcinogenesis. The elucidation of metabolic pathways in cells has also led to the synthesis of analogues of metabolites (eg, methotrexate, 5-fluorouracil) which may inhibit these pathways, and several of these analogues have provided a major contribution to cancer therapy (see chapter 18). Despite the above gains, the classical approach has offered relatively few insights into the molecular nature of the mechanisms involved in transformation. Recent discoveries of the nature, identification and possible actions of oncogenes (see chapter 5) have largely been due to the application of transfection and of the methods of recombinant DNA technology. A major challenge for current research will involve fusion of these newer techniques with those of classical biochemistry in attempts to relate oncogene function with cellular metabolism, particular emphasis being placed on elucidating mechanisms resulting in the central phenomena displayed by malignant cells, abnormal growth regulation and metastasis.

11.1.2 SOME CONSIDERATIONS ON METHODOLOGY

Many studies of tumor biochemistry involve the analysis of properties of tissue after its removal from a patient or animal. There is a large potential for artifacts introduced by changes in properties which take place during removal, storage and analysis of the tissue, and careful attention to methodology is therefore essential. Some of the important factors which may influence the interpretation of results are indicated in Table 11.1.

In seeking biochemical properties which characterise tumors, it is important to separate those properties that may be due merely to a rapid rate of cellular proliferation from those that are truly tumor specific. Thus it is important to study a variety of tumors, including those with a wide range of growth rates, and to compare their properties with those of appropriate normal tissues.

11.2 HISTORICAL DEVELOPMENT

11.2.1 GLYCOLYSIS IN TUMORS

Otto Warburg was the first investigator whose work had a significant and lasting impact on thinking about the biochemistry of tumors. Warburg (1930) measured the oxygen consumption and rates of aerobic and anaerobic glycolysis of tumors of animal and human origin. He observed that, whereas slices of normal tissues and tumors produced lactic acid from glucose or glycogen rapidly in the absence of oxygen (anaerobic glycolysis), virtually only the slices of tumors showed an ability to produce lactic acid from glucose in the presence of oxygen (aerobic glycolysis). Most tumors showed near-normal levels of respiration, but very high rates of anaerobic and aerobic glycolysis. High rates of anaerobic glycolysis were also found in growing or multiplying tissues (eg, embryonic tissue and testis), but in these tissues glycolysis was largely abolished by the presence of oxygen. Warburg and some of his contemporaries attempted to ascribe the above metabolic pattern (high rates of both anaerobic and aerobic glycolysis) to all cancer cells. They postulated that the high rate of aerobic glycolysis exhibited by tumors was attributable to damage to their respiratory-chain energy-coupling mechanisms due to neoplastic transformation. The increase of aerobic glycolysis thus represented a compensatory mechanism of the tumor cells to produce energy (later shown to be ATP) that was not able to be supplied in sufficient amounts because of the postulated damage. However, findings by Warburg himself, and others, revealed that certain normal tissues (eg, retina, renal medulla and myeloid cells of the bone marrow) could also use aerobic glycolysis to metabolize glucose.

Table 11.1. Some Factors that May Influence the Interpretation of Studies of Tumor Biochemistry

Factor(s)	Possible Influence on Results
Duration and method of storage of tissue	Autolytic change may have a profound influence on biochemical properties
Contaminating normal tissue, hemorrhage, infection	Measured properties may not reflect those of the tumor cells
Previous chemotherapy	Drugs may induce enzymes
Nutrition of host	Influences the concentrations of many metabolites and the activities of many enzymes
Rate of tumor growth	Many biochemical properties (eg, enzyme activities) are dependent on the rate of cell proliferation
Standardization of measurement of enzyme activities	Activators and inhibitors of enzyme activity may vary in different tissues and tumors. Isozyme profile may also differ
Tests for purity of subcellular fractions	Organelles from tumor and normal tissue may sediment at different rates

Subsequent studies of slowly growing tumors, such as Morris hepatoma 5123, showed that they displayed rates of aerobic and anaerobic glycolysis comparable to those of normal liver. These and other findings led many workers to doubt that a specific type of tumor metabolism really existed. Warburg's reports had suggested that the essential nature of the neoplastic cell had been revealed. But, as Greenstein (1954) stated, "Like so many similar examples in the field of cancer research, too much was claimed and too much was hoped for in the beginning."

11.2.2 MORRIS HEPATOMAS

In 1960 and 1961 a number of papers were published by Morris in collaboration with Potter, Pitot and others (see Potter, 1961) dealing with some of the biological and biochemical properties of transplantable rat hepatoma 5123, a tumor induced by ingestion of N-(2-fluorenyl)-phthalamic acid. This tumor exhibited many morphological, biological and biochemical characteristics closely resembling normal liver. A prime motivating factor for the biochemical analysis of this hepatoma had been the objective of finding a liver cancer cell that differed minimally from its normal counterpart. The Novikoff and Dunning hepatomas (Fig 11.1), which had been extensively studied, were found to display many differences in enzyme profile from normal liver, particularly the loss of many enzyme activities. However, many of these differences were probably irrelevant to the problem of carcinogenesis, and actually reflected changes due to tumor progression. If a hepatoma could be found that differed in only a few biochemical respects from liver (a "minimal-deviation hepatoma," Potter, 1961) it would help to narrow the spectrum of enzyme differences between liver and tumors to only a few that might be critical.

During the next few years, Morris developed some 50 hepatomas of slow, intermediate and fast growth rates. These were transplanted under defined conditions and were made available to other investigators. Their biological (eg, growth rates, karyotypes) and morphological (both light- and electron-microscopic) features were established and many biochemical studies were performed on them (Morris, 1975). A number of them were transferred to tissue culture, making it possible to do comparative studies both in vivo and in vitro. The availability of this series of hepatomas had a major impact on the biochemistry of cancer. Even the concept of "minimal deviation" was valuable, because it led many investigators to appreciate that not every biochemical alteration noted in a cancer cell had relevance to the process of carcinogenesis. Many of the studies described in the following sections were performed using Morris hepatomas.

11.3 ENZYMES IN CANCER CELLS

11.3.1 DERANGEMENTS OF THE REGULATION OF ENZYMES

Three of the more important mechanisms which regulate enzyme activity are indicated in Figure 11.2. Regulation by the end product or by phosphorylation–dephosphorylation acts rapidly (seconds), whereas mechanisms involving induction or repression are slower in onset (minutes to hours). Few significant alterations in the operation of the rapidly acting regulatory mechanisms have been reported between control and neoplastic cells. In particular, at the level of individual enzymes, no precise biochemical analogy exists to match the common statement that "cancer cells exhibit loss of feedback control." In contrast, mechanisms involving enzyme induction or repression frequently appear to be abnormal in tumors.

The majority of the studies comparing induction or repression of specific enzymes in control and tumor tissue have been performed on normal liver and on Morris hepatomas. The following examples illustrate

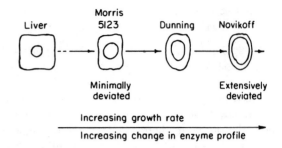

Figure 11.1. Diagrammatic representation of the concept of a minimal-deviation hepatoma (after Pitot, 1962). The Novikoff hepatoma is the fastest growing of the tumors indicated and lacks many of the enzymes found in liver. The Dunning hepatoma grows somewhat more slowly and possesses a number of enzymes that are absent from the Novikoff. The enzyme profile of the Morris hepatoma 5123 is much closer to liver, thus giving rise to the concept that it was a minimal-deviation hepatoma.

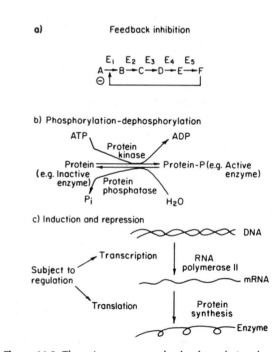

Figure 11.2. Three important methods of regulating the activities of enzymes. *a*, In feedback inhibition, the end product of a metabolic pathway usually inhibits the activity of the first, or committed, enzyme of the pathway. *b*, In a reaction catalysed by a protein kinase, the terminal phosphate of ATP (or GTP) is transferred to the hydroxyl groups of specific serine, threonine or tyrosine residues of an acceptor protein. The phosphorylation will either activate or inactivate various proteins. *c*, Induction signifies an increase of the rate of synthesis of a particular enzyme, repression signifies a decrease of its rate of synthesis. Induction can be due to increased transcription and/or decreased degradation of the specific mRNA species of the enzyme or to increased translation; opposite effects on transcription and translation are involved in repression.

these studies. When a rat on a normal chow diet is switched to a diet containing 90% protein, the activity of serine dehydratase in normal liver increases approximately 40-fold by 6 days after the switch. However, in Morris hepatoma 5123 (of intermediate growth rate), the activity of serine dehydratase was found to be high on the basal chow diet and was not affected by the change to the diet high in protein. The enzyme is described as "derepressed" (Fig 11.3a) by analogy with the similar phenomenon in bacteria. In contrast, in a number of sublines of the same hepatoma, the activity of this enzyme was found to be very low on the basal chow diet, but again the activity was not affected by the switch to the diet high in protein. The tumor enzyme showed lack of induction (Fig 11.3b), and there are other examples where tumor enzymes show lack of repression in response to manipulations that cause repression in normal liver (Fig 11.3c). A number of enzymes show characteristic diurnal variations in their activities. In the highly differentiated Morris hepatoma 7793, the activities of serine dehydratase and of two other enzymes were found to display diurnal variations, but these differed from the variations exhibited by control liver and thus reflected abnormal environmental regulation (Fig 11.3d).

As summarized in a review by Pitot (1975), the regulation of enzyme synthesis is generally abnormal in neoplasms. There is a tendency for tumor enzymes to be less responsive to normal control mechanisms, but each neoplasm may exhibit a unique pattern of abnormalities of regulation of its enzyme profile, with there being a remarkable diversity in the nature of the abnormalities of enzyme regulation noted.

11.3.2 THE MOLECULAR CORRELATION CONCEPT OF WEBER

Weber (1977) has proposed that gene expression and its quantitative and qualitative variations in neoplasia can be deduced from determination of the concentrations of specific, key enzymes. He calls this the molecular-correlation concept. The model system used to collect the data was the series of transplantable Morris hepatomas, with supporting data being obtained from certain rat kidney and mammary tumors of varying growth rate, and from human primary hepatomas.

Weber has suggested that early studies failed to detect a meaningful biochemical pattern in tumors because of the poor choice of parameters (enzymes, etc.) analysed. Biologic and other criteria for the identification of key enzymes are listed in Table 11.2. In contrast, non-key enzymes govern reversible reactions, are shared by both synthetic and catabolic pathways, exhibit high activities and are present in excess. Also,

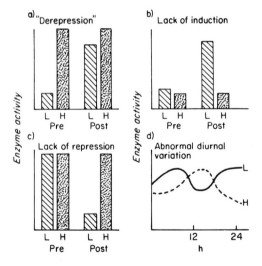

Figure 11.3. Diagrammatic representations of lack of control mechanisms of enzyme activity detected in certain hepatomas. The activities of the enzymes (eg, serine dehydratase, etc) studied in control liver (L) and those in the hepatomas (H) are indicated. In panels a, b and c, the activities in the left-hand side of each panel are those detected prior to the experimental manipulation affecting enzyme activity (eg, feeding of a diet high in protein) and those in the right-hand side of each panel are as measured at the completion of the manipulation. The ordinate in each panel represents enzyme activity, and in panel d the abscissa represents time in hours. Specific examples of each abnormality are given in Pitot (1975).

Table 11.2. Criteria for Identification of Key Enzymes*

I. *Biologic role*
   - Regulate rates and directions of opposing (or competing) metabolic pathways
   - Involved in overcoming thermodynamic barriers
   - Govern one-way reactions
   - Final common pathway of two or more metabolic pathways

II. *Place in pathway*
   - First in the reaction sequence
   - Last in the reaction sequence
   - Pathways in themselves
   - Operate on both sides of reversible reactions
   - One-way enzyme opposed by another one-way enzyme

III. *Regulatory property*
   - Possess relatively low activity in the pathway
   - Rate-limiting in pathway
   - Target of feedback regulation
   - Target of multiple regulation
   - Exhibit allosteric properties
   - Exhibit isozyme patterns

Note: After Weber (1977).

*Examples of enzymes in each of these categories are given by Weber (1977).

their activities are not markedly altered by endocrine and nutritional regulation and they do not correlate with transformation or neoplasia. Thus, one would expect to deduce little of value in respect to the biochemical properties of neoplastic cells by studying such enzymes.

The elaboration of the molecular correlation concept entailed the measurement of the activities of the key enzymes of a number of metabolic pathways using the full series of Morris hepatomas. The activities and concentrations of certain enzymes increase and those of the opposing enzymes decrease in parallel with the malignancy of the different tumors. More than 40 enzymes representing a variety of metabolic pathways have been found to correlate with growth rate. Other key enzymes were found to exhibit the same type of alterations (increase or decrease) in all Morris hepatomas; these enzymes are claimed to be enzymatic markers of malignant transformation. Some 13 or so enzymes involved in the metabolism of pentose phosphates, of purines and of pyrimidines are listed by Weber in this class.

The general biochemical features of hepatomas that correlate with malignancy are tabulated in Table 11.3. The overall trend is an increase of the activities of anabolic pathways and a diminution of the activities of the corresponding catabolic pathways. This is not surprising, considering that rapidly multiplying tumor cells must use anabolic pathways to support their growth.

Decreased catabolism of important metabolites is also of apparent biological advantage to the tumor cell.

Two specific examples of biochemical activities that show an excellent correlation with rate of tumor growth are illustrated in Figure 11.4. These are the ratio of the rate of incorporation of thymidine into DNA to the rate of degradation of thymidine to carbon dioxide (Fig 11.4a) and the activity of ribonucleotide reductase, a key enzyme catalysing the conversion of ribonucleotides to deoxyribonucleotides (Fig 11.4b).

The most important concept emerging from these studies is that many biochemical alterations exhibited

Table 11.3. Metabolic Changes Linked to Progression*

Biochemical Process	Direction of Change
Pyrimidine, RNA and DNA synthesis	increased
Pyrimidine catabolism	decreased
Purine synthesis	increased
Purine catabolism	decreased
Glucose catabolism	increased
Glucose synthesis	decreased
Protein synthesis	increased
Catabolism of certain amino acids	decreased
Urea cycle	decreased

*After Weber (1977). For further changes and for details of the individual enzymes involved, the reader is referred to this review.

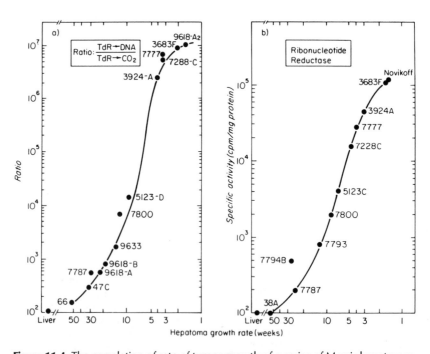

Figure 11.4. The correlation of rate of tumor growth of a series of Morris hepatomas with a, the ratio of incorporation of thymidine (TdR) into DNA to its degradation to carbon dioxide, and b, the specific activity of ribonucleotide reductase. Growth rate is indicated as the time between successive transplantations of the tumor. (Adapted from Weber, 1977 and Elford et al, 1970.)

by tumor cells are linked to the rate of tumor growth. The presence of a high activity of a particular enzyme in a tumor does not indicate that the increase of activity had a role in the initial process of transformation. Rather, as shown in Figure 11.4b for ribonucleotide reductase, the elevated activity may be part of the metabolic adaptation required by the tumor to sustain its high growth rate.

11.3.3 ISOZYMES

Isozymes (isozyme and isoenzyme are interchangeable terms) are different molecular forms of proteins with the same enzymatic specificity. Isozymes arise as a result of the presence of more than one structural gene. The multiple genes may be due to the presence of multiple gene loci or of multiple alleles. (Multiple forms of an enzyme due to variations in the extent of posttranslational modifications [eg, of glycosylation, phosphorylation, etc.] are not classified as isozymes).

Schapira et al (1963) reported that the aldolase that appeared in the plasma of humans with hepatic carcinomas was not the adult liver type (B), but rather was the fetal liver type (A); it was later shown that the liver tumors were the source of the type-A isozyme. A review by Ibsen and Fishman (1979) cites 22 examples of fetal isozymes produced by tumors, the enzymes involved being representatives of diverse metabolic pathways. Weinhouse (1983) has interpreted these changes as representing a misregulation of gene expression. He stresses that the isozymes that appear are not new enzymes; rather, they reflect a reactivation of the fetal genes and a repression of the adult genes. The expression of inappropriate fetal and ectopic proteins in tumors is a common and important phenomenon in neoplasia (see also sections 12.2.2 and 13.4.2); other examples of inappropriate expression of various proteins are listed in Table 11.4.

These changes in gene expression are probably not trivial, coincidental phenomena; rather, they reflect fundamental changes in gene regulation in neoplastic cells, and may confer distinct selective advantages to these cells (eg, replacement of an isozyme subject to hormonal control by one independent of such control).

11.4 METABOLIC CONTROL

11.4.1 CYCLIC NUCLEOTIDES AND PROTEIN KINASES

Cyclic AMP is formed from ATP by the action of adenylate cyclase and is converted to AMP by the action of phosphodiesterase. The regulation of both of these enzymes is complex. Considerable progress has been made recently in resolving the constituents of the hormone-sensitive adenylate cyclase system (Fig 11.5). Both stimulatory (R_s) and inhibitory (R_i) receptors have been distinguished. In addition, the activity of the catalytic component (C) is regulated by stimulatory (N_s) and inhibitory (N_i) nucleotide-binding components, comprised of two common (β and γ) and one different (α_s and α_i, respectively) polypeptide chains (see Hildebrandt et al [1984] for further details). The system has assumed additional importance as there is now evidence that the p21 product of the ras oncogene may act, at least in part, by chronically stimulating the activity of adenylate cyclase, possibly by "mimicking" the action of the N_s component (Marx, 1984). Agents that increase the activity of adenylate cyclase (Fig 11.5) lead to an increase in the intracellular levels of cyclic AMP; the same result can be produced by agents that inhibit the activity of the phosphodiesterase (eg, theophylline and caffeine).

The sole function of cyclic AMP in eukaryotic cells

Table 11.4. Expression of Inappropriate Fetal and Ectopic Proteins in Tumors and Cultured Transformed Cells

Synthesis of fetal enzymes

Tumor-associated fetal antigens (eg, CEA, alpha-1-fetoprotein)

Plasminogen activator

Angiogenesis factors

Growth factors (epidermal growth factor, platelet-derived growth factor, etc)

Polypeptide hormones

Products of cellular oncogenes

Note: Adapted from Weinhouse (1983).

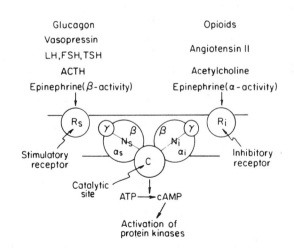

Figure 11.5. Schematic representation of the components of adenylate cyclase. (Adapted from Hildebrandt et al, 1984.)

appears to be the activation of certain protein kinases (cyclic AMP-dependent kinases); however, altering the flux of cyclic AMP in cells could alter the production of certain metabolites liberated during its biosynthesis (eg, pyrophosphate and protons), and these chemicals might affect cellular metabolism by other means. The mechanism of activation of the cyclic-AMP-dependent kinases has been shown to involve the dissociation of an inhibitory regulator subunit from the catalytic subunit; the latter subunit is then free to participate in catalysis. The majority of protein kinases in eukaryotic cells are not cyclic AMP-dependent.

The reaction catalysed by a protein kinase (Fig 11.2) generally involves transfer of the terminal phosphate of ATP (or GTP) to the hydroxyl group of specific serine and threonine residues of proteins. Of particular relevance to the understanding of the pathogenesis of virally induced cancer was the demonstration that some protein kinases transfer phosphate to the hydroxyl groups of certain tyrosine residues in proteins (Hunter and Sefton, 1980; see also chapter 5). When the protein to which a kinase transfers phosphate is an enzyme, the phosphorylation can result in either activation or inactivation of catalytic activity. Phosphorylation can also result in significant alteration of the biological functions of nonenzyme proteins. The phosphate groups can be removed by a class of enzymes known as protein phosphatases, and this will result in reversal of the process (activation or inactivation) caused by phosphorylation. These cycles of phosphorylation–dephosphorylation are important in the normal, short-term regulation of the activities of many key intracellular enzymes (Fig 11.2).

11.4.2 CYCLIC NUCLEOTIDES IN TUMORS

Numerous investigators have examined various aspects of cyclic nucleotides in transformed cells and tumors (see Prasad, 1981). The following approaches were used: (a) measurement of levels of cyclic nucleotides (cyclic AMP and cyclic GMP) in cultured cells or tumors in vivo, (b) attempts to alter the phenotypic properties of cancer cells by administration or addition of cyclic nucleotides or analogs (eg, dibutyryl cyclic AMP), (c) studies of the effects of administration of cyclic nucleotides on the growth of transformed or tumor cells, particularly in culture, and (d) measurements of the activities of adenylate cyclase, phosphodiesterase and other relevant enzymes.

Measurement of levels of cyclic nucleotides has provided conflicting data, certain transformed cells (eg, chicken and rat sarcoma cells) showing decreases of cyclic AMP and others (eg, rat and human mammary carcinoma cells) exhibiting increases. Where levels of

cyclic AMP were found to be low, there was a tendency for the levels of cyclic GMP to be elevated. One problem in interpretation of these studies arises because the data have been variably expressed relative to protein content, DNA content or cell size.

The addition of cyclic AMP and of dibutyryl cyclic AMP to tumor cells in culture can cause partial restoration of their phenotypic properties towards normal. Neuroblastoma cells have been most studied; cyclic AMP will cause long neurites to extend from these cells, their soma and nuclei to increase towards normal and their enzyme profiles to revert towards normal. Similar studies of glioma and sarcoma cells have revealed that their phenotypic properties are also restored towards normal, although all of the effects elicited disappear after the cyclic nucleotides are removed.

The addition of cyclic AMP or dibutyryl cyclic AMP to transformed cells usually inhibits their growth. However, in a number of experiments nonphysiological doses of these agents were employed, thus throwing doubt on the significance of the observed effects. Other experiments have demonstrated that the activity of adenylate cyclase in transformed cells is generally decreased, whereas the activity of phosphodiesterase is usually elevated.

Although the above results show a trend towards an association between malignancy and decreased levels of cyclic AMP, the several conflicting results make it impossible to draw general conclusions. Part of the confusion might be removed if there was a better understanding of the role of cyclic AMP in the replicative cycle of normal cells (Boynton and Whitfield, 1983).

11.4.3 PROTEIN KINASES AND MALIGNANCY

The discovery that the product of the src gene of Rous sarcoma virus was a tyrosine-specific kinase (Collett and Erikson, 1978; Hunter and Sefton, 1980) has had a dramatic impact on cancer research (see section 5.4). Because a tyrosine-specific protein kinase will phosphorylate a number of different substrates, it is apparent that the use of this enzyme by the oncogenic virus is an ingenious method of producing widespread pleiotropic effects, probably affecting a number of different cellular compartments (plasma membrane, cytosol, etc) and metabolic pathways.

Studies to evaluate the possibility that protein kinases of unusual specificity are involved in chemical carcinogenesis and in human malignancies are still in their infancy. Administration of certain promoting agents (eg, some types of phorbol esters) has been shown to result in an increase of the activity of protein kinase C, suggesting implication of this enzyme in the process of hepatocarcinogenesis. The possibility that subtle changes of the substrate specificities of enzymes other than protein kinases (eg, alteration of the specificity of a glycosyl transferase or of other enzymes involved in the post-translational modifications of proteins) is an important area for investigation.

11.4.4 CALCIUM AND CALMODULIN

It is well established that Ca^{2+} plays a key role in the regulation of a wide variety of cellular processes (Campbell, 1983), some of which are listed in Table 11.5. Interaction of a hormone with the cell surface may result in a rise in the intracellular concentration of free Ca^{2+}, which then affects one of the processes listed in Table 11.5. Thus, Ca^{2+} might be said, like cyclic AMP, to be a second messenger. However, it is usually a complex between Ca^{2+} and a specific intracellular Ca^{2+}-binding protein (calmodulin) that controls the subsequent metabolic effects. In addition, recent research has revealed that another second messenger, inositol triphosphate, is involved in the release of Ca^{2+} from intracellular stores prior to Ca^{2+} effecting its regulatory roles.

The entry of Ca^{2+} into cells, its level (both bound and free) in cells and its exit from cells must be carefully controlled; otherwise the balance among many of the processes shown in Table 11.5 would become disturbed. Some aspects of the control of these factors are shown in Figure 11.6. The concentration of free Ca^{2+} in the cytosol is usually less than $10^{-7}M$ and does not rise appreciably above $10^{-5}M$. The calcium-binding protein calmodulin is found in all mammalian cells and consists of a single highly conserved chain of 148 amino acids. Calmodulin has four high-affinity binding sites for Ca^{2+} that undergo large conformational changes when the cation is bound. Some of the enzymes and proteins whose activities are regulated by interaction with calmodulin are shown in Fig. 11.7. A schematic representation of how calmodulin interacts with Ca^{2+} and how the calmodulin–Ca^{2+} complex affects the ac-

tivity of a typical enzyme is presented in Figure 11.8. Calmodulin can contribute approximately 1% of the total protein of a mammalian cell. The effects of calmodulin will depend on which calmodulin-binding proteins are present. Also, different conformational states of calmodulin (as determined by the amount of Ca^{2+} bound) may exhibit different affinities for the various calmodulin-dependent enzymes.

Interactions between calmodulin and cyclic nucleotides can occur in several ways. First, calmodulin can affect the activity of adenylate or guanylate cyclase, enzymes involved in the formation of cyclic AMP and GMP respectively. Conversely, cyclic AMP can influence, by its action on dependent protein kinases, the activities of Ca^{2+} channels or pumps that control the entry to and exit from cells of Ca^{2+}. Third, both calmodulin and cyclic AMP may interact in different ways with a single target protein. The enzyme phosphorylase kinase is an excellent example of the latter:

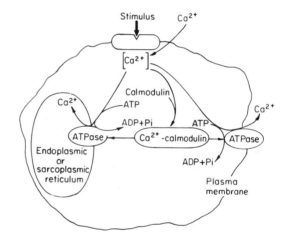

Figure 11.6. Schematic representation of the control of intracellular levels of calcium in a eukaryotic cell. The activities of the ATPases indicated are controlled by Ca^{2+}-calmodulin complexes. (Adapted from White et al, 1984.)

Table 11.5. Some Ca^{2+}-Dependent Reactions and Processes

Activation of certain enzyme systems (eg, glycogenolysis)

Inhibition of certain enzyme systems (eg, pyruvate kinase)

Activation of contractile and motile systems (eg, myofibrils, microtubules and microfilaments)

Hormonal regulation (eg, formation of cyclic AMP)

Membrane-linked functions (eg, excitation–contraction coupling in muscles, exocrine secretion, cellular adhesion

Note: Adapted from White, Middleton and Baxter (1984).

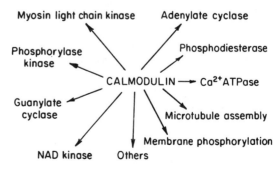

Figure 11.7. Some enzymes or cellular processes regulated by calmodulin. (Adapted from Cheung, 1980.)

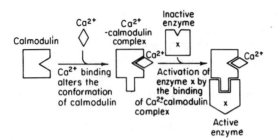

Figure 11.8. Schematic representation of the role of calmodulin in activating an enzyme. Free Ca^{2+} binds to calmodulin to form a Ca^{2+}-calmodulin complex; the conformation of calmodulin is altered by the binding of Ca^{2+}. The Ca^{2+}-calmodulin complex then binds to the inactive enzyme, converting the latter to a catalytically active form. For the sake of simplicity only one of the four Ca^{2+}-binding sites of calmodulin is shown. (Adapted from Alberts et al, 1983.)

calmodulin is actually a subunit (δ) of this enzyme, and the regulatory effects of two (α and β) subunits on the catalytic subunit (γ) are controlled by cyclic-AMP-dependent phosphorylation–dephosphorylation reactions.

The possibility that alterations of metabolic control mediated by calmodulin may occur in neoplasia (reviewed by Veigl et al, 1983) is attractive because of the pleiotropic nature of the biochemical alterations noted in cancer cells and because of the pleiotropic effects exerted by the protein itself (Fig 11.7). Calcium appears to be involved in control of cell division in some types of cells. In sea urchin eggs, Ca^{2+} activates cell division, while hepatocyte proliferation in regenerating liver appears to show an obligatory but transient requirement for Ca^{2+}. The division of certain cells in tissue culture is inhibited by lowering the concentration of Ca^{2+} from 1.0 to 0.1 mM, whereas the growth of corresponding transformed cells is not affected. Studies of calmodulin levels during the cell cycle have not revealed any dramatic changes. There is evidence that calmodulin is associated with the motility systems of various cells. For example, it is an activator of myosin light-chain kinase and may participate in the regulation of the polymerization of actin filaments. Other evidence indicates its involvement in Ca^{2+}-dependent microtubule assembly, which is necessary for formation of the mitotic spindle.

Certain drugs are potent inhibitors of the action of calmodulin. One of these, trifluoroperazine, blocks the spreading and migration of a variety of cell strains but not their attachment to the substratum.

Some transformed cells and tumor cells contain an unusual calcium-binding protein, oncomodulin (MacManus, 1979). This protein has been purified and shown to resemble parvalbumin, a protein thought to be involved in the contraction–relaxation cycle of mus-

cle. It has been postulated that oncomodulin and other similar Ca^{2+}-binding proteins that have been detected in tumor cells may be related to the known abnormal motility (a Ca^{2+}-dependent process) exhibited by some malignant cells. Further exploration of the nature and function of Ca^{2+}-binding proteins in tumor cells may prove important for the understanding of the abnormal properties of cancer cells.

11.4.5 PHOSPHOINOSITIDES

Calcium has been known to be involved in the response of some cellular hormone receptors for many years. Since 1983, there has been dramatic progress in the understanding of how these Ca^{2+}-linked receptors influence cellular metabolism through a pathway involving phosphoinositides (Berridge et al, 1985).

Hokin and Hokin (1953) found that administration of acetylcholine increased the turnover of phosphatidyl inositol (PtdIns; see Fig 11.9) in certain responsive tissues. In 1975, Michell proposed that an increase of the turnover of PtdIns generally accompanies the activation of Ca^{2+}-linked receptors and is the cause of the observed increase in the concentration of intracellular Ca^{2+}. Calcium-linked receptors include the muscarinic receptors for acetylcholine, alpha$_1$-adrenergic receptors for norepinephrine, thrombin receptors on platelets and one type of receptor for vasopressin. Subsequent work has shown that it is the polyphosphoinositide PtdIns(4,5)P_2 (Fig 11.9), rather than PtdIns, that is particularly important in the response of Ca^{2+}-linked receptors. A critical observation was that administration of acetylcholine to the iris enhances breakdown of PtdIns(4,5)P_2; this is accomplished by stimulation of a phospholipase C (located near the receptor: see Fig 11.10), which acts on PtdIns(4,5)P_2 to release diacyl-

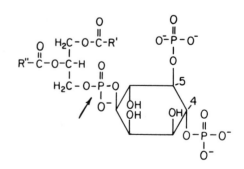

Figure 11.9. Structure of the polyphosphoinositide PtdIns (4,5)P_2. PtdIns has hydroxyl groups, not phosphates, on positions 4 and 5, and PtdIns(4)P has a phosphate on position 4 and a hydroxyl on position 5. Inositol is a hexahydroxy alcohol derived from glucose. The site where phospholipase C cleaves to form the two second messengers, DG and Ins(1,4,5)P_3, is indicated by the arrow.

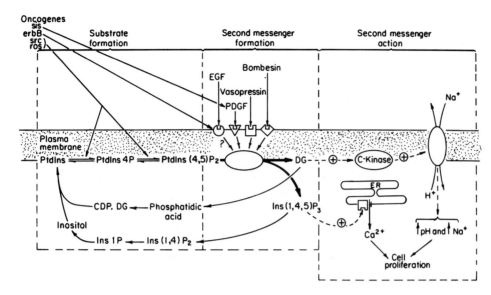

Figure 11.10. Polyphosphoinositide metabolism and cell growth. A variety of growth factors, all acting on separate receptors, stimulate the hydrolysis by phospholipase C, of PtdIns(4,5)P$_2$ to produce diacylglycerol (DG) and Ins(1,4,5)P$_3$. The latter is proposed to act on a specific receptor on the endoplasmic reticulum (ER) to mobilize Ca^{2+}. The other second messenger, DG, stimulates protein kinase C, which is thought to activate a Na$^+$/H$^+$ exchange carrier to increase intracellular pH. Both an increase of intracellular Ca^{2+} and of intracellular pH may stimulate cell proliferation. (Adapted from Berridge et al, 1985.)

glycerol (DG) and inositol triphosphate (Ins(1,4,5)P$_3$). Both of these products can act as second messengers. The latter appears to diffuse into the cytosol from the inner face of the plasma membrane and can cause release of Ca^{2+} from intracellular organelles, such as the endoplasmic reticulum and the sarcoplasmic reticulum. This release of Ins(1,4,5)P$_3$ appears to be a general consequence of the stimulation by agonists of Ca^{2+}-linked receptors.

Metabolism of phosphoinositides is important in the regulation of cell growth and in the mediation of effects of growth factors and some oncogene products (Fig 11.10). Thus, both epidermal growth factor (EGF) and platelet-derived growth factor (PDGF) (see also section 8.4.5) interact with their receptors to stimulate breakdown of PtdIns(4,5)P$_2$. The erb-B and sis oncogenes, which are homologous to genes coding for the EGF receptor and PDGF respectively, also affect this process. The products of the src and ras oncogenes appear to cause phosphorylation of PtdIns, resulting in the formation of PtdIns4P and PtdIns(4,5)P$_2$. Increases in the incorporation of radioactive phosphate into PtdIns4P, PtdIns(4,5)P$_2$ and phosphatidic acid have been shown to occur within 20 min after the induction of transformation by a temperature-sensitive mutant of Rous sarcoma virus. The Ca^{2+} mobilized from intracellular sites such as the endoplasmic reticulum by

Ins(1,4,5)P$_3$ may be involved in stimulation of cell proliferation.

Diacylglycerol released from PtdIns(4,5)P$_2$ by the action of phospholipase C is also a second messenger, stimulating the action of protein kinase C. The protein substrates for this kinase are still to be fully determined. However, present evidence indicates that one of these substrates may be a Na$^+$/H$^+$ exchange carrier (Fig 11.10; Berridge et al, 1985); the alkalinization of the cytoplasm resulting from increased activity of this carrier may influence the activity of a number of enzymes, and may also contribute to the stimulation of cell proliferation. The activity of protein kinase C in liver is increased by administration of certain tumor-promoting phorbol esters, suggesting that this enzyme may play a role in hepatocarcinogenesis (Nishizuka, 1984).

Advances in the understanding of factors which control cell metabolism are fundamental to cancer research. The emerging relationships among growth hormones, receptors, certain key enzymes of the plasma membrane (eg, phospholipase C and adenylate cyclase), Ca^{2+}, protein kinases and oncogene products are revealing not only how normal biochemical signalling events and growth regulatory processes are controlled, but also how these processes can become disturbed prior to (preneoplasia), during, or after (progression) the critical events of cell transformation.

11.5 THE PLASMA MEMBRANE

11.5.1 THE SURFACE OF MALIGNANT CELLS

The ability of tumor cells to metastasize is the most serious limitation to the efficacy of cancer treatment (see chapter 10). The interaction of one cell with another is a surface event; where this interaction is faulty, as in the case of metastasis, it appears logical to seek an explanation in the biochemistry of the cell surface.

The general structure of the plasma membrane of a normal cell is illustrated in Figure 11.11. The glyco-calyx or cell coat is made up of the oligosaccharide (glycan) chains of intrinsic membrane glycoproteins and glycolipids, as well as of adsorbed glycoproteins and proteoglycans.

Figure 11.12 summarizes in schematic form the major types of alterations found after neoplastic transformation (Nicolson, 1976; Friedman and Skehan, 1981).

The activities of some surface enzymes are frequently modified in malignant cells. The activity of collagenase is often elevated, and its release may play a role, along with other proteases, in destruction of normal tissue matrix and in tumor infiltration. Transformed cells may secrete a serine protease that converts serum plasminogen to plasmin (ie, plasminogen activator; Unkeless et al, 1973), which in turn hydrolyses fibrin. The secretion of the activator by virally transformed mouse, hamster, rat and chick cells, as well as by some human tumor cells, was found to be higher than from corresponding normal cells. It appears that the activity of this enzyme can play a role in determining morpholog-

ical properties of some transformed cells. However, extensive studies of malignant cells have shown no correlation between tumorigenicity and either fibrino-lytic activity or the production of plasminogen activa-tor (Skehan and Friedman, 1981).

The transport of a number of compounds (eg, glu-cose and some amino acids) into transformed cells is in-creased. Changes in the levels of cyclic nucleotides (section 11.4.2) may influence transport mechanisms, possibly acting via the phosphorylation of membrane proteins. Alterations in transport mechanisms might be relevant to the loss of growth regulation observed in tumor cells.

Lectins are proteins with two or more binding sites that interact specifically with certain sugars (see Ta-ble 11.6) and will thus bind to cell-surface receptor glycoproteins and glycolipids, causing agglutination. Many transformed cells are agglutinated at a lower con-

Table 11.6. Three Widely Used Lectins and the Specific Sugar Residues with Which They Interact*

Lectin	Sugars Recognized
Concanavalin A	β-D-glucose and β-D-mannose
Soybean lectin	D-galactose and N-acetyl-D-galactosa-mine
Wheat germ lectin	N-acetylglucosamine

Note: Adapted from Alberts et al (1983).

*Many other lectins recognizing various specific sugar residues are also available.

Figure 11.11. Schematic diagram of the plasma membrane and glycocalyx of a eukaryotic cell. Cholesterol and nonglycosyl-ated proteins of the plasma membrane are not indicated; some of the latter also traverse the bilayer, whereas others are attached loosely to either side of the bilayer. The glycoca-lyx is made up of the oligosaccharide chains of intrinsic mem-brane glycolipids and glycoproteins and also of adsorbed glycoproteins and proteoglycans. All of the carbohydrate chains are on the outside of the membrane. (Adapted from Alberts et al, 1983.)

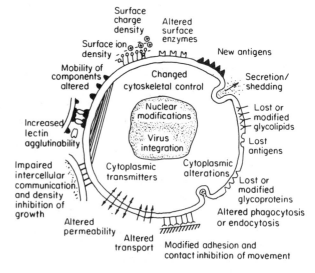

Figure 11.12. Schematic representation of alterations of the cell surface found after neoplastic transformation. (Adapted from Nicolson, 1976.)

Table 11.7. Some Functions of the Glycan
Moieties of Glycoproteins

- Clearance from plasma of certain glycoproteins
- Homing of lymphocytes
- Species-specific aggregation of certain cells
- Determinants of various blood-group substances
- Receptors on plasma membranes for certain hormones
- Modulation of certain physicochemical properties of proteins
- Stabilization against proteolysis
- Play role in proteolytic processing of precursors of certain glycoproteins
- Essential for the biological activity of a few glycoproteins (eg, hCG)
- Participate in membrane insertion, intracellular sorting and secretion of certain glycoproteins
- Involvement in embryonic development and differentiation
- Involved in cell contact-mediated interactions, including adhesion
- Possible involvement in determining sites of metastasis
- Possible determinants for cell killing by NK cells

centration of lectin compared to control cells, but the number of receptors on transformed cells appears similar to that on normal cells. Using electron and fluorescent microscopy, it has been shown that there is a greater relative mobility of lectin receptors on most transformed cells as compared to their controls. This increased mobility could be due to alterations in membrane fluidity, to changes in the structure of the receptor itself or to a variation in one or more of the membrane-associated cytoskeletal systems that restrict the mobility of components of the cell surface. Transformation often results in a partial disorganization of the cytoskeletal system, with an uncoupling of certain surface receptors from cytoplasmic transmembrane control. Cyclic nucleotides may be involved in the regulation of these events. Vinculin is a protein associated with adhesion plaques, which are thought to be involved in anchoring actin filaments to the plasma membrane. The tyrosine-specific kinase that is the product of the src gene of Rous sarcoma virus can phosphorylate tyrosine residues in vinculin; it is possible that this phenomenon is involved in the changes (eg, cell rounding and reduction of actin-containing stress fibers) observed after cell transformation by the virus.

11.5.2 GLYCOPROTEINS

Many of the proteins present on surface membranes contain covalently linked carbohydrates, and are thus glycoproteins. The oligosaccharide chains of these macromolecules extend outward from the cell into the external environment (Fig 11.11) and contain a variety of sugars (see Fig 11.13). Glycoproteins are classified according to the nature of the linkage between amino acid and carbohydrate. The major linkages present in membrane glycoproteins are the N-glycosidic linkage between asparagine and N-acetylglucosamine (GlcNAc) and the O-glycosidic linkage, serine (threonine)-N-acetylgalactosamine (GalNAc) (Fig 11.13). The biosynthesis of these two types of glycoproteins differs, that of the N-glycosidic class being more complex (reviewed by Schachter et al, 1985). The enzymes that transfer sugars onto the growing oligosaccharide chains of both types of glycoproteins are designated glycosyl transferases. The number and length of the oligosaccharide chains on glycoproteins can vary widely, so that carbohydrate can comprise from 1% to over 80% of the weight of a glycoprotein. A very large number of structures can be assembled from the permissible combinations of the sugars shown in Figure 11.13. Different oligosaccharides express different types of biological information (recognition sites, signals, etc), accounting at least in part for the wide range of functions attributed to glycoproteins. Glycoproteins on the cell surface have diverse functions, some of which are listed in Table 11.7 (Olden et al, 1985). Their role in the processes of adhesion and metastasis is under intensive investigation (see also section 10.4).

The glycoproteins on the surfaces of cells can be compared by a number of methods. One approach is to incubate cells with radioactive fucose and/or glucosamine, lightly trypsinize the cells to detach glycopeptides from the surface and then to extensively digest these glycopeptides with pronase to produce small fragments composed of oligosaccharide chains linked to only a few amino acids. These glycopeptides are then analysed by gel filtration, which will partly resolve them on the basis of molecular weight. Buck et al (1970) found that the radioactive fucose-containing glycopeptides obtained from virally transformed cells were of higher molecular weight and contained more N-acetylneuraminic acid (a sialic acid) than the equivalent glycopeptides of control cells. Additional studies on a variety of transformed cells and solid tumors from different species indicated that this was a consistent finding. Increased content of this sialic acid has been shown to correlate with metastatic potential in 29 tumor cell lines (Yogeeswaran, 1983).

There appears to be an increased degree of branching in the glycan chains of the glycoproteins of malignant cells, accompanied by a reduction in the content of mannose. The observed changes of glycoprotein structure in malignant cells may be due to increases or

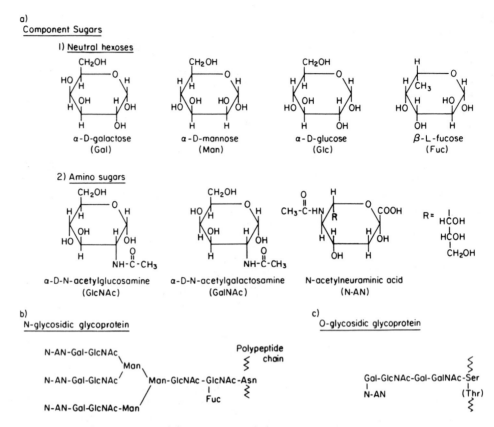

Figure 11.13. Some aspects of the structures of glycoproteins. *a*, Common sugars present in glycoprotein. *b*, Structure of one type of oligosaccharide chain present in an N-glycosidic glycoprotein. *c*, Structure of one type of oligosaccharide chain of an O-glycosidic glycoprotein.

decreases in the activities of certain of the key glycosyl transferases that control glycan structure. It is unlikely that a single type of alteration of glycosyl transferase activity will be found to be critical for the development of the alterations of oligosaccharide chains detected in tumor cells, but a small number of patterns of change (eg, those leading to certain patterns of branching) might be crucial.

Several cell-surface glycoproteins from normal and tumor cells have been purified and aspects of their structures and functions have been analysed (see Yogeeswaran, 1983; Smets and Van Beek, 1983). Examples are fibronectin and epiglycanin, whose properties are summarized in Table 11.8. Fibronectin appears to be important in cell adhesion, but does not appear to correlate with tumorigenicity. In contrast, epiglycanin does appear to play an important role in the tumorigenicity of the allotransplantable mouse TA3-Ha spontaneous mammary adenocarcinoma.

11.5.3 GLYCOSPHINGOLIPIDS

Glycosphingolipids (GSLs) are the other major class of glycoconjugates present on the surfaces of eukaryotic cells. The common sugars present in GSLs are glucose, galactose, N-acetylglucosamine, N-acetylgalactosamine and fucose; when N-acetylneuraminic acid is a constituent, the GSL is then called a ganglioside (Fig 11.14). Ceramide, which consists of a fatty acid covalently bound to the long-chain base sphingosine or one of its derivatives, is the universal backbone of the GSLs. The GSLs are synthesized by the sequential addition of individual sugars donated by appropriate nucleotide-sugars in reactions catalysed by individual glycolipid glycosyl transferases; like the glycoprotein glycosyl transferases, these enzymes are predominantly located in the Golgi apparatus. The GSLs are degraded by glycolipid hydrolases, which are lysosomal enzymes that are specific for catalysing the hydrolysis of the individual sugars of GSLs; deficiencies of these enzymes are responsible for various inborn errors of metabolism (eg Tay-Sachs disease, Gaucher's disease, etc). The majority of the GSLs in a cell are present on the plasma membrane, but smaller amounts may also be present on intracellular membranes of the endoplasmic reticulum and the Golgi apparatus. The sugar moieties of the GSLs have been shown to project from the surfaces of cells into the external environment (Fig 11.11); GSLs do not ap-

Table 11.8. Properties of Two Glycoproteins of the Cell Surface

Glycoprotein	Mol Wt	Class	Properties
Fibronectin	440,000	N-glycosidic	• Extrinsic protein. • Amount decreases after viral infections. • Involved in cell adhesion • Binds to collagen and to certain proteoglycans and gangliosides. • Probably no correlation with tumorigenicity.
Epiglycanin	500,000	O-glycosidic	• Role in masking H-2ᵃ histocompatibility antigens in the allotransplantable TA 3-Ha mouse mammary adenocarcinoma. • Probably involved in increasing metastatic potential.

Glucosylceramide   Ceramide-Glc

Lactosylceramide   Ceramide-Glc-Gal

GM₃: Ceramide-Glc-Gal
         | N-AN

GM₂: Ceramide Glc-Gal-GalNAc
         | N-AN

GM₁: Ceramide-Glc-Gal-GalNAc-Gal
         | N-AN

Figure 11.14. Schematic structures of certain of the more important glycosphingolipids (GSLs). Ceramide, the backbone of the GSLs, is comprised of a long-chain base, usually sphingosine, covalently linked to any one of a number of fatty acids. All of the GSLs depicted above, except glucosylceramide, can be synthesized from the preceding GSL by the addition of one sugar molecule donated by a nucleotide-sugar in a reaction catalysed by a specific glycolipid glycosyl transferase; glucosylceramide is synthesized by the addition of glucose to ceramide. GSLs that contain a sialic acid, usually N-AN, are called gangliosides. The simplest ganglioside shown above is GM₃. With respect to the nomenclature of the gangliosides, M represents a monosialoganglioside and the numerical subscripts (3,2,1) are assigned to each of the gangliosides indicated. For simplicity, the anomeric nature (α or β) and the positions of the individual linkages of the sugars to each other have been omitted. The various GSLs indicated in this figure can be separated from each other by thin-layer chromatography.

1. Blocked synthesis, due to deficiency of a specific glycolipid glycosyl transferase.
2. Neosynthesis, in which a change occurs in the synthesis of the type of GSL present, so that a GSL not normally found in adult tissue is detected; this usually involves activation of a specific transferase catalysing either addition of the same sugar in a different linkage or the addition of an entirely different sugar.
3. Loss of so-called "contact extension" of glycolipids. When some normal cultured cells come into contact with each other upon reaching confluence, an extension of the oligosaccharide chain of one or more of their glycolipids may be observed. This phenomenon is probably due to an increase of the activities of one or more glycosyl transferases that are involved in elongating the involved glycolipids. Contact extension may be associated with contact inhibition of cell growth in normal, but not in transformed, cells (see chapter 8).
4. Change of organisation of certain GSLs in membranes. A common finding is that whereas a particular glycolipid may be cryptic in control cells, it is more accessible (eg, to enzymes or antibodies) on the surfaces of transformed cells.

pear to be present on the inner surface of the plasma membrane.

The function of most GSLs is unknown. The ganglioside GM₁ has been shown to be a receptor for cholera toxin in intestinal epithelium and other cells. Other gangliosides are thought to be receptors for interferon and tetanus toxin.

A number of alterations of the composition of GSLs has been noted in transformed and tumor cells. Hakomori and Kannagi (1983) have classified these changes into four major classes.

Because of their presence on surface membranes and the fact that alterations of GSL profile are often observed in virus-transformed cells and in tumor cells, it has been suggested that GSLs may play a role in cell-surface phenomena such as adhesion, cell–cell interaction and possibly metastatic potential. Changes of glycolipid pattern have been detected in in vitro transformed cells, but generally speaking they have not been early changes following transformation. However, recent experiments involving transfection of certain oncogenes indicated that this procedure resulted in changes of glycolipid pattern, and thus suggest an important role for these alterations.

11.6 SUMMARY

Some generalizations regarding the biochemistry of cancer cells are (a) there is often evidence of expression of fetal gene products (eg, isozymes), (b) the regulation of the synthesis of enzymes (ie, mechanisms of enzyme induction and repression) is frequently disturbed, and (c) fast-growing tumors generally exhibit a predictable metabolic pattern largely consisting of an accentuation of certain anabolic pathways. The biochemical profile of a slow-growing tumor does not appear to differ appreciably from that of its parent tissue, except presumably in relation to those key changes (as yet to be defined) that led to transformation. Most of the biochemical changes noted in tumors do not relate directly to the basic mechanisms of transformation, but rather to the rate of cell proliferation.

Many alterations of biochemical processes (eg, transport, adhesion, etc) occurring at the plasma membrane have been documented, but molecular changes critical for the development of neoplasia have yet to be identified. Further structural studies of cell-surface glycoconjugates along with assays of the activities of appropriate glycosyl transferases may reveal changes in the biosynthesis of oligosaccharides that are important in generating abnormal surface macromolecules that contribute to loss of adhesion and to metastasis. Recent investigations have shown that certain products of oncogenes interact with enzymes of the cell surface that play central roles in the transduction of chemical signals to the interior (eg, adenylate cyclase, phospholipase C); continuation of these efforts should help clarify the precise mechanisms whereby malignant cells lose control of their regulation of growth and position.

REFERENCES

Alberts B, Bray D, Lewis J et al: *Molecular Biology of the Cell.* Garland, New York, 1983.

Berridge MJ, Heslop JP, Irvine RF, Brown KD: Inositol lipids and cell proliferation. *Trans Biochem Soc* 1985; 13:67–71.

Boynton AL, Whitfield JF: The role of cyclic AMP in cell proliferation: A critical assessment of the evidence. *Adv Cyclic Nucleotide Res* 1983; 15:193–294.

Buck CA, Glick MC, Warren L: A comparative study of glycoproteins from the surface of control and Rous sarcoma virus transformed hamster cells. *Biochemistry* 1970; 9:4567–4576.

Campbell AK: Intracellular calcium: Its universal role as regulator. John Wiley & Sons, New York, 1983.

Cheung WY: Calmodulin plays a pivotal role in cell regulation. *Science* 1980; 207:19–27.

Collett MS, Erikson RL: Protein kinase activity associated with the avian sarcoma virus src gene product. *Proc Natl Acad Sci USA* 1978; 75:2021–2024.

Elford HL, Freese M, Passamani E et al: Ribonucleotide reductase and cell proliferation. I. Variations of ribonucleotide reductase activity with tumor growth rate in a series of rat hepatomas. *J Biol Chem* 1970; 245:5228–5233.

Friedman SJ, Skehan P: Malignancy and the cell surface, in Cameron IL, Pool TB (eds): *The Transformed Cell.* Academic Press, New York, 1981, pp 67–134.

Greenstein JP: *Biochemistry of Cancer*, ed 2. Academic Press, New York, 1954.

Hakomori S-I, Kannagi A: Glycosphingolipids as tumor-associated and differentiation markers. *J Natl Cancer Inst* 1983; 71:231–251.

Hildebrandt JD, Codina J, Risinger R, Birnbaumer L: Identification of a γ subunit associated with the adenyl cyclase regulatory proteins N_s and N_i. *J Biol Chem* 1984; 259:2039–2042.

Hokin MR, Hokin LE: Enzyme secretion and the incorporation of P^{32} into phospholipids of pancreas slices. *J Biol Chem* 1953; 203:967–977.

Hunter T, Sefton BM: Transforming gene product of Rous sarcoma virus phosphorylates tyrosine. *Proc Natl Acad Sci USA* 1980; 77:1311–1315.

Ibsen KH, Fishman WH: Developmental gene expression in cancer. *Biochim Biophys Acta* 1979; 560:243–280.

MacManus JP: Occurrence of a low-molecular-weight calcium-binding protein in neoplastic liver. *Cancer Res* 1979; 39:3000–3005.

Marx JL: Oncogene linked to cell regulatory system: Analysis in yeast of the activity of the ras oncogene suggests that it works through adenylate cyclase, a major cell regulatory enzyme. *Science* 1984; 226:527–528.

Michell RH: Inositol phospholipids and cell surface receptor function. *Biochim Biophys Acta* 1975; 415:81–147.

Morris HP: Biological and biochemical characteristics of transplantable hepatomas, in Grundmann E (ed): *Handbuch der allgemeinen Pathologie.* Springer-Verlag, Berlin, 1975, vol 6, part 7, pp 277–334.

Nicolson GL: Transmembrane control of the receptors on normal and tumor cells. I. Cytoplasmic influence over cell surface components. II. Surface changes associated with transformation and malignancy. *Biochim Biophys Acta* 1976; 457:57–108, 458:1–72.

Nishizuka Y: The role of protein kinase C in cell surface signal transduction and tumor promotion. *Nature* 1984; 308:693–698.

Olden K, Bernard BA, Humphries MJ et al: Function of glycoprotein glycans. *Trends Biochem Sci* 1985; 10:78–82.

Pitot HC: Molecular pathogenesis of experimental liver cancer. *Fed Proc* 1962; 21:1124–1129.

Pitot HC: Metabolic controls and neoplasia, in Becker FF (ed): *Cancer: A Comprehensive Treatise*, ed 1. Plenum Press, New York, 1975, vol 3, chap 6, pp 121–154.

Potter VR: Transplantable animal cancer, the primary standard. *Cancer Res* 1961; 21:1331–1333.

Prasad KN: Involvement of cyclic nucleotides in transformation, in Cameron IL, Pool TB (eds): *The Transformed Cell.* Academic Press, New York, 1981, pp 235–266.

Schachter H, Narasimhan S, Gleeson P et al: Glycosyltrans-ferases involved in the biosynthesis of protein-bound oligosaccharides of the asparagine-D-glucosamine and serine (threonine)-N-acetyl-D-galactosamine types, in Martonosi AN (ed): *The Enzymes of Biological Membranes.* Plenum Press, New York, 1985, pp 227–278.

Schapira F, Dreyfus JC, Schapira G: Anomaly of aldolase in primary liver cancer. *Nature* 1963; 200:995–997.

Skehan P, Friedman SJ: Malignant transformation: *In vivo* methods and *in vitro* correlates, in Cameron, IL, Pool TB (eds): *The Transformed Cell.* Academic Press, New York, 1981, pp 8–66.

Smets LA, Van Beek WP: Carbohydrates of the tumor cell surface. *Biochim Biophys Acta* 1983; 738:237–249.

Unkeless JC, Tobia A, Ossowski L, Quigley JP, Rifkin DB, Reich E: An enzymatic function associated with transformation of fibroblasts by oncogenic viruses. I. Chick embryo fibroblast cultures transformed by avian RNA tumor viruses. *J Expl Med* 1973; 137:85–111.

Veigl ML, Vanaman TC, Sedwick WD: Calcium and calmodulin in cell growth and transformation. *Biochim Biophys Acta* 1983; 738:21–48.

Warburg O: *The Metabolism of Tumours.* Arnold Constable, London, 1930.

Weber G: Enzymology of cancer cells. *N Engl J Med* 1977; 296:486–493, 541–551.

Weinhouse S: Isoenzyme alterations, gene regulation and neoplastic transformation. *Advan Enzyme Regul* 1983; 21: 369–386.

White DA, Middleton B, Baxter M: *Hormones and Metabolic Control.* Edward Arnold, London, 1984.

Yogeeswaran G: Cell surface glycolipids and glycoproteins in malignant transformation. *Adv Cancer Res* 1983; 38:289–350.

BIBLIOGRAPHY

Alberts B, Bray D, Lewis J et al (eds): *Molecular Biology of the Cell.* Garland, New York, 1983.

Darnell J, Lodish H, Baltimore D: *Molecular Cell Biology.* Scientific American Books, W.H. Freeman and Co, New York, 1986.

12

Tumor Markers

Aaron Malkin

12.1 INTRODUCTION

It has long been recognized that in patients with cancer, blood samples may exhibit an abnormal biochemical profile. In particular, substances may be detected in body fluids which are produced by, or in association with, tumors. These substances have been termed tumor markers. In theory, tumor markers might be useful as an aid to tumor diagnosis and prognosis, as a method of assessment of tumor burden, and as a means for predicting recurrence before it can be detected clinically. They might be useful as a guide in the choice and scheduling of treatment. However, markers are not produced uniquely by tumors; their levels in blood differ quantitatively rather than qualitatively from normal. Also, the production of marker substances by tumor cells is likely to be heterogeneous among the cells of the tumor population.

A classification of substances that have been used or proposed as tumor markers is shown in Table 12.1. Basic properties of the markers and their detection in blood or urine will be described in the first part of the chapter. The factors which determine clinical usefulness of these markers will then be reviewed critically to allow an assessment of their current and future role in the management of cancer.

12.2 PROPERTIES OF TUMOR MARKERS

12.2.1 DETECTION OF MARKERS

Tumor markers occur in low concentrations in plasma and require sensitive techniques for their detection. Radioimmunoassay, immunoradiometric assay or enzyme-linked immunosorbent assays are variations on the same principle and are now the procedures of choice for the measurement of small quantities of protein in body fluids (Fig 12.1). All three procedures depend on the formation of antigen–antibody complexes. A purified preparation of a particular marker is used initially to prepare specific antibodies (usually monoclonal antibodies) which recognize the marker, and these antibodies are usually attached to a solid support such as sephadex beads. In a radioimmunoassay, the quantitation of tumor markers in serum depends on competition for binding to the antibodies between the unknown sample and a known amount of purified and labeled marker. With immunoradiometric or enzyme-linked immunosorbent assays, quantitation of an unknown sample is assayed by its binding to specific antibodies on the solid support, using labeled specific antibodies which form a "sandwich" around the marker antigen (Fig 12.1). The specificity of the fore-

Table 12.1. Classification of Tumor Markers Showing Selected Examples

Oncofetal protiens	Carcinoembryonic antigen (CEA)
	Alpha-fetoprotein (AFP)
Hormones	Human chorionic gonadotropin (hCG)
	Ectopic hormones
Enzymes	Prostatic acid phosphatase
	Alkaline phosphatase
	Lactic dehydrogenase
	Gamma glutamyl transpeptidase (GGT)
Immunoglobulins	
Tumor-associated antigens	CA-125
Miscellaneous markers	Polyamines
	Nucleosides
	Tissue polypeptide antigen (TPA)
	Isoferritins
	Acute-phase proteins

going procedures depends on the purity of the marker used to prepare antibodies and the specificity of these antibodies for the particular marker antigen.

Isolation and purification of tumor markers is laborious and except for relatively small molecules such as hCG, has not been particularly successful. No substance that is unique to tumors has been isolated to date. It follows, therefore, that antibodies raised against these markers may cross-react with related molecules. Although highly sophisticated techniques have been developed for the measurement of small quantities of markers caution should be exercised in interpreting the results of these assays.

12.2.2 ONCOFETAL PROTEINS

The oncofetal proteins are normally present during a variable period of embryonic or fetal life, do not disappear entirely in the adult, and reappear with certain malignancies. They are substances which appear to originate in the tumor itself and enter the circulation as a result of secretion by the tumor or as breakdown products of tumor cells. Classic examples of the oncofetal proteins include the carcinoembryonic antigen (CEA) and alpha-fetoprotein (AFP).

Carcinoembryonic antigen is a glycoprotein with a molecular weight of about 200,000 d and is found in the alimentary tract, liver and pancreas of fetuses between the second and sixth months of intrauterine life. It can be detected in normal adult tissues using sensitive immunohistochemical techniques and is present in small quantities in normal plasma. Elevated blood levels

of CEA are found in several nonmalignant diseases such as cirrhosis and chronic obstructive pulmonary disease, and modest elevations may occur in smokers. Reappearance of the protein, or other oncofetal proteins, in the presence of a variety of epithelial tumors (eg, colo-rectal cancer, breast cancer) has led to the suggestion that "de-repression" may be a characteristic of malignant growth or alternatively, that stem cells or other primitive progenitor cells populate the tumor. With the recent introduction of monoclonal antibodies to study the protein, there is evidence to suggest that immunologically distinct molecular forms exist. Whether they are characteristic of tumors of different organs remains to be determined. The half-life of CEA in plasma appears to be about 6–8 days. This estimate is based on the observation that elevated CEA levels return to normal in about two months following successful removal of a CEA-producing primary tumor.

Alpha-fetoprotein is an alpha$_1$-globulin and is a product of the fetal liver, gastrointestinal tract and yolk sac. The protein is normally present in the fetal circulation. There is good evidence to suggest that AFP functions as the fetal counterpart of adult albumin since there is considerable homology between the two proteins. Again, the protein gradually disappears from plasma during neonatal life to be replaced by albumin, but never entirely disappears in the adult. Marked increases in plasma AFP concentration are observed in about 80% of patients with hepatocellular carcinoma and about 60% of patients with nonseminomatous testicular tumors. Like CEA, AFP levels may be elevated in plasma in the presence of nonmalignant diseases, especially cirrhosis.

AFP has a half-life in plasma of about 5.5 days. A slower rate of disappearance of the protein, or failure of serum levels to return to normal following surgery, are strongly suggestive of the presence of residual disease.

12.2.3 HORMONES

Human chorionic gonadotropin (hCG) is produced normally by the syncytiotrophoblast cells of the placenta during pregnancy, and most pregnancy tests are based on its detection in serum or urine. Elevated levels of hCG are also found in the plasma of almost all women with tumors of placental origin (choriocarcinoma) and in 60% of men with testicular tumors. The hormone is a glycoprotein related to follicle-stimulating hormone (FSH), luteinizing hormone (LH) and thyroid-stimulating hormone (TSH). It consists of two polypeptide chains, termed alpha and beta. The alpha chain is homologous with the alpha chains of the other glycoprotein hormones; the beta chains exhibit some differ-

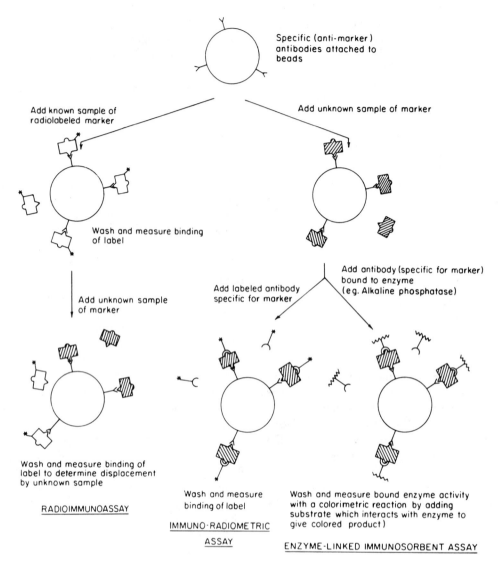

Figure 12.1. Schematic diagram of radio- or enzyme immunoassays. Several variations of these methods have been used to quantitate markers in body fluids.

ences. Thus use of hCG as a tumor marker depends on immunologic detection of the beta chain.

Modest elevations of hCG are sometimes observed in patients with tumors of other organs such as breast and large bowel. It is not clear whether this represents true ectopic hormone production, ie, hormone production by cells which do not normally produce the substance, or rather is due to increased synthesis and secretion of a material produced normally in small quantities by the organ in question (ie, eutopic production).

It has not yet been established whether the protein core of placental hCG is identical to that produced by tumors. However, there is great variation in the carbohydrate side chain of the hormone in patients with choriocarcinoma and testicular tumors, and large mo-

lecular forms, or free alpha or beta chains, can often be identified in the plasma of these patients. The large molecular forms probably represent prohormones which are incompletely processed and which would normally undergo translational modifications prior to secretion. hCG has a half-life in plasma of about 36–48 hr. This short half-life may be useful for early assessment of the efficacy of treatment.

Ectopic hormones can occasionally be secreted by tumors of nonendocrine organs and give rise to syndromes associated with overproduction of hormone (see section 13.4.2). The fact that the hormones produced are almost invariably polypeptides suggests that the responsible mechanism involves derepression of a single gene. Steroid biosynthesis is much more complex (see section 13.2), involving a cascade of enzymes, and unless genomically linked their activation would entail an unlikely series of events.

Bronchogenic carcinoma of the small-cell variety is the nonendocrine tumor most commonly associated with ectopic hormone production. Using immunochemical procedures, a great variety of hormones can be detected in the sera of these patients including ACTH, calcitonin and arginine vasopressin. In most patients, clinical sequellae are not observed because the synthesis of the hormone is disorganized. Prohormones and fragments of precursors appear in the patient's serum with far greater frequency than the active hormone itself.

There is some argument as to whether the secretion of polypeptide hormones in patients with small-cell lung cancer is indeed ectopic in origin. Immunohistochemical techniques have identified cells in the pulmonary bronchioles of the normal lung, which stain for a variety of polypeptide hormones. The cells are often referred to as "pulmonary endocrine" (or APUD = amine precursor uptake and decarboxylation) cells and it is suggested that small-cell lung cancer originates from them. The secretion of ectopic hormones is not unique to tumors since their production also occurs in patients with chronic obstructive pulmonary disease, albeit less frequently and at lower levels.

Ectopic hormone production has been studied most extensively in patients with small-cell lung cancer. While rare instances of ectopic hormone production have been described in other tumors, their role as markers is confined to small-cell lung cancer. Of the hormones investigated, calcitonin and arginine vasopressin appear to have the greatest potential usefulness. Preliminary evidence suggests that calcitonin reflects tumor burden and is a good prognostic indicator. Levels of arginine vasopressin may reflect the clinical response to treatment.

12.2.4 ENZYMES

Prostatic acid phosphatase is an enzyme secreted by the normal prostate gland. It can be differentiated from other phosphatases by chemical and immunological means. In patients with prostate cancer, abnormal levels indicate that the tumor has extended beyond the prostatic capsule. Synthesis and secretion of prostatic acid phosphatase is dependent on the action of testosterone and may be turned off by the administration of estrogens. Unfortunately the correlation between levels of acid phosphatase and total body burden of prostatic cancer has been rather poor, and consequently values of acid phosphatase are not used to stage the tumor.

Alkaline phosphatases exist as a number of isoenzymes

produced, for example, by liver, bone or placenta. Elevation of alkaline phosphatase in the plasma of patients with malignancy is usually due to overproduction by either liver or bone and indicates involvement of those organs by metastatic disease. A number of benign disorders are also associated with increased plasma levels of the enzyme. Placental alkaline phosphatase is a normal placental protein which is found occasionally in the plasma of patients with ovarian cancer, testicular seminomas and other tumors. It appears to be produced by the tumors themselves, and may have a role as a marker for monitoring the treatment of some seminomatous tumors.

Lactic dehydrogenase (LDH) is a tetramer comprised of combinations of two distinct polypeptide chains designated H for heart and M for muscle. Consequently there are five possible isoenzymes; the occasional aberrant form has also been described. Elevations of lactic dehydrogenase reflect tumor bulk in patients with lymphoma. In addition, enzyme levels are prognostic of outcome independent of conventional prognostic criteria in lymphoma. Measurement of total LDH and of ratios of the isoenzymes have been used as indicators of metastases or of tumor burden in other malignancies with little uniformity of opinion as to the value of these tests.

Gamma glutamyl transpeptidase (GGT), like the hepatic isozyme of alkaline phosphatase, may be elevated in the plasma of patients with hepatic metastases. The bulk of evidence suggests that elevated levels of the enzyme are due to canalicular obstruction, since increases in this enzyme usually parallel those in the hepatic form of alkaline phosphatase. Isozymes of GGT have been described, some of which may be tumor products.

12.2.5 IMMUNOGLOBULINS

In multiple myeloma and B-cell lymphomas there is often asynchronous synthesis of the polypeptide chains of immunoglobulins, and an excess of light over heavy chains is frequently formed. Excessive urinary excretion of light chains is almost pathognomonic of these disorders, although incomplete fragments of heavy chains or whole immunoglobulin molecules can be detected in serum or urine. Protein electrophoresis of these fluids will then show a sharp peak, indicating the presence of a monoclonal protein referred to in serum as an M-protein.

The use of immunoglobulin markers for diagnosis and for monitoring treatment of lymphoid tumors provides an example of what may be expected of an ideal tumor marker. There is evidence that the level of the M-protein reflects the total body burden of disease. While abnormal plasma levels of immunoglobulins can be found in many diseases and monoclonal peaks can occasionally be detected in the elderly population, the association of an M-protein and abnormal plasma cells is quite specific for multiple myeloma. In addition, there is a comparable degree of sensitivity since well over 90% of patients with this disease will have elevated plasma or urine levels of immunoglobulin or their components at presentation. However, genotypic and phenotypic alterations may sometimes occur in these tumors so that cells may be selected during treatment which have different rates of production of the markers than in the original tumor.

12.2.6 TUMOR-ASSOCIATED ANTIGENS

The widespread availability of techniques for the production of monoclonal antibodies has led to a renewed search for tumor-specific antigens. To do this, tissue cultures of homogeneous tumor cell lines have been established followed by the generation of monoclonal antibodies to the tumor cells. Antigens that are associated with tumors originating from specific organs have been detected, but antigens with absolute specificity have not been isolated for any type of cancer.

An example of this approach is the discovery of the ovarian antigen CA-125. The antigen was isolated and purified from an ovarian cancer cell line. Monoclonal antibodies were produced and an immunoradiometric assay developed. The antigen has proven useful for monitoring treatment of ovarian cancer, but may also be produced by other tumors such as those of the lung and large bowel.

An extension of the use of tumor markers for diagnostic purposes and as an adjunct in monitoring therapy involves the use of marker antibodies for tumor localization and treatment (see also section 20.3). Isotope-labeled antibodies to the markers CEA, AFP and hCG, for example, have been used to localize metastatic disease. At the same time, a great deal of experimental work is being directed to the use of antimarker antibodies in treatment. The antibodies are tagged with an isotope or conjugated with chemotherapeutic or toxic agents, the objective being to concentrate the therapeutic agent at the antigenic target: the tumor itself.

12.2.7 MISCELLANEOUS MARKERS

Polyamines, nucleosides and tissue polypeptide antigen (TPA) are potential markers which reflect cellular proliferation and are increased nonspecifically in patients with cancer. The polyamines spermine, spermidine and putrescine are products of ornithine decarboxylation and are found in increased concentrations in the urine whenever there is increased cell turnover. The nucleosides dimethyl guanosine and pseudouridine are components of transfer RNA. As with the polyamines, they are released into the circulation in excessive amounts with enhanced cellular proliferation. TPA is another nonspecific marker of cell turnover which has been investigated extensively over the past few years. While these markers of proliferation cannot be used for diagnostic purposes, they may be of some use in monitoring the effects of therapy. However, inflammatory or other nonmalignant processes also cause elevation in plasma levels of these substances and may therefore lead to spurious information about the magnitude of therapeutic response.

Isoferritins are complex protein molecules which exist in several isomeric forms. Acidic isoferritins occur in placenta and heart muscle and the basic isomers are characteristic of liver and spleen. While increases of total plasma ferritins are frequently observed in patients with cancer, the abnormalities are entirely nonspecific. It was hoped that measurement of ratios of acidic to basic forms might be indicative of malignancy. However, the weight of experimental evidence indicates that there is no consistent relationship between acidic and basic isomers of ferritin in patients with cancer.

Acute-phase proteins are under continued investigation as potential markers of malignancy. Most prominent among them are alpha$_1$-acid glycoprotein and C-reactive protein. These proteins are not specific for malignancy but are increased in many inflammatory conditions. If one could rule out accompanying nonmalignant processes, monitoring disease activity by measuring acute-phase proteins in the plasma might be worthwhile.

Increases in acute-phase proteins are usually accompanied by decreases in other proteins in the plasma, notably albumin. They are produced in the liver, and their synthetic process involves diversion of amino acids from the synthesis of other proteins such as albumin. Surprisingly, the function of the acute-phase proteins in cancer or other diseases is unknown, but their presence constitutes a manifestation of the severity of the process.

The above overview of properties of some of the more common tumor markers can be supplemented by referring to recent and comprehensive reviews (Rudden, 1981; Ewing et al, 1982).

12.3 CRITERIA FOR THE EVALUATION OF THE USEFULNESS OF TUMOR MARKERS

12.3.1 THE IDEAL MARKER

While scores of potential tumor markers have been described, very few have undergone rigorous appraisal. In the present section, criteria will be described which allow evaluation of the clinical potential of putative markers.

Ideally, biologic markers of tumor activity

1. should be sensitive and specific,
2. should reflect tumor burden,
3. should be prognostic of outcome,
4. should be predictive of recurrence, and
5. should lead to more effective treatment.

Unfortunately, few of the substances that are currently available approach this description of an ideal marker.

12.3.2 SENSITIVITY AND SPECIFICITY

The sensitivity of a marker refers to the proportion of patients with a particular tumor who have elevated plasma levels of the marker. Specificity is indicated by the proportion of patients who do not have this cancer, who have normal plasma levels of the marker (Fig 12.2). Ideally a marker will have high values of sensitivity and specificity.

A recurrent theme in the sequential evaluation of sensitivity and specificity of a marker substance is the initial finding of high values followed by disappoint-

ment as larger studies fail to confirm the results of a pilot investigation. This is illustrated in Figure 12.3 by plotting the proportion of patients with colo-rectal cancer, and of controls, who were found to have elevated levels of CEA as reported in the literature between 1969 and 1972 (Bodansky, 1974).

The initial report of an association between CEA and colo-rectal cancer suggested the discovery of a marker which was extremely sensitive and relatively specific (Thomson et al, 1969): 34 of 35 patients with colo-rectal cancer, studied at a time when tumor tissue was known to be present in the body, had plasma levels of CEA greater than 2.5 ng/ml, and 3 of 32 patients with cancerous lesions of digestive organs other than large bowel and rectum had elevated CEA levels, while none of 133 controls without colo-rectal cancer had elevated levels. Subsequent investigators found lower values of about 70% for the sensitivity of elevated levels of CEA in colo-rectal cancer, and variable levels of specificity. In a multicenter study indicated in Figure 12.3 by D, the original laboratory (M) was unable to confirm its own earlier findings. This sequence is not unusual and suggests caution in generalizing the results of preliminary data and the need for confirmatory evidence before drawing conclusions.

There are several reasons why preliminary results may not be confirmed in larger investigations. Initial studies usually choose patients from a hospital-based population who have advanced, bulky tumors. Plasma levels of a marker in these patients are unlikely to

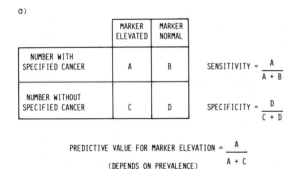

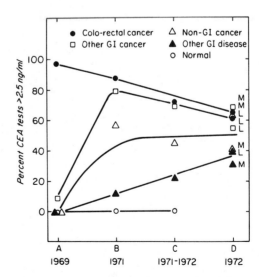

Figure 12.2. Sensitivity, specificity and predictive value. *a*, Patients with and without disease are classified as to the presence or absence of marker elevations. Predictive value depends on the proportion of patients with disease (ie, on prevalence). *b*, An example showing that for an uncommon disease both sensitivity and specificity may be high, but predictive value is low. This effect limits the value of markers in screening.

Figure 12.3. History of CEA. A shows results of the initial investigation of CEA in colo-rectal cancer and controls. B and C represent subsequent studies. D shows the results of a multicenter study on the use of CEA in colo-rectal cancer. In the last study there were four participating laboratories (L) as well as the original investigators from Montreal General Hospital (M). (From Bodansky, 1974, with permission.)

reflect those in patients with minimal disease, where marker studies have the highest potential for clinical use. False-positive results in control populations may be rare if these are drawn initially from healthy volunteers, or from patients with benign disease of unrelated organs. Marker elevation is usually more common in patients with other malignancies or in benign disease of the tissue in which the tumors under investigation have originated; such patients should be included as controls in larger studies.

Methods for assessing the sensitivity of a marker relate to the detection of early or minimal disease. Preoperative levels of the marker may be correlated with staging at surgery; postoperative elevations of the marker may be correlated with the presence of residual disease at operation, or with the subsequent development of recurrence in patients where there is no apparent residual disease. Attempts to relate plasma levels of markers to clinical data are limited because the clinical assessment of tumor bulk is usually rather imprecise.

Examples of the use of the foregoing criteria to measure sensitivity indicate that the CEA test is positive preoperatively in about 25% of patients with Dukes' stage A (ie, early) colo-rectal cancer. CA-125, a marker of ovarian cancer, is positive in about 80% of patients with minimal residual disease (<2 cm) following surgery.

The specificity of a marker may refer to cancer in general, or to one type of cancer. If a marker is proposed as specific for a particular type of tumor, the probability of false-positive tests due to tumors of other organs must be established. The frequency of marker elevation must be ascertained in healthy subjects of varying ages, in a variety of benign disorders, and particularly in benign diseases originating in the same organ as tumors that cause elevated plasma levels of the marker. If these criteria are applied to the ovarian antigen CA-125 it is found that the test is not specific for ovarian cancer, since elevation of plasma levels is found in an appreciable number of patients with other tumors, such as lung cancer. There is modest elevation in plasma levels of the marker in about 10% of patients with benign gynecologic disease, and more marked elevation in about 10% of patients with some other nonmalignant diseases such as cirrhosis of the liver.

One can enhance the specificity of a marker by adjusting the threshold for a positive test, but this is accompanied by a fall in sensitivity. The influence of threshold on values of specificity and sensitivity for use of CEA as a marker of colo-rectal cancer is illustrated in Table 12.2 (Miller, 1974). At a threshold level for CEA of 7.0 ng/ml, the specificity of marker elevation for colo-rectal cancer is 95%. But note that the sensi-

Table 12.2. Proportion of Colo-rectal Cancers Diagnosed by Using Different Threshold Values for Plasma Levels of CEA

Positive CEA Level (ng/ml)	Specificity	Sensitivity	
		All Colo-rectal Cancers	Dukes' A and B1
2.5 or more	71%	62%	28%
3.5 or more	80%	49%	12%
5.0 or more	90%	43%	8%
7.0 or more	95%	37%	4%

tivity for all colo-rectal cancers drops from 62% to 37% and for early disease (Dukes' stages A and B1) from 28% to 4%.

If several markers indicate the presence of a given type of cancer, use of a combination of markers will increase the sensitivity of tumor detection and if chosen appropriately may lead to only a small decrease in specificity. For example, Tormey et al (1975) evaluated a group of markers for breast cancer (Fig 12.4) and observed that in patients with metastatic disease, the CEA test was positive in about 70% of patients; dimethyl guanosine was positive and CEA negative in an additional 10–15%, while CEA and dimethylguanosine were negative with hCG positive in an additional 10%. The combined use of these markers led to an overall enhancement of sensitivity to about 95%.

The ideal choice of markers in combinations involves the selection of markers which individually are quite specific, and which are complementary. hCG and AFP

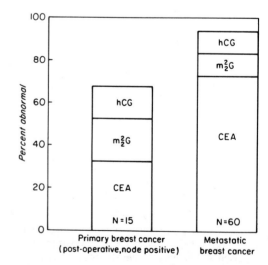

Figure 12.4. Use of multiple markers in patients with breast cancer. CEA = carcinoembryonic antigen; m_2^2G = dimethyl guanosine; hCG = human chorionic gonadotropin. (From Tormey et al, 1975, with permission.)

as markers of nonseminomatous testicular tumors are ideal in this respect; each marker, by itself, has a specificity of more than 90% and is positive in about 60% of patients bearing these tumors. There is some overlap, but the markers are complementary to the extent that one or other is positive in about 95% of patients.

The usefulness of a marker in screening is measured by the predictive value of a positive test, which depends not only on sensitivity and specificity but also on the prevalence of disease (Fig 12.2). This is illustrated by considering the use of a very sensitive marker with 90% specificity to screen for a common type of human cancer with a prevalence of 1 in 1000 people. For each 1000 people that are screened the marker would be elevated in 100 (since the specificity is 90%), but only 1 of these will have disease. Such a marker might have some use as an aid to diagnosis if patients are first preselected by the occurrence of symptoms, by performance of clinical and radiological tests, or in populations that are seriously at risk. hCG and AFP in testicular cancer, and immunoglobulin products in myeloma, are useful diagnostic aids when used in this way. However, for the majority of epithelial tumors markers are neither sufficiently sensitive nor specific for diagnostic purposes. To establish whether they can be used for monitoring the status of disease, information is required about the relationship between plasma levels of markers and tumor burden.

12.3.3 TUMOR BURDEN

There are two requirements if plasma levels of a marker are to be related to tumor burden. The frequency and level of marker elevation should increase with more advanced disease, and marker levels should fall in response to effective treatment.

Figure 12.5 indicates the probability of finding elevated levels of CEA in a large series of patients with breast cancer (Myers et al, 1978). The frequency of marker elevation is related to tumor burden as defined by clinical and pathological staging criteria. Figure 12.6 provides a comparison between pre- and posttreatment levels of CA-125 and CEA and response to treatment in patients with ovarian cancer (Bast et al, 1983). There is a good correlation with the type of response for CA-125 but not for CEA.

The data of Figures 12.5 and 12.6 indicate that the use of markers to monitor tumor bulk must be validated for each disease. While CA-125 reflects tumor burden in ovarian cancer and is relatively sensitive and specific for this disease, it is infrequently abnormal in patients with breast cancer (about 5%). By one criterion at least, CEA reflects tumor burden in breast cancer but is not sufficiently sensitive to be useful for monitoring treatment of ovarian cancer. There is one exception to this generalization: CA-125 is abnormal in only about 25% of mucinous ovarian tumors, while this type of ovarian tumor is one in which elevated levels of CEA after surgery give an 80% correlation with relapse. Under these rare circumstances, CEA levels might be used in conjunction with clinical criteria as an indication for further treatment.

12.3.4 PROGNOSIS

Marker determinations carried out preoperatively, postoperatively or sequentially following surgery might have potential in predicting prognosis, or help the cli-

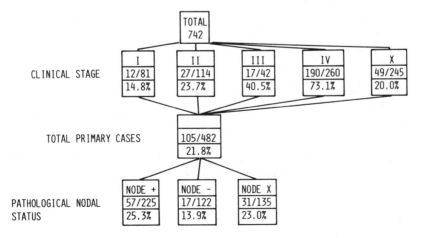

Figure 12.5. The proportion (and percentage) of patients with elevated CEA is indicated under each stage designation for patients with breast cancer. X = insufficient information for staging; NODE X = insufficient information for determining pathological nodal status. (Figures 12.5 and 12.7 are from Myers et al, 1978, with permission.)

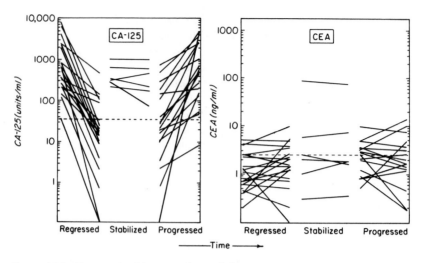

Figure 12.6. Changes in CA-125 and CEA following treatment of ovarian cancer. Regression, stabilization and progression were judged from usual clinical and radiologic criteria. (From Bast et al, 1983. Reported by permission of *The New England Journal of Medicine* 309:883–887, 1983.)

nician to decide on an appropriate program of therapy. Measured sequentially, marker levels could reflect the aggressiveness of the malignant process and help to individualize treatment.

Wang et al (1975) measured CEA levels in plasma pre- and postmastectomy in a group of patients with breast cancer and related the results to subsequent rates of recurrence. They observed that patients with an elevated CEA level postmastectomy were more likely to recur than those with a normal value of CEA. Unfortunately, the patients were not stratified by stage, so it could not be ascertained whether an elevated level of CEA was an independent risk factor for recurrence or whether the marker was simply associated with conventional prognostic criteria. Other studies suggest that CEA is an independent predictor of relapse. Myers et al (1978, 1979) studied two relatively homogeneous groups of patients with primary breast cancer: a group with stage 2 disease, and another with axillary-node involvement by pathological examination. These investigators found that a single abnormal CEA test determined postmastectomy was associated with a greater probability of recurrence (Fig 12.7). Tormey et al (1977a,b) showed that in a group of patients with metastatic breast cancer, all of whom received similar treatment, those with a normal CEA did better initially than those with an abnormal CEA although the level of hCG determined at the same time was not prognostic. Unfortunately, the value of prognostic information for metastatic breast cancer is limited because almost all patients die of their disease.

In patients with colo-rectal cancer, elevated preoper-

ative levels of CEA were found to be prognostic of recurrence independent of stage (Fig 12.8). Sculier et al (1985) observed that in a large series of patients with small-cell lung cancer, the CEA test was prognostic of survival independent of classical prognostic factors such as performance status and extent of disease. In ovarian cancer, studies at the University of Toronto have indicated that initial values of CEA following surgery are prognostic of relapse; however, when adjusted by log–rank analysis for stage, residual disease following surgery and pathologic grade, the test was no longer independently prognostic. Sequential CEA determinations in patients with ovarian cancer indicated that a persistently high value of CEA predicted an unfavourable prognosis, while rising, falling, variable or consis-

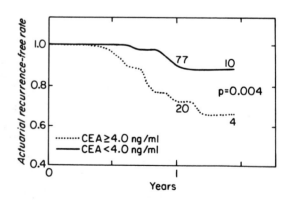

Figure 12.7. CEA and prognosis in Ca breast. Actuarial recurrence-free survival for the 225 patients with positive axillary nodes identified in Figure 12.5.

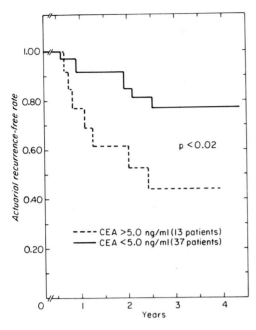

Figure 12.8. Preoperative levels of CEA and prognosis in colo-rectal cancer. Actuarial recurrence-free survival for 50 patients. (From Wanebo et al, 1978. Reprinted by permission of *The New England Journal of Medicine* 299:448–451, 1978.)

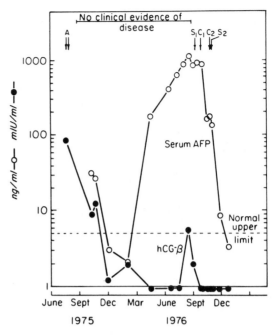

Figure 12.9. Rising levels of serum AFP and subsequent recurrence of disease in a patient with embryonal testicular cancer. The patient was treated initially (A) by orchiectomy followed by retroperitoneal lymph-node dissection. Following the rise in AFP, definite evidence of recurrence was documented in the pelvis using ultrasound (S_1). The patient received two courses of chemotherapy (C_1 and C_2) and a follow-up ultrasound (S_2) showed shrinkage of the mass.

tently normal values were not prognostic when adjusted for associated prognostic factors. However, conventional prognostic information may not always be available to the clinician, so that the prognostic value of markers may be useful even when they are not independently related to outcome.

The data reviewed above indicate that abnormal levels of CEA presage a poor prognosis in several types of cancer. This is due either to a reflection of tumor burden or to an association between CEA production and malignant properties of the tumor.

12.3.5 PREDICTION OF RECURRENCE

In patients with no evidence of disease, in whom marker levels have been consistently normal, the detection of rising levels should be predictive of recurrence. To be useful, marker elevation must provide significant lead time over clinical examination or ancillary diagnostic procedures for detecting recurrence. Monitoring gestational tumors with hCG or nonseminomatous testicular tumors with AFP and hCG are good examples of the utilization of sensitive, relatively specific markers as guides to further treatment (Fig 12.9). These tests are so reliable that only under exceptional circumstances are additional diagnostic procedures required for confirmation of the clinical state of the patient.

Unfortunately, markers are less reliable in predicting

for recurrence of epithelial tumors. Our group has studied patients with Dukes' stages B and C colo-rectal cancer in whom CEA tests were used to monitor progress after surgical removal of the primary (Fig 12.10). A rise in plasma CEA occurred 4–8 months before clinical recurrence occurred in 16 of 29 patients (sensitivity = 0.55). However, an elevation of CEA was also observed in 23 of 88 patients who did not show subsequent recurrence at the time of review, so that the specificity of the test (0.74) creates problems in interpretation if it is to be used as a guide to further treatment. Rigorous, controlled studies are required to ascertain whether markers exhibit any advantage over other diagnostic modalities or even thorough clinical examination in early detection of recurrent epithelial tumors.

12.3.6 GUIDANCE FOR TREATMENT

Measurement of plasma levels of hCG and AFP have proven to be invaluable in diagnosis and in monitoring treatment of choriocarcinoma and nonseminomatous testicular tumors. But markers would be of little value in these tumors in the absence of very effective treatment. As described above there are few data on the

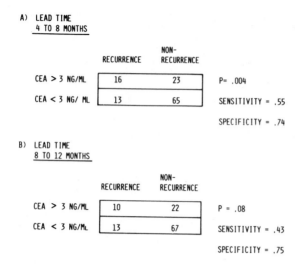

A) LEAD TIME
4 TO 8 MONTHS

	RECURRENCE	NON-RECURRENCE	
CEA > 3 NG/ML	16	23	P= .004
CEA < 3 NG/ML	13	65	SENSITIVITY = .55
			SPECIFICITY = .74

B) LEAD TIME
8 TO 12 MONTHS

	RECURRENCE	NON-RECURRENCE	
CEA > 3 NG/ML	10	22	P = .08
CEA < 3 NG/ML	13	67	SENSITIVITY = .43
			SPECIFICITY = .75

Figure 12.10. CEA and lead time to recurrence. The number of patients with and without recurrence is indicated at *a*, 4–8 months and *b*, 8–12 months after measurement of serum CEA.

capacity of markers to predict recurrence for other types of tumors. Of equal importance, the therapy that is available to treat recurrence of the common epithelial tumors is of limited efficacy.

The efficacy of second-look surgery based on a rising CEA has been investigated in patients with colo-rectal cancer (Steele et al, 1980; Fig 12.11). Two of 15

patients may have benefited from the surgery, but the study was uncontrolled and gives no indication of the probable outcome if intervention had taken place solely on the basis of results of the usual diagnostic tests and clinical examination. More recently patients with colo-rectal cancer were randomized into two groups—one treated with chemotherapy on the basis of a rising CEA and the other with the same chemotherapeutic regimen following detection of recurrence by other means. The disease-free interval and overall survival were identical in the two groups (Hine and Dykes, 1984; Fig 12.12).

The tendency to suggest that the markers used to monitor the common malignancies are of little value should be tempered with the realization that there have been few therapeutic triumphs in dealing with these tumors. The study of existing markers and the development of new and better ones are important both as a mechanism for learning about the biology of cancer, and as a guide to the use of more effective therapy, as it becomes available. Screening programs might then become a reality, earlier diagnosis a necessity, and monitoring of treatment an adjunct to good management.

12.4 SUMMARY

Several types of molecules produced by tumors may have potential use as markers of disease. Production of monoclonal immunoglobulins in myeloma, hCG in cho-

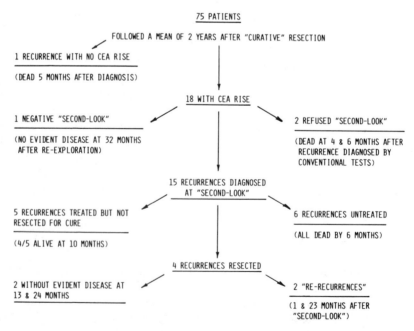

Figure 12.11. Outcome for 75 patients following "curative" resection for Dukes/Kirklin stages B-2 and C colo-rectal cancer. Eighteen patients who developed elevation of CEA levels were asked to undergo second-look surgery. (From Steele et al, 1980, with permission.)

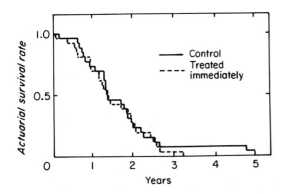

Figure 12.12. Actuarial survival for 52 patients with colo-rectal cancer who showed a rise in CEA after surgery. At the time of this rise the patients were randomised to start chemotherapy immediately or to receive identical chemotherapy when there was clinical evidence of disease (control). Survival is calculated from the time of randomization. (From Hine and Dykes, 1984, with permission.)

riocarcinoma, and hCG and AFP in nonseminomatous testicular cancers are highly sensitive and specific, and have been of great use in diagnosis and monitoring of treatment in these malignancies. Other markers are not sufficiently sensitive or specific to be used for screening purposes nor, with few exceptions, for diagnosis. Tumor markers reflect tumor burden and their major application lies in monitoring treatment. Some markers such as CEA appear to be prognostic of outcome and may be predictive of recurrence. Further studies are required for various markers and in a variety of tumors, to establish any advantage of markers in predicting recurrence over conventional diagnostic procedures and clinical examination.

Care is required in the design of studies to evaluate the clinical utility of newly discovered products of tumors that may have potential as tumor markers. Sensitivity and specificity must be based on patients with early or minimal cancer, with appropriate controls of similar age, and including a variety of other tumors and nonmalignant diseases.

REFERENCES

Bast RC Jr, Klug TL, St John E, et al: A radioimmunoassay using a monoclonal antibody to monitor the course of epithelial ovarian cancer. *N Engl J Med* 1983; 309:883–887.

Bodansky O: Reflections on biochemical aspects of human cancer. *Cancer* 1974; 33:364–370.

Ewing HP, Newsom BD, Hardy JD: Tumor markers. *Curr Prob Surg* 1982; 19:54–94.

Hine KR, Dykes PW: Prospective randomized trial of early cytotoxic therapy for recurrent colorectal carcinoma detected by serum CEA. *Gut* 1984; 25:682–688.

Miller AB: The Joint National Cancer Institute of Canada/American Cancer Society study of a test for carcinoembryonic antigen (CEA). *Cancer* 1974; 34:932–935.

Myers RE, Sutherland DJ, Meakin JW et al: Carcinoembryonic antigen in breast cancer. *Cancer* 1978; 42:1520–1526.

Myers RE, Sutherland DJ, Meakin JW et al: Prognostic value of postoperative blood levels of carcinoembryonic antigen (CEA) in breast cancer, in Lehmann FG (ed): *Carcino-Embryonic Proteins.* Elsevier/North-Holland, 1979, pp 133–138.

Ruddon RW: *Cancer Biology.* Oxford University Press, 1981.

Sculier, JP, Feld R, Evans WK et al: CEA: A useful prognostic marker in small cell lung cancer. *J Clin Oncol* 1985; 3:1349–1354.

Steele G Jr, Zamcheck N, Wilson R et al: Results of CEA-initiated second-look surgery for recurrent colorectal cancer. *Am J Surg* 1980; 139:544–547.

Thomson DMP, Krupey J, Freedman SO, Gold P: The radioimmunoassay of circulating carcinoembryonic antigen of the human digestive system. *Proc Natl Acad Sci USA* 1969; 64:161–167.

Tormey DC, Waalkes TP, Ahmann D et al: Biological markers in breast carcinoma. I. Incidence of abnormalities of CEA, HCG, three polyamines, and three minor nucleosides. *Cancer* 1975; 35:1095–1100.

Tormey DC, Waalkes TP, Simon RM: Biological markers in breast carcinoma. II. Clinical correlations with human chorionic gonadotrophin. *Cancer* 1977a; 39:2391–2396.

Tormey DC, Waalkes TP, Snyder JJ et al: Biological markers in breast carcinoma. III. Clinical correlations with carcinoembryonic antigen. *Cancer* 1977b; 39:2397–2404.

Wanebo HJ, Rao B, Pinsky CM et al: Preoperative carcinoembryonic antigen level as a prognostic indicator in colorectal cancer. *N Engl J Med* 1978; 299:448–451.

Wang DY, Bulbrook RD, Hayward JL et al: Relationship between plasma carcinoembryonic antigen and prognosis in women with breast cancer. *Europ J Cancer* 1975; 11:615–618.

BIBLIOGRAPHY

Ewing HP, Newsom BD, Hardy JD: Tumor markers. *Curr Prob Surg* 1982; 19:54–94.

Ruddon RW: *Cancer Biology.* Oxford University Press, 1981.

13

Hormones and Cancer

Donald J. Sutherland

Save us from a just review
when these humours are deciphered
and our treatments they recall,
Lest our mirth at barber surgeon
seen as grace before the fall.

13.1 INTRODUCTION

13.1.1 HORMONES AS INTERCELLULAR MESSENGERS

Cells communicate. Essentially all cells have been shown to respond to one or more of the ever-enlarging spectrum of cell products initially called humors, and more recently hormones and "growth factors." The first understanding of these processes was achieved in 1898 by Lewandowsky, who found that nerve cells were able to transmit signals to responding cells with which they were in close contact (Fig 13.1a). The nature of the "signal" was not appreciated, however, for many years. Bayliss and Starling, in 1902, initiated the modern era of "endocrinology" when they elucidated the association between an agent transported in the blood from cells in one part of the stomach to those in another which gave rise to the production of increased gastric acidity. The message, now known as gastrin, is an example of an endocrine hormone, ie, a substance produced by one group of cells (usually in a discrete endocrine gland) which is then transported by the circulation to act on cells of a geographically distant and phenotypically different tissue (Fig 13.1b). The term endocrine was introduced to distinguish this "internal" secretion from the exocrine type of secretion, in which a cell product is excreted via a duct such as in the production of sweat, milk or bile (Fig 13.1c).

It has been demonstrated more recently that cells can produce substances, usually referred to as growth factors, that can act on phenotypically different cells in their immediate environment, ie, a paracrine effect (Fig 13.1d). Such factors appear to be important in homeostasis, and may stimulate proliferation of tissue in response to stress or injury. Finally, Todaro and collaborators (eg, Sporn and Todaro, 1980) have provided evidence that certain cells may not only produce and release a message but may respond to this same signal (an autocrine effect) through a receptor mechanism similar to that described for cells responding to endocrine and paracrine stimuli (Fig 13.1e). The implications of this positive-feedback system in relationship to the growth of tumor cells have been discussed in section 8.4.5.

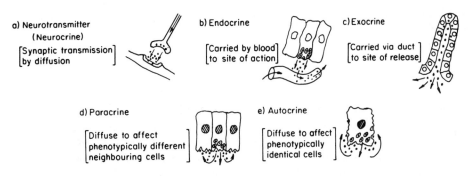

Figure 13.1. Different types of humoral signals. *a, Neurotransmission*, in which signals are transmitted by a diffusible substance at synapses between nerves, or between nerve and muscle. *b, Endocrine*, in which hormones are carried by blood to their site of action. *c, Exocrine*, in which substances are released into a duct. *d, Paracrine*, in which mediators diffuse to influence neighboring cells that are phenotypically different. *e, Autocrine*, in which growth factors act on the cells which produced them, as well as on neighboring cells.

Initially, each hormone was considered to be a unique product of a single type of cell because of the regionalization of tissues with similar function which occurs in higher animals. More recently, it has been recognized that multiple tissues within the same organism may produce identical, biologically active products. It is now known that even unicellular organisms are capable of producing materials which are similar or identical to the polypeptide substances which in vertebrates have been demonstrated to induce hormone effects. Thus exocrine and endocrine functions of cells might be considered extensions of pheromone communication, a term used to designate intercellular chemical messengers produced in one organism that regulate target cells in another. In this model the eukaryotic host is represented by a large number of individual organisms which, although derived from a single cell, have become functionally unique entities through their divergent pathways of differentiation.

Normal or eutopic production and secretion of hormones is limited usually to a group of cells located in a specific gland, even though low levels of production may be found in other tissues. Thus although human chorionic gonadotropin may be detected by immunological methods in most cells, the appearance of this substance in the serum is normally a sensitive marker for pregnancy. Malignant cells derived from tissues which do not normally release measurable quantities of hormones may do so, giving rise to ectopic hormone formation; endocrine symptoms may then develop related to the uncontrolled release of hormone, leading to alterations in other cell populations.

Tumors may also express hormone receptors that are not found in the tissue of origin. The possibility of aberrant receptor function provides a mechanism by which autonomous growth could result from inappropriate responses to ambient levels of physiological hormones which surround all tissues.

In this chapter hormones will be interpreted in a limited sense as agents which have been recognized to act on cells at a distance and whose principal effects are mediated following transport of the factor through the circulation (ie, endocrine hormones). Growth factors with autocrine and paracrine function are described in chapter 8. The substances to be discussed in this chapter are merely the more easily recognized examples of a vast array of signals influencing cellular behaviour.

13.1.2 TYPES OF HORMONES AND FACTORS CONTROLLING THEIR PRODUCTION

Endocrine hormones may have a variety of chemical structures. These include amino acids such as thyroxine, small peptides such as vasopressin, and proteins such as insulin and parathyroid hormone. In addition, an extensive array of steroid hormones with a basic structure similar to cholesterol has been described. Tissues which are capable of responding to these products require the appropriate receptors, which are typically located on the plasma membrane for water-soluble hormones, and intracellularly for lipid-soluble hormones. The effects elicited by hormones can be instantaneous, delayed, or have a biphasic pattern. The response to a given message depends not only on the type of hormone, but also on the nature of the receptor. Thus different tissues may have opposite responses to the same hormone; for example, smooth muscle at one site may contract in response to epinephrine (adrenalin), whereas at another it will relax.

Under physiological conditions homeostatic mechanisms operate to regulate the production of hormones. Some of these mechanisms involve simple feedback loops. For example, the regulation of the production of parathyroid hormone (which acts to increase the level of calcium in the blood) and calcitonin (which acts to decrease the level of calcium in the blood) are modulated directly by the level of free calcium in the blood (Fig 13.2a). Other homeostatic mechanisms depend on feedback loops of varying complexities and may involve hormones produced at several sites. Two examples of these with important implications for the treatment of some types of tumors are shown in Figure 13.2b. The secretion of steroid hormones by both adrenal and gonadal tissues is influenced by hormones secreted by the pituitary gland. In turn, secretion of these pituitary hormones is influenced both by the levels of steroid hormone acting on the pituitary and by releasing factors arising in the hypothalamus. Finally, the secretion of these releasing factors is modified by the levels of adrenal and gonadal hormones in the circulation as well as by neurological signals to the hypothalamus.

13.2 STEROID HORMONES

13.2.1 STRUCTURE AND CLASSIFICATION

All natural steroids share a common chemical structure and have additional chemical groups bound to the steroid nucleus which confer specificity to their actions as estrogens, androgens, progestins, glucocorticoids, or mineralocorticoids (Fig 13.3). Each class of steroids has distinct physiological effects and several have been implicated by epidemiological or experimental studies to act as cofactors in the development of cancer. In addition, several steroids are useful as pharmacological agents in the treatment of cancer, or as replacement factors following ablative surgery.

Synthesis of steroid hormones appears to be limited to specialized cells in the adrenal gland, testis and ovary. The steroid hormones are derived from cholesterol (Fig 13.3a), which is obtained from food or synthesized from acetyl coenzyme A. Subsequent metabolic modifications require migration of precursor molecules between enzymes located in both mitochondria and endoplasmic reticulum before a mature product is formed (Fig 13.4). Ectopic production of functional steroid hormones has not been observed, indicating the low probability for the simultaneous appearance and coordinated action of the necessary enzymes for the production and release of these specialized messages.

Androgens. Androgens of high potency such as testosterone (Fig 13.3b) are produced primarily by the testis under the influence of luteinizing hormone (LH) on

Figure 13.2. Examples of hormonal mechanisms which maintain control of physiological factors. *a*, Simple feedback loop illustrating the action of parathyroid hormone and calcitonin to maintain calcium levels in the blood. *b*, More complex feedback loops which act to maintain sex-hormone production by the gonads and glucocorticoid production by the adrenal gland.

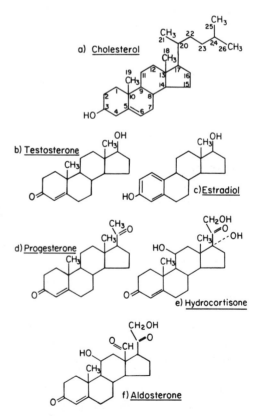

Figure 13.3. Molecular structure of some important steroid hormones that are produced by the adrenal glands or gonads.

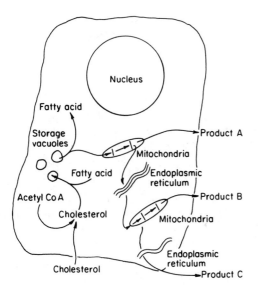

Figure 13.4. Schematic illustration of the synthesis of steroid hormones by cells of the adrenal gland or gonads. Depending on the hormone synthesized (products, A, B, and C), the precursor steroid may migrate between enzymes in mitochondria and the endoplasmic reticulum before the mature hormone is synthesized and released.

Leydig's cells. The production of testosterone is quite constant in the adult male, although serum levels of LH fluctuate widely. Certain tissues possess a specific enzyme (5-alpha reductase) which acts on testosterone to form an androgen with even higher activity, namely 5-alpha-dihydrotestosterone (DHT). This latter compound is required for hormone effects to occur in certain androgen-responsive tissues, and leads to normal sexual maturation of the prostate, seminal vesicle, epididymis, phallus, and scrotum, as well as development of secondary sexual characteristics of males, such as growth of facial hair. Androgens also tend to stimulate growth of prostatic tumors, and their removal or inhibition plays a major role in therapy of this malignancy (section 13.6.3).

Less potent androgens (eg, androstenedione) are produced in both sexes by the adrenal gland and by the ovary in women. Such androgens contribute to adolescent growth and are important in maintaining normal anabolic function throughout life without giving rise to masculinization.

Estrogens. The most biologically active estrogen, estradiol (Fig 13.3c), is produced predominantly by the parafollicular cells in the premenopausal ovary under the coordinated stimulation of luteinizing hormone (LH) and follicle-stimulating hormone (FSH). The LH level maintains stromal-cell production of androstenedione, a necessary precursor of estrogen production; the

FSH level stimulates conversion of androgen precursors into estrogens by the parafollicular cells. This reaction is known as aromatization, since estrogens have an aromatic ring (Fig 13.3c) whereas androgens do not. Inhibition of the aromatase reaction has been used in the treatment of breast cancer.

Serum levels of estradiol increase during the first part of the menstrual cycle (Fig 13.5). Increasing levels of estradiol stimulate the hypothalamus at mid-cycle to produce a surge of gonadotropin-releasing hormone (GnRH). The consequent increase in levels of LH and FSH induces ovulation and allows maturation of the parafollicular cells, giving rise to increased levels of progesterone. Subsequently, unless fertilization of the ovum occurs with implantation and release of human chorionic gonadotropin by the products of conception, the corpus luteum which has begun to develop at the site of ovulation atrophies. The production of both estrogen and progesterone declines (Fig 13.5). This fall initiates menstrual bleeding, and an increase in secretion of LH and FSH, with a further round of maturation of parafollicular cells. The entire process is repeated with each menstrual cycle in which ovulation occurs. If ovulation fails to occur the level of progesterone in the second or luteal phase of the cycle does not rise, leading to prolonged unimpeded estrogen action.

Estrogens act to develop and maintain uniquely feminine tissues such as the uterus and breast by promoting cellular proliferation in these tissues. They also have metabolic effects ranging from alterations in sugar metabolism to stimulation of the production of binding proteins for other hormones.

In addition to the ovarian source of estrogen, continuous noncyclical production of less potent estrogens occurs through peripheral aromatization of androgens of

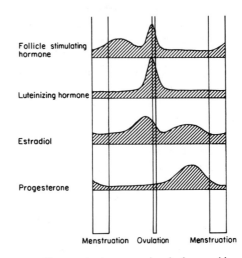

Figure 13.5. Changes in the serum level of several hormones during a normal menstrual cycle.

adrenal origin. Peripheral aromatization occurs chiefly in adipose tissue, and the production of these estrogens is increased with obesity. The level of estrogens derived from this source is insufficient to maintain a full estrogenic effect, but has been suggested as a predisposing factor in the appearance of certain tumors.

Progesterone. Progesterone (Fig 13.3d) levels increase following ovulation, stimulated initially by the action of FSH and LH on the corpus luteum (Fig 13.5). Progesterone causes cell differentiation (eg, in the uterus) and tends to arrest proliferative effects of estrogenic stimulation. Analogues of progesterone are used in the treatment of breast and other cancers.

Glucocorticoids. These hormones (eg, hydrocortisone, Fig 13.3e) are synthesized in the adrenal gland under the influence of adrenocorticotrophic hormone (ACTH) released from the pituitary. The level of ACTH is influenced not only by an inherent diurnal rhythm and by the level of circulating glucocorticoids which act both on the pituitary and on the hypothalamus, but also by "stress" which can override the other controls through hypothalamic or cortical effects (Fig 13.2). The glucocorticoids play a major role in carbohydrate metabolism through promotion of the synthesis of glucose and breakdown of glycogen in the liver, elevation of blood sugar, and metabolism of protein. In addition, these steroids have major anti-inflammatory effects at pharmacological doses, and are used in the therapy of lymphomas and breast cancer.

Mineralocorticoids. Mineralocorticoids (Fig 13.3f), primarily aldosterone, are also produced by the adrenal cortex. The secretion of aldosterone is controlled by an elaborate series of interlocking mechanisms which respond to alterations in intravascular volume and electrolyte balance. Its principle effect is on renal tubular function, with consequent alterations in sodium and potassium retention or excretion.

Many synthetic steroids have been developed which possess increased potencies for each of the above classes of hormone action. In some instances the potency reflects alterations in structure which resist metabolism and therefore prolong the hormonal effect. For example, dexamethasone is a glucocorticoid with greatly increased potency primarily due to the introduction of a nonmetabolizable fluorine. Some modifications of structure have led to effects that are not associated with naturally occurring steroids, including carcinogenicity. For example, the use of the synthetic estrogenic compound diethylstilbestrol (DES; Fig 13.6) has been associated with clear-cell adenocarcinoma in the vagina in the offspring of women who have taken this medication

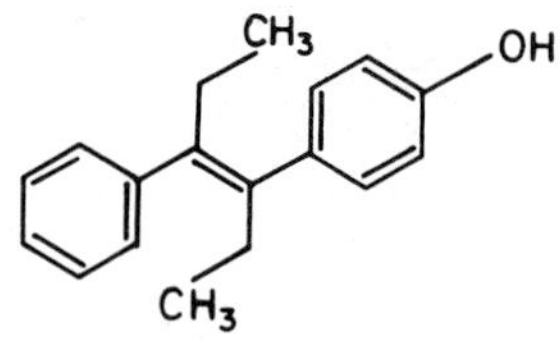

Figure 13.6. Molecular structure of the synthetic estrogen diethylstilbestrol (DES) that has been used widely in the treatment of breast and prostatic cancer.

in pregnancy, as well as a possible increase in the incidence of breast tumors in patients taking the drug (section 13.5.2).

13.2.2 STEROID RECEPTORS

The effects of the lipid-soluble steroid hormones are mediated through their association with intracellular receptors. Receptors for estrogens, progestins, glucocorticoids, androgens and mineralocorticoids have been characterized by physical and biochemical techniques. The receptors appear to be polypeptides, which may have multiple units and which may undergo modification subsequent to association with their specific steroid molecule. Tissues lacking receptors for specific steroids do not manifest physiological responses to these steroids. The presence of receptors does not, however, ensure that a tissue will respond to steroids. The level of receptor protein in a cell may itself depend on the hormonal milieu; thus the presence of progesterone receptor appears to depend on the presence of estrogen receptor (Sarrif and Durant, 1981), and the number of progesterone receptors can be augmented by the administration of estrogens.

Estimation of the cellular content of receptors for specific steroid hormones has been emphasized since the discovery that the concentration of receptor could predict for response to hormonal treatment in breast cancer (section 13.6.2). Some of the techniques which are available for quantitating the amount of a steroid receptor in tissue are presented in Figure 13.7. Most studies depend on the binding of a labeled steroid to its receptor, and the single-point dextran-coated charcoal-competition assay has been used most widely. More information can be obtained by measuring the sedimentation velocity of the steroid-receptor complex in a sucrose density gradient, or by measuring its association constant using Scatchard analysis, but time and expense prevent the routine use of these methods clinically. Most of the methods do not account for receptors already occupied by steroids; thus estimates of estrogen-receptor content are of little value in tissue

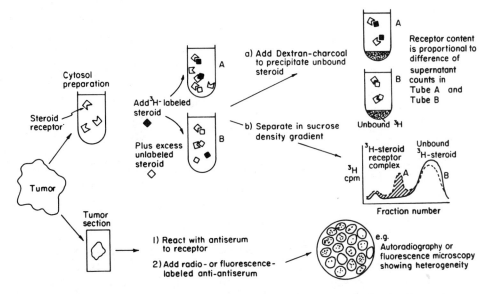

Figure 13.7. Several methods that are used to detect and quantitate the levels of steroid receptors in tumors. These methods rely on addition of a known quantity of ³H-labeled steroid with or without excess unlabeled steroid. *a*, Dextran-coated charcoal is added and absorbs all steroid that is not tightly bound to its receptor. Thus receptor content may be determined by the difference in ³H counts between the tubes as shown. *b*, Bound and unbound steroid is separated in a sucrose density gradient. Other methods of molecular separation (eg, gel-exclusion chromatography and gel electrophoresis) use the same principle. *c*, Histochemical or autoradiographic methods, antisera specific for the receptor (usually a monoclonal antibody) is applied to a tumor section. A second antibody, directed against the first, is added and may be detected by fluorescence, by labeling and autoradiography, or by a counter stain. This method gives information about heterogeneity of receptor content among the individual cells.

from patients who are receiving pharmacological doses of estrogen or some antiestrogens.

Considerable effort is being directed toward developing monoclonal antibodies which might allow localization of steroid receptors within a single cell. Previous use of ultracentrifugation to separate cellular components had suggested that steroid receptors were located in the cytoplasm of the cell. More recently, the use of monoclonal antibodies has suggested that most of the receptors are intranuclear, and that previous results were influenced by methods used in cell separation (King and Greene, 1984). Separation of cellular components using cytochalasin B has also suggested that estrogen receptors are in the nuclear fraction, even though older methods of analysis had indicated that the receptors were cytoplasmic (Welshons et al, 1984).

Use of monoclonal antibodies to quantitate steroid receptors has the advantage that the techniques may be automated by using flow cytometry (section 9.4). This technique, or the use of labeling and autoradiography, may be used to assess heterogeneity of receptor content among the cells of a population (Buell and Trembley, 1983; Van et al, 1984).There appears to be considerable variation in the content of estrogen receptors

among the cells of primary breast cancers, and between primary tumors and their metastases.

13.2.3 MECHANISMS OF ACTION OF STEROID HORMONES

Steroid molecules are hydrophobic and their transport in serum is facilitated by interaction with carrier proteins. Alteration in the levels of these binding proteins is important in controlling the biological expression of both androgens and estrogens. Thus the serum concentration of sex-hormone-binding globulin (SHBG), which is known to be the principal transporter for potent estrogens and androgens, is influenced by thyroid function and by the degree of obesity. Patients with hypothyroidism and/or obesity have lower levels of SHBG, a setting in which free estrogen will be higher. In the obese patient, production of estrogens from androgens in the peripheral adipose tissue will also be increased. Thus obese and/or hypothyroid women will be subjected to excess estrogen effect.

A current model illustrating the major events which occur when steroids enter cells is shown in Figure 13.8. Irrespective of the initial site of intracellular binding

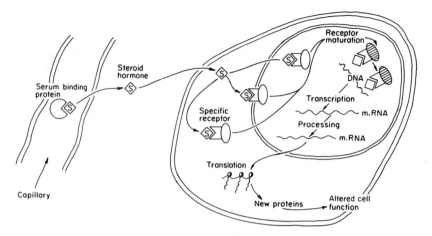

Figure 13.8. Schematic illustration of the interaction of steroid hormones with their target cells.

with their receptor, steroids are preferentially retained by responsive tissues. The mechanism(s) by which steroid hormones effect changes in the cell phenotype involve interaction of the steroid–receptor complex with the nuclear chromatin. This interaction may stimulate the transcription of specific sequences of mRNA (see section 13.5.4), suggesting that changes in cellular properties are due to changes in the expression of genes. Multiple effects are seen, some of them initiated after short delays and others appearing after prolonged periods.

13.3 NONSTEROID HORMONES

13.3.1 GENERAL PROPERTIES

Most of the nonsteroid hormones are polypeptides whose complete amino acid sequence is known, and for many of them the location of the gene(s) responsible for their production has been defined. Nonsteroid hormones may be produced ectopically by several types of cancer and may influence cells through mechanisms similar to those of polypeptide growth factors (section 8.4.5). The synthesis and release of polypeptide hormones is shown schematically in Figure 13.9. All nucleated cells are capable of the initial steps of DNA transcription and translation, but an excretory mechanism is usually restricted to cells which normally secrete a polypeptide product. The absence of an excretory mechanism in most cells may explain the relative infrequency of ectopic hormone production by tumors.

13.3.2 MECHANISMS OF ACTION

Nonsteroid hormones act typically through the formation of a second messenger in a process which cata-

lytically augments the initial signal provided by the hormone or first messenger. For many hormones the second messenger is cyclic adenosine monophosphate (cAMP; Sutherland, 1972) and Figure 13.10 indicates the essential elements in this pathway. A hormone interacts with a specific receptor located in the plasma membrane of the target cell. The receptor migrates randomly in this lipid bilayer, activating a guanine-nucleotide-binding protein (GNBP) which becomes phosphorylated from guanosine triphosphate (GTP), releasing guanosine diphosphate (GDP). The activated GNBP then interacts with adenylate cyclase, allowing the formation of cAMP from adenosine triphosphate (ATP) in the presence of magnesium. Subsequently, the cAMP binds to the regulator subunit of cAMP-dependent protein kinase. This binding allows dissociation of the catalytic subunit from the regulatory subunit, and the free catalytic subunit (ie, the activated protein kinase) can then transfer a phosphate group from ATP to various intracellular proteins (see also section 11.4.1).

The cAMP-dependent protein kinases phosphorylate an extensive array of proteins which in their turn elicit a cellular response. Some of these events may lead to alterations in the ionic permeability of the cell membrane, permitting sodium and calcium to enter the cell. Considerable evidence suggests that the production of cAMP and the influx of calcium, as well as release of calcium from intracellular stores, act in a synergistic manner to augment the cellular response to hormones.

Recent advances in our understanding of growth factors and the action of oncogenes have provided new insight into a second mechanism by which hormones may influence cellular function (Berridge and Irvine, 1984). This pathway involves binding of hormones to

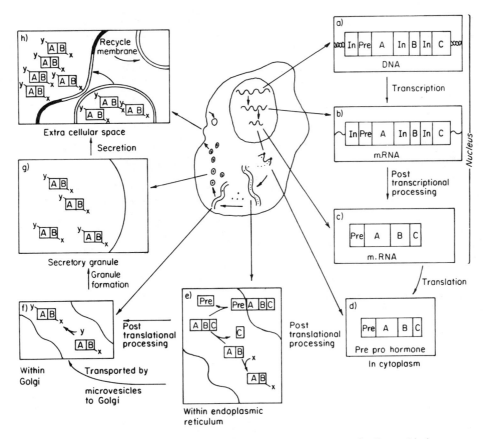

Figure 13.9. Schematic illustration of the biosynthesis and secretion of polypeptide hormones. The gene encoding the hormone, *a*, is transcribed (*b*) and the introns (In) are spliced out (*c*). The mRNA migrates to the cytoplasm where it is translated into a protein or polypeptide that is a precursor of the final hormone (*d*). Posttranslational processing takes place in the endoplasmic reticulum and the Golgi apparatus (*e,f*), and the mature hormone is packaged in a secretory granule (*g*) which fuses with the cell membrane to allow excretion (*h*).

a cell-surface receptor and subsequent activation of phosphodiesterase to hydrolyse phosphatidylinositol 4,5 bisphosphate to inositol triphosphate (IP$_3$) and diacylglycerol (see section 11.4.5). Diacylglycerol can interact with protein kinase C, which in turn may activate other membrane-bound enzymes by phosphorylation. Inositol triphosphate has been shown to liberate calcium stores from the endoplasmic reticulum, and the increase in free cytoplasmic calcium may mediate cellular response by a pathway involving cAMP. In the above reactions IP$_3$ acts as a "second messenger" instead of cAMP, and is resynthesized in a cyclical pathway. Several hormones and growth factors have been found to act through this mechanism, including angiotensin and platelet activating factors in the liver, vasopressin in the sympathetic ganglia, angiotensin in the adrenal cortex and glucose in the pancreatic islet cells.

13.4 HORMONE PRODUCTION BY TUMORS

13.4.1 TUMORS OF ENDOCRINE GLANDS

Tumors may develop from hormone-producing cells (or more likely from their stem-cell precursors) within an endocrine gland. Provided that the normal coordinated series of events necessary for the production and release of hormones remains intact, the tumor may continue to produce hormones. Such tumors may, however, lose the ability to respond to the normal homeostatic mechanisms that control hormone production and may therefore produce hormones autonomously, giving rise to endocrine syndromes.

When endocrine tissue becomes malignant there is often a decline in the coordinated production and/or release of mature hormones. This change is relative rather than absolute, however, and the degree of differ-

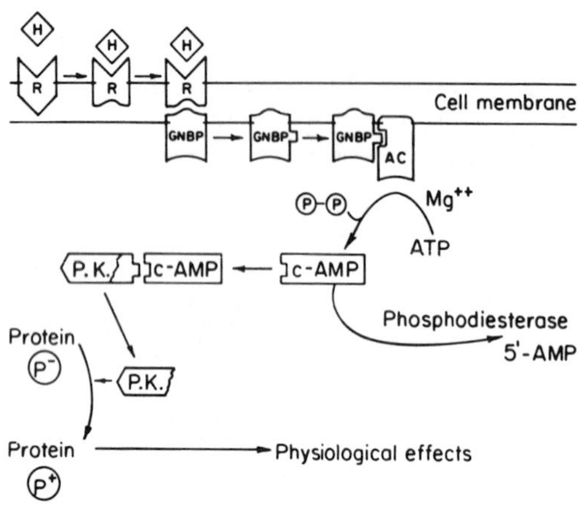

Figure 13.10. Cyclic AMP as a second messenger for hormone action. The hormone (H) interacts with a specific receptor (R) in the cell membrane. The receptor interacts with a guanine-nucleotide-binding protein (GNBP) which, after phosphorylation, interacts with the enzyme adenylate cyclase, allowing formation of cAMP from ATP. Subsequently cAMP may be inactivated by phosphodiesterase or may serve as a source of high-energy phosphate for the cAMP-dependent protein kinases.

entiation in many tumors correlates roughly with their hormone production. Thus, anaplastic tumors may produce little if any hormone, whereas well-differentiated tumors usually synthesize and secrete the hormone product normal for that tissue. Even if cells in the tumor produce hormone less efficiently than cells in the normal gland, the increased number of tumor cells and their autonomous production may result in high levels of circulating hormone. Table 13.1 shows examples of hormones associated with neoplasia in endocrine tissues and the common presenting symptoms.

In two well-recognized familial syndromes, adenomas and/or carcinomas arise in tissues which secrete hormones. These are the multiple endocrine neoplasias type 1 and type 2 (MEN1 and MEN2). The disorders are inherited as autosomal dominant traits with variable penetrance. The tissues involved and the frequency of abnormality in family members with disease is shown in Table 13.2.

13.4.2 ECTOPIC PRODUCTION OF HORMONES

Tumors arising in nonendocrine tissues may occasionally synthesize molecules possessing hormonal activity. Some of the syndromes (known as paraneoplastic syndromes) which may arise from this ectopic production of hormones are presented in Table 13.3. All of the syndromes are rare, occurring with less than 5% of tumors of any given histologic type.

Tumor cells which secrete hormones ectopically must inherit from their stem cells the ability not only to transcribe and translate hormonal messages, but they must also possess the posttranscriptional and posttranslational machinery necessary for the modification of precursor molecules and the ability to secrete a mature product. Malignant transformation of a stem cell may allow expression of genes that would not normally be expressed by tissues of the same histological origin. The potential for multiple pathways of differentiation and for generation of subclones with varying properties (section 8.3) might lead to only some cells in a tumor producing hormones ectopically.

Tumors derived from cells of the embryonic neural crest may preferentially retain the ability to produce hormones ectopically, since these cells possess the necessary capacity for posttranslational activity that is required for the synthesis of functional hormones (Fig

Table 13.1. Examples of Hormones Associated with Neoplasia of Endocrine Tissue and of the Clinical Effects of Hormone Production

Tissue of Origin	Hormone	Biochemical	Symptoms
Pituitary	growth hormone		gigantism visual-field defects
Pituitary	prolactin		abnormal milk production visual-field defects
Islet cells of pancreas	insulin	↓blood sugar	fainting, weakness, sweating, mental disorders, convulsions, coma
Islet cells of pancreas	gastrin		peptic ulcers, diarrhea (Zollinger–Ellison syndrome)
Adrenal medulla	epinephrine, norepinephrine	↑blood sugar	hypertension, anxiety
Adrenal cortex	hydrocortisone	↑blood sugar ↓potassium ion	Cushing's syndrome: ↓weight, easy bruising, round face, weakness, hirsutism, osteoporosis, cessation of menses

Table 13.2. Characteristics of Patients Presenting with Multiple Endocrine Neoplasia

	Tissue	% Expression in Patients with Syndrome		Hormone(s) Which May Be Produced
MEN1 (Werner's syndrome)	pituitary	65		prolactin, growth hormone, ACTH
	parathyroid	90		parathyroid hormone
	pancreas	80		insulin, gastrin, VIP, glucagon, PP
MEN2* (Sipple's syndrome)		(a)	(b)	
	thyroid	100	100	calcitonin
	adrenal medulla	20	30	catecholamines
	parathyroid	30	<5	parathyroid hormone
	ganglioneuromas	0	100	—

ACTH = adrenocorticotrophic hormone;
VIP = vasoactive intestinal peptide;
PP = pancreatic polypeptide.

*MEN2 may be separated into two syndromes as shown.

Table 13.3. Selected Hormones Formed Ectopically and Their More Common Clinical Effects*

Tumor	Hormone	Symptoms	Biochemical
Small-cell Ca of lung, pancreatic tumors	antidiuretic hormone	confusion convulsions, coma	$\downarrow Na^+$
Small-cell Ca of lung, carcinoid, islet-cell Ca of pancreas, medullary thyroid Ca	adrenocorticotrophic hormone or corticotrophin-releasing hormone	proximal muscle weakness, polyuria, edema, pigmentation changes	$\downarrow K^+$ $\uparrow$Blood Sugar
Multiple myeloma	osteoclast activity factor	constipation, polyuria, polydipsia, vomiting, psychosis, coma	$\uparrow Ca^{++}$
Squamous-cell Ca of lung, renal carcinoma, hepatomas	parathyroid hormone		
Breast carcinoma	prostaglandins		
Renal carcinoma hepatoma, bronchogenic carcinoma, adrenal carcinoma	human chorionic gonadotropin	precocious puberty in boys, irregular menses	

*Very rare examples of the ectopic secretion by tumors of almost all of the nonsteroid hormones have been documented.

13.9). These cells have been referred to as the APUD (amine precursor uptake and decarboxylation) cells because of their biochemical properties. They may occur as nests of cells in many tissues and give rise to a variety of tumors including, possibly, small-cell carcinomas of the lung. In addition, Odell and Wolfsen (1980) have provided evidence that cells in most types of tumors produce ectopic hormones, although secretion is inefficient in cells which do not normally secrete molecular products. In these tumors the cytoplasm of the cells may contain large amounts of immunologically identifiable hormone even though the product may not possess the ability to activate normal receptors and/or the cells may be unable to secrete the product.

The number of recognized ectopic hormone syndromes is increasing and many systemic effects that occur in cancer patients, including depression and cachexia, may be caused by the secretion of cell products which have as yet unrecognized biological activities.

13.5 HORMONES AND CANCER CAUSATION

13.5.1 HORMONES AND DIFFERENTIATION

Many hormones have profound effects on differentiation. Perhaps the most dramatic example is provided by the tadpole: if the normal thyroid gland is removed, metamorphosis into a frog is prevented, but subsequent administration of thyroxine, the principle thyroid hormone, will allow the process to proceed.

Androgen action provides a further example in which the importance of tissue receptors is emphasized. In one form of testicular feminization, genotypic males lack the ability to respond to testosterone because although they possess intra-abdominal testicles and adequate serum concentration of testosterone, their androgen-dependent tissues lack functional receptors and therefore masculinization of these tissues cannot occur.

In the above examples the lack of an intact hormone-receptor system at a critical period of development prevents morphogenesis. The observed effects are essentially all or none. In many tissues, however, hormones are required not only for the initiation of differentiation but their continued presence is required to maintain differentiated features. For example, removal of estrogen will result in marked atrophy of the vaginal mucosa, endometrium, and breast epithelium in females, while the removal of androgens will result in prostatic atrophy and loss of potency in males. These effects may be reversible since the potential for normal differentiation remains, and administration of the missing hormone will often restore tissues to their differentiated state.

Cancer may be considered as a disorder of differentiation in which relatively immature cells continue to proliferate, failing to respond to homeostatic mechanisms that are normally responsible for tissue organization and morphology (section 8.2). Thus it is not surprising that several hormones known to affect differentiation may influence the development of cancer.

13.5.2 CANCER IN MAN

Epidemiological evidence strongly implicates a number of hormones as, at the very least, permissive for the development of several types of human tumor.

Carcinoma of the endometrium has been found in clinical association with diabetes, obesity and nulliparity. This association probably reflects the summation of a series of endocrine events each of which may predispose to high levels of free estrogen. Thus nulliparity frequently accompanies failure of ovulation and provides prolonged estrogen stimulation without the "protective" action of intermittent progestin secretion following ovulation. These conditions frequently occur in obese women whose increased adipose tissue continuously metabolizes adrenal androgens to estrogens. Also, there is a correlation between adiposity and decreased levels of sex-hormone-binding globulin. This association will increase the serum level of free estrogen by providing fewer binding sites for the increased estrogen produced, and will therefore increase the biological effect of these estrogens (Siiteri et al, 1980).

Further evidence that endometrial carcinoma is influenced by estrogen is suggested by the observation that endometrial carcinoma is found with increased frequency in patients with estrogen-secreting theca-granulosa cell tumors of the ovary (Dockerty et al, 1951). Epidemiological studies have also reported an increase in the incidence of endometrial cancer following treatment of women with exogenous estrogen (eg, Antunes et al, 1979) although others dispute the observation. The hypothesis that unopposed action of estrogens leads to endometrial carcinoma was initially proposed by Novak and Yui in 1936. The excess estrogen probably acts as a promotor on initiated cells in the endometrium.

Prostatic cancer in men appears to depend on the presence of potent androgens such as testosterone. Evidence for this requirement is provided by the absence of prostate cancer in eunuchoid men (Moore, 1944), and by the low incidence of prostatic cancer in patients with cirrhosis (Robson, 1966). In cirrhosis, liver impairment interferes with metabolism of estrogens produced by aromatization of androgens; there is thus a high estrogen effect leading to low levels of LH with coincident fall in production of testosterone. Growth of prostate cancer is supported by normal levels of androgens and may be accelerated by administration of exogenous androgens or by the increase in endogenous androgens which occurs initially during treatment with gonadotropin-releasing analogues (see section 13.6.3).

The incidence of breast cancer in women is weakly associated with the number of years of ovarian function as manifested by years of active menstruation, with later age at first pregnancy, and with the prolonged administration of estrogen in certain forms of sequential contraceptive pill (Pike et al, 1983). There may also be an increase in the incidence of breast cancer in women who have taken DES therapeutically. These results suggest that the incidence of breast cancer may be influenced by estrogen; experiments in animals described below indicate that estrogen might sometimes act indirectly through elevation of the serum levels of the pituitary hormone, prolactin.

Birth control pills with certain types of estrogens and progestins have been associated with hepatic adenomas and more rarely with hepatic carcinoma (section 2.2.6). Another unfortunate causative relationship between hormone administration and cancer resulted from the former administration of DES to some pregnant women to prevent miscarriage: the female offspring of the women have shown a high incidence of an unusual form of carcinoma of the vagina during adolescence.

Whether synthetic hormones such as DES act primarily through physiological mechanisms available to naturally occurring hormones, or whether the observed association with carcinoma represents an independent phenomenon, is not clear. Synthetic hormones are often designed to potentiate absorption, resist metabolism, or increase tissue retention and are frequently administered at supraphysiological doses. Their accumulation, retention and therapeutic actions which mimic naturally occurring hormones probably depend on receptor action; nevertheless their tumor-promoting effects might be independent. It appears, however, that endogenous hormones can act either as promoters or as permissive agents which allow sufficient cell proliferation for an initiated cell to generate a tumor. Hormones may also act indirectly through induction of secondary hormones that in their turn are permissive for the expression of a tumor's growth potential.

13.5.3 ANIMAL MODELS

Several animal models have clarified the relationship between hormone action and the induction of cancer. One example (Fig 13.11) is the development of thyroid cancer associated with continuous stimulation of this gland with thyroid-stimulating hormone (TSH) (Matovinovic et al, 1968; Doniach, 1970). This polypeptide arises from cells in the pituitary, and increased levels of TSH are produced in the presence of decreased levels of thyroid hormone, as well as in response to trophic factors from the hypothalamus.

It is possible to block the production of thyroid hormone by thyroid cells with suitable metabolic inhibitors. Animals treated with such an inhibitor initially develop hyperplastic glands which revert to normal morphology when the blocking drug is discontinued. With longer treatment the thyroid tissue becomes invasive and can be transplanted into syngeneic animals treated with the same metabolic inhibitor of thyroid hormone formation. Once again reversal of the metabolic blockade will result in atrophy of the invasive thyroid tissue. With continued treatment a final stage

arises in which thyroid cells become completely autonomous and invasive and no longer regress on removal of the metabolic inhibitor. This experiment demonstrates that continuous stimulation of the thyroid gland allows the development of cancer. It is uncertain, however, whether the metabolic inhibitor acts as the initiator in the presence of TSH acting as a promoter or permissive agent, or whether TSH is itself acting as an initiator.

Another useful model is provided by the induction of mammary tumors in certain strains of rat with the carcinogen dimethylbenzanthracene (DMBA). In these animals, the simultaneous presence of prolactin is required for maximum tumor production, since removal of the pituitary or blocking of prolactin release by means of drugs results in decreased tumor incidence. Even when tumors are actively growing, hormonal

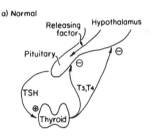

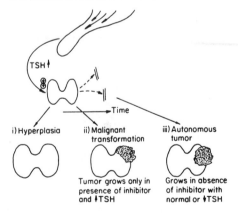

Figure 13.11. Animal model which demonstrates that continuous hormonal stimulation of the thyroid gland can lead to malignant transformation. *a*, Under normal conditions the thyroid hormones T_3 and T_4 are synthesized in response to thyroid-stimulating hormone (TSH) produced by the pituitary gland. T_3 and T_4 in turn inhibit production of TSH, allowing for controlled production of the hormones. *b*, Application of a drug which inhibits production of T_3 and T_4 removes feedback inhibition of TSH leading to continuous stimulation of the thyroid gland. Depending on the duration of inhibition the result is (1) reversible hyperplasia, (2) an invasive and transplantable tumor which depends on TSH for continued growth, or (3) an autonomous tumor that is no longer hormone dependent.

manipulations which alter either directly or indirectly the level of serum prolactin influence profoundly the rate of tumor growth. Removal of the pituitary and/or removal of the ovaries may cause tumors to regress. The effect of estrogens on the growth of these tumors occurs predominantly if not entirely through alterations in the release of prolactin by the pituitary. Thus tumors in animals with grafted pituitaries that secrete prolactin continuously do not regress when estrogen levels are lowered, and suppression of prolactin will prevent the growth stimulation of estrogen in the intact rat.

From the time of initiation some DMBA-induced mammary tumors fail to respond to hormone manipulation. These nonresponsive tumors have been shown to lack estrogen receptors (Mobbs, 1966). Thus, while the stimulus for hormone-responsive tumor growth is prolactin, the responsiveness of tumors can be assessed by measuring their estrogen receptor levels. Tumors lacking this receptor apparently do not require the presence of prolactin as a trophic factor for their growth. Tumors which regress following the removal of trophic stimuli frequently do not completely disappear and reintroduction of the trophic factor will result in the reappearance of the tumor. These carcinogen-induced mammary tumors thus share many features with the human disease: variable responsiveness to hormones that is predicted by estrogen receptor content, and incomplete eradication of tumors by hormonal therapy.

In the transplantable Shionogi carcinoma 115, an androgen-dependent murine tumor of breast origin, cells derived from hormone-dependent tumors require androgen for their continued growth on transplantation (Fig 13.12). Although cells from these tumors will not usually grow in castrated males or female animals, they will grow in normal males or litter mates of either gender given androgen. Subsequent withdrawal of the androgens will usually cause tumor regression, but the tumors will frequently regrow if androgen is reintroduced. Cells derived from hormone-dependent tumors may remain dormant for a long period of time when implanted into an androgen-deprived host, yet administration of androgens will allow them to grow. On transplantation, cells derived from hormone-dependent tumors occasionally form tumors in the absence of androgens. Subsequent analysis of these tumors typically reveals that the cells have acquired the ability to grow without androgen and have become "autonomous." The Shionogi tumor therefore shares several features with human prostate cancer: most cancers regress when initially deprived of androgen, but subsequently progress to hormone-insensitive disease.

Finally a model for hormone modulation of tumor initiation, progression, and treatment has been developed by R.L. Noble using the Nb rat (eg, Noble, 1982). Normally these animals have a low spontaneous rate of carcinoma in the adrenal cortex and breast which can be augmented by subcutaneous implants of estrone or diethylstilbestrol pellets. In a similar way an increased

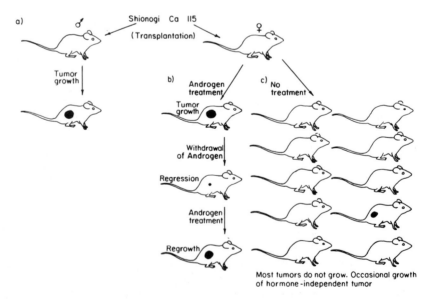

Figure 13.12. The transplantable Shionogi carcinoma 115 is a useful model for human prostatic cancer. a, The tumor grows routinely when transplanted into syngeneic male mice, or b, into androgen-treated female mice. In these animals withdrawal of androgen usually leads to regression but not to cure. c, Transplantation into untreated female (or castrated male) mice does not usually lead to tumor growth, but occasional growth of an androgen-independent tumor is observed.

incidence of prostate carcinoma was observed when pellets of testosterone propionate were implanted. From the results of experiments in which pieces of developing tumor were transplanted into Nb rats either with or without hormone treatment, a model for tumor progression has been developed. This model suggests that complete removal of the putative tumor-initiating hormone may potentiate the appearance of autonomous tumors and give rise to an accelerated rate of growth. This interesting model suggests that current approaches which attempt to utterly deprive tumors of growth-promoting factors may potentiate the expression of autonomous cell populations.

13.5.4 THE MURINE MAMMARY TUMOR VIRUS

The murine mammary tumor virus (MMTV) is an RNA-containing virus which induces breast carcinoma in mice (Hynes et al, 1984). This virus may be acquired during suckling from animals which excrete it in milk, or as proviral DNA present in the germ line (see also section 4.4). It is possible to infect cell lines with this virus in vitro, and in both cell lines and intact mice, the expression of viral RNA is augmented by the presence of a potent glucocorticoid such as dexamethasone.

When MMTV is endogenous to the germ-line DNA, only certain sites of integration of proviral DNA (Mtv-1 and Mtv-2) have been associated with the onset of carcinoma. Most of the tumors which arise are responsive to hormones and require prolactin, progestins and estrogens for their growth. Some tumors may develop during pregnancy but will usually regress at parturition. The incidence of tumors increases with the number of pregnancies.

Initially tumors contain more copies of integrated MMTV DNA per cell than normal tissues in the same animals; however, with progression from the hormone-responsive to the autonomous state the amount of MMTV DNA per cell declines.

Tumors arising from milk-acquired infection have variable hormone responsiveness, and the number of sites of integration of proviral DNA in tumor cells is variable. Few copies of the provirus can be detected by hybridization techniques in normal tissues of mice, but multiple copies are found in cells of the mammary tumors; thus cells either express the malignant phenotype because of amplification of viral DNA sequences, or in the process of progression integrate multiple copies of the provirus. The latency period for generation of tumors tends to be long and tumors often appear after intensive hormonal stimulation such as occurs with pregnancy. These studies suggest that although mammary tumor virus may be present in all cells, in only a minority of cells will events give rise to malignant transformation.

Glucocorticoid hormones increase transcription of DNA sequences complementary to MMTV into RNA, and they also influence posttranscriptional events including phosphorylation and glycosylation of the proteins arising from these mRNAs (Fig 13.13; Parker, 1983). Recent studies have demonstrated that glucocorticoid action results from binding of the glucocorticoid–receptor complex to a specific region within the MMTV proviral DNA (Scheidereit et al, 1983) and that this region is homologous to other regions within native cellular DNA which bind the glucocorticoid–receptor complex. Cloning techniques have shown that areas within the long terminal repeat of MMTV proviral DNA can be joined in a plasmid vector to other genetic markers such as the thymidine kinase gene, and that after integration into cellular DNA these regions will express their gene products under the control of glucocorticoid. These studies with MMTV suggest mechanisms by which steroid hormones may influence gene expression in target cells.

At this time MMTV is not known to contain or directly activate any known oncogene. The regions of DNA which contain the MMTV proviral genome can be detected by hybridization methods (see section

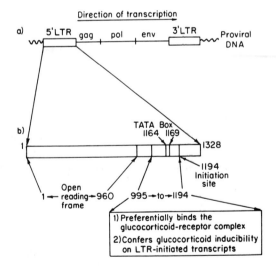

Figure 13.13. Organization of MMTV proviral DNA (ie, DNA that is complementary to RNA of the virus that is integrated into mammary cells). *a*, Proviral DNA showing long terminal repeats (LTR) and the genes coding for viral group-specific antigens (gag), reverse transcriptase (pol) and envelope proteins (env). *b*, Magnified illustration of 5′ end indicating the initiation site for transcription which is close to the TATA box, and the region where the glucocorticoid–receptor complex can bind to the DNA and can initiate this transcription. Numbers refer to bases from the 5′ end.

A3.3); however, transfection of DNA from the regions into other cells does not appear to cause malignant transformation, although another region in the genome does possess this potential. Interestingly, the region that is capable of causing this transfection is shared by MCF-7 cells, a cell line derived from a patient with breast cancer.

13.6 HORMONES AND CANCER TREATMENT

13.6.1 GENERAL CONSIDERATIONS

A number of hormonal manipulations have evolved as useful treatments for tumors of the breast, prostate and endometrium, with occasional responses seen in other types of tumors. In breast cancer, the probability of response to hormonal manipulation has been shown to correlate with the presence of specific classes of receptors in the tumor cells (Table 13.4). Elevated receptor levels have been demonstrated in other tumors such as carcinomas of the colon and pancreas; nevertheless, these tumors which are derived from hormonally unresponsive tissues do not usually respond to hormones.

When hormone manipulations are effective in causing tumor regression the effects may be as follows.

1. Primary, through removal of hormones which directly stimulate tumor growth.
2. Secondary, through blockade of production or release of other trophic factors which are the direct stimulus for tumor growth. These factors may be produced by (a) the tumor cell (autocrine), (b) the immediate neighboring cells (paracrine), (c) distant endocrine glands.

A few patients with endocrine-responsive tumors may have temporary disappearance of all evidence of disease following hormonal therapy; measurable tumor regression or relief of symptoms is observed in about 80% of

patients with prostate cancer, 30–40% of patients with breast cancer, and 30% with endometrial cancer. Although effectiveness of hormonal manipulations in individual patients is established, it has been difficult to substantiate an increase in the median survival of the total population. Inevitably the tumors regrow, and although sequential responses to a series of hormonal manipulations may occur with certain tumors the patient will ultimately develop tumors unresponsive to any hormonal manipulation. Many tumors that arise in hormone-responsive tissues do not respond to hormonal manipulations at all.

Probable explanations for the above observations are

1. a fundamental insensitivity of the stem cells and their progeny to hormone manipulation;
2. the prior existence of populations unresponsive to hormones;
3. the induction of nonresponsive clones by hormone manipulation; or
4. the failure of adequate suppression by current modalities of treatment of the spectrum of factors known and unknown that can stimulate tumor growth.

13.6.2 BREAST CANCER

Hormonal treatment of breast cancer classically involved removal of the ovaries (hence reducing estrogen) in premenopausal women, and administration of pharmacological doses of estrogen (usually DES, see Fig 13.6) in postmenopausal women. These measures led to initial regression of tumors in some 30–40% of patients. Hormonal treatment on relapse involved either the administration of progestins, androgens or glucocorticoids, or surgical ablation of the adrenal or pituitary gland; a second response was observed in about 50% of those patients who had a response to initial hormonal manipulations. More recently the antiestrogen drug tamoxifen (Fig 13.14) has become the initial hormone treatment of choice for both pre- and post-

Table 13.4. Summation of Several Trials Correlating Estrogen and Progesterone Receptors with Response to Endocrine Manipulation in Patients with Breast Cancer

	Rate of Response (%) to Hormonal Treatment
ER+ PR+	67/91 (74%)
ER+ PR−	20/71 (28%)
ER− PR+	3/6 —
ER− PR−	9/63 (14%)

Note: Adapted from McGuire (1978).

ER = estrogen receptor, PR = progesterone receptor.

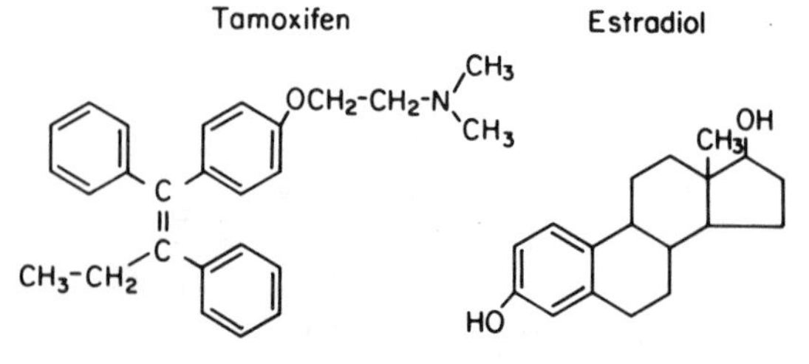

Figure 13.14. Molecular structure of the antiestrogen drug tamoxifen, which is used widely in the treatment of breast cancer. The estrogen estradiol is shown for comparison.

menopausal women with breast cancer: the rate of response is unchanged, but the drug has minimal toxicity and avoids an operation. The evolution of treatment presents a paradox: how can the addition of estrogen and the blocking of estrogen activity both lead to tumor regression in postmenopausal patients? The most likely explanation is that pharmacological doses of DES lead to blockage of estrogen response, rather than the stimulation caused by smaller doses of naturally occurring estrogens.

Although all the mechanisms of action of tamoxifen are not fully elucidated, its major antiestrogen effects are due to competition with estradiol for the high-affinity estrogen receptor, and binding to this receptor. Binding does not lead to an estrogenic response in most tissues, and leaves the cell refractory to further estrogen stimulation. The result may be death of malignant cells that are dependent on estrogen for their survival.

There is also evidence that antiestrogens may influence cells by binding to a protein distinct from the steroid receptor (Sutherland et al, 1980), but the relevance of such binding to clinical effects is unclear.

Progestational agents (eg, medroxyprogesterone) tend to abrogate trophic effects of estrogen, while the aromatase inhibitor aminoglutethimide inhibits the synthesis of naturally occurring estrogens. Ablative procedures (ie, removal of ovaries, adrenal gland or pituitary) are used less often now that equally effective drugs are available. These methods act to decrease estrogen stimulation either directly (oophorectomy), through removal of the precursor necessary for estrogen formation (adrenalectomy), or removal of the trophic hormones ACTH, FSH and LH (Table 13.5) necessary for estrogen formation (hypophysectomy). Whether there are additional benefits related to the effects of hypophysectomy (ie, decreased prolactin) is not clear.

Table 13.5. Effects of Treatment for Breast Cancer which Influence Estrogen Synthesis or Action*

	1° Effect	2° Effect	3° Effect
Ablative			
Ovarian	↓estrogens	—	—
Adrenal	↓androgens	↓estrogens	—
Pituitary	↓ACTH	↓adrenal and ovarian androgens	↓estrogens
	↓FSH	↓estrogens	
	↓LH	↓ovarian androgens	↓estrogens
Additive			
Diethylstilbestrol	occupy estrogen receptor	↓estrogen action	
	↓FSH	↓estrogens	
	↓LH	↓ovarian androgens	↓estrogens
Tamoxifen	occupy estrogen receptor	↓estrogen action	—
Progestin	occupy progestin receptor	↓estrogen receptor	↓estrogen action
Androgens	occupy androgen receptor	↓estrogen receptor	↓estrogen action
	↓FSH	↓estrogens	
	↓LH	↓ovarian androgens	↓estrogens
Glucocorticoid	occupy glucocorticoid receptor	↓adrenal androgens	↓estrogens
Aminoglutethimide	inhibits conversion of androgen to estrogen	↓estrogens	

*Note: treatments have other effects, direct and indirect, that could contribute to inhibition of tumor growth. Effects of treatment may result from (1) inhibition of primary action of hormone on tumor, (2) inhibition of formation of autocrine growth factors by tumor, or (3) alterations in other hormones (eg, FSH, LH, prolactin, ACTH, TSH) needed for (1) or (2) above.

The above treatments all tend to decrease estrogen levels or estrogen effects, but it is not certain that this decrease in estrogen effect is the direct cause of tumor regression in hormone-responsive tumors. Thus estrogens have been shown to stimulate the release of growth factors which are necessary for tumor cell growth, at least in tissue culture. Also, estrogens influence the levels of other hormones such as prolactin, and the importance of this hormone in some experimental cancers has been described in section 13.5.3. Nevertheless, the observation that human breast cancer may respond to hormonal therapy in the presence of normal or elevated levels of prolactin suggests that prolactin is rarely a prime regulator of tumor growth in women.

The presence of estrogen and progesterone receptors in primary breast cancer increases with the age of the patient and is associated with a better prognosis than for receptor-negative tumors (Clark et al, 1984). Data summarized in Table 13.4 indicate that receptor content of tumors is a major but imperfect indicator of hormonal response. Study of animal models has suggested that the failure of receptor-positive tumors to respond may have several explanations (Sibley and Tomkins, 1974).

1. The hormone–receptor complex fails to mature or, if binding takes place in the cytoplasm, to enter the nucleus.
2. The hormone–receptor complex fails to bind to DNA.
3. The hormone–receptor complex binds to DNA but fails to initiate the changes normally associated with this event.
4. The hormone–receptor complex may function normally but remains a coincidental marker of differentiation associated with another, as yet unknown, true effector molecule.

Response to hormone manipulation by tumors that appear to lack receptors may occur for artifactual reasons, such as lack of epithelial cells in the sample, or improper handling of the sample leading to denaturation of the heat-labile receptors.

Considerable heterogeneity in receptor content has also been demonstrated within large tumor specimens, perhaps on the basis of local clonal selection. Heterogeneity may occur among the metastatic clones arising from the initial tumor (Holdaway and Bowditch, 1983). Assays on multiple sequential biopsies show that about 15–20% of estimates of the content of both estrogen and progesterone receptors will change from negative to positive or vice versa (Hull et al, 1983; Gross et al, 1984). If 40% of those switching from negative to posi-

tive were to respond to subsequent hormonal manipulation, an observed response rate in receptor-negative tumors of about 8% would be anticipated, and a similar number of patients who had initially receptor-positive tumors would not be expected to respond to hormone treatment. Finally, the relationship between estrogen receptor and response to hormone treatment may be one of association rather than cause and effect, and some divergence between the presence of receptor and response to treatment would be anticipated.

13.6.3 PROSTATE CARCINOMA

Androgens are required for the development of prostate cancer, which is estimated to become evident clinically in about 4% of men. In addition, autopsy studies have shown that latent tumors are present in a much larger percentage of elderly men dying of other causes (8–46%). Hormonal manipulation designed primarily to decrease serum androgens has been reported to effect improvement in symptoms of up to 80% of patients with prostate carcinoma, but cure does not result from such treatments. Endocrine manipulations used to treat patients with prostate carcinoma include surgical ablation of the testes, adrenals, and the pituitary, as well as treatment with estrogens or antiandrogens. More recently synthetic gonadotropin-releasing-hormone (GnRH) agonists have been used with or without coincident treatment with antiandrogens.

The prime aim of all treatments is to deprive the prostatic tumor of trophic androgens. Surgical ablation of the testes removes 95% of the circulating potent androgens. At progression, adrenalectomy will remove the remaining 5% as well as other weaker androgens and results in a further response in some patients. Administration of estrogens has similar therapeutic effects to removal of the testes. Although estrogens may have some direct effect on the prostatic tumor, their major mechanism of action is believed to be due to suppression of LH with subsequent decline in endogenous androgen secretion by the testis.

Two potent antiandrogens, cyproterone acetate and flutamide, have been used to treat patients with prostatic cancer. These agents have multiple effects, but their principal action is to inhibit binding of testosterone or dihydrotestosterone to the androgen receptor.

Treatment with synthetic GnRH agonists initially causes increased release of LH and FSH, with subsequent increase in testosterone. Continued administration of the GnRH agonist, however, causes pituitary desensitization with a decrease in the number of pituitary GnRH receptors and a subsequent decline in LH and FSH levels; there is a resultant fall in release of gonadal hormones. In addition, GnRH agonists have demonstrated some growth-inhibiting effects on breast cancer cells in vitro (Miller et al, 1985). Use of GnRH agonists can cause an initial "flare" in some patients due to increased secretion of testosterone.

Receptors for androgens have been detected in prostatic tissue and their presence correlates with the responsiveness of the tumor to hormonal manipulations. In addition, Bruchovsky and Wilson (1968) have demonstrated that the enzyme 5-alpha-reductase produces high-potency androgen metabolites in target tissues like the prostate; hence the level of this enzyme in prostatic carcinoma might provide additional information indicating patients likely to respond to hormone manipulation. The problems associated with acquisition of tumor biopsies, technical problems with receptor assays, and the high level of responsiveness to endocrine manipulation in patients with prostate carcinoma have prevented extensive studies of clinical correlation with receptor content of the type that has been achieved in breast cancer.

13.6.4 OTHER TUMORS

Progesterone analogues (eg, medroxyprogesterone and megestrol acetate) lead to remission of endometrial cancer in about 30% of patients. Estrogen- and progesterone-receptor determinations have been undertaken on endometrial carcinomas and their presence correlates with response to progesterone treatment. Typically, patients that respond to progestins have very high levels of progesterone receptor in their tumor tissue with lower but measurable levels of estrogen receptor. There is, however, a direct relationship between the degree of differentiation and the receptor level; thus studies of receptor content add little in determining which patients will respond to hormonal manipulation.

Renal carcinomas may regress on rare occasions when progestins or androgens are administered. Some of these tumors have both estrogen and progesterone receptors. Other tumors which do not usually respond to endocrine manipulation, but which also contain estrogen and/or progesterone receptors, include carcinoma of the ovary, melanomas, carcinoma of the colon, carcinoma of the pancreas, and meningiomas. Some of these tumors have been observed to alter their rate of growth during pregnancy, suggesting that some endocrine factor may potentiate their growth. In these tumors the presence of hormone receptors might indicate the possibility of response to unidentified hormones, and that therapeutic manipulation might become possible if the responsible hormone(s) could be identified.

13.7 SUMMARY

Hormones are secreted molecules which act as intercellular messengers, through mechanisms that involve specific receptors. They include substances produced by endocrine glands which reach target cells via the blood stream, as well as growth factors which act on neighboring cells, or even directly on the cells which generate the message.

Steroid hormones are synthesized only by specialized cells in the adrenal gland, ovary or testis, and ectopic production of steroid hormones by tumors originating in other tissues has not been observed. Most cells retain the ability to transcribe and translate mRNA fragments into polypeptide hormones. Some cells possess in addition mechanisms for the appropriate posttranscriptional modification of these messages and/or for the release of functional product that can be recognized as hormones. In tissues normally engaged in production and secretion of hormones these separate functions are under physiological control. Some tumors possess one or more of these mechanisms and symptoms may occur because products capable of interacting with receptors are produced ectopically and are released into the systemic circulation.

Hormones exert their effects on target cells by binding to specific receptors which interact with the genome to cause alterations in gene expression. The influence of the hormone–receptor complex on transcription of DNA may lead to induction of tumors and may facilitate their growth in endocrine-responsive tissues such as breast, endometrium, and prostate. Water-soluble hormones tend to bind to receptors on the cell surface leading to a sequence of intracellular events involving phosphorylation of proteins. There are similarities between the effects of these latter hormones and the products of activated oncogenes.

Steroid hormones are used in the treatment of tumors derived from endocrine-responsive tissue such as breast, prostate and endometrium; but treatment of advanced cancer with hormones is not curative. The limited efficacy of hormonal treatment may reflect (a) a fundamental insensitivity of the stem cell or its progeny to hormone manipulation, (b) the prior existence of subpopulations of cells unresponsive to hormones, (c) the induction of nonresponsive clones by hormone manipulation, or (d) the failure of adequate suppression of all the hormonal factors, known and unknown, which stimulate growth of the tumor.

The interaction of hormones and growth factors with cancer demonstrates that some malignant cells may respond partially to physiological control mechanisms.

Improved understanding of these interactions may lead eventually to improved control of the malignant process.

REFERENCES

Antunes, CMF, Strolley PD, Rosenshein NB: Endometrial cancer and estrogen use. Report of a large case-control study. *N Engl J Med* 1979; 300:9–13.

Berridge MJ, Irvine RF: Inositol triphosphate, a novel second messenger in cellular signal transduction. *Nature* 1984; 312:315–321.

Bruchovsky N, Wilson JD: The conversion of testosterone to 5α-androstan-17β-ol-3-one by rat prostate *in vivo* and *in vitro*. *J Biol Chem* 1968; 243: 2012–2021.

Buell RH, Tremblay G: The localization of ^{3}H-estradiol in estrogen receptor-positive human mammary carcinoma as visualized by thaw-mount autoradiography. *Cancer* 1983; 51:1625–1630.

Clark GM, Osborne CK, McGuire WL: Correlations between estrogen receptor, progesterone receptor, and patient characteristics in human breast cancer. *J Clin Oncol* 1984; 2:1102–1109.

Dockerty MB, Lovelady SB, Foust GT Jr: Carcinoma of the corpus uteri in young women. *Am J Obstet Gynecol* 1951; 61:966–981.

Doniach I: Experimental thyroid tumors, in Smithers D (ed): *Tumors of the Thyroid Gland*. E. & S. Livingstone, Edinburgh, 1970, Chap 5, pp 73–79.

Gross GE, Clark GM, Chamness GC, McGuire WL: Multiple progesterone receptor assays in human breast cancer. *Cancer Res* 1984; 44:836–840.

Holdaway IM, Bowditch JV: Variation in receptor status between primary and metastatic breast cancer. *Cancer* 1983; 52:479–485.

Hull DF III, Clark GM, Osborne CK et al: Multiple estrogen receptor assays in human breast cancer. *Cancer Res* 1983; 43:413–416.

Hynes NE, Groner B, Michalides R: Mouse mammary tumor virus: Transcriptional control and involvement in tumorigenesis. *Adv Cancer Res* 1984; 41:155–184.

King WJ, Greene GL: Monoclonal antibodies localize oestrogen receptor in the nuclei of target cells. *Nature* 1984; 307:745–747.

Matovinovic J, Leahy MS, Armstrong WF, Hill HC: The effect of environment on the growth and function of rat thyroid transplant tumors, in Inman DR, Young S (eds): *Thyroid Neoplasia*. Academic Press, New York, 1968, pp 211–247.

McGuire WL: Hormone receptors: their role in predicting prognosis and response to endocrine therapy. *Sem Oncol* 1978; 5:428–433.

Miller WR, Scott WN, Morris R et al: Growth of human breast cancer cells inhibited by a luteinizing hormone-releasing hormone agonist. *Nature* 1985; 313:231–233.

Mobbs BG: The uptake of tritiated oestradiol by dimethyl-benzanthracene-induced mammary tumours of the rat. *J Endocrinol* 1966; 36:409–414.

Moore RA: Benign hypertrophy and carcinoma of prostate. *Surgery* 1944; 16:152–167.

Noble RL: Tumor progression—endocrine regulation and control, in Bruchovsky N, Goldie JH (eds): *Drug and Hormone Resistance in Neoplasia*. CRC Press, Boca Raton, FL, 1982, Vol 1, pp 157–183.

Novak E, Yui E: Relation of endometrial hyperplasia to adenocarcinoma of the uterus. *Am J Obstet Gynecol* 1936; 32:674–698.

Odell WD, Wolfsen AR: Hormones from tumors: Are they ubiquitous? *Am J Med* 1980; 68:317–318.

Parker M: Enhancer elements activated by steroid hormones? *Nature* 1983; 304:687–688.

Pike MC, Henderson BE, Krailo MD et al: Breast cancer in young women and use of oral contraceptives: Possible modifying effect of formulation and age at use. *Lancet* 1983; 2:926–929.

Robson MC: Cirrhosis and prostatic neoplasms. *Geriatrics* 1966; 21:150–154.

Sarrif AM, Durant JR: Evidence that estrogen-receptor-negative, progesterone-receptor-positive breast and ovarian carcinomas contain estrogen receptor. *Cancer* 1981; 48: 1215–1220.

Scheidereit C, Geisse S, Westphal HM, Beato M: The glucocorticoid receptor binds to defined nucleotide sequences near the promoter of mouse mammary tumor virus. *Nature* 1983; 304:749–752.

Sibley CH, Tomkins GM: Mechanisms of steroid resistance. *Cell* 1974; 2:221–227.

Siiteri PK, Nisker JA, Hammond GL: Hormonal basis of risk factors for breast and endometrial cancer, in Iacobelli S, et al (eds): *Hormones and Cancer*. Raven Press, New York, 1980, pp 499–505.

Sporn MB, Todaro GJ: Autocrine secretion and malignant transformation of cells. *N Engl J Med* 1980; 303:878–880.

Sutherland EW: Studies on the mechanism of hormone action. *Science* 1972; 177:401–408.

Sutherland RL, Murphy LC, San Foo M et al: High-affinity anti-oestrogen binding site distinct from the oestrogen receptor. *Nature* 1980; 288:273–275.

Van NT, Raber M, Barrows GH, Barlogie B: Estrogen receptor analysis by flow cytometry. *Science* 1984: 224: 876–879.

Welshons WV, Lieberman ME, Gorski J: Nuclear localization of unoccupied oestrogen receptors. *Nature* 1984; 307: 747–749.

BIBLIOGRAPHY

Alberts B, Bray D, Lewis J et al: Chemical signaling between cells, in *Molecular Biology Of The Cell*, Garland Publishing, New York, pp 717–768.

Fletcher RF: *Lecture Notes on Endocrinology*. Blackwell Scientific Publications, Oxford, 1982.

Wilson JD, Foster DW (eds): *Textbook of Endocrinology*. W.B. Saunders, Philadelphia, 1985.

14

Immunology Related to Cancer

Richard G. Miller

14.1 INTRODUCTION

Most of us have had one or more of the common childhood diseases, such as measles, mumps or chickenpox. We got better. This was our immune system doing its job. Our response to these childhood diseases can teach us a lot about how our immune system works. These diseases are all caused by infectious agents which are foreign to our body. Somehow, the immune system can recognize this foreignness, respond to it, and eliminate it from the system. The recognition process has memory and is specific. Usually one gets a disease such as mumps only once, implying that on a second infection there is a memory response which eliminates the infectious agent before there are any clinical symptoms. Such protection against one disease does not confer protection against a second, implying the existence of specificity. For many infectious diseases, protection can be artificially conferred by injection of a nonviable or nonpathogenic form of the infectious agent. This is the basis of protective immunization and remains perhaps the single most effective intervention of medical science to date.

If a foreign agent can be recognized by the immune system, it is said to be antigenic, and if the immune system can also mount an active response against it,

the agent is said to be immunogenic. Not all antigens are immunogenic. Under some circumstances an antigenic material can induce a state in which an effective immune response against the antigen is actively suppressed.

Many investigators have proposed that tumor cells are antigenic and that one of the major functions of the immune system is to eliminate such cells before they can form large tumors. If so, the immune system has been ineffective in a patient with a progressing tumor. Before reviewing the possible role of the immune system in tumor development and progression it is necessary to describe briefly some of the basic biology of the immune response.

14.2 BIOLOGY OF THE IMMUNE RESPONSE

14.2.1 ANTIBODIES

The ability to mount a secondary immune response immediately on exposure to antigen can be transferred from an immune animal to a nonimmune animal. This procedure has been used to define two different kinds of immunity: humoral immunity, in which serum alone can transfer the response, and cell-mediated immunity, in which cells must be transferred. In humoral immunity, the effectors of the response are soluble protein molecules called antibodies, whereas in cell-mediated immunity, the effectors are cells.

Figure 14.1a shows the structure of one type of antibody molecule. It is composed of four polypeptide chains, two identical large chains referred to as heavy (H) chains and two identical small chains, referred to as light (L) chains. They are joined together by disulfide bonds as indicated in the figure. This molecule has two identical sites, capable of recognizing and binding to the antigen which the molecule can recognize. Analysis of the amino acid sequence of many different antibody molecules of many different specificities has shown that each chain consists of a "constant" or "C" region showing relatively little variation, and a variable or "V" region showing substantial variation. Further analysis has shown that the antigen-combining site is made up of elements from the V regions of the H and L chains (V_H and V_L). Thus the V regions of the molecule determine its specificity (Fig 14.1). The C region appears to determine its biological function. Thus the C region can be recognized by binding sites on various kinds of cells such as phagocytes and/or by the complement enzyme system which can bind to it and then cause lysis of the cell to which the antibody is bound.

A comparison of the V_L, C_L and V_H sequences of antibody molecules indicates significant homologies as well as differences, suggesting that over evolutionary time they all evolved from duplicated copies of a single primitive gene. Analysis of C_H suggests that it consists of three such duplicated genes. Each of the segments corresponding to the hypothetical primitive gene codes for a single polypeptide "domain" and each domain has a similar looped structure formed by disulfide bonds (Fig 14.1b). This basic domain structure is found in several types of immunologically important molecules.

Antibody is secreted by plasma cells, with each plasma cell secreting a single kind of antibody. Much of our knowledge of the structure of antibody molecules has been derived from studies of the protein (myeloma protein) secreted by plasma-cell tumors (myelomas). Plasma cells are mature endstage cells that appear to have a relatively short lifespan. They are produced when antigen enters the animal and, in a complex series of cell interactions not yet fully understood, activates B lymphocytes. These then proliferate and differentiate to form plasma cells.

Each B lymphocyte is programmed in its DNA to make an antibody molecule of a single specificity. The B lymphocyte makes a special form of this molecule, which is not secreted but remains anchored to the outer surface of the cell membrane where it can serve as a membrane receptor for binding antigen to the B cell. Different B cells will have receptors of different specificities, there being for mammals and birds more than 10^7 different specificities in all. An antibody response can occur when an antigen is recognized by and binds to a B cell through this antigen receptor. This leads to proliferation and differentiation of the B cell with the formation of plasma cells which actively secrete the receptor in the form of soluble antibody. If there is no B cell with a receptor capable of binding a particular foreign material then there will be no immune response against that material. B cells with appropriate receptor specificities must exist prior to the introduction of a foreign material into the system. This mechanism for production of specific antibodies is referred to as clonal selection (Burnet, 1959; Fig 14.2).

The ability to make 10^7 different antibody molecules is not present in newborn animals. Instead, it is acquired during development and throughout life as new B cells are produced. Lymphocyte stem cells carry multiple, different copies of genes arranged in families, each of which codes for a different part of the receptor (Fig 14.3). During development one member of each family is selected to make up a single gene coding for a complete receptor chain. In addition, there appears to be a high rate of somatic mutation during the process, which continues even after the B cell has been activated by antigen. Since the more effectively a B cell recognizes antigen the more it will be driven to proliferate, this provides an opportunity for antigen to select and stimulate B cells with higher affinity for the anti-

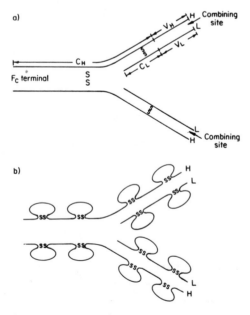

Figure 14.1. *a,* Structure of an antibody molecule (IgG). *b,* Structure of an antibody molecule emphasizing the presence of domains.

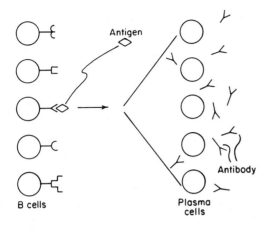

Figure 14.2. The theory of clonal selection.

gen. Apart from this last step, the process appears to be largely random and undirected, yet it is remarkably successful in producing B cells capable of recognizing the vast majority of infectious agents.

14.2.2 T CELLS AND REGULATION OF ANTIBODY PRODUCTION

Figure 14.4 indicates the concentration of specific antibodies in an animal as a function of time after exposing it to antigen. There is first a lag phase with no measurable response, then a rise to some peak value, and finally a fall to a value approaching the baseline. It was assumed previously that the rise was driven directly by the presence of antigen, and that the fall occurred as the immune response removed antigen

from the system. However, the process is now known to be under the control of regulatory cells. These regulatory cells are also lymphocytes and arise ultimately from the same stem cell as B lymphocytes. However, they follow a very different pathway of development in which the thymus plays an important, although still not understood, role. These cells, called T lymphocytes, also express antigen-specific surface receptors although, as will be described below, the way in which they recognize antigens is rather different than for B cells.

There are several different kinds of T cells which perform different functions. Some T cells are directly cytotoxic (see section 14.2). The regulatory T cells are of two types: helper T cells (T_H) and suppressor T cells (T_S). Both are antigen specific in much the same way as B cells and both are induced into activity by the presence of the antigen which they recognize. This activation involves a complex set of cell interactions of which the details remain controversial. T_H cells are required for the development of plasma cells from B cells, and they stimulate antibody production (Fig 14.4). T_S cells are produced later in a normal immune response and appear to act by blocking the T_H pathway. Thus, they inhibit antibody production through a process of active suppression.

14.2.3 RECOGNITION OF SELF

An essential property of the normal immune response is the ability to distinguish foreign antigens from self-antigens. For example, humans have B cells which can recognize both bovine albumin and chicken albumin; antibodies can be produced which will distinguish

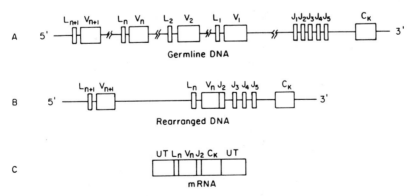

Figure 14.3. Immunoglobulin light-chain gene (mouse C_K gene family). At top, *a*, is shown the germ-line state of the DNA. There are a series of V genes, each with its own leader (L), a series of J genes, and a single C_K gene. The middle, *b*, shows the DNA in a B cell. Gene V_n has been translocated immediately adjacent to J_2. At bottom, *c*, the whole sequence L_n to C_K plus some untranslated tails (UT) has been transcribed into mRNA. All introns, as well as J_3–J_5, have been spliced out. The UT sections will not be translated into protein. The leader sequence is translated but later cleaved off. See Nisonoff (1982).

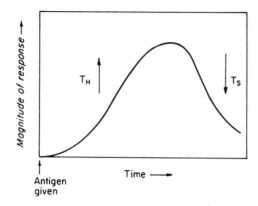

Figure 14.4. Time course of a normal immune response.

between them. These two albumins are neither very different from each other nor from human albumin. It seems likely that the process which produces B cells capable of recognizing and distinguishing between bovine and chicken albumin will also produce B cells capable of recognizing human albumin. These, if present, are not normally activated. One is said to be "tolerant" of self.

The mechanism by which tolerance to self is established remains unclear. One hypothesis is that all self-reactive cells are deleted at a specific stage of B-cell development. Thus a B cell reacting with a self-antigen (or any other antigen) during this special stage would be deleted. An alternative hypothesis is that regulatory T cells prevent the activation of self-reactive cells: T_S could become activated before T_H and stop the development of an antibody response before it has even started. In support of this mechanism, it has been shown that normal individuals have B cells capable of recognizing self-antigens and that these B cells are normally not activated.

A failure in the immune system's ability to distinguish between self and nonself appears to be at the origin of many human diseases. Autoimmune diseases are those in which self components are mistakenly treated as nonself and are actively attacked by the immune system. These include organ-specific diseases such as juvenile-onset diabetes, in which a specific immune response destroys the insulin-producing cells of the pancreas, and multiple sclerosis, in which the myelin sheath insulating nerves is specifically destroyed. They also include some systemic diseases such as rheumatoid arthritis and systemic lupus erythematosis, which are characterized by high levels of antibody against DNA and other self-antigens. There may also be diseases in which nonself components, which should be recognized by the immune system and destroyed, are treated as self and not attacked. Some investigators have proposed

that some forms of cancer fall into this category. Assuming that tumors do have antigens, there are at least three reasons why the immune response may fail to destroy the tumor:

1. there are no B cells or cytotoxic T lymphocytes (CTL) capable of recognizing the tumor;
2. there are no T_H cells capable of recognizing the tumor;
3. T_S cells become activated before T_H cells, thus preventing B-cell and CTL activation.

14.2.4 TRANSPLANTATION IMMUNITY

We now turn to the second major type of specific immunity, an immune response in which the effectors are antigen-specific T cells rather than antibody molecules. Historically, our knowledge in this area developed from studies of the rejection of tumor grafts. If a normal tissue (eg, skin) is transplanted from one unrelated human to another, it is rejected by an immunological process. This occurs because the donor and host carry different alleles of genes coding for normal components of the cell surface, known as histocompatibility antigens, and these differences are recognized by the immune system (Fig 14.5). Tumor cells transferred from one individual to another would also be rejected because they express normal histocompatibility antigens, but they may also have some additional cell-surface components unique to the tumor cell. An antigen that is present on tumor cells but not on normal cells of the same individual (indicated by C in Fig 14.5) is referred to as a tumor-specific transplantation antigen (TSTA).

Histocompatibility antigens were discovered accidentally in experiments attempting to transplant tumors

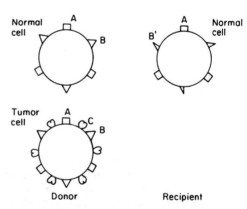

Figure 14.5. Tumor-specific and histocompatibility antigens. Both the normal cell-surface components, B, and the tumor-specific cell-surface components, C, are potentially antigenic in the recipient.

from one mouse to another. Attempts to transplant a spontaneous tumor from its host of origin to a new host were almost uniformly unsuccessful. Careful analysis of the few successful transplants suggested that the donor and recipient were genetically identical either as a result of accidental or deliberate inbreeding. These results provided the initial incentive for the establishment of many different strains of inbred mice (Klein, 1975).

The standard protocol for creating a new inbred mouse strain is to select a brother and sister from a litter, mate them, select a brother and sister from the ensuing litter, mate them and so forth. After 20 generations of inbreeding in this manner, the probability of a particular genetic locus remaining heterozygous is less than 1%. Transplants of normal tissue, such as skin, can be successfully made between mice of the same inbred strain since they share the same histocompatibility antigens; this is referred to as a syngeneic transplantation. Transplants of normal tissue between mice of two different inbred strains almost invariably fail unless special measures are taken to prevent immunological rejection, and even then these special measures often do not work. Such transplants are referred to as allogeneic transplants. Differences in histocompatibility antigens are potent barriers to transplantation. Transplants between two different species, such as rat and mouse or man and baboon, are referred to as xenogeneic transplants and also usually fail. In an outbred population such as man syngeneic transplants can be done only between identical twins.

14.2.5 TUMOR-SPECIFIC TRANSPLANTATION ANTIGENS

When a spontaneous tumor arising within an inbred strain designated strain A is transplanted syngeneically (ie, to another mouse of the same strain) the tumor will often grow; when transplanted to a mouse of another inbred strain (strain B) the tumor is almost invariably rejected. Success or failure of the tumor graft seems to be determined by the same rules as for normal tissues (ie, to be determined by differences in histocompatability antigens). However, this result does not necessarily indicate the absence of tumor-specific antigens. Consider a particular tumor (call it P) which can be transplanted within strain A and which normally grows progressively. The tumor is transplanted into the flank of a strain A mouse, allowed to grow and then excised. If the same mouse is rechallenged at some later time with the same tumor P, it may be actively rejected (Fig 14.6). This result provides strong evidence for the existence of tumor-specific antigens against which the mouse has been immunized during prior growth of the tumor. A second unrelated tumor, Q, also freely trans-

plantable within strain A, will usually still grow within the mouse immunized against tumor P, implying that tumor-specific antigens vary from tumor to tumor.

14.2.6 CONGENIC RESISTANT MOUSE STRAINS

The nature of histocompatibility (H) antigens has been studied through the development of congenic resistant mouse strains (Klein, 1975). Congenic mice are identical with those of an inbred strain at all genetic loci but one; however, this locus codes for an H antigen and therefore prevents successful transplantation of tissue. Figure 14.7 illustrates one scheme for developing such mice, using a simplified example in which there is only one H gene, with strain A carrying allele "a" (therefore genotype $^a/a$) and strain B carrying allele "b" (therefore genotype $^b/b$). Thus the tumor P (genotype $^a/a$) will grow in A but not in B. Generation 1 consists of a cross between these two strains. All mice are genotype $^a/b$. H genes appear to be codominately ex-

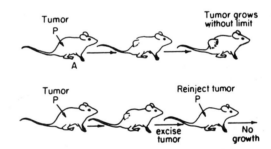

Figure 14.6. Demonstration of tumor-specific antigens.

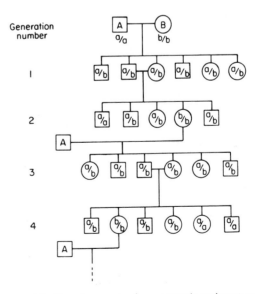

Figure 14.7. Development of a congenic-resistant mouse strain.

pressed, so that these mice express the same H allele as the tumor and the tumor will grow in all of them. These mice are now brother–sister mated and the genotype of their progeny (generation 2) will be ᵃ/ₐ, ᵃ/ᵦ or ᵇ/ᵦ. The ᵇ/ᵦ mice can be identified because they are the only ones in which the tumor will not grow. One such mouse is mated with an A mouse; the progeny (generation 3) are once again all ᵃ/ᵦ and the tumor will grow in all of them. Once again, brother–sister mating is undertaken, and a mouse is chosen in which the tumor does not grow, establishing that it is ᵇ/ᵦ. This mouse is mated with strain A and so on. Each breeding back to strain A roughly halves the amount of genetic material still present from strain B, but by testing with the tumor at each stage, the retention of the H gene from strain B is ensured. Eventually a mouse is produced which is entirely strain A except for a very short piece of chromosome carrying the H antigen and a little neighboring genetic material from strain B. The mouse and its inbred progeny are designated A.B and are referred to as belonging to a congenic resistant mouse strain.

14.2.7 THE MAJOR HISTOCOMPATIBILITY COMPLEX (MHC)

Using the above and other strategies, more than 50 different H genes have been identified in the mouse. When they are classified on the basis of the strength of the rejection reaction they produce, one locus is found to be associated with strong rejection, and the others weak. The locus which determines a strong rejection reaction is called the major histocompatibility complex (MHC), "complex" because it has been subsequently discovered to include several closely linked genes. Although the MHC was first defined in studies of allograft rejection, many other immunological phenomena are also governed by the MHC. For example, it appears to play a central role in cell–cell recognition.

The genes of the MHC code for products which can be grouped into three different classes. Class I products are glycoproteins which are expressed on the surfaces of all cells. Class II products are glycoproteins which are expressed only on some of the cells actively involved in the immune system. Class III products form part of the complement enzyme system and will not be discussed further. The MHC has been best defined in the mouse, where it is called the H-2 complex. It has been quite well defined in man through study of human leukocyte antigens and is therefore referred to as the HLA complex (Nisonoff, 1982).

In the mouse, there are three different genes coding for class I gene products. All three are expressed on the surfaces of all cells. They are called K, D and L (or H-2K, H-2D, H-2L). K and D are extremely polymorphic. The products of all three class I genes consist of three domain-like structures similar to those found in immunoglobulins. On the cell surface the class I molecule associates noncovalently with a fourth domain-like structure, an invariant molecule called beta-2-microglobulin (Fig 14.8a). Class II products are coded for in a subregion of the MHC designated as the I region. Two class II products, referred to as Ia antigens (I-A and I-E), are expressed on the surfaces of some immunocompetent cells of mice (Fig 14.8b). In man there are also three different class I loci, called A, B and C (or HLA-A, HLA-B and HLA-C) whose products are found on the cell surface in association with human beta-2-microglobulin. The details of human class II gene products (ie, HLA-DR) are only now being worked out, but there appear to be at least three.

Each inbred strain of mice is given a name. Some of the commonly used strains have names such as DBA/2, C3H, C57BL/6 and C57BL/10. The C57BL/10 strain (B10) has been used as the "background" for carrying MHC genes from a large number of different strains. Thus the strain B10.D2 is a congenic resistant strain which is C57BL/10 everywhere except for the MHC

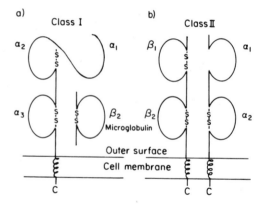

Figure 14.8. Structure of the major histocompatibility complex. *a*, Class I molecules. These are found on the surfaces of all (or nearly all) cells. They are composed of two noncovalently linked chains, α and β. The α chain is composed of three domains (α₁, α₂ and α₃) and a C terminal transmembrane portion. The β chain is a single molecule comprising a single domain and referred to as β₂ microglobulin. In man, the class I molecules are HLA-A, B and C, corresponding to H-2K, L and D in the mouse. Different class I molecules differ extensively from each other in all three chain domains. For a given molecule (eg, HLA-A) individual-to-individual variations are mostly in the α₁ and α₂ domain. *b*, Class II molecules. These are found only on B cells, some activated T cells and on cells which can present antigen to T cells (dendritic cells, macrophages and at least some epithelial cells). They are composed of two noncovalently associated chains, α and β, each comprised of two domains and a C-terminal transmembrane portion. In man, the total number of class II molecules is not yet definitely established. In mouse, there are two class II molecules, I-A and I-E, coded for by four genes, Aα, Aβ, Eα and Eβ.

locus, which has been transferred from the DBA/2 (abbreviated D2) strain. Mice of each strain carry a particular set of genes (known as a haplotype) coding for all the different MHC products. The particular set of genes carried by the DBA/2 mouse (and the B10.D2 mouse) has been arbitrarily named d haplotype, or to be H-2^d. The class I and class II molecules are then referred to as, for example, K^d, D^d, I-A^d, ... The strains C57BL/10 and C57BL/6 carry the b haplotype and expresses molecules K^b, D^b, I-A^b, ... Lists of inbred strains and their MHC haplotypes are regularly updated. These inbred strains have played an important role in studies of transplantation and tumor-associated immune responses.

14.2.8 CYTOTOXIC T LYMPHOCYTES AND MHC RESTRICTION

As stated above, many normal tissues (eg, skin) and spontaneous tumors of mice may be transplanted to animals of the same strain but are rejected by other strains. For example, P815 is a tumor which will grow in its strain of origin, DBA/2, and therefore has an MHC haplotype H-2^d. The tumor is rejected when it is injected into B10 mice. Following intravenous injection the number of tumor cells increases steadily in the spleens of DBA/2 mice, but peaks and then declines after injection into B10 mice (Fig 14.9). It appears that some active process is eliminating the tumor cells from the B10 mice by 5–6 days after injection. When spleen cells are taken from such an animal and mixed in vitro with tumor cells, the tumor cells are actively destroyed. Within the spleen-cell suspension is a subpopulation of cytotoxic effector cells which can move around, recognize a tumor cell, attach to it, transfer something as yet not identified to it, detach, and move on to find another target. A short time later, the tumor cell spontaneously lyses. These cytotoxic effector cells belong to the T-cell lineage and are referred to as cytotoxic T lymphocytes or CTLs. They are directed against class I MHC products of the tumor cell (or of normal cells if these are used in grafting) as is illustrated in Table 14.1. Here one sees that a DBA/2 target, syngeneic to the stimulating tumor cells, is lysed as is an H-2-identical but otherwise different target (B10.D2). H-2-different "third-party" targets (eg, B10.BR) and self-targets are not lysed.

Although CTL can act as potent mediators of graft rejection, their primary role is probably the elimination of virus-infected cells. If strain B10 mice are infected with virus V_1, CTLs will be produced which kill B10 cells infected with the virus. A curious and poorly understood phenomenon emerges when cells from other mouse strains infected with the same virus are tested as targets: only virally infected cells with the same MHC

haplotype as strain B10 are killed (Table 14.2). This phenomenon is referred to as MHC restriction.

The current interpretation of MHC restriction is that cytotoxic T cells with specificity for virally infected cells recognize a complex of some part of the virus together with a class I MHC product; such cells are thus simultaneously specific for (self) MHC and (foreign) virus.

As described earlier, T helper cells are involved in antibody production. Like B cells, they are antigen specific but like CTLs, they are also MHC restricted, although in this case the restriction is to class II MHC products. For a T helper cell to become activated, anti-

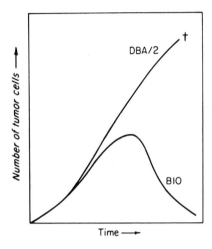

Figure 14.9. Growth of P815 (H-2^d) tumor cells in DBA/2 (H-2^d, syngeneic) or B10 (H-2^b, allogeneic) mice.

Table 14.1. Ability of B10 (H-2^b) CTL Raised Against P815 (H-2^d) to Kill Target Cells from Various Mouse Strains

Target Cell	H-2	Lysis	Comment
DBA/2	d	Yes	Syngeneic to P815
B10	b	No	Self
B10.BR	k	No	Third party
B10.D2	d	Yes	H-2 identical to P815

Table 14.2. CTL Lysis of Virus-Infected Cells is MHC Restricted*

Target Cell	H-2	Lysis	Comment
B10-V_1	b	Yes	Original stimulus
B10-V_2	b	No	Lysis is virus specific
B10.D2-V_1	d	No	Lysis is MHC restricted
B10.BR-V_1	k	No	Lysis is MHC restricted
BalB.b-V_1	b	Yes	Lysis is MHC restricted

*CTLs are from B10 mice infected with virus V_1.

gen must be presented to it on the surface of an antigen-presenting cell (APC) in association with class II MHC gene products. Such cells include macrophages, dendritic cells, B cells and epithelial cells exposed to immunological insult.

The T-cell receptor has recently been identified (Yanagi et al, 1984; Hedrick et al, 1984) and is known to be comprised of two chains, α and β, each composed of two immunoglobulin-like domains (Fig 14.10). The N terminal domains of both the α and β chains are variable (like immunoglobulin heavy and light chains) and appear to confer antigen specificity, but it is not known how MHC restriction is related to this structure. It may be important that the α–β dimer structure is always found in the membrane associated with several other molecules which also appear to play a role in T-cell recognition. Thus, in man, the α–β dimer structure (referred to as T_i) is always found in a one-to-one noncovalent association with an invariant glycoprotein called T3. T cells seeing antigen in association with class I MHC (usually CTLs) carry an invariant glycoprotein T8; those seeing antigen in association with class II MHC (usually T_H) carry another invariant glycoprotein T4. Other molecules (eg, LFA1, LFA2, etc) also appear to be involved in the recognition process.

MHC restriction is likely to impose important limitations to the potential use of CTLs in immunotherapy of cancer. Presumably CTLs reactive against tumor antigens would also see these antigens in association with class I MHC products. Given that the MHC is extremely polymorphic it is unlikely that CTLs from one patient would kill tumor cells from a second, even if the two tumors had the same antigen.

14.3 TUMOR IMMUNITY

14.3.1 IMMUNE SURVEILLANCE

The major role of the immune system is to discriminate between "self" and "nonself" and to actively eliminate invading "nonself." The concept of immune surveillance postulates that all tumors are nonself and that a principal job of the immune system is to destroy tumors as they arise. This concept assumes that all tumor cells carry nonself components (tumor-specific antigens) that are recognized by the immune system. Views on whether or not this is true are highly polarized and, over time, the consensus opinion has swung several times from one extreme to the other. It now appears that some tumors are almost certainly immunogenic in the sense that they have determinants that can be recognized by receptors on T cells and/or B cells, whereas others almost certainly are not. There is another type of poorly understood immunity, referred to as "natural immunity," which shows specificity for

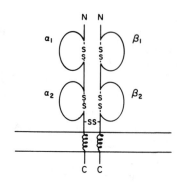

Figure 14.10. Structure of the T-cell receptor. The T-cell receptor is composed of two chains, α and β, each of about 45 kd molecular weight and held together by a disulfide (–S–S–) bond. Each chain contains two domains and a C-terminal transmembrane portion. The N terminal α_1 and β_1 domains are thought to comprise the antigen-recognizing part of the molecule and show substantial variation from one T cell to another; α_2, β_2 and the transmembrane portions are nearly invariant.

tumor cells as opposed to normal cells. It is mediated by cells: natural killer (NK) cells and macrophages. The determinants recognized are still uncharacterized.

The following two sections describe (a) underlying biological processes which may give rise to tumor-specific antigens in some tumors and in other tumors may not, and (b) how tumor-specific antigens are operationally defined.

14.3.2 BASIS FOR THE EXISTENCE OF TUMOR-SPECIFIC ANTIGENS

A tumor cell differs from a normal cell in that it is no longer subject to normal growth control. There are a number of different pathways for producing loss of growth control and only some of these are likely to produce tumor-specific antigens. The complete pathway to transformation is almost certainly a complex, multistep process. The following discussion focuses on some of the processes that may lead to formation of tumor-specific antigens (see, for example, Klein and Klein, 1985). Changes in tumor cells associated with progression, particularly those involved in formation of metastases (sections 8.3 and 10.4), may also lead to the appearance of new tumor-specific antigens.

There are a number of oncogenic DNA viruses which can play a primary role in tumor induction. An example is the Epstein-Barr virus (EBV) which is associated with Burkitt's lymphoma (section 4.3.9). Transformed cells carry viral antigens which can stimulate an immune response. Some of the tumors which occur in immunosuppressed patients appear to fall in this category.

Some spontaneous tumors may be caused by the uncontrolled and abnormal activation of a normal cellular gene. A gene which when activated in this way can produce loss of growth control is called an oncogene (section 5.3). One mechanism for producing the activation is a chromosomal translocation which brings the oncogene into association with and under the control of a gene or genes which are normally activated. This is unlikely to produce a new antigen so that tumors formed in this way are unlikely to be immunogenic. Another mechanism is insertion into the DNA of the transcription-controlling element of an RNA virus (the long-terminal repeat or LTR) in such a way that the oncogene is now activated (section 4.4.3). This may produce tumor-specific antigens if viral genes are also transcribed and translated. A third mechanism is direct alteration of the oncogene itself such that it is now actively transcribed. The product of this mutated oncogene may or may not be immunogenic, depending upon the extent of the alteration away from the self-product.

14.3.3 DETECTION OF TUMOR-SPECIFIC ANTIGENS

Early attempts to detect tumor-specific antigens focussed on studies of tumor cell lines of animal origin which could be maintained in vitro and which would grow in a syngeneic host. It was often possible to immunize animals such that the transplanted tumor would no longer grow because of an active immunologically based rejection process (Fig 14.6). In this way, tumor-specific transplantation antigens (TSTAs) could be defined for essentially all transplantable tumors. However, transplantable tumors may be poor models for spontaneous tumors: during their long life in vitro, they may accumulate a multitude of alterations, making them much more immunogenic. When similar experiments have been performed with spontaneous tumors, it has been difficult to define TSTAs (Hewitt et al, 1976).

A tumor-specific antigen on a spontaneous human tumor can only be defined through some kind of experimental procedure. The most widely used procedure has been characterization of serum taken either directly from a patient with a tumor or from an animal immunized with tumor cells from the patient. The serum, after absorption with cells from a range of normal tissues, is then tested for its ability to recognize the tumor cell. Many antigens on tumor cells have been described on the basis of such testing, but most of these are not truly tumor specific. Instead, they are normal cell-surface structures which, as well as being expressed on tumor cells, are expressed either at a high level on a small population of normal cells or at low levels on many normal cells. Such antigens are better referred to as tumor associated. A well-characterized example of

such an antigen is carcino-embryonic antigen (CEA). CEA is present at high levels on (and is secreted by) certain tumor cells. However, it is also present at low levels on normal intestinal mucosa, in much higher levels in normal embryos, and can be induced to high levels of expression in many pathological conditions not involving malignancy. An immune response against such an antigen would not be tumor specific and should normally be prevented by the mechanisms of self-tolerance. However, the detection and monitoring of the levels of such antigens may be useful for following the clinical course of disease (see chapter 12).

Clearly, viral antigens can be tumor specific. However, almost all other antigens that appeared initially to be tumor-specific have been found subsequently to be merely tumor associated (Zalcberg and McKenzie, 1985). B-cell lymphomas have been shown to provide an interesting exception: the unique immunoglobulin molecule coded for by the initial transformed cell is expressed by all of its progeny and serves as a marker antigen for the whole malignant clone. It is probable that receptors of T lymphocytes will provide a similar unique marker antigen (Minden et al, 1985).

The characterization of possible tumor-specific antigens has been greatly facilitated by the development of monoclonal antibodies (see section 20.3). Such antibodies have high specificity and can be produced in large quantities. Future work with monoclonal antibodies may define unique tumor-specific antigens, perhaps associated with unique products of oncogenes.

14.4 POTENTIAL MECHANISMS FOR ANTITUMOR IMMUNITY

There are a number of possible mechanisms by which the immune system could destroy tumor cells. Stimulation of these mechanisms provides the basis for immunotherapy (see chapter 20). One family of mechanisms is based on the recognition of the types of antigens discussed in the previous section by antibody or T cells. A second family of mechanisms can be linked together under the rubric "natural immunity." The nature of the determinants recognized remains unclear but is different from the determinants recognized by B cells and T cells.

14.4.1 MECHANISMS DEPENDENT ON ANTIBODIES

Antibody specific for a tumor antigen could bind to a tumor cell and activate the complement system to kill the tumor cell. This would be direct killing by the antibody. Alternatively many cells have receptors for the F_c terminal of antibodies. Some of these cells, called K cells, when so coated with an antibody will kill cells which the antibody recognizes. This is referred to as ADCC (antibody-dependent cellular cytotoxicity).

14.4.2 CYTOTOXIC T LYMPHOCYTES (CTLs)

Cytotoxic T lymphocytes (CTLs) play an important role in rejection of foreign-tissue grafts and may be important in antitumor immunity. These effector cells may be obtained with specificities against cell-surface determinants such as tumor-associated antigens. Cloned lines of CTLs can be established and expanded in vitro for periods of months and even years, through the use of medium containing T-cell growth factor (also known as interleukin 2). Cloned lines of CTLs with specificities for tumor-associated antigens of transplantable tumors have been injected into tumor-bearing animals and have produced tumor regression and even cure (eg, Mills et al, 1980).

CTLs may play an important role in rejection of some tumors, particularly those with a viral etiology. A particular problem with applying CTL lines therapeutically in man is that toxicity of CTLs depends on specificities for both major histocompatibility antigens and tumor-associated antigens. Thus even if a given type of tumor has the same tumor-associated antigens in different patients, CTL lines raised from the cells of one patient will probably be active only against the tumor in that patient because different patients will rarely share the appropriate MHC determinants. There are promising preliminary attempts at cloning tumor-specific CTLs from tumor biopsies with the objective of infusing them back into the patient (Rosenberg, 1984). This approach has potential for production of a large number of active cells that are not foreign to the host, but requires that the tumor be controlled by conventional means while the CTLs are established and expanded in culture.

14.4.3 NATURAL KILLER CELLS

Natural killer (NK) cells are a subpopulation of lymphocytes which may, without prior sensitization, spontaneously kill certain tumor cells. They have been studied extensively in both mouse and man. In man, their action may be determined by purifying lymphocytes from peripheral blood, mixing them with appropriate radioactively labeled tumor cells and monitoring tumor-cell lysis by the presence of radiolabel in the culture supernatant. Significant killing may often be seen after less than an hour of incubation. Cells from different tumors have differing sensitivities to killing by NK cells, and many tumors of myeloid or lymphoid origin are particularly sensitive. Killing is nonspecific in the sense that a single NK cell can kill many different kinds of tumor cells, although the range of tumor cells that

may be attacked by a particular NK cell is unknown. The structures recognized on tumor cells do not appear to involve the major histocompatibility complex (MHC) because killing of NK-sensitive tumor cells can be obtained irrespective of the MHC of the NK-cell donor. Tumor-cell sensitivity may be due in part to differences in cell-surface glycosylation (Pohajdak et al, 1984).

The origin of NK cells is unclear but human NK cells can be distinguished from both B cells and T cells on the basis of a surface marker (HNK-1 or Leu7, Abo and Balch, 1981) and because they contain characteristic cytoplasmic granules (Timonen et al, 1981). Cloned NK cell lines can be established in vitro using conditions similar to those used to clone T cells; on appropriate manipulation of the culture conditions, cloned lines of cytotoxic T lymphocytes can be shown to lose their original specificity and to become NK-like in their ability to kill certain tumor cells but not others (Brooks, 1983). It is possible that culture conditions might be manipulated to provide cells with therapeutic potential; however, both surface markers and range of specificity of these cells differ from those of freshly isolated NK cells.

Natural killer cells may have a role in the regulation of differentiation since some early progenitors of lymphocytes and bone marrow cells are sensitive to lysis by NK cells (Hansson et al, 1982). They may also constitute a system of immune surveillance against some tumors. Mice with normal immunity except for severely depressed NK-cell function (carrying the beige mutation) have a high incidence of spontaneous tumors; in contrast, athymic nude mice which are severely deficient in mature functional T cells have normal or elevated levels of NK cells and no increase in incidence of spontaneous tumors. Humans with the Chediak-Higashi syndrome have depressed NK-cell activity and an increased incidence of lymphoid malignancy (Roder et al, 1982). High levels of NK cells have also been correlated with inhibition of metastases from some, but not all, experimental tumors in mice (see section 10.2.4). Patients with tumors generally have depressed NK cell activity, but whether this is a contributing cause or an effect of their disease is not clear at the present time.

14.4.4 MACROPHAGES

Macrophages, like NK cells, appear to have mechanisms for distinguishing tumor cells from normal cells, but as for NK cells, the nature of these mechanisms is unknown. The major function of macrophages is thought to be processing and presentation of antigens: immunogenic fragments become associated with MHC determinants on the macrophage surface, where they are presented to T cells. Normal body constituents, such as serum proteins, are not processed, so that macrophages presumably have the ability to discriminate between self and nonself, but the mechanisms responsible for this discrimination are unknown. As discussed in section 20.4, macrophages can be activated to kill tumor cells.

14.5 SUMMARY

The immune system can remove foreign agents from the body. It has specificity and memory. An immune response develops when lymphocytes capable of recognizing an antigen are activated. Lymphocytes are of two main types: B cells and T cells. Activated B cells produce antibody, a soluble, antigen-specific protein which can bind to the antigen eliciting its production and as a result may facilitate its removal. T cells are of three main types: cytotoxic T lymphocytes, T helper cells and T suppressor cells. Cytotoxic T lymphocytes can destroy cells which they recognize. T helper and T suppressor cells are regulatory cells and are involved in the activation of both B cells and cytotoxic T lymphocytes. T cells can only detect antigens on the surface of another cell where they see it in association with an appropriate product of the major histocompatibility complex (MHC). Thus T cells have a dual specificity for (foreign) antigen and (self) MHC. T cells can recognize foreign MHC products directly. Both B and T cells can distinguish more than 1,000,000 different foreign determinants. This capacity continues to develop throughout life. It remains unclear how this is done without also producing autoreactive cells; ie, how does the immune system maintain tolerance to self?

Tumor cells may contain surface antigens which differ from those on most normal cells, but such antigens can usually also be found on at least some types of normal cells. Such antigens are best referred to as tumor associated. Some tumors express antigens which are truly tumor specific and have grown despite the presence of a potential immune response against them. Mechanisms for antitumor immunity include cell killing by antibody and complement, antibody-dependent cell-mediated cytotoxicity, and lysis by cytotoxic T lymphocytes. NK cells and macrophages can also distinguish between tumor and normal cells; how they do this is unknown at the present time.

REFERENCES

Abo T, Balch CM: A differentiation antigen of human NK and K cells identified by a monoclonal antibody (HNK-1). J Immunol 1981; 127:1024–1029.

Brooks CG: Reversible induction of natural killer cell activity in cloned murine cytotoxic T lymphocytes. Nature 1983; 305:155–158.

Burnet FM: The Clonal Selection Theory of Acquired Immunity. Cambridge Univ. Press, Cambridge, 1959.

Hansson M, Beran M, Andersson B, Kiessling R: Inhibition of in vitro granulopoiesis by autologous allogeneic human NK cells. J Immunol 1982; 129:126–132.

Hedrick SM, Cohen DI, Nielsen EA, Davis MM: Isolation of cDNA clones encoding T cell-specific membrane-associated proteins. Nature 1984; 308:149–153.

Hewitt HB, Blake ER, Walder AS: A critique of the evidence for active host defense against cancer, based on personal studies of 27 murine tumours of spontaneous origin. Br J Cancer 1976; 33:241–259.

Klein J: Biology of the Mouse Histocompatibility-2 Complex: Principles of Immunogenetics Applied to a Single System. Springer-Verlag, New York, 1975.

Klein G, Klein E: Evolution of tumors and the impact of molecular oncology. Nature 1985; 315:190–195.

Mills GB, Carlson G, Paetkau V: Generation of cytotoxic lymphocytes to syngeneic tumors by using co-stimulator (interleukin 2): in vivo activity. J Immunol 1980; 125:1904–1909.

Minden MD, Toyonaga B, Ha K et al: Somatic rearrangement of T-cell antigen receptor gene in human T-cell malignancies. Proc Natl Acad Sci USA 1985; 82:1224–1227.

Nisonoff A: Introduction to Molecular Immunology. Sinauer Assoc., Sunderland, MA, 1982.

Pohajdak B, Wright JA, Greenberg AJ: An oligosaccharide biosynthetic defect in conconavalin A-resistant chinese hamster ovary (CHO) cells that enhances NK reactivity in vitro and in vivo. J Immunol 1984; 133:2423–2429.

Roder JC, Haliotis T, Laing L et al: Further studies of natural killer cell function in Chediak-Higashi patients. Immunology 1982; 46:555–560.

Rosenberg SA: Adoptive immunotherapy of cancer: Accomplishments and prospects. Cancer Treat Rep 1984; 68:233–255.

Timonen T, Ortaldo JR, Herberman RB: Characteristics of human large granular lymphocytes and relationship to natural killer and K cells. J Expl Med 1981; 153:569–582.

Yanagi Y, Yoshikai Y, Leggett K et al: A human T cell-specific cDNA clone encodes a protein having extensive homology to immunoglobulin chains. Nature 1984; 308:145–149.

Zalcberg JR, McKenzie IFC: Tumor-associated antigens—An overview. J Clin Oncol 1985; 3:876–882.

BIBLIOGRAPHY

Golub ES: The Cellular Basis of the Immune Response: An Approach to Immunobiology. Sinauer Assoc., Sunderland, MA, 1977.

Nisonoff A: Introduction to Molecular Immunology. Sinauer Assoc., Sunderland, MA, 1982.

PART 3

BIOLOGY UNDERLYING
CANCER TREATMENT

15

Cellular Basis of Radiotherapy

Richard P. Hill

15.1 INTRODUCTION

Since their discovery by Roentgen almost a century ago, X-rays have played a major role in modern medicine. The first recorded use of X-rays for the treatment of cancer occurred within about one year of their discovery. Subsequently there has been intensive study of X-rays and other ionizing radiations, and their clinical application to cancer treatment has become increasingly sophisticated. The next two chapters will review the biological effects of ionizing radiation and the application of that knowledge to cancer treatment. The important application of ionizing radiation in assisting the diagnosis of cancer will not be discussed because it is beyond the scope of this book.

The present chapter will deal initially with the basic physical properties of ionizing radiations, and their interaction with biological matter. Many of the important concepts have been discussed in chapter 7 and will only be described briefly here. The effect of energy deposition in tissue will then be discussed with emphasis on the inhibition of the ability of cells to divide and continue to proliferate. Various factors which are known to influence the effect of radiation on cells will be described.

15.2 INTERACTION OF RADIATION WITH MATTER

15.2.1 TYPES OF RADIATION AND ENERGY DEPOSITION

X-rays and γ-rays constitute part of the continuous spectrum of electromagnetic (EM) radiation which includes radio waves, heat and visible and ultraviolet (UV) light (see Fig. 7.1). All types of EM radiation can be considered as moving packets (quanta) of energy called photons. The amount of energy in each individual photon defines its position in the electromagnetic spectrum. X-ray or γ-ray photons carry more energy than heat or light photons and are at the high-energy end of the EM spectrum. They differ only in the way that they are produced (γ-rays are emitted from the nucleus while X-rays result from energy losses from electrons).

When EM radiation interacts with matter energy is absorbed by the atoms or molecules. Individual photons of X-rays (but not UV light) are sufficiently energetic that their interaction with matter can result in the complete displacement of an electron from its orbit around the nucleus of an atom. Such an atom is left with a net positive charge and is thus an ion; hence the term *ionizing radiation*. An interaction which transfers energy but does not completely displace an electron produces an "excited" atom or molecule and is called an *excitation*.

When X-ray photons interact with tissue they give up energy by one of three processes: the photoelectric effect, the Compton effect and pair production. The relative importance of these processes depends on the energy of the individual photons (see section 7.2). All three processes produce secondary electrons that move through the tissue. These secondary electrons give up their kinetic energy by interacting with the atoms and molecules in the tissue to cause further ionizations and excitations.

In the energy range most widely used in radiotherapy (100 keV to 10 MeV) the Compton effect is the most important mechanism leading to deposition of energy in biological materials. This energy-transfer process involves a billiard-ball-type collision between the photon and an outer orbital electron of an atom, with partial transfer of energy to the electron and scattering of the photon into a new direction. The photon (and the electron) can then undergo further interactions, causing more ionizations and excitations, until its energy is dissipated.

An electron is a charged particle and it is possible with modern particle accelerators to irradiate directly with electrons or with other charged particles such as those listed in Table 15.1. Energy may be absorbed directly by the atoms and molecules, causing ionization and excitation and creating secondary electrons. The deposition of energy in matter by moving charged particles is chiefly a result of electrical field interactions and depends both on the velocity and on the charge of the particle (see section 7.2). Detailed discussion of the mechanisms involved is given in Johns and Cunningham (1983). Neutrons have no charge and do not interact with atomic electrons to produce ionizations. They deposit energy by collision with nuclei, particularly hydrogen nuclei (protons), and thereby transfer their energy to create moving charged particles, which, in turn, can cause ionizations and excitations.

15.2.2 LINEAR ENERGY TRANSFER AND ENERGY ABSORPTION

As a charged particle moves through matter it transfers energy by a series of interactions which occur at random. Because of the discrete nature of these energy-loss events the amount of energy released in small volumes (≤ 1 μm^3) demonstrates large variations from one volume to another due to statistical fluctuations (Rossi, 1962). The average energy lost by a particle over a given path length is known as the linear energy transfer (LET). The concept of LET is discussed in more detail in section 7.2, where it is indicated that energy loss by charged particles in matter is inversely related to their velocity. Thus, as a particle slows down it loses energy more and more rapidly and reaches a maximum rate of energy loss (the Bragg peak) just before it comes to rest (see Fig 15.1). The LET of a charged particle thus varies along the length of its track. Average LET values for a number of different types of ionizing radiation are given in Table 7.1.

The importance of LET is that the biological effect of a radiation dose depends on its LET (see section 15.6.1), and it is therefore necessary to know the LET at each point in an irradiated volume in order to predict the biological response. When EM radiation (eg, 1.25 MeV γ-rays produced by decay of ^{60}Co) is used to irradiate tissue, electrons are set in motion in the tissue and because of their small mass ($1/1860 \times$ mass of proton) they are easily deflected and their track through the tissue is tortuous. Each electron track has a Bragg peak at its termination and a range of LET values

Table 15.1. Some Types of Ionizing Radiation

Radiation	Charge
Electromagnetic	
x-rays	none
γ-rays	none
Particles	
Electrons (or β-rays)	negative
Protons	positive
Neutrons	none
α-particles (He nuclei)	positive
negative π-mesons	negative
heavy charged ions (eg, C, Ne, Ar)	positive

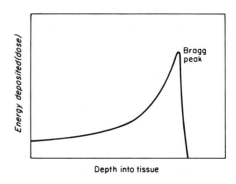

Figure 15.1. Schematic illustration of the energy deposition by a charged particle along its track in tissue. The particle has a high velocity at the left-hand side of the figure but as it loses energy it slows down until it comes to rest in the region of the Bragg peak.

along its track, but both the initiation and termination points of the electron tracks occur at random in the tissue, so that the LET spectrum is similar at all depths. A similar result occurs if the irradiation is with a primary electron beam.

In contrast, if a beam of mono-energetic heavy charged particles (eg, protons, He or Ne nuclei) is used to irradiate the tissue, the tracks of the particles are much straighter, because their much larger mass reduces the chance of significant deflection and the Bragg peak occurs at a similar depth in the tissue for all particles. Thus, for each type of particle and each energy, there is a region in the tissue where a relatively large amount of energy is deposited (at high LET). This feature of irradiation with heavy charged particles makes them potentially attractive for some therapeutic applications (see section 16.5).

Radiation dose is measured in terms of the amount of energy absorbed per unit mass and is quoted in grays (1 J/kg—see section 7.2). It is not, however, the total amount of energy absorbed which is critical for the biological effect of ionizing radiation. A whole-body dose of 5 grays (Gy) would result in the death (due to bone marrow failure) of many animals, including man, yet the amount of energy deposited, if evenly distributed, would cause a minimal temperature rise of only about 10^{-3}°C. The total amount of energy deposited is much less than that absorbed by drinking a warm cup of coffee. It is the size and localized nature of the energy-deposition events caused by ionizing radiations which is the reason for their efficacy in damaging biological systems.

15.2.3 DIRECT AND INDIRECT EFFECT

The interactions leading to energy deposition discussed in the last section occur very rapidly (see Fig 15.2), and generate chemically reactive free electrons and free radicals (molecules with unpaired electrons). Many different molecules in cells will be altered as a

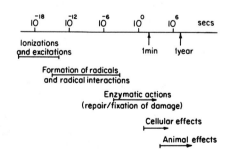

Figure 15.2. Approximate time scale for events occurring during and after the treatment of tissue with ionizing radiation.

result of *direct* energy absorption. In addition, energy may be transferred from one part of a large molecule to another or from one molecule to another, giving rise to *indirect* effects. Since cells are more than 70% water, most of the energy deposited in cells is absorbed in the water and radiochemical studies have demonstrated that a number of reactive radicals are produced (see section 7.2). Most of the indirect effects of radiation involve interaction of these radicals with other molecules in the cell. The OH· radical, an oxidizing agent, is regarded as being the most damaging. Subsequent to the initial physical and radiochemical events, a series of biochemical and biological interactions occur, most of which are poorly understood. The net result may be altered cellular and tissue function which is expressed hours, days, weeks or even years later (see Fig 15.2).

15.3 BIOLOGICAL EFFECTS OF RADIATION

15.3.1 MOLECULAR DAMAGE

The random nature of the energy-deposition events means that radiation-induced changes can occur in any molecule in a cell; it is generally believed that damage to DNA is the most crucial, particularly in relation to cell killing. This damage may include single- or double-strand breaks in the sugar–phosphate backbone of the molecule, alteration or loss of bases, or formation of cross-links between the DNA strands or between the DNA and chromosomal proteins. Evidence to support the critical role of DNA damage comes from experiments in which the cytoplasm or nuclei of cells have been irradiated either with microbeams or by incorporating radioisotopes into specific macromolecules. Many experiments have also indicated a direct correlation between the DNA content and the sensitivity of different organisms such as viruses, bacteria and cells to radiation treatment.

Although a number of recently developed techniques, such as alkaline elution, have allowed study of specific DNA lesions caused by radiation, such as single- or double-strand breaks, the nature of the DNA damage responsible for cell death remains unclear. Many lesions in DNA can be partially or completely repaired (see section 7.4); thus the expression of DNA damage at the cellular level is complex. It has been suggested that unrepaired or incorrectly repaired double-strand breaks are the critical lesions, but this remains to be proven. That DNA repair capacity can influence cellular radiosensitivity is clear from studies of cells from patients with ataxia telangiectasia (AT), an inherited disease associated with deficiency in DNA repair capacity. Fibroblasts from patients with AT are significantly

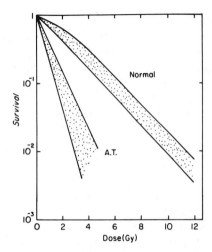

Figure 15.3. Survival of cultured fibroblasts following treatment with ^{60}Co γ-rays delivered under hypoxic conditions. The range of values for cells derived from five normal subjects and nine patients with ataxia telangiectasia (A.T.) are shown. (Adapted from Paterson et al, 1979.)

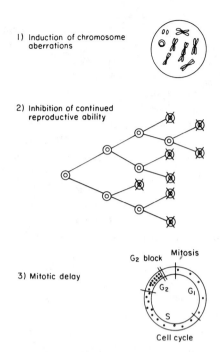

Figure 15.4. Schematic illustration of some of the cellular effects of radiation. (1) Three types of aberration are shown—a dicentric chromosome, a ring chromosome and two acentric fragments. (2) After irradiation, lethally damaged cells may divide a few times but eventually all the progeny will cease dividing or lyse (crossed cells). (3) Cells in G_2 phase are blocked for a period of time in their progression through the cell cycle and the progression of cells in other phases is slowed.

more sensitive to γ-irradiation than similar cells from normal patients (see Fig 15.3).

15.3.2 CELLULAR EFFECTS

Radiation damage to the macromolecules in cells can result in a wide range of cellular effects, some of which are illustrated in Figure 15.4. Inhibition of specific biochemical processes in cells, such as DNA, RNA or protein synthesis, respiration, or substrate metabolism, usually requires quite large doses (10–100 Gy). Chromosome aberrations, which are discussed in section 7.3, can, however, be detected in cells entering mitosis after radiation doses of less than about 1 Gy. Inhibition of the continued reproductive ability of cells is an important consequence of radiation, both because it occurs at relatively low doses (a few grays) and because it is the major aim of irradiation of malignant disease; a tumor is controlled if its stem cells are prevented from continued proliferation.

Most types of cells do not show morphological evidence of radiation damage until they attempt to divide, and following doses of less than about 10 Gy, lethally damaged cells may divide a few times before their progeny undergo lysis and disappear from the population. Following larger doses of radiation (>20 Gy) cells can express their damage in interphase and lyse without entering mitosis. Thus nondividing cells may be killed by high doses, while they show little evidence of damage from lower doses. A few cell types, notably small lymphocytes and spermatocytes, undergo interphase

death following low doses (~1 Gy). The mechanism(s) involved in interphase death is poorly understood.

Radiation damage also delays the progression of cells through the cell cycle. There is a rapid drop in the mitotic index in an irradiated cell population because both lethally damaged and surviving cells cease to enter mitosis, whilst the cells already in mitosis continue their progression. After a period of time, which depends on both the cell type and the radiation dose, cells begin to re-enter mitosis (Fig 15.5); this time is known as the mitotic delay. Mitotic delay appears to be largely due to a block of cell-cycle progression in G_2 phase, which may involve inhibition of the synthesis of proteins necessary for mitosis. Cells in G_1 and S phases are also delayed in their progression through the cell cycle, but to a lesser extent than cells in G_2 phase. Thus after doses larger than a few grays, the cells which enter mitosis first can be those which were irradiated in the G_1 or S phases. The cell population will be partially synchronised as a result of the radiation-induced cell-cycle delay. Even after doses as high as 10 Gy most cells divide at the end of the cycle in which they were

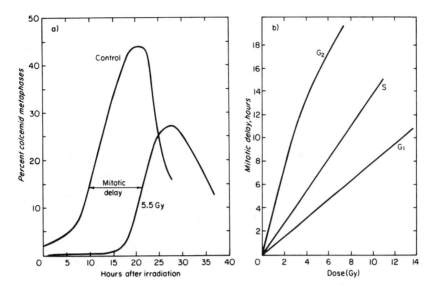

Figure 15.5. The effects of irradiation on the progression of cells into mitosis after the treatment. *a*, At time zero, the cells were placed in medium containing colcemid, a drug which arrests cells in mitosis, and the percentage of cells which accumulated in mitosis is plotted as a function of time. The decline in the curves at late times is a result of cells escaping the drug-induced block or dying. The mitotic delay due to a radiation dose of 5.5 Gy displaces the curves for the radiation-treated cells to the right. *b*, Cells were irradiated when in different phases of the cell cycle and the mitotic delay observed is plotted as a function of radiation dose. (Adapted from Elkind and Whitmore, 1967.)

irradiated. However, the surviving cells may continue to experience delays in their progression through the next and subsequent cycles.

15.4 ASSAYS FOR PROLIFERATIVE CAPACITY

15.4.1 IN VITRO ASSAYS

A cell which retains unlimited proliferative capacity after radiation treatment is regarded as having survived the treatment, whilst one which fails to proliferate is regarded as having been killed, even though it may undergo a few divisions or remain intact in the cell population. Assessing survival of cells after radiation thus depends on the demonstration that they retain the ability to produce a large number of progeny, ie, to produce a colony (see section 8.2). One of the commonest ways to assess cell survival is to use an in vitro plating assay (Puck and Marcus, 1956; see Fig 15.6a). Cells grown in culture are irradiated either before or after preparation of a suspension of single cells. The cells are then counted and serial dilutions are plated in tissue culture dishes with appropriate medium and incubated at 37°C. The cells attach to the surface of the tissue culture dish, and those which retain proliferative capacity

divide and grow to form discrete colonies of cells. After a number of days of incubation, which depends on the growth rate of the cells, the plates are removed from the incubator and the colonies are fixed and stained so that they can be counted easily.

Cells which do not retain proliferative capacity following irradiation (ie, are killed) may also divide a few times but form only very small "abortive" colonies. If a colony contains more than 50 cells (ie, is derived from a single cell by at least six division cycles) it is usually capable of continued growth and can be regarded as having arisen from a surviving cell. The plating efficiency (PE) of the cell population is calculated by dividing the number of colonies formed by the number of cells plated. Untreated cells rarely have a PE of 1 (more usually it is 0.5–0.8); thus the ratio of the PE for the irradiated cells to the PE for control cells is calculated to give the fraction of cells surviving the treatment (cell survival). If a range of radiation doses is used then these cell-survival values can be plotted to give a survival curve, such as the ones shown in Figure 15.10.

Technical advances, which permit in vitro growth of cells taken directly from many tumors, have allowed the in vitro assay method to be extended to the study of the radiation sensitivity of tumor cells treated in vivo. The procedure is often called an in vivo–in vitro assay and

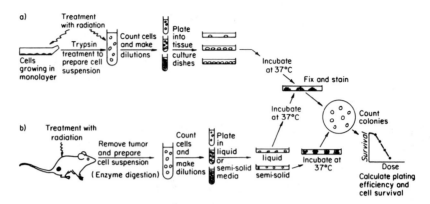

Figure 15.6. Schematic diagram of *in vitro* plating assays to assess cell survival. *a,* Assay for the radiation sensitivity of cells growing in culture. *b,* In vivo–in vitro assay for the sensitivity of tumor cells grown and irradiated in vivo.

is outlined in Figure 15.6b. Control and treated tumors are removed from their respective host animals and cell suspensions are prepared using one of a variety of enzyme dissociation procedures. Serial dilutions are then made and the cells are plated in tissue culture dishes either in liquid media, where they attach to the surface of the dish and may grow to form colonies, or in semi-solid media (agar or methylcellulose in nutrient media) where they grow to form colonies in suspension. The colonies are counted and cell survival is calculated as described above.

15.4.2 IN VIVO ASSAYS

A number of assays are also available for estimating cell survival by transplantation of irradiated and control cells in vivo. One of the earliest of these approaches is the endpoint-dilution technique of Hewitt and Wil-

son (1959). This technique (Fig 15.7) was used originally to determine the radiation sensitivity of a transplantable leukemia which grew in the livers of mice. More recently it has been used to study the radiosensitivity of cells in solid tumors. After treatment of the tumors in vivo, cell suspensions are prepared from treated and control tumors. The cells are counted and serial dilutions injected subcutaneously or intramuscularly into groups of recipient animals. The animals are then observed to determine which injection sites give rise to tumors. The percent of tumors which develop is plotted as a function of the cell number injected and the number of cells required for 50% tumor takes (the TD_{50} value) is determined. The ratio of the TD_{50} value obtained for cells from untreated control tumors to that obtained from the radiation-treated tumors gives the cell survival.

The above technique has also been adapted (Clifton,

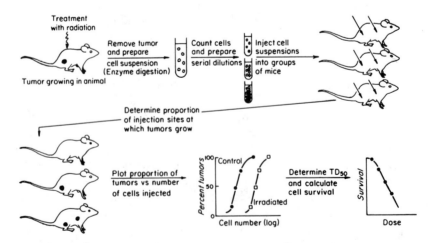

Figure 15.7. Schematic diagram of the application of the endpoint dilution assay to determine the radiation sensitivity of tumor cells treated in vivo.

1980) to the study of the radiosensitivity of the cells of a number of normal tissues (eg, mammary gland, thyroid gland). Cell suspensions are prepared from the glands of irradiated and control animals. Serial dilutions are then injected into the mammary fat pads in recipient animals. The animals are treated such that the growth of the injected cells is stimulated (eg, by separate transplantation with a hormone-producing tumor). After an appropriate period of time the recipient animals are killed, growth of the transplanted cells is assessed by microscopic examination of the mammary fat pad, and a TD_{50} value determined.

A number of methods have also been developed for assessing the ability of cells to form colonies in vivo. The best known of these is the spleen-colony method described in section 17.2.3, which has been used to assess both the radiation and drug sensitivity of bone marrow stem cells (see, for example, McCulloch and Till, 1962). A similar procedure has been used to study the radiation or drug sensitivities of lymphoma cell populations which can also form spleen colonies.

An analogous method, which has been used to examine radiation and drug sensitivities of the cells of solid tumors, is the lung-colony assay (Hill and Bush, 1969; see Fig 15.8). In this technique cell suspensions, prepared from treated or untreated solid tumors, are injected intravenously into groups of recipient mice. The cells arrest in the lungs of the animals and grow to form tumor nodules, which can be counted 2–4 weeks later depending on the growth rate of the tumor cells. Cell

survival is calculated as the ratio of the colony-forming efficiencies of irradiated and control cells.

15.4.3 IN SITU ASSAYS

Some ingenious colony-forming assays have been developed to study the radiation response of stem cells in situ in some proliferative tissues, including skin, GI tract, testis, cartilage, and certain tumors. An example is the technique used to study the sensitivity of individual crypt stem cells in the small intestine (Withers and Elkind, 1970, Fig 15.9). Radiation doses which are sufficient to reduce the number of surviving crypt cells to a low level are given to groups of mice. The surviving cells grow rapidly to form regenerating crypts, which can be identified in histological sections made about 3–4 days after radiation treatment. The fraction of crypts which are capable of regenerating can then be calculated and plotted as a function of radiation dose to give a survival curve for intestinal crypts. The number of cells in each crypt which are capable of regenerating the crypt (ie, the crypt stem cells) is greater than 1 (probably about 80; Potten and Hendry, 1985). Consequently, crypt survival does not reflect individual cell survival unless radiation doses sufficient to reduce the probable number of stem cell survivors to less than 1 per crypt are used. The low-dose initial part of the cell-survival curve thus cannot be determined directly and only the final slope of the survival curve is obtained.

15.4.4 SURVIVAL CURVES

The various techniques described above have been used to obtain survival curves for a wide range of malignant and normal cell populations. In general, for low LET radiations (eg, X- or γ-rays) these curves have the

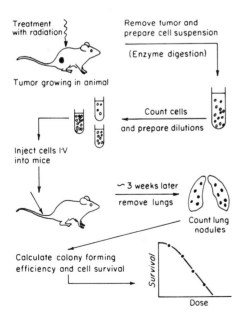

Figure 15.8. Schematic diagram illustrating the use of the lung colony assay to determine the radiation sensitivity of tumor cells treated in vivo.

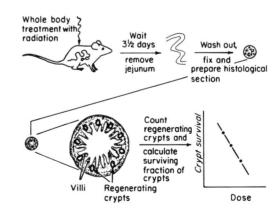

Figure 15.9. Schematic diagram describing the in situ assay used to determine the radiation sensitivity of individual crypt stem cells in the small intestine.

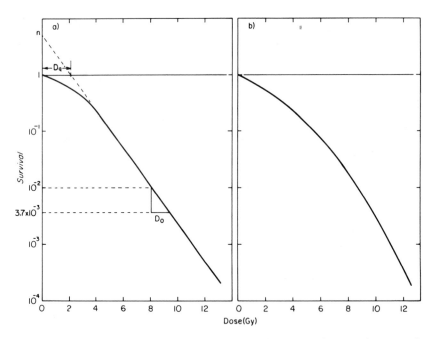

Figure 15.10. Survival curves for cells treated with low LET radiation. The survival is plotted on a logarithmic scale against dose plotted on a linear scale. Parts *a* and *b* of the figure demonstrate two different shapes which have been widely observed.

shape illustrated in Figure 15.10a, in which cell survival is plotted on a log scale as a function of dose on a linear scale. At low doses there is evidence of a shoulder region, but at higher doses the curve becomes steeper and straight so that survival decreases exponentially with dose. For some types of cells the survival curve appears to be continually bending downwards on a semilogarithmic plot (see Fig 15.10b), and often the accuracy of the data is such that either shape could adequately fit the data over the first two or three decades of survival. The survival curve in Figure 15.10a can be characterized by the parameters D_0, which represents the slope of the straight-line part of the curve, and n or D_q, which represents the size of the shoulder. The derivation of these parameters will be discussed in section 15.5.

A large number of cell-survival curves have been derived for malignant and normal cell populations. These demonstrate that D_0 values for almost all mammalian cells are quite similar (about 1–2 Gy for irradiation with X- or γ-rays given under aerobic conditions). There are no consistent differences in D_0 values between malignant and normal cells. For low LET radiations the size of the shoulder varies considerably between different cell lines, ranging from essentially no shoulder ($D_q = 0$ Gy) for bone marrow cells to large shoulders ($D_q > 3$ Gy) for many other types of cells. The shape of the shoulder region of the survival curve also varies between different cell lines (see section 16.2.1). The size of the shoulder reflects the ability of

cells to accumulate and repair radiation damage and will be discussed in more detail in section 15.6.3.

15.5 MATHEMATICAL MODELS OF CELL SURVIVAL

15.5.1 SINGLE-HIT KILLING

Many different mathematical models have been proposed to define the shapes of survival curves. All of these are based on the concept of the random nature of energy deposition by radiation. The earlier models, which are discussed in detail by Elkind and Whitmore (1967), were based on the idea that a specific target (or targets) had to be inactivated for cells to be killed. Thus the number of targets (dN) inactivated by a small dose of radiation (dD) should be proportional to the initial number of targets N and to dD, so that

$$dN \propto N\,dD \qquad \text{or} \qquad dN = -(1/D_0)N\,dD \;, \qquad (15.1)$$

where $1/D_0$ is a constant of proportionality and the negative sign is introduced because the number of active targets N decreases with increasing dose. This equation can be integrated to give

$$N = N_0 \exp(-D/D_0) \;, \qquad (15.2)$$

where N_0 is the number of active targets present at zero dose. If it is assumed that cells contain only a single target which must be inactivated for them to be killed then the fractional survival of a population of cells

$N/N_0 = \exp(-D/D_0)$. This also represents the probability that any individual cell will survive the radiation dose D.

Equation 15.2 gives a single-hit survival curve which is a straight line on a semilogarithmic plot originating at a surviving fraction of 1 at zero dose (see Fig 15.11, line a). Survival curves of this shape have been obtained for cells in the bone marrow, and for many types of cell treated with high LET radiation (see section 15.6.1). If D is put equal to D_0 in eq (15.2) then $N = N_0 e^{-1} = 0.37N_0$, so that D_0 represents the dose required to reduce cell survival from any value N to $0.37N$.

15.5.2 THE MULTITARGET MODEL

In the derivation of the single-hit survival equation it is assumed that the cell contains a single target which can be inactivated by a single hit. If instead it is assumed that a cell contains n identical targets each of which must be inactivated by a single hit to cause cell death, a different equation may be derived to represent cell survival. From eq (15.2) the probability of an individual target not being inactivated (ie, surviving) is $\exp(-D/D_0)$; thus the probability that any individual target will be inactivated is $1 - \exp(-D/D_0)$. The probability that all n targets in a cell will be inactivated is thus $[1 - \exp(-D/D_0)]^n$, and the probability that *not* all n targets will be inactivated (ie, that the cell will survive) is $1 - [1 - \exp(-D/D_0)]^n$. This gives the multitarget single-hit equation

$$N = N_0\{1 - [1 - \exp(-D/D_0)]^n\} \ . \qquad (15.3)$$

A plot of this equation leads to a survival curve with a shoulder at low doses and a straight-line section on a semilogarithmic plot as shown in Figure 15.11, line b. The parameters D_0, n and D_q can be determined for this curve as shown in Figure 15.10(a). At doses which are large compared to $D_0 (D \gg D_0)$, eq (15.3) reduces to $N = N_0 n \exp(-D/D_0)$, which is similar to eq (15.2). The straight-line part of the survival curve thus extrapolates to a value n at zero dose and has a slope defined by D_0. As indicated in the previous section, the D_0 value is the dose required to reduce cell survival for any value N to $0.37N$ in the *straight-line region* of the survival curve. The quasi-threshold dose D_q is the dose at which the extrapolated straight-line section of the survival curve crosses the dose axis (survival = 1) and is a measure of the size of the shoulder. It can be obtained by setting $N = N_0$ for the extrapolated straight line derived from the survival curve, giving $D_q = D_0 \ln n$.

For this model, the extrapolation number n theoretically represents the number of targets per cell. However, it is no longer believed that this is a useful concept in understanding how radiation inactivates cells. Rather, the size of the shoulder is regarded as giving

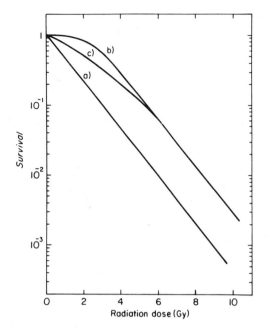

Figure 15.11. Survival curves defined by some of the mathematical equations discussed in the text. *a*, Single-hit (single-target) survival curve defined by eq (15.2). *b*, Multitarget survival curve defined by eq (15.3). *c*, Composite survival curve resulting from both multitarget and single-hit components defined by eq (15.4).

an indication of the repair capacity of cells. Equation (15.3) can fit survival-curve data reasonably well at dose levels greater than a few grays, and its parameters (D_0 and n) have been widely used to characterize survival curves for different types of cells. The utility of the model does not, however, prove that its underlying assumptions are correct.

One limitation of eq (15.3) is that it predicts that a certain amount of damage must be accumulated in a cell before it is killed, ie, that, at very low doses, the survival curve should be parallel to the dose axis or have an initial slope of zero. This is contrary to experimental data, which indicates that, for most cell populations irradiated with X- or γ-rays, the survival curve has a finite initial slope (see Fig 15.11, line c). This observation can be accommodated by modifying eq (15.3) to allow for an additional single-hit mechanism by which cells may be killed. Thus eq (15.3) would have a single-hit component added to give

$$N = N_0 \exp(-D/D_s)\{1 - [1 - \exp(-D/D_0)]^n\} \ . \qquad (15.4)$$

The extra parameter D_s defines the initial slope of the survival curve.* This equation has been used as the basis for a model to predict the responses of human

---

*The final slope of the survival curve (D_0') is modified and is given by $D_0' = D_0 D_s/(D_0 + D_s)$.

tumors and normal tissues to different fractionated radiation regimes (see section 16.4.3).

15.5.3 THE LINEAR-QUADRATIC MODEL

An alternative model for analysing cell survival after irradiation assumes that multiple lesions, induced by radiation, interact to cause cell killing. The lesions which interact could be caused by a single ionizing track, giving a direct dependence of cell killing on dose, or by two or more separate tracks, giving a dependence of lethality on higher powers of dose. The assumption that two lesions must interact to cause cell killing gives an equation which can fit most experimental survival curves quite adequately, at least over the first two to three decades of survival. The equation

$$N = N_0 \exp(-\alpha D - \beta D^2) \qquad (15.5)$$

is known as the linear-quadratic equation. The parameters α and β are assumed to describe the probability of the interacting lesions being caused by a single track or two independent tracks, respectively. The linear-quadratic equation defines a survival curve which is concave downwards on a semilogarithmic plot and never becomes strictly exponential (see Fig 15.10b). However, the curvature is usually small at high doses. Values for α and β vary considerably for different types of cells. Typical values of α are in the range $1-10^{-1}$ Gy^{-1} and of β are in the range $10^{-1}-10^{-2}Gy^{-2}$.

Alternative equations with formats similar to the linear-quadratic equation can be derived by making various biological assumptions, eg, concerning the capacity of cells to repair radiation damage and the effect of radiation treatment on that capacity. These models are discussed in more detail in the book edited by Meyn and Withers (1980). Many different biological models can be proposed which produce equations which can fit survival-curve data within the limits of experimental error. These equations and their parameters can be used to characterize different cell-survival curves, but a good fit of a given equation to the survival data does not validate the underlying biological assumptions.

15.6 FACTORS WHICH INFLUENCE CELL SURVIVAL

15.6.1 RADIATION QUALITY AND RBE

The biological effect of radiation depends on its effective LET. The difference in survival curves for X− or γ-rays (low LET) and for fast-neutron (high LET) irradiation is illustrated in Figure 15.12. In general both the slope (D_0) and the shoulder (n) of the sur-

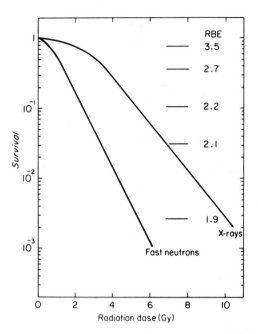

Figure 15.12. Comparison of survival curves for low LET (X-ray) and high LET (fast-neutron) irradiation. The RBE is calculated as indicated in the text and varies at different levels of survival.

vival curve are reduced for higher LET radiations. The biological effectiveness of different types of radiation can be characterized by a parameter known as the radiobiological effectiveness (RBE). The RBE is defined as the ratio of the dose of a standard type of radiation to that of the test radiation which gives the same biological effect. The standard type of radiation is usually taken as 200- or 250-kVp X-rays. ^{60}Co γ-rays are also used as a standard for comparison studies, although their RBE relative to 250-kVp X-rays is about 0.9. Because the extrapolation number of the survival curve is reduced for high LET radiation, the RBE varies with the dose or the survival level at which it is determined (see Fig 15.12). Thus the RBE increases as the dose at which it is determined is reduced.

The relationship between the RBE and the LET of different types of radiation (see Fig 15.13) is complex (Barendsen, 1968). The RBE rises to a maximum at an LET of about 100 keV/μm before declining again. The rise in RBE indicates that increase in the density of energy deposition events increases biological damage, but there is an optimum (~100 keV/μm) beyond which the extra energy deposited is wasted on cells which have already been killed (ie, there is an overkill phenomenon). The reduction in the shoulder of the survival curve for higher LET radiations also depends on the LET. At very high LET values (>~100 keV/μm) the shoulder on the survival curve is completely eliminated

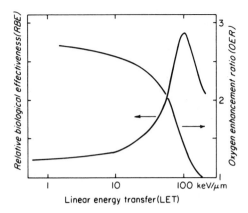

Figure 15.13. Illustration of the dependence of the RBE (left-hand axis) and the OER (right-hand axis) on the LET of the radiation. The actual value of the RBE depends on the level of biological damage being examined.

and there is essentially no repair. This indicates that as the LET increases an increasing proportion of the observed cell killing is due to single-hit (nonrepairable) damage.

15.6.2 CELL CYCLE POSITION

The various phases of the cell growth cycle have been discussed in section 9.3.1. In a growing cell population the cells will be distributed asynchronously throughout this cycle. A number of techniques have been devised which allow cell populations to be synchronised in one of the phases of the cell cycle. These techniques have been reviewed (Whitmore, 1971; Grdina et al, 1984) and include (see Fig 15.14) (a) the selective detachment of mitotic cells from monolayers, (b) separation of cells on the basis of volume, (c) the introduction and subsequent removal of a metabolic block (eg, excess thymidine), (d) the use of agents (eg, high-specific-activity H^3-thymidine or hydroxyurea) which kill cells exposed during the S phase of the cell cycle, and (e) direct sorting on the basis of DNA content using a fluorescence-activated cell sorter (see section 9.4.3).

Terasima and Tolmach (1961) used the mitotic shake-off technique to demonstrate that the radiosensitivity of HeLa cells differs in different phases of the cell cycle. Similar findings have been reported for many other cell lines and survival curves for Chinese hamster cells synchronised in different phases are shown in Figure 15.15a. If a single radiation dose is given to cells in different phases (ie, a vertical cut is taken through the curves in Fig 15.15a) then a pattern of cell survival, as a function of cell cycle position like that in Figure 15.15b, is obtained. The figure shows that Chinese hamster cells in late S phase have the highest probability of survival after radiation (ie, are the most resistant)

and that cells in G_2/M phases are the most sensitive. Different cell lines have different patterns of sensitivity and resistance throughout the cell cycle, but many cell lines appear to have a resistant period in S phase and to be sensitive in G_2 phase. These results have been obtained for cell lines growing in vitro. Recent studies using centrifugal elutriation (to separate cells on the basis of their volume and hence their position in the cell cycle) have shown that tumor cells growing and treated in vivo also demonstrate variations in radiosensitivity in different phases of the cell cycle (Grdina, 1980; Keng et al, 1984). However, these studies indicate that the pattern of sensitivity and resistance throughout the cell cycle may be different for the same cells growing in vivo or in vitro.

Regardless of these differences, the varying radiosensitivity as a function of cell-cycle phase demonstrated in Figure 15.15 means that the surviving cells in irradiated asynchronous populations will be partially synchronised, since those in the resistant phase(s) have a higher probability of survival than those in sensitive phases. Thus, after irradiation, the surviving cells may progress through the cell cycle as a cohort, moving initially into phases in which they would be more sensitive to a subsequent dose of radiation. Because of the variable rate at which cells progress through the cycle, the synchrony will decay rapidly.

15.6.3 REPAIR

Some of the radiation damage in cells can be repaired. This repair is the major mechanism underlying the clinical observation that a larger total dose can be tolerated when the radiation dose is fractionated. Elkind and Sutton (1960) showed that the shoulder on the survival curve reflects the accumulation of sublethal damage that can be repaired. They determined survival curves for Chinese hamster cells following treatment with two doses of radiation separated by a variable time interval. Their results are illustrated in Figure 15.16. When the cells were incubated at 37°C for 2.5 hr between the first and second radiation treatments, the original shoulder of the survival curve was partially regenerated and it was completely regenerated when the cells were incubated for 23 hr between the treatments (Fig 15.16a). When the interval between two fixed doses was varied (Figure 15.16b) there was a rapid rise in survival as the interval was increased from zero (single dose) to about two hours. This was followed by a decrease before the survival rose again to a maximum level after about 12 hr. This pattern of recovery is due to two processes. Repair of sublethal damage (SLDR) accounts for the early rise in survival. Since cells which survive radiation tend to be synchronized in resistant

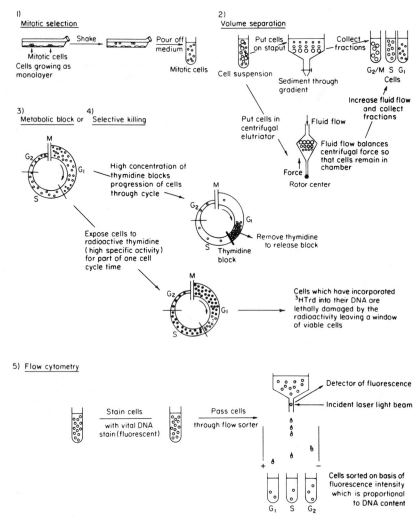

Figure 15.14. Schematic diagram illustrating some of the methods used for selecting cells synchronized in different phases of the growth cycle. (1) Selection of mitotic cells by shake-off. (2) Separation of cells according to their size either by allowing the cell suspension to sediment through a gradient at unit gravity or by spinning the suspension in a centrifugal elutriator. (3) Accumulation of cells at a particular point in the cell cycle (G_1/S boundary) by blocking their progress past this point using a high concentration of thymidine. (4) Selective killing of cells which pass through S phase by allowing them to incorporate radioactive thymidine (high specific activity) which kills them. A similar effect can be achieved with the drug hydroxyurea which kills cells in S phase and also blocks them at the G_1/S boundary. (5) Sorting of cells on the basis of DNA content using a fluorescence-activated cell sorter.

phases of the cell cycle, their subsequent progression (inevitably into more sensitive phases) leads to the reduced survival at four hours. Further progression and desynchronization explains the increase in survival at later times. This pattern of SLDR has been demonstrated for a wide range of cell lines in vitro and in vivo using many of the assay procedures described in section 15.4.

The repair capacity of the cells of many tissues in

vivo has been demonstrated using either the cell-survival assays described in sections 15.4.2 and 15.4.3 or the functional assays described in section 16.2.2. An increase in total dose is required to give the same level of biological damage, when a single dose (D_1) is split into two doses (total dose D_2) with a time interval between them (see Fig 15.17). The difference in dose ($D_2 - D_1$) is a measure of the repair by the cells in the tissue. Provided that the two doses are each larger than

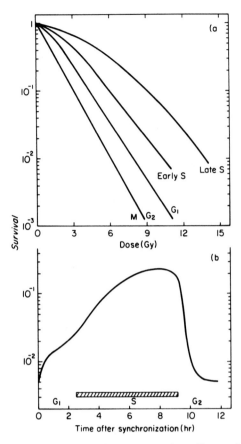

Figure 15.15. The effect of position in the cell growth cycle on cellular radiosensitivity. *a*, Survival curves for Chinese hamster cells irradiated in different phases of the cell cycle. *b*, The cells were selected in mitosis and irradiated with a fixed dose as a function of time of incubation after synchronization. The pattern of cell survival reflects the changing cellular sensitivity as the cells move through the cell cycle. (Adapted from Sinclair, 1968.)

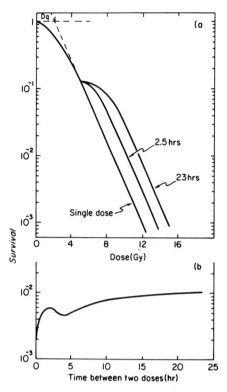

Figure 15.16. Illustration of the repair of sublethal damage which occurs between two radiation treatments. *a*, Survival curves for a single-dose treatment or for treatments involving a fixed first dose followed after 2.5 or 23 hr of incubation (at 37°C) by a range of second doses. *b*, The pattern of survival observed when two fixed doses of irradiation were given with a varying time interval of incubation (at 37°C) between them. (Adapted from Elkind and Sutton, 1960.)

those which generate the shoulder region of the survival curve, and that there is sufficient time between them for full repair but not for substantial cell proliferation, then the difference $D_2 - D_1$ should be equivalent to the D_q value.

The capacity of different cell populations to undergo SLDR is reflected by the width of the shoulder on their survival curve, ie, the D_q or $D_2 - D_1$ value. Thus survival curves for bone marrow cells have little or no shoulder ($D_q \approx 0$ Gy) and the cells demonstrate little or no repair, whilst other cells (eg, jejunal crypt cells) demonstrate a large repair capacity ($D_2 - D_1$ value of 4–5 Gy). The rate at which SLDR takes place also varies from tissue to tissue, but repair is usually complete within two to six hours of a radiation treatment. The underlying mechanism(s) responsible for SLDR are not established but are presumed to relate to repair of DNA damage (see section 7.4).

The extent of SLDR can be influenced by intercellular contact. Certain cell lines can be grown such that they form multicell clusters (spheroids) either in or on the surface of semisolid media or in suspension (see section 9.6.2). It was demonstrated (see Sutherland and Durand, 1976) that the radiation survival curve for cells from spheroids had a larger shoulder than when the same cells were grown and irradiated as monolayers. This larger shoulder reflected increased repair capacity (SLDR) for cells which had been grown in three-dimensional contact with other cells. The cell-contact phenomenon has been demonstrated for a number of cell types, including cells of tumors growing in vivo, but it is not always observed. The underlying mechanism for the effect remains unclear but may involve (a) modified damage and/or repair of DNA by cells in contact, (b) differences in cellular metabolism due to growth in contact, or (c) transfer of important molecules between the cells in contact. Many tissues irradiated in vivo demonstrate a larger amount of SLDR (as measured by values of $D_2 - D_1$) than would be ex-

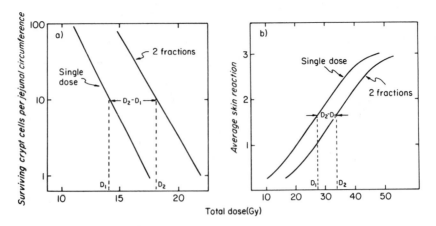

Figure 15.17. Repair of radiation damage in vivo. *a*, Survival curves for murine intestinal crypt cells γ-irradiated in situ with a single dose or with two equal fractions given three hours apart. (Modified from Withers et al, 1974.) *b*, Average skin reaction following X-irradiation of mouse skin with a single dose or two fractions given 24 hr apart. The technique used to determine these curves is described in section 16.2.2.

pected on the basis of D_q values typically observed for cell lines growing in culture; this may be due to a cell-contact effect occurring in vivo.

Cell survival can be influenced by the postirradiation conditions of the treated cells. If cells are held under suboptimal growth conditions (eg, low temperature, nutrient deprivation or density inhibition) for a period of time between irradiation and plating, survival is often greater than if the cells are placed in optimal growth conditions immediately after irradiation. This indicates that radiation damage, which is potentially lethal to cells able to continue their progress through the growth cycle soon after irradiation, may be repaired if the cells are maintained under suboptimal growth conditions. Repair of this potentially lethal damage (PLDR) usually results in a change in the slope of the cell-survival curve and occurs over times similar to that required for SLDR (see Fig 15.18). It is not known whether PLDR represents the expression of a different repair process from that which occurs in SLDR. The two types of repair are defined by the experimental procedures which are used to demonstrate their existence, but they may represent two expressions of the same underlying mechanism.

PLDR can also occur in vivo. When some irradiated tumors are left in situ for a number of hours before excision and assay (by the in vivo–in vitro assay procedure described in section 15.4.1) the survival level is higher than for immediate excision and assay (Hahn et al, 1974). This increased survival has the same characteristics as shown in Figure 15.18, and because relatively large (~20 Gy) radiation doses must be given to the tumors for the phenomenon to be observed, it is

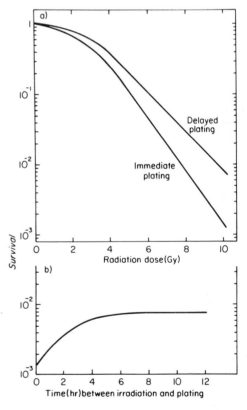

Figure 15.18. Illustration of the repair of potentially lethal damage which can occur after a radiation treatment if cells are held under suboptimal growth conditions. *a*, Survival curves obtained for cells plated in standard growth conditions immediately after irradiation or held for a few hours under suboptimal growth conditions before being plated. *b*, Pattern of survival observed following a fixed radiation dose when cells are held under suboptimal growth conditions for different periods of time before plating. (Adapted from Little, 1973.)

believed that it represents PLDR in the hypoxic cells in the tumor (see section 15.6.4), which would be expected to be under poor nutrient conditions. An analogous phenomenon has been observed for normal mammary and thyroid cells when they are assayed using the excision assays described in section 15.4.2. If the cells are left in their original host for 24 hr after irradiation, before excision and transplantation, there is an increase in the shoulder of the observed survival curve but no change in slope (Mulcahy et al, 1980). In this case the cells would not be expected to be hypoxic but would most likely be out of the cellular growth cycle.

15.6.4 THE OXYGEN EFFECT AND HYPOXIA IN TUMORS

The biological effects of radiation are influenced by oxygen. Cells irradiated in the presence of air are about three times more sensitive than cells irradiated under conditions of severe hypoxia (see Fig 15.19a).

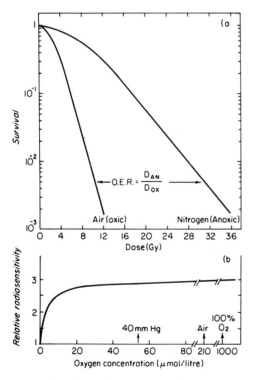

Figure 15.19. The effect of oxygen as a radiosensitizer. *a*, Survival curves obtained when cells are treated with low LET radiation in the presence (air) or absence (nitrogen) of oxygen. The oxygen enhancement ratio (OER) is calculated as indicated and as described in the text. *b*, The relative radiosensitivity of cells is plotted as a function of oxygen concentration in the surrounding medium, to illustrate the dependence of the sensitizing effect on oxygen concentration. (Adapted from Chapman et al, 1974.)

The sensitizing effect of different concentrations of oxygen is shown in Figure 15.19b. At very low levels of oxygen the cells are resistant but, as the level of oxygen increases, their sensitivity rises rapidly to almost maximal levels at oxygen concentrations above about 35 μmol/L (equivalent oxygen partial pressure ~25 mmHg). The oxygen concentration at which the sensitizing effect is a half of maximum (the K_m value) is about 5 μmol/L (3–4 mmHg).

The degree of sensitization afforded by oxygen is characterized by the oxygen enhancement ratio (OER) which is defined (see Figure 15.19a) as the ratio of doses required to give the same biological effect in the absence or the presence of oxygen. The OER for a wide range of cell lines in vitro and for most tissues in vivo, irradiated with X-rays or γ-rays (ie, low LET radiations), is in the range 2.5–3.3. At doses greater than about 3 Gy, it is usually found to be independent of the dose or survival level at which it is measured. For high LET radiations the OER is reduced, declining from a value of about 3 for low LET radiations to a value of 1 for radiations with LET values greater than about 200 keV/μm (see Fig 15.13).

For X- or γ-ray doses less than 3 Gy (ie, in the shoulder region of the survival curve), recent work has suggested that the OER may be reduced to about 80% of its value at higher doses (Skarsgard et al, 1986). The reason for this reduction is unclear but may relate to the greater importance of single-hit killing in this region of the survival curve. As noted above and in section 15.6.1, high LET radiations are more likely to kill cells by a single-hit mechanism and these radiations demonstrate a lower OER value. A reduction of the OER at low doses may be clinically important since the individual treatments of a fractionated course of radiation are usually of this size .

Most normal tissues have an average oxygen concentration equivalent to a partial pressure (PO$_2$) of about 40 mmHg and are fully sensitive to radiation. Some tissues in the body may have lower PO$_2$ levels (eg, liver, cartilage, brain) but it has been demonstrated, in particular, that most tumors contain a significant proportion of cells which are hypoxic and hence maximally resistant to radiation. The presence of hypoxic cells in tumors was suggested by the work of Thomlinson and Gray (1955). These authors examined histological sections of human bronchogenic carcinoma and observed that the tumors contained "cords" of viable cells surrounded by stroma containing blood vessels. At the center of these viable regions there were often areas of necrosis (see Figs 9.16, 9.17 and 15.21). The width of the viable regions of cells between the stroma and the necrotic areas was found to be reasonably constant (100–150 μm) and equivalent to the calculated distance which oxygen would be expected to be able to diffuse through the tumor. This implies that at the edge of the necrotic regions there could be viable cells at very low oxygen tensions. Similar tumor cords have subsequently been observed in a large number of other tumors.

These histological studies provide indirect evidence of the existence of hypoxic cells in tumors. Direct evidence was provided by the experiments of Powers and Tolmach (1964), who studied the radiation sensitivity of the cells of a solid lymphosarcoma growing subcutaneously in a mouse. The tumor was irradiated in situ and cell survival was assessed using an endpoint dilution assay. The results are illustrated schematically in Figure 15.20a. The survival curve was found to have two components; at low doses the line is quite steep but at high doses it is much shallower. The difference in slope is a factor of approximately 3, suggesting that the two components may represent the survival of two subpopulations of cells, which are well oxygenated and hypoxic, respectively. This was confirmed by further studies, which demonstrated that cells which survived high doses of radiation were not intrinsically more resistant and that the relative position of the more resistant part of the survival curve (the tail) could be altered by modifying oxygen delivery to the tumor (see Fig 15.20b). Similar results have been obtained with a wide range of other tumors.

The proportion of hypoxic cells in tumors can be estimated (see Fig 15.20b) from the ratio (S_{air}/S_{anox}) of the cell survival obtained for tumors in air-breathing animals irradiated with a large dose to that obtained for tumors irradiated with the same dose under anoxic conditions (eg, tumor blood supply clamped or animal killed prior to the irradiation). It is assumed that the tumors made deliberately anoxic contain 100% hypoxic cells and that the radiation survival curve for the naturally occurring hypoxic cells is the same as that for the cells made deliberately anoxic. The proportion of naturally occurring hypoxic cells in the lymphosarcoma studied by Powers and Tolmach was estimated to be about 1% using the above method. Most other tumors treated in air-breathing animals contain a larger proportion, in the range 10–20%. While there are no direct measurements to indicate the proportion of hypoxic cells in human tumors there is strong indirect evidence that a significant fraction of hypoxic cells does exist in at least some human tumors. Human melanomas xenografted

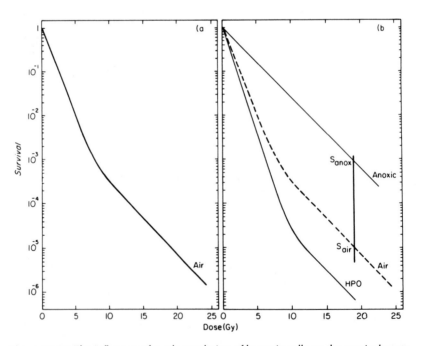

Figure 15.20. The influence of a subpopulation of hypoxic cells on the survival curve obtained for an irradiated tumor. *a*, The curve was obtained when the tumors were irradiated in situ in air-breathing animals and demonstrates two components with different slopes. *b*, The curves marked Anoxic and HPO were obtained when the animals were killed or given high-pressure oxygen to breathe prior to the irradiation respectively. The broken line marked Air is from *a*. The fraction of cells which were hypoxic in the tumor in air-breathing animals can be estimated as described in the text. (Modified from Powers and Tolmach, 1964.)

into immune-deficient mice have been found to have a proportion of hypoxic cells ranging from 5–10% to 80–90% (see Rofstad, 1985).

Two general models have been proposed to explain the existence of hypoxic cells in tumors (see Fig 15.21). The tumor "cord" model discussed earlier implies that hypoxic cells exist at the limits of the diffusion range of oxygen away from blood vessels. The hypoxic cells in such cords presumably remain hypoxic for a period of time, until the division of cells, closer to the blood vessels, causes them to be pushed so far away from the vessel that they die and become necrotic (assumed to happen because of lack of oxygen and other nutrients). Such cells are often referred to as chronically hypoxic cells, although there is evidence that in rapidly growing tumors (doubling time of a few days) the length of time that they exist under hypoxic conditions may be less than a day.

An alternative model (Brown 1979, Franko and Sutherland, 1979) to explain hypoxic cells in tumors is that flow in tumor blood vessels fluctuates, and therefore that regions of tumors supplied by one or more blood vessels may become hypoxic for short periods of time as a result of intermittent blood-flow stoppages. According to this model, cells may be hypoxic for only short periods of time and, at any given time, different

cells will be hypoxic depending on which blood vessels are not carrying oxygenated blood. These two models for hypoxia in tumors are not mutually exclusive. Recent studies have suggested that both mechanisms can be responsible for hypoxic cells in tumors (Chaplin et al, 1986). The relative importance of the two mechanisms is probably different for different tumors.

Hypoxic cells in tumors are of interest because they may influence the efficacy of clinical radiation treatments. Further discussion of this issue is given in chapter 16.

15.7 SUMMARY

Ionizing radiations cause damage to cells and tissues by depositing energy as a series of discrete events. It is the size of these individual energy-deposition events occurring in small volumes ($<1~\mu m^3$) which is critical for the biological effects of ionizing radiations. Different types of radiation have different abilities to cause biological damage, because of the densities of the energy deposition events which are produced. The relative biological effectiveness (RBE) of densely ionizing (high linear energy transfer or high LET) radiations is greater than that of low LET radiations.

Radiation can cause damage to any molecule in a

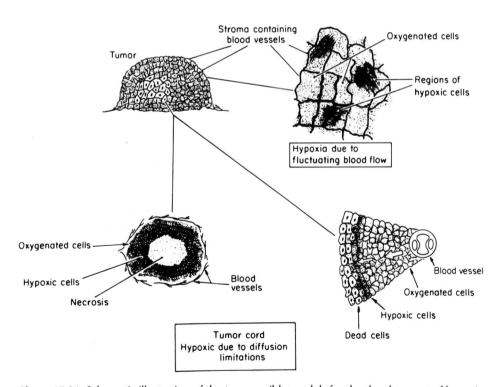

Figure 15.21. Schematic illustration of the two possible models for the development of hypoxia in tumors. Hypoxia may arise as a result of diffusion limitations in the tumor cord model or as a result of fluctuating blood flow.

cell, but it is generally believed that damage to DNA is most crucial in relation to cell lethality. One of the most radiation-sensitive functions of cells is the ability to maintain continued proliferative potential (ie, to retain clonogenic capacity). Many different assay procedures have been developed for assessing the clonogenic capacity of both normal and malignant cells, and these have been used to obtain radiation survival curves for a wide range of different cell types. For X- or γ-rays, survival curves for most mammalian cells have a shoulder region at low doses, while at higher doses the survival decreases approximately exponentially with dose. There are no systematic differences observed between normal and malignant cells. The slope (D_0) of the exponential (high-dose) region of the survival curve is quite similar for most mammalian cells, but there are differences in the low-dose shoulder region.

Various factors can influence the response of cells to radiation treatment. Following treatment with low LET radiation, cells can repair some of their damage over a period of a few hours; thus if the treatment is prolonged or fractionated it is less effective than if given as a single acute dose. Following high LET radiation, there is little repair of damage and cells are killed more effectively (ie, the slope of the survival curve is steeper for high LET radiations). Position in the cell-proliferation cycle also influences radiation sensitivity; cells in S phase are often more resistant than cells in the G_2/M phases, but there is variability between cell types. Oxygen acts as a radiation sensitizer such that cells treated with low LET radiation, in the absence of oxygen, require approximately three times the dose to produce a given level of cell killing, as is required for cells irradiated in the presence of oxygen (ie, the oxygen enhancement ratio [OER] is about 3). The OER is reduced for high LET radiations. Most experimental tumors have been demonstrated to contain a significant fraction (~10%) of hypoxic cells, which are resistant to radiation, whereas most normal tissues contain relatively few hypoxic cells.

REFERENCES

Barendsen, GW: Responses of cultured cells, tumours and normal tissues to radiations of different linear energy transfer. *Curr Top in Radiat Res* 1968; 4:293–356.

Brown JM: Evidence for acutely hypoxic cells in mouse tumours and a possible mechanism for reoxygenation. *Br J Radiol* 1979; 52:650–656.

Chaplin DJ, Durand RE, Olive PL: Acute hypoxia in tumors: Implications for modifiers of radiation effects. *Int J Radiat Oncol Biol Phys* 1986; 12: 1279–1282.

Chapman JD, Dugle DL, Reuvers AP, et al: Studies on the radiosensitizing effect of oxygen in Chinese hamster cells. *Int J Radiat Biol* 1974; 26:383–389.

Clifton KH: Quantitative studies of the radiobiology of hormone-responsive normal cell populations, in Meyn RE, Withers HR, (eds): *Radiation Biology in Cancer Research.* New York, Raven Press, 1980, pp 501–513.

Elkind MM, Sutton H: Radiation response of mammalian cells grown in culture. I. Repair of x-ray damage in surviving Chinese hamster cells. *Radiat Res* 1960; 13:556–593.

Elkind MM, Whitmore GF: *The Radiobiology of Cultured Mammalian Cells.* New York, Gordon and Breach, 1967, pp 351–353.

Franko AJ, Sutherland RM: Radiation survival of cells from spheroids grown in different oxygen concentrations. *Radiat Res* 1979; 79:454–467.

Grdina DJ: Variations in radiation response of tumor subpopulations, in Meyn RE, Withers HR, 1980, pp 353–363.

Grdina DJ, Meistrich ML, Meyn RE et al: Cell synchrony techniques. I. A comparison of methods. *Cell Tissue Kinet* 1984; 17:223–236.

Hahn GM, Rockwell S, Kallman RF et al: Repair of potentially lethal damage in vivo in solid tumor cells after X-irradiation. *Cancer Res* 1974; 34:351–354.

Hewitt HB, Wilson CW: A survival curve for mammalian cells irradiated in vivo. *Nature* 1959; 183:1060–1061.

Hill RP, Bush RS: A lung colony assay to determine the radiosensitivity of cells of a solid tumor. *Int J Radiat Biol* 1969; 15:435–444.

Johns HE, Cunningham JR: *The Physics of Radiology,* ed 4. Springfield, IL, Charles Thomas, 1983, pp 167–216.

Keng PC, Siemann DW, Wheeler KT: Comparison of tumour age response to radiation for cells derived from tissue culture or solid tumours. *Br J Cancer* 1984; 50:519–526.

Little JB: Factors influencing the repair of potentially lethal radiation damage in growth-inhibited human cells. *Radiat Res* 1973; 56:320–333.

McCulloch EA, Till JE: The sensitivity of cells from normal mouse bone marrow to gamma radiation in vitro and in vivo. *Radiat Res* 1962; 16:822–832.

Meyn RE, Withers HR (eds): *Radiation Biology in Cancer Research.* New York, Raven Press, 1980.

Mulcahy RT, Gould MN, Clifton KH: The survival of thyroid cells: in vivo irradiation and in situ repair. *Radiat Res* 1980; 84:523–528.

Paterson MC, Smith PJ, Bech-Hansen NT et al: Gamma ray hypersensitivity and faulty DNA repair in cultured cells from humans exhibiting familial cancer proneness, in Okada S, Imamura M, Terashima T et al (eds), *Proceedings of the 6th International Congress of Radiation Research.* Japanese Association for Radiation Research, 1979, pp 484–495.

Potten CS, Hendry JH (eds): *Cell Clones: Manual of Mammalian Cell Techniques.* Edinburgh, Churchill-Livingstone, 1985, pp 50–60.

Powers WE, Tolmach LJ: Demonstration of an anoxic component in a mouse tumor-cell population by in vivo assay of survival following irradiation. *Radiology* 1964; 83:328–336.

Puck TT, Marcus PI: Actions of x-rays on mammalian cells. *J Exp Med* 1956; 103:653–666.

Rofstad EK: Human tumour xenografts in radiotherapeutic research. *Radiother Oncol* 1985; 3:35–46.

Rossi HH: Distribution of radiation energy in the cell. *Radiology* 1962; 78:530–535.

Sinclair WK: Cyclic X-ray responses in mammalian cells in vitro. *Radiat Res* 1968; 33:620–643.

Skarsgard LD, Harrison I, Durand RE, Palcic B: Radiosensitization of hypoxic cells at low doses. *Int J Radiat Oncol Biol Phys*, 1986; 12:1075–1078.

Sutherland RM, Durand RE: Radiation response of multicell spheroids: An in vitro tumour model. *Curr Top Radiat Res* 1976; 11:87–139.

Terasima T, Tolmach LJ: Changes in the X-ray sensitivity of HeLa cells during the division cycle. *Nature* 1961; 190: 1210–1211.

Thomlinson RH, Gray LH: The histological structure of some human lung cancers and the possible implications for radiotherapy. *Br J Cancer* 1955; 9:539–549.

Whitmore GF: Natural and induced synchronous cultures. *In Vitro* 1971; 6:276–285.

Withers HR, Elkind MM: Microcolony survival assay for cells of mouse intestinal mucosa exposed to radiation. *Int J Radiat Biol* 1970; 17:261–267.

Withers, HR, Mason K, Reid BO, et al: Response of mouse intestine to neutrons and gamma rays in relation to dose fractionation and division cycle. *Cancer* 1974; 34:39–47.

BIBLIOGRAPHY

Elkind MM, Whitmore GF: *The Radiobiology of Cultured Mammalian Cells*. New York, Gordon and Breach, 1967.

Hall EJ: *Radiobiology for the Radiologist*, ed 2. Hagerstown, MD, Harper and Row, 1978.

Johns HE, Cunningham JR: *The Physics of Radiology*, ed 4. Springfield, IL, Charles Thomas, 1983.

Meyn RE, Withers HR (eds): *Radiation Biology in Cancer Research*. New York, Raven Press, 1980.

Potten CS, Hendry JH (eds): *Cell Clones: Manual of Mammalian Cell Techniques*. Edinburgh, Churchill-Livingstone, 1985.

16

Experimental Radiotherapy

Richard P. Hill

16.1 INTRODUCTION

Radiation treatment of tumors inside the body requires that the radiation must pass through normal tissue. Furthermore, the tendency for malignant tumors to infiltrate surrounding normal tissue means that a radiation treatment field must encompass a margin of normal tissue around the known extent of a tumor. Radiation damage is not specific for tumors and thus, for most treatments, the dose of radiation which can be delivered to a tumor is limited by the damage to normal tissue and the consequent risk of complications.

Therapeutic efficacy can be improved either by increasing the effective radiation dose delivered to the tumor relative to that given to surrounding normal tissue, or by devising an approach which will increase the response of the tumor relative to that of the surrounding normal tissue. The former approach implies improvement in the physical aspects of radiation therapy. An example is the introduction of high-energy X- and γ-ray treatment procedures over the last quarter century, which have been very effective in improving the results of treatment of patients with deep-seated tumors. Further improvements may be possible using more sophisticated methods for treatment planning or from the use of high LET radiation beams, particularly

heavy ions. The second approach implies understanding the response of cells and tissues to radiation treatment. The empirical development of multifractionated treatments, which involve giving 2–2.5 Gy fractions daily for 4–7 weeks is an example of this approach. Exploration of possible ways to exploit the oxygen effect or to modify existing fractionation schedules may offer further improvements. Our current understanding of biological factors which may influence the outcome of radiation therapy is discussed in this chapter.

16.2 DOSE RESPONSE AND THERAPEUTIC RATIO

16.2.1 TUMOR CONTROL

The emphasis in the last chapter on the cellular effects of radiation treatment reflects a general belief that the response of tissues and particularly tumors can be understood in terms of the response of the cells within those tissues.

Tumor response to radiation treatment can, however, also be assessed by techniques which do not directly measure tumor cell survival (see Fig 16.1). A sufficiently large dose of radiation will delay the growth of tumors, and this growth delay can be determined by

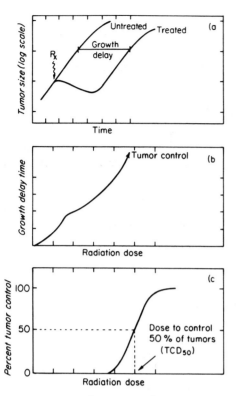

Figure 16.1. Illustration of two assays for tumor response. In a, growth curves for groups of treated and untreated tumors are shown and the measurement of growth delay indicated. Growth delay is plotted as a function of radiation dose in b. At large doses some of the tumors may not regrow and the percentage of controlled tumors can be plotted as a function of dose as in c.

measuring the size of untreated and irradiated tumors as a function of time to generate growth curves. The delay in growth is the difference in time for untreated and treated tumors to grow to a defined size (equal or larger than that at the time of irradiation). The time difference is a measure of tumor response and can be plotted as a function of radiation dose to give a tumor-growth-delay curve. The shape and position of this curve will be different for different treatments. The curve shown in Figure 16.1b has a change in slope, which could be interpreted as indicative of the presence of a fraction of hypoxic cells in the tumor (in analogy with the change in slope of the tumor-cell survival curve shown in Fig 15.20a). As the radiation dose is increased the tumor-growth delay will become larger until in some tumors it becomes infinite, ie, the tumors will be permanently controlled. Further increases in dose will result in an increasing proportion of tumors being permanently controlled. The percentage of controlled tumors if plotted as a function of dose gives a dose-control curve.

Tumors contain a fraction of cells which have a large

proliferative capacity (ie, tumor stem cells — see section 8.2) and, to achieve tumor control, all the tumor stem cells must be killed. Thus the dose of radiation required to control a tumor depends both on the intrinsic radiation sensitivity of the stem cells and on their number. From a knowledge of the survival curve for the cells in a tumor it is possible to predict the expected level of survival following a given single radiation dose. A simple calculation, using eq (15.3) and typical survival curve parameters for well-oxygenated cells ($D_0 = 1.3$ Gy, $D_q = 2.1$ Gy), indicates that a single dose of 26 Gy of X- or γ-rays might be expected to reduce the probability of survival of an individual cell to about 10^{-8}. For a tumor containing 10^8 stem cells this dose would thus leave, on average, one surviving cell. Because of the random nature of radiation damage there will be statistical fluctuation around this value. Therefore, following irradiation of a group of identical tumors, each containing 10^8 well-oxygenated stem cells, in some tumors there would be no surviving stem cells, whilst in others there would be 1, 2 or more. The statistical fluctuation expected from random cell killing by radiation follows a Poisson distribution; the probability, P_n, of a tumor having n surviving cells when the average number of cells surviving is a is given by

$$P_n = \frac{a^n e^{-a}}{n!} \qquad (16.1)$$

For tumor control the important probability is P_0, which is the probability that a tumor will contain no surviving cells (ie, $n = 0$). From eq (16.1):

$$P_0 = e^{-a} \qquad (16.2)$$

so for $a = 1$, as in the example above, the probability of control would be $e^{-1} = 0.37$.

Different radiation doses will of course result in different values of a. For example, for identical tumors each containing 10^8 cells, a dose which reduces the survival level to 10^{-9} will give $a = 0.1$ (ie, 10 cells surviving in 100 tumors) with an expected probability of control of $e^{-0.1} = 0.90$. From such calculations it is possible to construct a tumor control versus dose curve which shows a sigmoid relationship (Fig 16.2, solid line). The slope of the dose–control curve for this ideal group of tumors is dependent on the shape of the underlying cell-survival curve in the region of dose required to achieve cures.

The solid curve in Figure 16.2 represents a group of identical tumors each containing 10^8 tumor stem cells. If the tumors had contained 10^{10} stem cells then the curve would have been displaced by a dose sufficient to reduce survival by two orders of magnitude (Fig 16.2, long dashed line). These dose–control curves illustrate

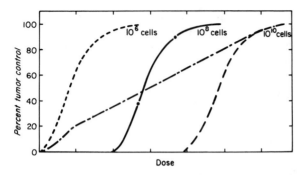

Figure 16.2. Percent tumor control plotted as a function of dose for single radiation treatments. Theoretical curves for groups of tumors containing different numbers of tumor stem cells are shown. The points on the curve labeled "10^8 cells" are derived as discussed in the text. The composite curve (short and long dashes) was obtained assuming a group containing equal proportions from the three individual groups.

that the dose of radiation required to control a tumor depends on the number of stem cells that it contains. Thus a large tumor may be expected to require a larger dose for control than a small tumor, assuming that each contains the same proportion of stem cells.

In clinical practice, groups of tumors are not identical. Tumors will vary in size, in their proportion of stem cells, and possibly in the radiosensitivity of their cells. Thus a dose–control curve for a group of human tumors will be a composite of ones similar to those shown in Figure 16.2. Such a composite is shown in the figure for a mixed group of tumors comprised of equal proportions of tumors containing 10^6, 10^8 and 10^{10}

stem cells. The slope of the composite dose–control curve is less than that for the individual groups of tumors. Any other factors which contribute to the heterogeneity of the group of tumors will further accentuate this reduction in slope. Fractionation of the radiation treatment and heterogeneity among tumors in all the various factors involved in such treatment, which will be discussed in section 16.3, will also result in a decrease in the slope of the dose–control curve. Thus a dose–control curve derived from a clinical study will be influenced by many factors, and its slope is likely to be very shallow if the group of tumors is heterogeneous. In this case it would be desirable to seek a way of assigning the tumors to more homogeneous groups, so that patients with significant differences in prognosis could be identified.

Intrinsic variations in the radiation sensitivity of different cells (or cell types) have until recently been regarded as a relatively minor factor influencing the dose of radiation required to control a tumor. This situation arose because in the high-dose regions of the cell-survival curves the slopes (represented by D_0 values — see section 15.4.4) fall in a narrow range of 1–2 Gy for nearly all mammalian cells. Recent emphasis on the low-dose shoulder region of survival curves, which is the part of the curve relevant to the individual doses of most fractionated radiotherapy regimens, has highlighted the variability which occurs between different cell lines.

The survival curves illustrated in Figure 16.3a are similar at high doses, but show differences in the survival level attained following low doses. Even small dif-

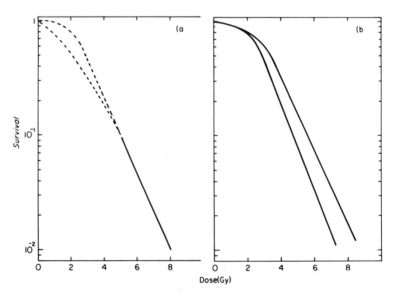

Figure 16.3. Illustration of variability observed in cell survival curves. *a,* Different shoulders with the same high-dose region. *b,* The same extrapolation number *n* but high-dose regions with slightly different slopes (D_0 values 1.35 Gy and 1.15 Gy).

ferences can be important, because they are likely to be magnified during the multiple doses given in fractionated radiotherapy (see section 16.3.2). The upper survival curve in Figure 16.3a indicates that survival following a dose of 2 Gy is 0.8. Assuming that each fraction of a multiple-dose treatment is equally effective (a simplifying assumption which ignores some of the issues to be discussed in section 16.3), the survival following 30 fractions of 2 Gy would be $0.8^{30} \simeq 10^{-3}$. In contrast, for the lower curve in Figure 16.3a, the survival level following 2 Gy is 0.5, so that survival after 30 fractions would be $0.5^{30} \simeq 10^{-9}$. Thus small differences in survival at low doses can potentially translate into very large differences during a treatment course containing many fractions.

A small change in the slope of the survival curve leading to a factor of 2 or more differences in survival at higher doses, as illustrated in Figure 16.3b, would result in a much smaller difference during fractionated therapy because only a small number of large doses can be given without exceeding the tolerance of normal tissues (eg, survival following 8 fractions of 5 Gy would be $0.16^8 \simeq 5 \times 10^{-7}$ for the shallower curve and $0.08^8 \simeq 10^{-9}$ for the steeper curve).

Analysis of results available for a large number of human tumor cell lines (Fertil and Malaise, 1985; Deacon et al, 1984) indicates that survival curves can vary quite considerably even for cells of similar histopathological types (see Fig 16.4). It is the size of the shoulder of the curves which varies most widely. When the different cell lines were grouped, according to the likelihood that human tumors of similar histopathological types would be controlled by radiation treatment, results such as those in Table 16.1 were obtained. In this table the mean survival at 2 Gy is shown for the different groups. There is a trend towards higher survival values for the tumor groups expected to be less radiocurable. An analysis by Steel of the growth delay, induced by single radiation doses, in a range of different types of human tumors growing as xenografts in immune-deficient mice suggests a similar correlation (see Rofstad, 1985). Substantial further work is needed to confirm these observations, but the results support the idea that some of the intertumor differences in radiation response observed clinically may reflect differences in intrinsic cellular radiosensitivity.

The radiocurability of a tumor depends both on the radiosensitivity of the tumor stem cells (ie, their underlying survival characteristics) and the number of such cells in the tumor. The terms "radiosensitive" and "radioresistant" have also been used to describe, respectively, tumors that regress rapidly or slowly after radiation treatment. The use of these terms in this context can be misleading, however, because the rate of regression may not correlate with the ability to cure a tumor

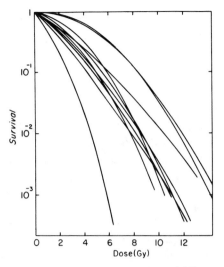

Figure 16.4. Survival curves for a number of different human melanoma cell lines. The lines were drawn to be continuously curving and conform to the linear-quadratic model (see chapter 15). (Adapted from Fertil and Malaise, 1981.)

Table 16.1. Values of the Surviving Fraction at 2 Gy for Human Tumor Cell Lines

Tumor Cell Type*	No. of Lines	Mean Survival at 2 Gy (Range)
1 Lymphoma Neuroblastoma Myeloma Small-cell lung Ca Medulloblastoma	14	0.20 (0.08–0.37)
2 Breast Ca Squamous cell Ca Pancreatic Ca Colo-rectal Ca Non-small-cell lung Ca	12	0.43 (0.14–0.75)
3 Melanoma Osteosarcoma Glioblastoma Hypernephroma	25	0.52 (0.20–0.86)

*Tumor types are grouped (1–3) approximately in decreasing order of their likelihood of local control by radiation treatment. (Modified from Deacon et al, 1984.)

with tolerable doses of radiation. A better term to describe a tumor which regresses rapidly after treatment is radioresponsive; this term describes the effect observed and avoids confusion with intrinsic cellular radiosensitivity. The rate of response of a tumor (or normal tissue) depends on the proliferative rate of its cells. Thus a tumor which contains a large proportion of proliferating cells will tend to express radiation damage to its cells early and will regress rapidly. Although radioresponsive, the tumor may contain surviving stem cells which will eventually be responsible for its recurrence.

16.2.2 NORMAL TISSUE RESPONSE

Radiation treatment can cause loss of function in normal tissues. In renewal tissues, such as bone marrow or gastrointestinal tract, loss of function may be correlated with loss of proliferative activity of stem cells. In other tissues loss of function may occur through damage to more mature cells. Many functional assays have been developed and used to assess radiation dose response. The simplest of these is the determination of the dose of radiation given either to the whole body or to a specific organ which will cause death of 50% of the treated animals within a specified time (LD_{50}). The relationship between lethality and radiation dose is usually sigmoidal in shape, and some experimentally derived relationships for different normal tissues are shown in Figure 16.5. Dose–response relationships for normal tissues are generally quite steep and well defined. There are, however, significant differences in the doses required to achieve a given endpoint (eg, LD_{50}) between different species of animals and even between different strains of the same species. Values of the LD_{50} for different species of animals given whole-body irradiation and dying due to bone marrow failure are given in Table 16.2.

Functional assays have been widely used to assess the radiation response of skin. Following irradiation, skin will develop erythema and, at higher doses, desquamation and ulceration. These changes occur as a result of changes in vascular permeability, the death of basal cells, and the inability of the survivors to replace the outer layers of cells, which are lost due to normal "wear and tear" processes. Numerical scoring systems have been set up to assess skin damage, and these systems can be used to generate dose–response curves as illustrated in Figure 16.6. Other functional assays which have been used to assess radiation damage to different normal tissues are listed in Table 16.3.

The effects of radiation treatment on normal tissues can be divided into two categories: the early or acute responses, which occur within a few weeks of radiation treatment, and the late or chronic responses, which may take many months to develop. Acute responses occur primarily in tissues with rapid cell renewal and occur because cell division is required to maintain the function of the organ. Since most cells express radiation damage during mitosis, there is early death and loss of cells killed by the radiation treatment. Following irradiation of skin, for example, the expression of radiation damage depends on the relative rates of cell loss and cell

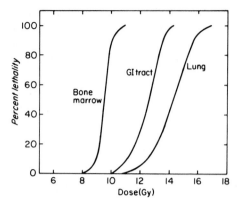

Figure 16.5. Three different curves indicating percent lethality plotted as a function of radiation dose for the same strain of mouse. The "bone marrow" and "GI tract" curves were obtained using whole-body irradiation and assessing lethality prior to day 30 or prior to day 7 respectively, since death due to damage to the GI tract occurs earlier than that due to bone marrow failure. The curve labeled "lung" was obtained by assessing lethality 180 days after local irradiation to the thorax.

Table 16.2. Approximate LD_{50} Values for Different Animals

Animal*	LD_{50} (Gy)
Mouse	7–9
Rat	7–9
Hamster	7–9
Rabbit	7–9
Gerbil	10–11
Dog	2–3
Goat	2–3
Sheep	1–2
Monkey	3–5
Man	3–5

Note: Modified from Hall, 1978.

*Deaths assessed at 30 days except for man (60 days).

proliferation of the basal cells, so that acute skin reactions occur more rapidly in murine (7–10 days) than in human skin (2–3 weeks). When the GI tract is irradiated, villus cells lost into the lumen are not replaced adequately by division of the surviving crypt cells (see section 9.5.2) and the expression of acute injury occurs even more rapidly in mouse (4–7 days) and man (8–10 days).

Late responses tend to occur in organs whose parenchymal cells divide infrequently (eg, liver or kidney) or not at all (eg, central nervous system or muscle) under normal conditions. Depletion of the parenchymal cell population due to entry of cells into mitosis, with the resulting expression of radiation damage and cell death, will be slow or nonexistent, depending on the cell

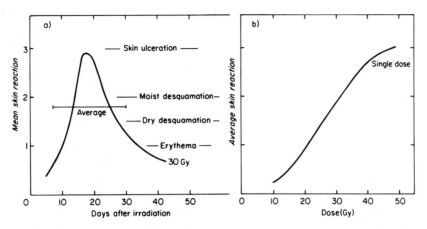

Figure 16.6. Assessment of the response of mouse skin to irradiation. *a,* The skin reaction (mean of a group of mice) assessed on an arbitrary scale as indicated is plotted as a function of time after a dose of radiation (30 Gy). The average reaction calculated over a certain time range (eg, 7–30 days) as indicated is determined and plotted as a function of radiation dose as shown in *b.*

Table 16.3. Functional Assays for Radiation Damage

Tissue	Assay Endpoint
Bone marrow	LD_{50}, depletion of different cell types
GI Tract	LD_{50}, weight loss, protein or electrolyte leakage
Lung	LD_{50}, breathing rate, CO uptake
Kidney	LD_{50}, urine output
Bladder	Urination frequency
Skin	Acute reactions, late deformities or skin contraction, hair loss, telangiectasia
CNS	LD_{50} (brain), paralysis (spinal cord)

kinetics in the tissue involved. In parallel with expression of damage occurring in the tissue parenchymal cells, damage to the connective tissue and vasculature of the organ may also develop, leading to fibrosis and progressive impairment of its circulation. If the damage to the circulation is severe enough, secondary parenchymal cell death will occur due to nutrient deprivation. This loss of functional cells may induce other parenchymal cells to divide, causing further cell death as they express their radiation damage. The end result may be functional failure of the organ involved. The relative importance of direct radiation damage to the parenchymal cells, as compared to secondary damage due to connective tissue and vascular injury, in causing late effects is unknown. It is probable that it varies between organs, depending on factors such as cellular kinetics and vascular supply.

Early responding tissues also contain connective tissue and vasculature and can express late damage after their surviving parenchymal cells have repopulated the tissue. Thus months to years after the early desquamation has healed there may be progressive development of atrophy of human skin and eventually, if the radiation dose was sufficiently high, tissue necrosis.

Although tissues may repair damage and regenerate after irradiation, previously irradiated regions have a reduced tolerance for subsequent radiation treatments. This indicates the presence of residual injury. The influence of previous irradiation on the response of rodent skin to subsequent treatment (6 months later) has been found to be greater for late damage than for early damage (see Hornsey and Field, 1980).

16.2.3 THERAPEUTIC RATIO

The dose of radiation which can be delivered to a tumor is limited by the possibility of serious normal tissue damage (or complications). The choice of dose for a given tumor must thus be based on an assessment of the relative probabilities of tumor control and normal tissue complications. Whether a certain risk of developing complications is regarded as acceptable depends both on the tissue(s) and the severity of the damage involved, and it must be compared to the probability of benefit from the treatment (eradicating the tumor) in order to determine the overall gain from the treatment. This gain can be estimated for an average group of patients (see Bush 1979 for discussion) but it may vary for individual patients depending on their particular characteristics (eg, age). The balance between the probabilities for tumor control and normal tissue complications gives a measure of the therapeutic ratio of a treatment.

Although the concept is expressed in mathematical terminology, the therapeutic ratio is ill defined in numerical terms. The concept is illustrated in Figure 16.7, which shows theoretical dose–response curves for tumor control and normal tissue complications. These two curves have been drawn parallel to one another for simplicity. The therapeutic ratio is often defined as the percentage of tumor cures which are obtained at a given level of normal tissue complications (ie, by taking a vertical cut through the two curves at a dose which is clinically acceptable). The problem with this approach is that the ratio between these two numbers—the therapeutic ratio—is different at different levels of complications and tumor control. An approach more in keeping with the definition of other ratios, such as RBE and OER, is to define the therapeutic ratio in terms of the ratio of radiation doses (D_2/D_1) required to produce a given percentage (usually 50%) of tumor control and complications. It is thus a measure of the horizontal displacement between the two curves. It remains imprecise, however, because it depends on the shape of the dose–response curves for tumor control and severe normal tissue complications.

The curves shown in Figure 16.7a depict a situation in which the therapeutic ratio is favourable since the tumor-control curve is displaced to the left of that for severe normal tissue complications. The greater this displacement the more radiocurable the tumor. If the two curves are close together (see Fig 16.7b) or the curve for tumor control is displaced to the right of that for complications, the therapeutic ratio is unfavourable since a high level of complications must be accepted to achieve even a minimal level of tumor control.

16.3 FRACTIONATION

16.3.1 OVERVIEW

Radiation treatment of cancer is usually given as a series of daily fractions of 2–2.5 Gy given 5 or 6 days/week for 4–7 weeks. The use of fractionated treatment arose from studies of French radiotherapists in the early part of the century. Seminal among the studies were those of Regaud (see del Regato, 1976) who demonstrated that with fractionated treatment to a ram's testis it was possible to achieve sterilization without significant damage to the scrotal skin, while with a single dose it was difficult to obtain sterilization even if a dose sufficient to produce severe skin damage was given. Many empirical modifications of fractionation regimes evolved from these early studies and there is now a general consensus that the therapeutic ratio is significantly improved by such treatment. Many of the underlying biological effects occurring during fractionated radiation treatment have been identified over the last 25 years, and the improvement of the therapeutic ratio may be explained in terms of the biological response of tissue. The most important processes occurring during fractionated treatment are the so-called "4 'R's," repair, repopulation, redistribution and reoxygenation. Each of these is described below and their relative effects during fractionated radiation are discussed.

16.3.2 REPAIR

The repair of radiation damage has been described in section 15.6.3. The shoulder on the survival curve after single radiation doses is indicative of the capacity of the cells to accumulate and repair radiation damage. If multiple doses are given with sufficient time between the fractions for repair to occur, survival curves for cells

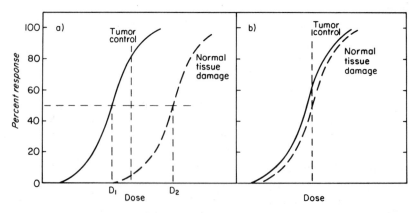

Figure 16.7. Illustration of the concept of a therapeutic ratio in terms of dose–response relationships for tumor control and normal tissue damage. See the text for discussion of the two parts of the figure.

treated with fractionated irradiation will be similar to those illustrated in Figure 16.8. The broken lines in this figure represent the effective slope of the survival curve for different fractionated treatments. This effective slope depends on the size of the individual dose fractions, becoming shallower as the fraction size is reduced. This effect is well illustrated by survival curves for the crypt cells of murine colonic mucosa irradiated with different numbers of fractions (see Fig 16.9).

When the size of the individual dose fractions is large enough that survival for each fraction is represented by the exponential portion of the survival curve then the dose-equivalent amount of repair (D_r) after each dose fraction is equal to the value of D_q (defined in section 15.6.3), regardless of the size of the dose fraction. However, if the size of the dose fraction is such that the survival is represented by the curvilinear, shoulder region of the survival curve, as for most dose fractions used clinically, then the D_r value will be less than D_q. In this situation D_r will be maximal when equal-sized dose fractions are given (Hornsey, 1967). Thus if a certain total dose is given with unequal fraction sizes it would be expected to produce more damage than the same total dose given in equal fraction sizes (see section 16.4.1 for further discussion of this issue).

The single-dose survival curve for most cells has a finite initial slope, due to a single-hit nonrepairable component (section 15.5.2), so that there is a limit below which further reduction of the fraction size will no longer reduce the effective slope of the survival curve (see Fig 16.8). At this limit all the repairable damage is being repaired between each fraction so that the cell killing is entirely due to nonrepairable events. The fraction size at which this limit is reached is likely to be different for different cell populations but, for many, it is expected to be less than the 2–2.5 Gy fractions widely used in conventional fractionation regimens (Fowler, 1984).

The effect of reducing the rate at which the radiation dose is given is similar to that of reducing fraction size.

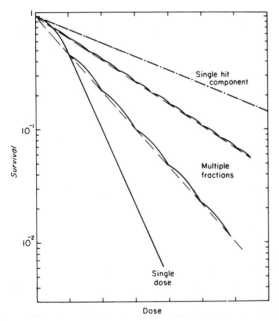

Figure 16.8. The influence of fractionating the radiation treatment on the shape of cell survival curves. When repair occurs between the fractions, the shoulder of the survival curve is repeated for every fraction. The curve labeled "single-hit component" is discussed in the text.

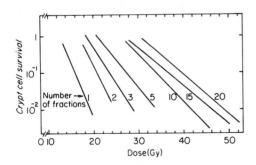

Figure 16.9. Survival curves obtained for murine intestinal crypt cells following different fractionated treatments. The fractions were given three hours apart to minimize the influence of proliferation of surviving cells during the course of the fractionated treatments. (Modified from Withers and Mason, 1974.)

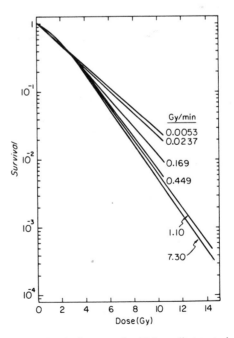

Figure 16.10. Survival curves for HeLa cells treated with γ-irradiation given at different continuous dose rates. (Modified from Hall, 1972.)

Dose rates above about 1 Gy/min result in a cell survival curve similar to the single-dose curve shown in Figure 16.8. At lower dose rates repair is able to occur during the course of the treatment, leading to a survival curve with a shallower slope (Fig 16.10). The major effects of dose rate on the slope of the survival curve occur in the range 1–0.01 Gy/min (Hall, 1972).

16.3.3 REPOPULATION

In tumors and in normal tissues which contain proliferating cells, cell division may occur during the course of fractionated treatment. Furthermore, as cellular damage and cell death occur during the course of the treatment, the tissue may respond with an increased level of cell proliferation. The effect of cell proliferation during treatment, known as repopulation or regeneration, will be to increase the number of cells at risk during the course of the treatment and reduce the overall response. The effect is most important in early-responding normal tissues or tumors whose stem cells are capable of rapid proliferation (eg, skin, GI tract) and will be of little consequence in late-responding slowly proliferating tissues (eg, liver), which do not suffer much early cell death and hence do not produce an early proliferative response to the radiation treatment. Repopulation will therefore decrease the early damage to normal tissue and the response of tumors following fractionated treatment to a greater extent than it will decrease late damage to normal tissue. Repopulation is likely to be more important towards the end of a course of treatment, when sufficient damage has accumulated (and cell death occurred) to induce a regenerative response. The regenerative response in mouse skin during and following fractionated treatment with doses of 3 Gy is illustrated in Figure 16.11. There is a period of about 10 days of treatment before significant repopulation occurs, after which a rapid regenerative response is observed. It can be anticipated that regenerative responses may be very important in reducing acute responses during split-course treatments.

16.3.4 REDISTRIBUTION

Variation in the radiosensitivity of cells in different phases of the cell cycle results in the cells in the more resistant phases being more likely to survive a dose of radiation (see section 15.6.2). During a course of fractionated treatment, proliferating cells may move from one phase of the cell cycle to another between the radiation doses. Since some of the surviving cells will redistribute into more sensitive parts of the cell cycle, this effect will tend to make the whole population more sensitive to fractionated treatment compared to a single

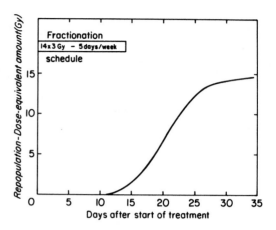

Figure 16.11. Illustration of the effect of the regenerative response in mouse skin which occurs during the course of a fractionated treatment. The repopulation which occurs is plotted in terms of the extra (single) radiation dose, required to be given at different times after the start of the 3-Gy/day schedule, in order to produce a constant level of acute skin reaction. (Modified from Denekamp, 1973.)

dose. The effect of this process on cell survival is shown in Figure 16.12, where the effect has been calculated for a course of 2 Gy fractions given to Chinese hamster cells, using the survival curves for different phases of the cell cycle shown in the insert (and in Fig 15.15). Two different rates of redistribution were assumed, giving the two lower curves. These curves can be compared to the upper curve, which was calculated assuming no redistribution. Since redistribution inevitably involves cell proliferation the survival will also be influenced by repopulation. The broken line in the figure indicates that the influence of repopulation substantially reduces the effect of redistribution. Both redistribution and repopulation are important only in rapidly proliferating cell populations. It should be noted that not all cell lines show such large differences in radiosensitivity between cells in different cell-cycle phases. The effect of redistribution will be correspondingly less for these types of cells.

In many normal tissues (and tumors) stem cells can be in a resting phase (G_0) but can be recruited into cycle to repopulate the tissue. There is some evidence that cells in cycle are slightly more sensitive to radiation than G_0 cells, possibly because G_0 cells may repair potentially lethal damage (section 15.6.3). Recruitment of resting cells into the proliferative cycle, during the course of fractionated treatment, may therefore tend to increase the sensitivity of the whole population. Neither recruitment nor redistribution would be expected to have much influence on late damage, which occurs predominantly as a result of injury to tissues in which the rate of proliferation is slow.

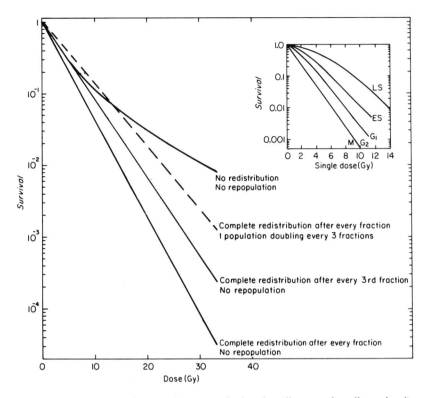

Figure 16.12. Theoretical survival curves calculated to illustrate the effect of redistribution on the level of cell killing following treatment with 2 Gy fractions. The inset curve indicates sensitivities in different phases of the cell cycle and is reproduced from Figure 15.15. The curves in the main body of the figure were calculated using these curves and assuming an asynchronous cell population containing 5% cells in M, 30% cells in G_1, 25% cells in early S (ES), 25% cells in late S (LS) and 15% cells in G_2. Redistribution and/or repopulation were assumed to occur as indicated on the individual lines.

16.3.5 REOXYGENATION

Hypoxic cells in tumors dominate their response to large single doses of radiation (see section 15.6.4), even if only a very small fraction of the tumor stem cells are hypoxic (Fig 16.13). After a dose of radiation the proportion of the surviving cells which are hypoxic will be elevated. However, with time, some of the surviving hypoxic cells may gain access to oxygen, and hence become more sensitive to a subsequent radiation treatment. This process of reoxygenation has been shown to occur in many animal tumors. The mechanism is poorly understood but may result from increased or redistributed blood flow, reduced oxygen utilization by radiation-damaged cells, or rapid removal of radiation-damaged cells so that the hypoxic cells become closer to functional blood vessels (Kallman, 1972). Experimental observations of the time course of reoxygenation and of the above processes suggest that different mechanisms may be involved in different tumors.

Regardless of the biological mechanism(s) involved, reoxygenation can theoretically result in a substantial increase in the sensitivity of tumors during fractionated treatment, as illustrated in Figure 16.14. In this figure, there are three survival curves for treatment with 2 Gy fractions: one for a tumor containing no hypoxic cells, one for a tumor containing 10% hypoxic cells which do not reoxygenate, and the third for a tumor in which there were initially 10% hypoxic cells, but after each fraction reoxygenation reduced the proportion of survivors which remained hypoxic at the time of the next fraction to 10%. The survival curve for the tumor containing 10% hypoxic cells which do not reoxygenate is dominated at higher doses by the hypoxic cells, which are the most radioresistant cell population. In contrast, the survival curve for the reoxygenating tumor-cell population lies close to the curve for a fully oxygenated population.

Reoxygenation has been shown to occur in almost all rodent tumors that have been studied, but both the extent and timing of this reoxygenation are variable among animal tumors (see Fig 16.15). Experiments to demonstrate reoxygenation directly cannot be performed on human tumors, but this process almost certainly does

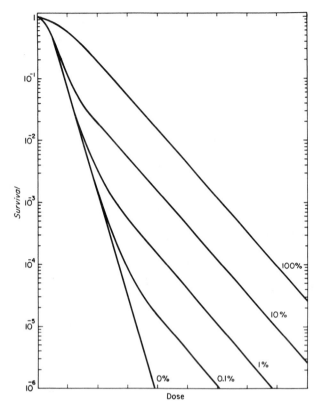

Figure 16.13. Hypothetical survival curves which would be obtained following (single) radiation doses given to tumors containing different fractions of hypoxic cells.

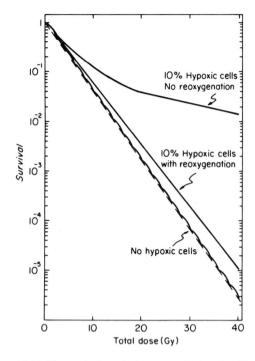

Figure 16.14. Theoretical survival curves calculated to illustrate the influence of reoxygenation on the level of cell killing in a tumor following treatment with 2 Gy fractions. It was assumed that the tumor initially had 10% hypoxic cells and that reoxygenation was sufficient to maintain this level among the surviving cells throughout the treatment.

occur and is probably a major reason why fractionating treatment leads to an improvement in therapeutic ratio (as compared to single large doses) in clinical radiotherapy.

The variable rates of reoxygenation in animal tumors imply the possibility of similar variations in human tumors. Studies with human melanomas xenografted into immune-deficient mice have demonstrated such variability, although it must be noted that the stroma and vascular structure in such tumors is derived from their murine host (Rofstad, 1985). These results suggest that daily fractionation schedules may not be optimal for all tumors. Large single radiation doses were used to induce the reoxygenation in the animal tumors illustrated in Figure 16.15. Reoxygenation will probably be less extensive following smaller fractionated doses, and the kinetics of the process may be different. Experimental studies with animal tumors using fraction sizes of 2–3 Gy are very limited but seem to indicate that although reoxygenation occurs, it may not be sufficient to prevent the hypoxic cells from influencing the response of the tumor to the radiation treatment (Hill, 1986).

Whether reoxygenation is sufficient during conven-

tional fractionated treatment of most human tumors to prevent hypoxic cells from influencing tumor control probability is unknown. Results from clinical trials with modifiers of the oxygen effect (see section 16.5), which are currently the only available approach to addressing this issue, suggest that the answer to this question may be different for different tumors.

16.4 TIME AND DOSE RELATIONSHIPS

16.4.1 OVERVIEW

Repair and repopulation can be expected to increase the total dose required to achieve a given level of biological damage (an isoeffect) when radiation treatment is fractionated. Redistribution and reoxygenation would be expected to reduce the required total dose for an isoeffect. Reoxygenation applies mostly to tumors (since they contain hypoxic cells) whilst repopulation and redistribution apply to both tumor and proliferating normal tissues. Repair is an important factor in the response of nearly all tissues. It is often difficult to dissect the influence of the individual factors. However, the fact that the total dose used in clinical fractionation regimes is much larger than the isoeffective single dose,

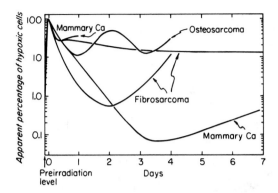

Figure 16.15. The apparent percentage of surviving cells, which were hypoxic in the tumor, is plotted as a function of time after a single radiation dose (10–15 Gy) given to a number of different rodent tumors. The initial (preirradiation) percentage of hypoxic cells was 1–15% for the different tumors but, immediately after the radiation dose, essentially all the surviving cells were hypoxic. As a function of time after the first radiation dose, second radiation doses were given to allow determination of the fraction of hypoxic cells among the survivors of the first dose. (Modified from Hill, 1986.)

and increases with length of treatment, implies that repair and repopulation are the dominant factors which determine (normal tissue) response to fractionated radiotherapy. These two factors depend respectively on the fraction size (and number) and the overall time of the treatment.

Fowler and Stern (1963) addressed the question of the relative importance of repair and repopulation with studies of the response of pig skin to fractionated radiation. Pig skin was chosen because it has a structure similar to that of human skin. Their data are summarized in Table 16.4, which shows the total dose required to produce a given level of early skin reaction. An increase in the number of fractions from 5 to 20 delivered over a constant time of 28 days necessitated a large increase in total dose, whereas an increase in the duration of treatment from 4 to 28 days when the fraction number (5) remained constant required a smaller increase. These results suggest that repair of sublethal damage between fractions is the more important of the

Table 16.4. Single and Fractionated Doses Required for a Fixed Level of Acute Reaction in Pig Skin

No. of Fractions	Overall Time	Total Dose
1	<1 day	20 Gy
5	4 days	36 Gy
5	28 days	42 Gy
20	28 days	~60 Gy

Note: Adapted from Fowler and Stern (1963).

parameters, and that repopulation plays a lesser but still significant role over the course of a four-week treatment. If the fractionated treatment had been extended to longer times the contribution of repopulation would have been greater for the early skin-reaction endpoint used in these studies.

The finding that the biological effect of radiation depends on the fractionation schedule used for its delivery has significant implications for the planning of therapy. To obtain the maximum dose to a tumor while minimizing dose to surrounding normal tissue, the radiotherapist will often use a number of overlapping radiation beams. The dose at any given location will be calculated by summing the doses given by the various individual beams and the dose distribution will be represented by a series of isodose curves (cf contours on a map) joining points which are expected to receive equal percentages of the dose at a particular point (usually within the tumor). These isodose lines must be viewed with caution, because the same total dose may not give the same biological effect if the doses delivered by the individual beams are of unequal size and they are not given in close temporal proximity (within approximately one hour). For example, it was noted in section 16.3.2 that equal-sized dose fractions allow for maximum repair; thus regions which receive unequal contributions from different beams would repair less of the radiation damage than regions where the contributions were equal. The biological effect would then be different at different points on the same isodose line.

16.4.2 ISOEFFECT CURVES

When different fractionation schedules are identified which give the same level of biological effect the results can be presented in the form of an isoeffect curve. One of the earliest attempts to derive an isoeffect curve was that of Strandqvist (1944), who made observations of skin response and tumor recurrence following treatment of carcinoma of the skin and lip. The total dose used to treat each tumor was plotted against the overall treatment time, using logarithmic scales. Strandqvist drew a line through these data points which he believed represented the optimal treatment schedules (ie, total doses given over different times which minimized tumor recurrence without causing excessive skin damage). Essentially this line (Fig 16.16a) represented the maximum total doses, given over different time periods, which could be tolerated by the skin.

Experiments specifically designed to examine the response of pig skin (which is similar in structure to human skin) were performed by Fowler and his colleagues (see Fowler, 1971). An isoeffect curve derived from some of these studies is shown in Figure 16.16b.

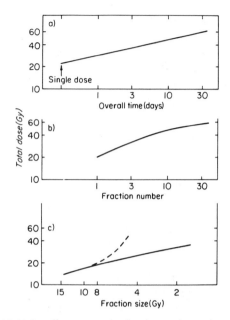

Figure 16.16. Isoeffect curves for fractionated treatments plotted in three different formats. *a*, Line plotted by Strandqvist (1944) to define normal tissue tolerance and control of carcinoma of the skin and lip using the axes of total dose and overall treatment time. *b*, Isoeffect curves for damage to pig skin plotted as total dose versus number of fractions. (Adapted from Fowler, 1971.) *c*, Isoeffect curve for the crypt cells of the mouse intestine plotted as total dose versus fraction size using an inverted scale. The solid line is for fractions given 3 hr apart and the broken line for fractions given 24 hr apart. (Adapted from Withers and Mason, 1974.)

In this plot the horizontal axis represents fraction number, since this is a more important variable than overall treatment time (section 16.4.1). Isoeffect curves can also be drawn with total dose plotted as a function of fraction size (Fig 16.16c), thus emphasizing the importance of fraction size in determining the effect of fractionated treatments (section 16.3.2).

All of these isoeffect curves demonstrate the requirement for increased dose to give the same biological effect using greater times or fraction numbers. This is largely due to repair, but the continuing rise of these curves at large fraction numbers or small fraction sizes is probably due to the effect of repopulation. The implication of the finite initial slope to a cell survival curve is that at small fraction sizes all repairable damage is repaired and cell killing occurs as a result of single-hit nonrepairable events (see section 16.3.2). Thus reduction in the fraction size beyond a certain point would not result in a further increase in dose required to achieve the isoeffect, and hence the isoeffect curves in Figure 16.16 should become parallel to the dose-fraction axis if repopulation was not occurring. The effect of repopulation, occurring in a rapidly proliferating tis-

sue, is demonstrated in Figure 16.16c, which is for mouse jejunal crypt cells and is derived from data similar to that shown in Figure 16.9. The solid line represents the results when the fractionated treatments were given with three-hour intervals, so that the treatment was completed within a few days and repopulation was relatively small. The broken line indicates the effect of increasing the fraction interval to 24 hr when substantial repopulation results in a large increase in the total dose required to produce the isoeffective level of damage.

The effect of reoxygenation on an isoeffect curve for tumor control can be seen in Figure 16.17, which shows results for treatment of mouse mammary tumors. When fractions were given either daily or on alternate days, tumor control was achieved with a lower total dose when it was given as two fractions rather than as a single dose. The total dose required for tumor control then increased at larger fraction numbers. This tumor demonstrates extensive reoxygenation (see Fig 16.15) and for two fraction treatments this reoxygenation made the tumor more sensitive despite the effects of repair. For larger numbers of fractions repair and repopulation became more important even though reoxygenation continued to occur. A curve of similar shape can be drawn through isoeffect data for human breast tumors, although the results are less clear cut (Howes and Field, 1968). Animal tumors which show less extensive reoxygenation than the mouse mammary tumors discussed above (eg, a mouse fibrosarcoma) do not show a dip in isoeffect curves (see Fig 16.17) even though it can be demonstrated that reoxygenation is occurring.

Experimental studies performed mainly in rodents have established isoeffect curves for different normal tissues using endpoints of either early or late radiation damage. Some of these isoeffect curves are shown in

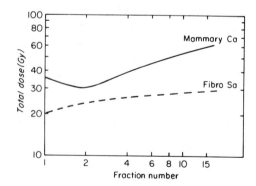

Figure 16.17. Isoeffect curves for two different experimental tumors. Tumor control was the isoeffective endpoint for the mammary carcinoma (adapted from Fowler et al, 1974) whilst a fixed level of cell survival was used for the fibrosarcoma. (Adapted from Hill and Bush, 1977.)

Figure 16.18, with the broken lines representing early responses and the solid lines late responses. The iso-effect lines for late responses are steeper than those for early responses. This implies a greater capacity for the repair of damage which is expressed late than for damage which is expressed early after radiation treatment (Thames et al, 1982). The reasons for this difference are unknown but could reflect greater repair of potentially lethal damage in tissues which have little or no cell proliferation, or an effect of redistribution to reduce the effective repair in proliferating tissues which show early damage. The results in Figure 16.18 imply that fractionated treatments which result in equal levels of early damage will give reduced levels of late damage if the individual fraction size is small and increased levels of late damage if the individual fraction size is large. Possibilities for exploiting this effect are discussed in section 16.5.5.

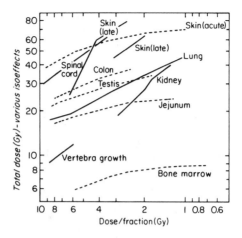

Figure 16.18. Isoeffect curves for a number of rodent tissues obtained using a variety of different cell survival or functional assays. The total dose required to obtain a fixed level of tissue damage is plotted as a function of the dose/fraction. The displacement of the curves on the vertical axis is a result of the fact that different isoeffective endpoints were used for the different tissues. (Modified from Thames et al, 1982.)

16.4.3 MODELS FOR ISOEFFECT

A straight line on a log–log plot implies a power-law relationship, and the isoeffect line drawn by Strandqvist (Fig 16.16a) can be represented by the relationship

$$\text{total dose} \propto (\text{time})^n \qquad (16.3)$$

where the exponent n is obtained from the slope of the line. Strandqvist's line gave $n \simeq 0.3$, consistent with the "cube-root law" which was used by early radiotherapists as a guide to modifying fractionation schedules. Subsequently Ellis (1969) developed the concept of the Nominal Standard Dose (NSD) in which he postulated that the total dose (D), tolerated by normal tissues, was related to the number of fractions (N) and overall treatment time (T) by the relationship

$$D = (\text{NSD})N^{0.24}T^{0.11} \qquad (16.4)$$

This formula is similar to eq (16.3) above but emphasizes the importance of fraction number. It is based on clinical data for cure of squamous cell carcinoma and for tolerance of skin.

The NSD equation and two mathematical derivatives (CRE—Kirk et al, 1971, and TDF—Orton and Ellis, 1973) have been quite widely applied in radiotherapeutic practice. The clinical experience (combined with extensive animal experimentation) has indicated that the NSD equation predicts isoeffect doses for the response of skin and oral mucosa reasonably well for fraction numbers between about 10 and 30 given in overall times of less than about 6 weeks (Fowler, 1983). For late responses of skin and other organs the exponent of fraction number N in the equation is too small and the exponent of time T too large. The result is that

the NSD tends to overpredict tolerance doses for small numbers of large fractions and underpredict them for large numbers of small fractions. Modifications have been proposed for tolerance of a number of different organs (see Ellis, 1985) but the original NSD equation and its related formulae are useful only in making minor changes to fractionation schedules without causing large changes in late normal tissue damage.

The NSD equation has also been used to calculate values of NSD for treatments with disparate fractionation regimes. The tumors treated by the regimes have then been grouped, according to the NSD values calculated, for analysis of dose/response, on the assumption that equal NSD values mean biologically equivalent treatments. This procedure may introduce substantial error, because there is relatively little information available on isoeffect relationships for tumors and they may be quite different from tumor to tumor. Extreme caution is therefore required in interpreting the results of such analyses.

An alternative to the empirical derivation of isoeffect relationships is to assume that equal levels of survival of cells within a tumor or normal tissue will lead to equal levels of damage (ie, isoeffect) and to develop an equation to predict isoeffective treatments based on radiobiological and cell-kinetic parameters. The values of these parameters for individual normal tissue and tumors can then be calculated by obtaining the "best fit" of the derived equation to available clinical data which define isoeffect relationships.

Cohen (1983), in particular, has developed this

approach to calculate isoeffect relationships for tolerance of a wide range of normal tissues and for control of tumors. Cohen's model assumes a cell-survival equation (the composite multitarget equation or linear quadratic equation — see section 15.5), a growth constant to describe repopulation and a factor to allow for field size (or tumor volume). It can also allow for the fraction of hypoxic cells in a tumor and the rate of reoxygenation. The method uses computer programs to fit values of the individual parameters to the available clinical data. Unfortunately, appropriate clinical data are often very limited. Thus this approach is likely to suffer from similar problems to those which affect empirical formulae such as NSD (ie, extrapolations beyond the existing data base are potentially subject to large errors). One attractive feature of such a model, however, is that it can be combined with the dose calculations associated with treatment planning and used to predict contour lines joining points of equal cell survival (ie, isosurvival lines) for comparison with calculated isodose lines, which were discussed in section 16.4.1.

16.5 APPROACHES TO IMPROVING THE THERAPEUTIC RATIO

Most radiation treatments which are aimed at controlling a local tumor are limited by the tolerance of the irradiated normal tissue. Improving the therapeutic ratio thus requires knowledge of the possible reasons for the failure of radiation treatment to control the tumor and/or of ways of increasing the tolerance of normal tissue. The preceding sections of this chapter have discussed a number of radiobiological factors which could influence tumor control by, or normal tissue tolerance to, fractionated radiation treatment. Some of these factors are (a) the number of stem cells that a tumor contains, (b) the level of hypoxia in the tumor and the extent of reoxygenation, (c) the growth kinetics of the tumor and critical normal tissue cells, (d) the repair capacity of the cells and (e) the intrinsic radiosensitivity of the cells. A number of these factors are potentially susceptible to manipulation to improve the therapeutic ratio.

The factors are unlikely to be of equal importance in all tumors, even those of a specific histopathological type. Ideally, it would be desirable to identify which particular factors are likely to influence the radiocurability of individual tumors, so that only tumors which can be expected to benefit from a particular modification in treatment are studied. The development of predictive assays for tumor radiocurability has been the goal of many workers, but no tests of accepted reliability are available (see Peters et al, 1984 for review). Thus clinical studies of treatment modifications are likely to include some tumors which can benefit and

some which cannot, making statistical assessment of any benefit of the modified treatment more difficult. Various approaches to improving the therapeutic ratio are discussed in the present section.

16.5.1 INCREASE IN OXYGEN DELIVERY

Hypoxic cells represent a radiation-resistant subpopulation in tumors which does not exist (or only to a very minor extent) in most normal tissues. The therapeutic ratio might thus be improved by eliminating the influence of these cells on tumor response. Reoxygenation during fractionated radiotherapy reduces the effect of hypoxic cells but reoxygenation is variable from tumor to tumor in animals and may be inadequate for at least some tumors in man.

A number of clinical studies have demonstrated the negative effect of anemia on patient prognosis, and in many centres blood transfusions are used to maintain patients at normal hemoglobin levels during treatment. There is evidence that this procedure may improve tumor control and survival for patients with carcinoma of the cervix (Bush et al, 1978). Experimental studies have suggested that other conditions such as chronic respiratory disease, giving low arterial oxygen tensions, or smoking, which increases the carboxyhemoglobin content of the blood, may also influence tumor response by affecting the level of hypoxia (Siemann et al, 1978a, b). It would be desirable to correct all such conditions influencing oxygen delivery to tissue prior to radiotherapy.

Oxygen delivery to tumor cells may be increased by giving animals or patients high-pressure (200–300 kPa) oxygen (HPO) to breathe before and during radiation treatment. An increase in the dissolved oxygen concentration in blood plasma should result in greater diffusion of oxygen into the hypoxic regions. Studies with animal tumors have demonstrated that the use of HPO will indeed sensitize them to radiation, particularly when used with fractionated treatments (Suit et al, 1977). Clinical studies with HPO as an adjuvant to radiation therapy have demonstrated improved results for patients with tumors of the head and neck or cervix (Table 16.5 and Fowler, 1985 for review). Many other trials were inconclusive, however, and the improvements seen were not sufficient to outweigh the difficulties, dangers and extra expense involved in treating patients in high-pressure oxygen chambers.

There are many possible reasons why these trials failed to show a positive result. In relation to the original reason for using HPO (to sensitize hypoxic cells), these include (a) the extra oxygen was only able to diffuse to some of the hypoxic cells, and (b) tumor control was not limited by hypoxic cells, either because of effective reoxygenation or because very few hypoxic cells

Table 16.5. Summary of Clinical Trials Testing Sensitization of Hypoxic Cells

Sensitizing Agent	No. of Trials	Significant Benefit	Margin in Favor	No Benefit
Hyperbaric oxygen*	15	3	6	6
Misonidazole**	33	5	2	26

*Adapted from Fowler (1985).

**Adapted from Dische (1985).

existed in the tumors. The results of the positive trials, however, do indicate that hypoxic cells are present in some tumors, and that reoxygenation is not sufficient in these tumors to prevent the hypoxic cells from influencing the probability of tumor control during fractionated radiation treatment.

More recently the possibility of improving oxygen delivery to tumors by infusing artificial blood substitutes such as perfluorocarbon emulsions is under investigation. The solubility of oxygen in these emulsions is much greater than in plasma, so that infusion combined with breathing carbogen (95% O_2 + 5% CO_2) can increase the oxygen-carrying capacity of the blood. Initial studies have indicated that this approach can reduce the proportion of hypoxic cells in some animal tumors (Rockwell, 1985).

16.5.2 SENSITIZERS

An alternative approach to the use of hyperbaric oxygen involves the use of drugs which can mimic the radiosensitizing properties of oxygen. These drugs, known as hypoxic-cell radiosensitizers, must be able to diffuse to all parts of a tumor to be effective. Development of radiosensitizers was based on the idea that the radiosensitizing properties of oxygen are probably due to its electron affinity (Adams and Dewey, 1963) and that other electron-affinic compounds might act as sensitizers. A large number of electron-affinic compounds have been found to be sensitizers of hypoxic cells in vitro and their efficacy as sensitizers has been found to be directly related to their electron affinity. Many of these compounds are highly reactive and are not effective in vivo. However, a family of compounds, the nitroimidazoles (Fig 16.19), has been found to contain members which can sensitize hypoxic cells both in vitro and in animal tumors. The most extensively studied of these compounds is misonidazole, which can sensitize hypoxic cells in vitro in a dose-dependent fashion and does not sensitize oxygenated cells (Fig 16.20). The extent of the sensitization can be assessed in terms of a sensitizer enhancement ratio (SER) which is analogous to the OER discussed in section 15.6.

When misonidazole is administered 30–60 min before a single radiation dose given to tumor-bearing

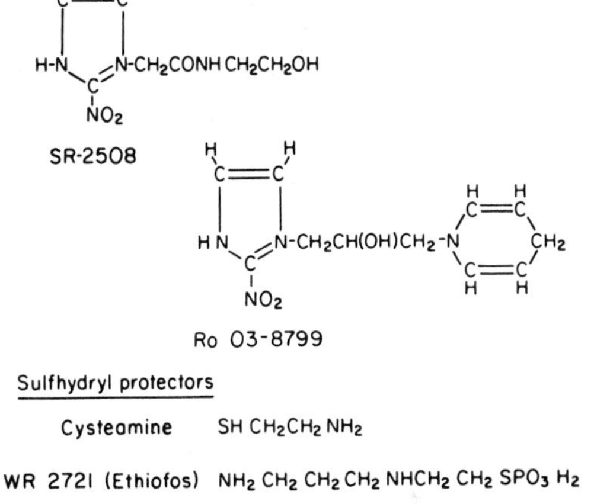

Figure 16.19. The structure of some nitroimidazole sensitizers and sulfhydryl protectors.

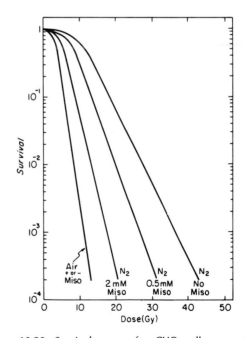

Figure 16.20. Survival curves for CHO cells treated with γ-irradiation under anoxic conditions (N_2) in the presence of different concentrations of misonidazole or under well-oxygenated conditions (air) in the presence or absence of the highest concentration of misonidazole (2 mM). (Modified from Whitmore et al, 1978.)

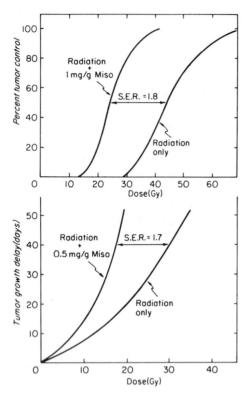

Figure 16.21. In vivo studies to illustrate the sensitizing effect of misonidazole. *a,* Tumor control versus dose curves for murine mammary tumors treated with X-irradiation in the presence or absence of misonidazole (1 mg/g) (modified from Sheldon et al, 1974). *b,* Growth delay versus dose curves for murine mammary tumors treated in the presence or absence of misonidazole (0.5 mg/g).

animals, results similar to those in Figure 16.21 can be obtained. In Figure 16.21a tumor cure is plotted as a function of radiation dose and substantial reduction of the dose required to cure 50% of the tumors is observed in the drug-treated group. An enhancement ratio is obtained from these results by taking the ratio of the radiation doses given in the drug's absence, to that in the presence of the drug, to achieve 50% tumor control. Enhancement ratios may be calculated in an analogous manner using other endpoints for tumor response (eg, growth delay—see Fig 16.21b). Sensitizer enhancement ratios depend on the drug concentration in the tumor at the time of radiation. There is a good correspondence between the values obtained for tumors in vivo and the results from in vitro studies. If misonidazole is combined with fractionated radiation doses the SER is reduced, largely because of reoxygenation occurring between the fractions (see Hill, 1986).

Many hypoxic cell radiosensitizers, such as the nitroimidazoles, have also been found to exhibit a preferential toxicity for hypoxic cells in the absence of radiation. This toxicity is dependent on both drug concentration and time of exposure, and appears to require the metabolic reduction of the drug. The reason for the preferential toxicity is that reduction is much more efficient under hypoxic conditions. Because the reduced products of the drug bind inside the cells, radiolabeled misonidazole is being studied for its potential as a marker for hypoxic cells. It would be anticipated that much higher concentrations of the drug would be bound to hypoxic cells than to oxygenated cells. Experimental studies confirm this prediction and the use of radiolabeled misonidazole is being evaluated in patients to provide direct evidence of the presence of hypoxic cells in human tumors (Urtasun et al, 1986).

Some hypoxic cell radiosensitizers have undergone clinical trials and many trials are still in progress (for review see Dische, 1985). Metronidazole was tested first in a randomised trial of the treatment of glioblastoma. This trial gave a significant improvement in survival time for the group of patients treated with the drug, but the control group had unexpectedly poor survival, probably due to the altered fractionation schedule used in the study to accommodate the drug treatments. Thus although there was no therapeutic advantage the trial did demonstrate that sensitization could be obtained in human tumors.

Misonidazole is a much better sensitizer in experimental studies and has been used in a number of trials. Only a few of these trials have shown a significant improvement in tumor control for patients treated with the drug when compared to best current treatment regimes (see Table 16.5). Most of these trials have been for tumors of the head and neck. Possible reasons for the failure of most of the trials to give a therapeutic gain include those which limit the potential benefits of HPO, but an important consideration is that, because of the neurotoxicity of the drug, doses which could be given to the patients were much lower than those required to give maximum sensitization in animal tumors. Drug concentration in the tumors in patients was probably sufficient to produce only a small amount of sensitization.

Current studies are focusing on drugs which are either as good sensitizers as misonidazole but less toxic or are more effective sensitizers without an equivalent increase in toxicity. Two such drugs (see Fig 16.19) are being tested in clinical trials. One drug, SR 2508 was developed on the premise that a compound with reduced lipophilicity would be less able to penetrate nervous tissue and hence would be less neurotoxic (Brown et al, 1981). The drug is as effective as misonidazole as a sensitizer and larger doses can be tolerated by patients. The second drug, Ro 03-8799 is slightly more electron affinic than misonidazole and has a basic side chain which appears to result in increased drug concentrations in tumors relative to plasma (possibly because the pH in tumors tends to be more acidic than in normal tissues; see Chapter 21). Both drugs thus act as more effective sensitizers than misonidazole at maximally tolerated doses. Results of clinical trials using these drugs will be available within a few years.

Some drugs can sensitize cells to irradiation but are not specific for hypoxic cells. The halogenated pyrimidines, bromodeoxyuridine (BrdUrd) or iododeoxyuridine (IdUrd) are incorporated into DNA in place of thymidine and as a result make cells more sensitive to irradiation by virtue of increasing the damage caused to the DNA. These drugs can thus sensitize proliferating cells and, if a greater amount of BrdUrd is incorporated into tumor cells than surrounding normal tissue, a preferential sensitization could be achieved. Therapeutic advantage has been demonstrated for rapidly growing tumors in mice following injection of bromodeoxycytidine (which is rapidly converted to BrdUrd in vivo) presumably because less drug was taken up in the murine normal tissue than in the tumor (Brown et al, 1971). Clinical studies of the use of halogenated pyrimidines in treatment have been limited, however, by increased normal tissue effects (Bagshaw et al, 1967). There has recently been a revival of interest in these agents for possible application in the clinic (see, for example, Kinsella et al, 1985) for tumors at sites where acute normal-tissue effects are not limiting for the radiation dose which can be tolerated.

Sensitization of cells may also be possible using drugs which interfere with the molecular processes involved in the repair of DNA. A number of different drugs have been studied, particularly those which may sensitize cells by inhibiting the repair of potentially lethal damage (Nakatsugawa, 1984). The potential role for such drugs in clinical treatment is likely to be limited by their lack of specificity for tumors as compared to normal tissues, but they might be useful in the treatment of tumors (eg, melanoma) whose cells have a large capacity for repair.

Anticancer drugs may also interact with radiation to cause increased toxicity, but in most cases the result is consistent with additive cytotoxic effects. Important interactions are reviewed in section 19.4.

16.5.3 RADIOPROTECTORS

Drugs which protect cells from the effects of radiation might improve the therapeutic ratio if they were more effective in normal tissues than in tumors. Radiation protectors fall into two classes, those which induce hypoxia and those which contain sulfhydryl groups which can interact with and modify damage caused by radiation-produced radicals. Sulfhydryl compounds are effective as protectors against low LET radiation but have relatively little effect against high LET radiation. A drug such as cysteamine (see Fig 16.19) can increase

the dose of radiation required for lethality of animals by a factor of about 1.8. A thiophosphate compound, known as WR2721 or ethiofos (see Fig 16.19), which is broken down in vivo to give a sulfhydryl, can give a greater degree of protection at tolerated doses in mice (up to a factor of about 3). There is experimental evidence that normal tissues may be protected by the drug to a greater degree than tumors, although there is considerable variability in the degree of protection observed in different normal tissues (Yuhas et al, 1980; Denekamp et al, 1983). This is probably either because of poor drug delivery and penetration into tumors or because of a reduction in the level of protection in hypoxic cells. Unfortunately, the toxicity of the compound in humans appears to be such that dose levels required to produce maximum protection in mice are unlikely to be achieved in patients. Although other radioprotectors are being developed, such compounds are less attractive clinically than hypoxic-cell radiosensitizers, since they require an increase in the radiation dose and are thus not "fail-safe."

Cells contain their own sulfhydryls, both free and protein bound. These compounds may act as natural protectors and depletion of these compounds in the cell can result in sensitization. Glutathione (GSH) is the major non-protein-bound sulfhydryl in cells and a number of compounds, including some of the hypoxic-cell radiosensitizers, have been shown to reduce the level of glutathione in cells. There is evidence that reduced GSH levels in cells can alter their response to radiation treatment, and inhibitors of GSH production in cells are being examined as possible sensitizing agents (Bump et al, 1982).

Compounds which induce hypoxia have not been studied for potential use in therapy but deliberate induction of hypoxia through the use of a tourniquet to cut off blood flow to a limb has been investigated. By making all of the treated region equally hypoxic, the approach should result in an increase in the total dose tolerated and reduce the differential advantage of hypoxic tumor cells. Clinical trials of this approach used a small number of large dose fractions, which were given because of the difficulties associated with the induction of hypoxia. The results demonstrated enhanced late reactions and any therapeutic gain was minimal (Suit et al, 1973).

16.5.4 HIGH LET RADIATION

The use of high LET radiations might contribute to improvements in the therapeutic ratio in two different ways. First, heavy-charged-particle beams, because most of their energy is deposited in tissue at the end of particle tracks (ie, the region of the Bragg peak—see section 15.2), can be used to give improved depth–dose distributions for deep-seated tumors (Fig 16.22). Neutron beams are not useful in this regard since they do not demonstrate a Bragg peak and depth–dose distributions are similar to those for low LET radiation.

The second potentially beneficial aspect of high LET radiations are their specific radiobiological properties. The oxygen enhancement ratio is reduced at high LET (see section 15.6), so that hypoxic cells are protected to a lesser degree. Studies with fast neutron irradiation have indicated that the OER is in the range 1.5–2.0, and for heavy-ion beams it may be lower. Thus high LET radiation is potentially useful in the treatment of tumors which contain hypoxic cells and where reoxygenation, between fractions of conventional radiation is not sufficient to overcome the radioresistance that they cause.

Cells also exhibit reduced capacity for repair (both SLDR and PLDR) following high LET radiation relative to that following low LET radiation. This property leads to an increased RBE (section 15.6) for fractionated treatment relative to single doses, with the RBE increasing as the fraction size decreases (see Fig 16.23). Isoeffect relationships (see section 16.4.2) for high LET irradiation are reduced in slope as a result of this reduced repair. If tumor cells had a greater capacity for repair than cells in the critical normal tissues it would be possible to reduce this difference by using high LET radiation. Some types of tumor cells apparently show a high degree of PLDR, which may correlate with a poor clinical response (Guichard et al, 1984). Such tumors might be more effectively treated with high-LET radiation.

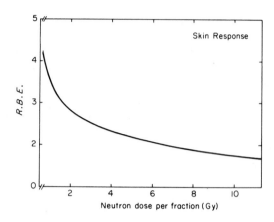

Figure 16.23. The RBE of fractionated fast neutron irradiations plotted as a function of the size of individual dose fractions. Acute reactions in mouse, rat and human skin were assessed following fractionated irradiation with fast neutrons or 250-kV X-rays and RBE values determined at equivalent levels of reaction. The single line fits all the data. (Adapted from Field and Hornsey, 1975.)

The variation in radiosensitivity with position in the cell cycle is also reduced for high LET radiation, and in general there is reduced variability in response between different cells. This reduction in variability together with the increased slope (D_0 value) of cell survival curves for high LET irradiation means that dose–response relationships for tumors and normal tissues (see section 16.2) would be expected to be steeper than those for low LET radiations. This effect could be beneficial, if the tumor dose–control curve is shallow relative to the dose–response curve for the critical normal tissue, but it makes careful dosimetry very important since small changes in dose could translate into large changes in response.

A comparison of various different radiations in relation to their potential physical or biological therapeutic advantages is shown in Figure 16.24. The vertical axis represents the potential gain due to improved depth–dose distributions while the horizontal axis represents that due to the biological aspects of increased LET. The expected gains with protons are largely confined to improved dose distributions, while for neutrons any gains are likely to be related to the biological factors. Negative pions and heavy ions can give both advantages, but it is likely that they will only have limited applicability because they are very expensive to produce and only a few places in the world have suitable facilities.

Although the various radiobiological aspects of high LET irradiation can potentially lead to an improved therapeutic ratio, this will not be the case for all tumors. In fact, high LET radiations could be disadvantageous for some tumors because they reduce the

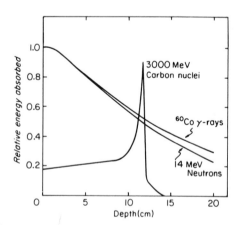

Figure 16.22. Depth–dose distributions for three different types of radiation. The energy deposited decreases as a function of depth into the body for both γ-rays and 14-MeV neutrons. For the 3000-MeV carbon nuclei energy deposition increases to a peak (the Bragg peak) at a depth of about 12 cm. The vertical scale relates to the three types of radiation independently and does not provide an intercomparison. (Modified from Hall, 1978.)

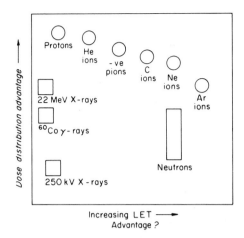

Figure 16.24. Schematic comparison of the possible therapeutic advantage of using different types of radiation. The vertical axis represents the advantage due to improved depth–dose distribution. The horizontal axis represents increasing LET, which may give an advantage for the treatment of some tumors but not others. (Adapted from Raju, 1980.)

possibility of exploiting differences (eg, in repair capacity) which exist in the response of different cells and tissues to low LET radiations. Thus the problem is to identify patients with tumors likely to benefit from high LET radiotherapy.

As discussed above, the biological aspects may not always lead to a therapeutic advantage. Such an advantage can only be established by clinical trials. Clinical studies using high LET radiations have been most extensive with fast neutrons, although a small number of patients have been treated with negative pions or heavy ions and trials are in progress with protons. The results of clinical trials with neutrons have suggested that tumors at certain sites (eg, salivary gland adenocarcinomas, soft-tissue sarcomas, squamous-cell carcinomas) may benefit from such treatment (see Wambersie et al, 1984). Neutron treatments have, however, been associated with an increase in complications and randomised trials have yet to demonstrate convincingly that a real therapeutic gain can be achieved (see Duncan, 1983).

16.5.5 MODIFIED FRACTIONATION SCHEDULES

Results from animal studies suggest that the repair of damage expressed late after radiation may be greater than that of damage expressed early (see section 16.4.2). Since tumors are thought to respond to fractionated treatments like early-responding normal tissues, this difference in repair capacity might be exploited to obtain a therapeutic gain (Withers, 1985). This can be achieved by reducing the fraction size

below that used conventionally (from 2–2.5 Gy to 1–1.5 Gy). More fractions would be required, and these would have to be given more than once per day if the treatment time was not to be prolonged. Such a treatment protocol is termed hyperfractionation. The increase in dose, expected to be tolerated by late-responding normal tissues treated with hyperfractionation, should give increased tumor response. An increase in early normal tissue reactions would also be expected so that hyperfractionation could only be used in situations where an increase in early reactions would not be dose limiting. The rationale for hyperfractionation does not consider reoxygenation, but because there is no change in overall treatment time it is assumed that reoxygenation will not be much different than for a conventional fractionation scheme.

Shortening of the overall treatment time might also improve the therapeutic ratio, since it will reduce the time for repopulation in the tumor. The tolerance of late-responding normal tissues should be relatively little affected. Reduced treatment time can be achieved either by reducing the number of fractions or by giving more than one fraction per day (with fractions given 4–6 hr apart to allow for repair). The latter option, often called accelerated fractionation, is preferable because increasing fraction size (which would be necessary with reduced fraction number) leads to a relative increase in damage to late-responding tissues. Accelerated fractionation may be detrimental if it reduces reoxygenation of tumors between fractions. It is likely to be beneficial particularly for rapidly reoxygenating and repopulating tumors in sites where acutely responding tissues (which will also have less time for repopulation) would not become dose limiting.

16.6 SUMMARY

Radiotherapeutic treatment of cancer usually involves giving 20–30 individual dose fractions of 2–2.5 Gy spread over a period of 4–6 weeks. In general, such conventional treatments have a better therapeutic ratio than single doses because they have been found to give greater tumor control at tolerable levels of normal tissue damage. Experimental studies with cells in culture and with animal models identified four factors (the "four R's") which are likely to influence response to fractionated treatment. These are repair of radiation damage, repopulation of damaged tissues by proliferation of surviving cells, redistribution of proliferating cells through the cell cycle and reoxygenation of hypoxic cells. Repair and repopulation are the reasons why cells and tissues can tolerate a larger total dose when it is fractionated. They occur both in tumors and normal tissues, although repopulation probably has a minor effect on the late radiation damage which occurs in slowly proliferating normal tissues and is often dose limiting. Reoxygenation, which occurs primarily in tumors, seems likely to be a major factor responsible for the improved therapeutic ratio obtained with fractionated treatment compared to single doses.

Different fractionated schedules which give equal levels of normal tissue response or tumor control can be expressed in the form of isoeffect relationships, which are usually plotted as log (total dose) vs log (overall time or number of fractions). For fractionated treatments in clinical practice such an isoeffect plot can be approximated by a straight line, implying a power-law relationship between total dose and overall time or fraction number. This relationship has been formalised into a number of different mathematical equations such as the NSD equation, designed to predict isoeffective treatments. Isoeffect relationships for late-responding tissues tend to be steeper than those for acutely responding tissues, implying greater capacity for repair of damage that leads to late effects. The difference in the isoeffect relationships for early and late damage implies that reducing fraction size will reduce damage to late-responding tissues to a greater extent than to early-responding tissues or tumors. A therapeutic gain might therefore be achieved by using hyperfractionation, where treatment with smaller dose fractions is given several times per day.

Other approaches to improving the therapeutic ratio have included attempts to reduce the resistance due to hypoxic cells in tumors. Hyperbaric oxygen breathing prior to and during treatment has met with limited success and studies are in progress using drugs capable of specific sensitization (and toxicity for) hypoxic cells. High LET radiations are also being studied because certain types can give improved depth–dose distributions as compared to X-rays or γ-rays, and there are certain radiobiological attributes of high LET irradiation (eg, reduced OER) which may lead to a therapeutic advantage.

REFERENCES

Adams GE, Dewey DL: Hydrated electrons and radiobiological sensitization. *Biochem Biophys Res Commun* 1963; 12: 473–477.

Bagshaw MA, Doggett RLS, Smith KC et al: Intra-arterial 5-bromo-deoxyuridine and x-ray therapy. *Radiology* 1967; 99:886–894.

Brown JM, Goffinet DR, Cleaver JE, Kallman RF: Preferential radiosensitization of mouse sarcoma relative to normal skin by chronic intra-arterial infusion of halogenated pyrimidine analogs. *J Natl Canc Inst* 1971; 47:75–89.

Brown JM, Yu Ny, Brown DM, Lee WW: SR-2508:A 2-nitroimidazole amide which should be superior to mis-

onidazole as a radiosensitizer for clinical use. *Int J Radiat Oncol Biol Phys* 1981; 7:695–703.

Bump EA, Yu NY, Brown JM: Radiosensitization of hypoxic cells by depletion of intracellular glutathione. *Science* 1982; 127:544–545.

Bush RS: Endpoints for evaluating treatment, in *Malignancies of the Ovary, Uterus and Cervix*. London, Edward Arnold, 1979, chap 1.

Bush RS, Jenkin RDT, Allt WEC et al: Definitive evidence for hypoxic cells influencing cure in cancer therapy. *Br J Cancer* 1978; 37(Suppl III):302–306.

Cohen L: *Biophysical Models in Radiation Oncology*. Boca Raton, FL, CRC Press, 1983.

Deacon J, Peckham MJ, Steel GG: The radioresponsiveness of human tumours and the initial slope of the cell survival curve. *Radiother Oncol* 1984; 2:317–323.

Del Regato JA: Our history and heritage: Claudius Regaud. *Int J Radiat Oncol Biol Phys* 1976; 1:993–1001.

Denekamp J: Changes in the rate of repopulation during multifraction irradiation of mouse skin. *Br J Radiol* 1973; 46:381–387.

Denekamp J, Rojas A, Stewart FA: Is radioprotection by WR-2721 restricted to normal tissues? in Nygaard OF, Simic MG (eds), *Radioprotectors and Anticarcinogens*. New York, Academic Press, 1983, pp 655–679.

Dische S: Chemical sensitizers for hypoxic cells: A decade of experience in clinical radiotherapy. *Radiother Oncol* 1985; 3:97–115.

Duncan W: A clinical evaluation of fast neutron therapy, in Steel GG, Adams GE, Peckham MS, (eds), *The Biological Basis of Radiotherapy*. Amsterdam, Elsevier, 1983, pp 277–286.

Ellis F: Dose, time and fractionation: a clinical hypothesis. *Clin Radiol* 1969; 20:1–7.

Ellis F: Is NSD-TDF useful to radiotherapy? *Int J Radiat Oncol Biol Phys* 1985; 11:1685–1697.

Fertil B, Malaise EP: Inherent cellular radiosensitivity as a basic concept for human tumor radiotherapy. *Int J Radiat Oncol Biol Phys* 1981; 7:621–629.

Fertil B, Malaise EP: Radiosensitivity of human cell lines is correlated with radioresponsiveness of human tumors: Analysis of 101 published survival curves. *Int J Radiat Oncol Biol Phys* 1985; 11:1699–1708.

Field SB, Hornsey S: The RBE for fast neutrons: The link between animal experiments and clinical practice, in Nygaard OF, Adler HI, Sinclair WK (eds), *Radiation Research; Biomedical, Chemical and Physical Perspectives*. New York, Academic Press, 1975, pp 1125–1135.

Fowler JF: Experimental animal results relating to time–dose relationships in radiotherapy and the "ret" concept. *Br J Radiol* 1971; 44:81–90.

Fowler, JF: A critical look at empirical formulae in fractionated radiotherapy, in Fletcher GH, Nervi C, Withers HR (eds), *Biological Bases and Clinical Implications of Tumor Radioresistance*. New York, Masson, 1983, pp 201–204.

Fowler JF: What next in fractionated radiotherapy? *Br J Cancer* 1984; 49(Suppl VI):285–300.

Fowler JF: Chemical modifiers of radiosensitivity—theory and reality: A review. *Int J Radiat Oncol Biol Phys* 1985; 11: 665–674.

Fowler JF, Denekamp J, Sheldon PW et al: Optimum fractionation in x-ray treatment of C_3H mouse mammary tumours. *Br J Radiol* 1974; 47:781–789.

Fowler JF, Stern BE: Dose–time relationships in radiotherapy and the validity of cell survival curve models. *Br J Radiol* 1963; 36:163–173.

Guichard M, Weichselbaum RR, Little JB, Malaise EP: Potentially lethal damage repair as a possible determinant of human tumor radiosensitivity. *Radiother and Oncol* 1984; 1:263-269.

Hall EJ: Review article: Radiation dose–rate: a factor of importance in radiobiology and radiotherapy. *Br J Radiol* 1972; 45:81–97.

Hall EJ: *Radiobiology for the Radiologist*, ed 2. Hagerstown, MD, Harper and Row, 1978.

Hill RP: Sensitizers and radiation dose fractionation: Results and interpretations. *Int J Radiat Oncol Biol Phys* 1986; 12: 1049–1054.

Hill RP, Bush RS: Dose fractionation studies with a murine sarcoma under conditions of air or carbogen breathing. *Int J Radiat Oncol Biol Phys* 1977; 2:913–919.

Hornsey S: The recovery process in organised tissue, in Silini G (ed), *Radiation Research*. Amsterdam, North-Holland, 1967, pp 587–603.

Hornsey S, Field SB: Slow repair and residual injury, in Meyn RE, Withers HR (eds), *Radiation Biology in Cancer Research*. New York, Raven Press, 1980, pp 489–499.

Howes AE, Field SB: The oxygen effect: A new look at "Friedman and Pearlman." *Br J Radiol* 1968; 41:554–555.

Kallman RF: The phenomenon of reoxygenation and its implications for fractionated radiotherapy. *Radiology* 1972; 105:135–142.

Kinsella TJ, Russo A, Mitchell JB: A Phase 1 study of intravenous iododeoxyuridine as a clinical radiosensitizer. *Int J Radiat Oncol Biol Phys* 1985; 11:1941–1946.

Kirk J, Gray WM, Watson ER: Cumulative radiation effect. Part I: fractionated treatment regimes. *Clin Radiol* 1971; 22:145–155.

Nakatsugawa S: Potentially lethal damage repair and its implications in cancer treatment, in Sugahara T (ed), *The Modification of Radiosensitivity in Cancer Treatment*. Japan, Academic Press, 1984, pp 221–250.

Orton CG, Ellis F: A simplification in the use of the NSD concept in practical radiotherapy. *Br J Radiol* 1973; 46: 529–537.

Peters LJ, Hopwood LE, Withers HR, Suit HD: Predictive assays of tumor radiocurability. *Cancer Treatment Symposia* 1984; 1:67–74.

Raju, MR: *Heavy Particle Radiotherapy*. New York, Academic Press, 1980.

Rockwell S: Use of a perfluorochemical emulsion to improve oxygenation in a solid tumor. *Int J Radiat Oncol Biol Phys* 1985; 11:97–103.

Rofstad EK: Human tumor xenografts in radiotherapeutic research. *Radiother Oncol* 1985; 3:35–46.

Sheldon PW, Foster JL, Fowler JF: Radiosensitization of C_3H mouse mammary tumours by a 2-nitroimidazole drug. *Br J Cancer* 1974; 30:560–565.

Siemann DW, Hill RP, Bush RS: Smoking: The effect of chronic reductions in the arterial partial pressure of oxygen on the radiation response of an experimental tumor. *Br J Radiol* 1978a; 51:992–996.

Siemann DW, Hill RP, Bush RS: The influence of carboxyhemoglobin (HbCo) in tumour oxygenation and response to radiation. *Int J Radiat Oncol Biol Phys* 1978b; 4:657–662.

Strandqvist M: Studien Uber die kumulative wirkung der rontgenstrahlen bei fracktionierung. *Acta Radiologica Suppl.* LV, 1944.

Suit HD, Howes AE, Hunter N: Dependence of response of a C_3H mammary carcinoma to fractionated irradiation on fractionation number and intertreatment interval. *Radiat Res* 1977; 72:440–454.

Suit HD, Russell WO, Martin RG: Management of patients with sarcoma of soft tissue in an extremity. *Cancer* 1973; 31:1247–1255.

Thames HD, Withers HR, Peters LJ, Fletcher GH: Changes in early and late radiation responses with altered dose fractionation: Implications for dose–survival relationships. *Int J Radiat Oncol Biol Phys* 1982; 8:219–226.

Urtasun RC, Chapman JD, Raleigh JA et al: Binding of ^3H-misonidazole to solid human tumors as a measure of tumor hypoxia. *Int J Radiat Oncol Biol Phys* 1986; 12:1263–1267.

Wambersie A, Battermann JJ, Breteau N: Survey of the clinical results of neutrontherapy. *J Eur Radiother* 1984; 5: 120–131.

Whitmore GF, Gulyas S, Varghese AJ: Sensitizing and toxicity properties of misonidazole and its derivatives. *Br J Cancer* 1978; 37(Suppl III):115–119.

Withers HR: Biologic basis for altered fractionation schemes. *Cancer* 1985; 55:2086–2095.

Withers HR, Mason KA: The kinetics of recovery in irradiated colonic mucosa of the mouse. *Cancer* 1974; 34:896–903.

Yuhas JM, Spellman JM, Culo F: The role of WR-2721 in radiotherapy and/or chemotherapy, in Brady LW (ed), *Radiation Sensitizers*. New York, Masson, 1980, pp 303–308.

BIBLIOGRAPHY

Brown JM (ed): Chemical modifiers of cancer treatment. *Int J Radiat Oncol Biol Phys* 1986; 12:1019–1545.

Fowler JF: What next in fractionated radiotherapy? *Br J Cancer* 1984; 49(Suppl VI):285–300.

Hall EJ: *Radiobiology for the Radiologist*, ed 2. Hagerstown, MD, Harper and Row, 1978.

Meyn RE, Withers HR (eds): *Radiation Biology in Cancer Research*. New York, Raven Press, 1980.

Raju, MR: *Heavy Particle Radiotherapy*. New York, Academic Press, 1980.

Steel GG, Adams GE, Peckham MJ (eds): *The Biological Basis of Radiotherapy*. Amsterdam, Elsevier, 1983.

17

Biological Properties of Anticancer Drugs

Ian F. Tannock

17.1 INTRODUCTION

This chapter is the first of three which deal with the scientific basis for cancer chemotherapy. It will introduce the more important anticancer drugs and their biological properties, as well as experimental methods that are used to determine their activity; the second chapter will describe the pharmacology of anticancer drugs, and the third will give an overview of experimental chemotherapy.

The first documented clinical use of chemotherapy was in 1942 when the alkylating agent nitrogen mustard was used to obtain a brief clinical remission in a patient with lymphoma (Gilman, 1963). Following this initial demonstration that a chemical agent might cause remission of a human malignancy, a large number of drugs have been developed and tested for potential clinical activity. Figure 17.1 indicates the historical development of those anticancer drugs which have achieved wide clinical usage, as well as other landmarks such as the initial use of important drug combinations. About 30 cytotoxic drugs (excluding hormonal agents) are cur-

rently (1986) licensed for use in North America and several new agents are undergoing clinical trials.

Anticancer drugs can be classified into a number of families (see Fig 17.2) based on their biochemical activities or their origins. These families include the alkylating agents, antimetabolites, and natural products which have anticancer activity. Numerous drugs with a related structure have been synthesized and their biological activities have been assessed. This study of structure–activity relationships has produced several alkylating agents that are in current clinical usage, such as cyclophosphamide and melphalan. Alkylating agents have one or two side chains that are electron deficient, and which will bind to electron-rich groups of biological molecules. Their major mechanism of lethal activity is thought to involve interaction with bases of DNA (section 18.3).

The development of a second major class of compounds followed the unravelling of biochemical pathways in intermediate metabolism. Drugs were synthesized which resembled normal metabolites, and which could compete as substrates for enzyme activity

278

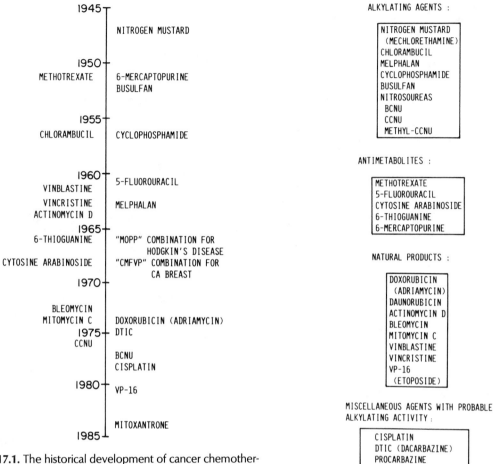

Figure 17.1. The historical development of cancer chemotherapy. Dates are approximate, and indicate the availability of drugs or combinations for use in North America.

Figure 17.2. Major families of drugs that are used in cancer chemotherapy.

(section 18.4). Examples of these antimetabolites (Fig 17.2) are methotrexate, an analog of the vitamin folic acid, which is essential for transfer of methyl groups in several biosynthetic reactions; and 5-fluorouracil, which closely resembles the bases thymine and uracil that are constituents of DNA and RNA respectively. Most antimetabolites inhibit nucleic acid synthesis either directly or indirectly, and tend to be active mainly against proliferating cells.

Other new drugs are heterogeneous and include derivatives of naturally occurring species (antibiotics) and synthesized chemicals (eg, cisplatin). Several naturally occurring compounds have important antitumor activity. The anthracyclines such as doxorubicin (Adriamycin) are planar multiring structures that are thought to intercalate between turns of the double helix in DNA. The vinca alkaloids (vincristine and vinblastine) are derived from the periwinkle plant; they bind to tubulin and disrupt the mitotic spindle. Cisplatin is a very active compound derived by chemical synthesis, and its activity may be due in part to alkylating

properties. The pharmacology of each of these compounds is reviewed in chapter 18.

17.2 CELLULAR EFFECTS OF DRUGS

17.2.1 TYPES OF CELL DAMAGE

The concept was introduced in chapter 8 that tumors contain a population of cells, known as stem cells, which have a very large potential for cell proliferation. Stem cells may constitute only a small proportion of the total cells in a human tumor, whereas most of the cells in transplantable tumors of animals may be stem cells. If the aim of tumor treatment is cure or long-term remission, then the critical assessment of drug effect is lethality for stem cells. In practice, the survival of such cells after treatment is assessed by their ability to produce colonies of progeny of a defined minimum size. Thus, measurement of cell survival after drug treatment is analogous to that for radiation, and involves the use of a clonogenic assay (see section 15.4). Other types of damage, leading to transient changes in cell metabolism and proliferation, and loss of nonclonogenic cells, occur frequently after drug treatment. These effects may lead to normal-tissue toxicity (section 17.5), and may contribute to tumor remission (ie, to transient changes in tumor volume) but not to cure.

17.2.2 NONCLONOGENIC ASSAYS

Many investigators have sought to assess the cellular toxicity of anticancer drugs by a variety of methods that do not measure reproductive potential in a clonogenic assay (see Table 17.1).

Each of the endpoints in Table 17.1 has been proposed as a method for predicting the inhibition of reproductive potential by drugs without the need to do clonogenic assays. Their purpose was to assess the response of human tumors to individual drugs, usually following incubation of tumor cells with the drug in vitro. Unfortunately, most of these endpoints correlate poorly with loss of reproductive integrity as measured by a clonogenic assay (eg, Roper and Drewinko, 1976). Cells that are visibly damaged and whose membranes become permeable to dyes or radioisotopes have almost certainly lost their clonogenic capacity; however, a large number of lethally damaged cells may appear normal and may exclude dyes or retain isotopes at short intervals after treatment. Some lethally damaged cells may continue to have normal macromolecular synthesis for several hours after treatment, while other cells which are destined to survive may have transient changes in their metabolism. Despite the above problems, many nonclonogenic assays have been quite successful in predicting clinical resistance when applied after drug treat-

ment of biopsies from human tumors (ie, if a drug has no effect in the assay it usually has no effect in the patient donating the biopsy). Unfortunately the assays have a much poorer record in predicting the rarer patient with drug sensitivity, and they have not led to improvement in patient survival when drugs selected by an in vitro assay were used in comparison to empirical treatment in randomized clinical trials (Nissen et al, 1978).

17.2.3 COLONY-FORMING ASSAYS

Colony-forming and other assays which allow quantitation of stem cells were described in detail in section 15.4 as methods for assessment of the lethal effects of radiation. The same assays are used also for assessing the lethal effects of drugs (Table 17.2). The major modification for assessment of drug effects is that whereas even high doses of radiation may be delivered over a few seconds or minutes, some drugs may require exposures of several hours in order to exert lethal effects on cells. The biological effectiveness of a drug is dependent on both the concentration of the drug and the duration of exposure. Thus, it is usual to relate cell survival after drug treatment both with drug concentration (for a constant exposure time) and with duration of exposure (at a constant drug concentration).

The simplest assay for assessing drug-induced lethality is to expose cells that will grow in tissue culture to the drug, followed by plating of different dilutions of cells in Petri dishes. Colony-forming assays in culture may also be used for study of drug effects in vivo by using tumors that have the ability to generate colonies in vitro following removal and dissociation of the tumor. Assessment of colony formation after treatment of transplanted tumors allows for drug metabolism and other aspects of in vivo pharmacology, while toxicity to

Table 17.1. Nonclonogenic Assays That Have Been Used to Assess Drug Activity

- Microscopic evidence of cell damage, such as disruption of cells
- Damage to cell membranes, as measured by failure to exclude dyes such as trypan blue, or loss of radioactivity (eg, ^{51}Cr) from prelabeled cells
- Impairment of macromolecular synthesis, usually assessed by measuring the uptake of ^{3}H-thymidine into DNA, ^{3}H-uridine into RNA, or ^{3}H-amino acids into proteins
- Changes in proliferative parameters such as thymidine-labeling index
- Formation of micronuclei in cells
- Exchange of sister chromatids detected at mitosis as an assay of damage to DNA

Table 17.2. Assays That Have Been Used to Quantitate Stem Cells After Drug Treatment

- Colony formation on plastic or glass in liquid medium
- Colony formation in semisolid medium such as dilute agar or methylcellulose
- Serial dilution of cells into multiwell plates to establish the minimum number of cells that will lead to growth
- Serial dilutions of cells implanted into syngeneic animals to establish the TD-50 (ie, the number of cells which lead to growth of tumors in 50% of animals)
- Formation of spleen colonies after intravenous injection of hematological cells into irradiated mice (see Fig 17.3)
- Formation of metastatic lung colonies after intravenous injection of tumor cells

colony-forming cells of bone marrow can be assessed by removal and culture of marrow in the same experiment.

The spleen-colony assay (Fig 17.3) has been used widely for assessing the effects of drugs on survival of pluripotent colony-forming cells of mouse bone marrow (termed CFU-S) and of syngeneic transplantable leukemias and lymphomas of mice. The method, developed by Till and McCulloch (1961), involves intravenous injection of bone marrow from drug-treated and control mice into syngeneic mice that have received a dose of radiation (~9 Gy) that would have been lethal in the absence of such an injection. Recognizable colonies may be observed in the spleens of recipients about 7–10 days later and cell survival is estimated by the ratio of number of colonies derived from treated and from untreated inocula. The method may also be adapted to compare the drug sensitivities of rapidly and slowly proliferating cells (eg, Van Putten et al, 1972), and has been an important source of information about the relationship between drug activity and proliferative rate.

17.2.4 CLONING ASSAYS FOR HUMAN TUMORS

Courtenay et al (1976) and Hamburger and Salmon (1977) have developed assays using semisolid agar and enriched media that support colony growth from cell suspensions derived from a variety of human tumors. These assays were described in section 8.2 and have been important in the study of human tumor biology. They have also been used widely in attempts to predict clinical response to specific drugs (Selby et al, 1983).

There is evidence for a correlation between clinical response and in vitro response of tumor cells in a human-tumor clonogenic assay. Thus we can state the following:

1. Cells from human tumors of a single histologic type appear to have a response in vitro that is similar to the known clinical behavior of such tumors.
2. An assay that predicts for drug resistance is correct in about 90% of cases, whereas the prediction of clinical drug sensitivity is correct in about 40–70% of patients.
3. The response rate of a group of patients treated with drugs selected by the assay was higher than that of a group of empirically treated patients for whom the test was not performed. (Von Hoff et al, 1983)

Although a correlation is established between in vitro and clinical response, this does not prove the benefit of the test for individual patients. Many biological and technical problems are associated with the assay and

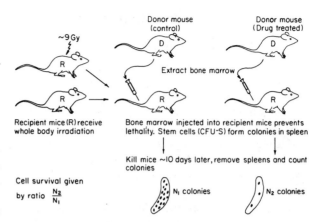

Figure 17.3. The spleen-colony assay used to assess the effects of anticancer drugs against colony-forming cells (CFU-S) in mouse bone marrow.

currently limit its appropriate use to a research setting (Table 17.3). Despite these problems, the clonogenic assay has a sound biological basis for study of drug effects against cells from primary human tumors. Careful experimental design may minimize artifacts, and the assay might have some potential as part of a screening procedure for new agents. Considerable improvement is required before it can serve as a useful guide for the treatment of individual patients.

Table 17.3. Problems Associated with the Use of Human Tumor Clonogenic Assays in Prediction of Response to Chemotherapy

- Low plating efficiency (typically 0.001–1.0%) limits the number of tumors that form adequate colonies for assessment of drug effects.
- The tissue-culture environment may lead to selection of some colony-forming cells from a heterogeneous group of clonogenic cells in the original tumor.
- It is difficult to obtain a pure suspension of single cells without causing cellular damage. Residual clusters or clumps of cells may cause artifacts by confusion with colonies.
- The assay allows only short exposure to drugs in culture, and this may not disclose the effects of cell-cycle-phase-specific agents.
- There is potential for large errors in assessment of "response" in both the assay and in patients.
- Predictive values of all assays depend on prevalence. Thus assays are only useful if (for example) the predictive value for drug resistance exceeds its prevalence among the treated patients (frequently >80%).
- A requirement for validation of all assays is use of a positive control such as radiation, where the relationship between survival and dose may be predicted.

7.3 CELL SURVIVAL

17.3.1 CELL-SURVIVAL CURVES

For several drugs, the proportion of cells surviving treatment is found to be exponentially related to drug concentration. Thus, following the practice for radiation (section 15.4), cell-survival curves are usually plotted using a logarithmic axis for cell survival (S) and a linear axis for drug dose or concentration (D); exponential survival curves are then represented by a straight line (Fig 17.4).

Exponential cell-survival curves are expected if cell lethality is due to a simple chemical interaction between molecules of the drug and a molecular "target" in the cell. The relationship is then analogous to the interaction of ionizing events due to radiation with a molecular target (thought to be DNA). The equation which describes the relationship between cell survival and dose was derived in section 15.5 and was shown to be

$$S = \exp(-D/D_0) \qquad (17.1)$$

Here D_0 is the drug concentration required to reduce survival to $1/e$, or 0.37. Thus a smaller value of D_0 represents the effect of a more potent drug.

Tumors and normal tissues may be expected to contain cells that are heterogeneous with respect to proliferative state, intrinsic drug sensitivity and possibly in proficiency for repair of drug-induced damage. In addition, limited diffusion of some drugs may lead to varying dosage to cells within the population. Each of these factors may influence the shape of the cell-survival curve after drug treatment, so that departures from an exponential relationship between cell survival and dose occur more commonly than for radiation. As discussed in subsequent sections, the shape of the dose–survival relationship may give important clues to the mechanisms underlying drug activity.

17.3.2 PROLIFERATIVE RATE

The spleen-colony assay (Fig 17.3) has been used to compare the effects of drugs on cell survival of slowly proliferating bone marrow precursors (CFU-S) with either rapidly proliferating murine lymphoma cells, or with CFU-S that have been induced to proliferate (eg, Bruce et al, 1966; Van Putten et al, 1972). Two basic types of survival curve were obtained. For many drugs, including most of the alkylating agents and 5-fluorouracil, cell survival was exponentially related to dose, and most drugs had greater activities against proliferating cells (Fig 17.4a). For other drugs, survival decreased exponentially at low drug doses, but if the

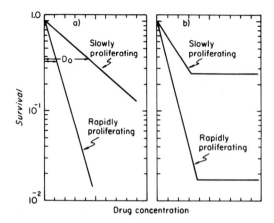

Figure 17.4. Model cell survival curves for rapidly and slowly proliferating cells generated following a short duration of exposure to varying concentrations of drugs, *a*, for drugs that are not cell-cycle-phase specific, and, *b*, for drugs that are active in only one phase of the cell cycle.

exposure time was short there was no further decrease in survival above a threshold concentration, leading to a plateau on the cell-survival curve (Fig 17.4b). The plateau level of cell survival was always lower for rapidly proliferating cells. Drugs which show this pattern of survival are now known to act primarily at one phase of the cell cycle (see following section); they include most of the antimetabolites and tubulin-binding agents such as methotrexate, cytosine arabinoside, 6-thioguanine, 6-mercaptopurine, vincristine and vinblastine. An increase in concentration of these drugs with a short exposure time gives no further cell kill once a threshold is exceeded since all cells in the drug-sensitive phase of the cycle are killed and no others are affected. An increase in exposure time with constant drug concentration may allow more cells to enter the drug-sensitive phase, leading to an exponential relationship between cell survival and exposure time (Bruce et al, 1969). However, many drugs also inhibit the transit of surviving cells through the cell cycle.

In vitro assays are also available for studying drug activity for cells with different rates of proliferation. Cells in culture grow exponentially when conditions are ideal; however, as cell crowding increases and nutrients in the media are rapidly consumed, proliferation slows because of an increase in cell-cycle time and/or a decrease in growth fraction (Fig 17.5). Cell death increases to equal the rate of cell production, and the number of cells reaches a maximum, or "plateau" level. Survival curves have been obtained for many drugs following treatment of rapidly proliferating cells in exponential phase and slowly proliferating cells in plateau phase. In general, the results of such experiments are in agreement with data obtained by the spleen-colony

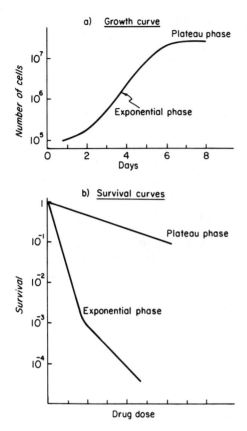

Figure 17.5. *a,* Typical sigmoid growth curve for cells in culture. During exponential phase cells are cycling rapidly, but there is minimal cell proliferation during plateau phase. *b,* Survival curves for treatment of exponential- and plateau-phase cells are similar to those obtained for doxorubicin by Twentyman and Bleehen (1975).

assay and by other methods. Most drugs have greater sensitivity for rapidly proliferating cells. Exceptions include the nitrosoureas (BCNU, CCNU), bleomycin and cisplatin, which in most laboratories have shown little selectivity when tested in this way (eg, Twentyman and Bleehen, 1975).

For drugs which show an exponential relationship between cell survival and dose, their relative sensitivity for rapidly and slowly proliferating cells may be expressed as the ratio of doses required to achieve the same level of cell kill (Fig 17.4a). Values of this ratio generally lie between 1.0 and 2.0 for alkylating agents, but cyclophosphamide has greater specificity for cycling cells with values in the range of 2.0–5.0 when tested in the spleen-colony assay against proliferating and nonproliferating cells of the same type. 5-Fluorouracil, doxorubicin and bleomycin also show marked selectivity for proliferating cells (Data reviewed in Tannock, 1978). Thus proliferative rate is a major determinant of drug activity.

17.3.3 CELL CYCLE PHASE SPECIFICITY

Information about the activities of drugs at different phases of the cell cycle has been obtained by treatment of cells that have been synchronized in tissue culture (Nias and Fox, 1971; see also section 15.6.2). As cells progress in a cohort around the cell cycle, drug administration may be timed to treat a population that is enriched for cells in G_1, S, G_2 or mitotic phase. Alternative methods for studying drug effects involve separation of asynchronous cells on the basis of cell-cycle phase either before or immediately after drug treatment, followed by assessment of colony formation.

Procedures used to separate cells must not, of course, influence cell viability. At least two methods have been used. Flow cytometry using a vital dye such as Hoechst 33342 may separate cells on the basis of DNA content (section 9.4), but may be subject to artifact if the dye has direct toxicity or if it may enhance the activity of anticancer drugs (Pallavicini et al, 1979). Alternatively, cells may be separated by size or density using centrifugation; cell separation has been automated by using centrifugal elutriation, which allows rapid separation of a large number of cells (eg, Meistrich et al, 1977). Since cells increase in size as they pass through the cell cycle, fractions can be obtained which are enriched for cells in G_1, S, or G_2 phase; these populations can then be assessed for drug sensitivity.

The above methods have demonstrated that almost all drugs show variations in lethal toxicity around the cell cycle (eg, Mauro and Madoc–Jones, 1970; Fig 17.6). Many of the antimetabolites exert lethal toxicity only for cells that are synthesizing DNA, whereas methotrexate and doxorubicin have maximum toxicity for S-phase cells, but have some activity during other phases of the cycle. Studies using thymidine labeling or

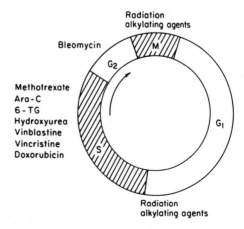

Figure 17.6. Phases of the cell cycle in which anticancer drugs show selective lethal toxicity.

flow cytometry have demonstrated that many of these drugs also inhibit either the onset or continuation of DNA synthesis in cells which survive treatment (eg, Tobey, 1972). Such studies of nonlethal progression delay are always subject to problems of interpretation because of difficulty in recognizing surviving cells, as opposed to lethally damaged cells prior to their lysis. Vincristine and vinblastine are known to disrupt formation of the mitotic spindle, leading to arrest of cells in mitosis. Experiments with synchronized cells have shown, however, that lethal effects of these drugs occur when cells are in S phase, presumably when formation of the mitotic spindle is initiated. Many alkylating agents (eg, nitrogen mustard, melphalan) have similar phase activity to that observed most often for radiation (see section 15.6.2) with two peaks of maximum lethal activity, one in G_2-M phase and one near the G_1-phase/S-phase boundary. Bleomycin acts mainly in G_2 phase and mitosis, while cisplatin may have greater activity for some cells in G_1 phase, with little or no phase specificity for others.

The relative specificity of most drugs for one or more phases of the cell cycle leaves a partly synchronized population of surviving cells after treatment. Several investigators have proposed that such synchrony may allow scheduling of anticancer drugs to maximize killing of tumor cells by giving subsequent treatments when a large number of survivors are again in a drug-sensitive phase. In practice, the wide spread of cell-cycle times observed in vivo leads to rapid loss of synchrony, and heterogeneity of the tumor cell population and of drug distribution make this difficult to apply clinically (Tannock, 1978). The most important determinant of clinical scheduling is recovery from normal tissue toxicity (see section 17.5).

17.3.4 DRUG RESISTANCE

Survival curves obtained for mammalian cells treated with radiation under aerobic conditions tend to fall within a rather narrow range of sensitivities. In contrast, when different mammalian cells are treated with the same drug, survival curves may show a very wide range of sensitivities. The mechanisms underlying such drug resistance are reviewed in section 19.2.

Intrinsic sensitivities to drugs may differ not only between cell populations, but also among the cells of a single population. Indeed, the induction or selection of a drug-resistant subpopulation in human tumors can be the major factor limiting the efficacy of clinical chemotherapy. Even if drug-resistant cells are present initially only at low frequency (eg, one drug-resistant cell per 10^5 drug-sensitive cells), their selective advantage during drug treatment will lead to their rapid emergence

as the dominant cell population. The presence of such drug-resistant cells will be disclosed by the presence of a drug-resistant "tail" on the cell-survival curve. Survival curves with a terminal part of shallow slope may indicate a population that is drug resistant for many reasons, including a population that is spared in a drug-resistant phase of the cell cycle (cf Fig 17.4b). If a population of cells has been selected that has intrinsic and stable drug resistance, the survival curve will demonstrate resistance when the initial surviving cells are expanded and again treated with the same agent.

17.3.5 REPAIR OF DRUG-INDUCED DAMAGE

When cells are treated with radiation they may accumulate a certain amount of repairable damage, and this leads to a shoulder on the cell-survival curve. Ability to repair some types of damage depends on the cellular environment (see section 15.6.3). Less is known about cellular repair of damage caused by anticancer drugs. Comparison of cell survival following single and divided doses of treatment, which first suggested repair of radiation damage, has been performed infrequently for drugs. Such experiments are more difficult to interpret than for radiation because lethal effects of drugs often take place over several hours and it is difficult then to define an interval between doses; results are also confounded by the greater dependence on cell-cycle phase of many drugs, so that the distribution of cells among drug-sensitive and drug-resistant phases may change dramatically between treatments. Strong evidence for the existence in cells of repair mechanisms for damage caused by some anticancer drugs is provided by studies of drug effects against cells derived from patients with one of the clinical syndromes that are due to deficiency of DNA repair enzymes (eg, ataxia telangiectasia). Marked sensitivity of such cells, or of other repair-deficient mutant cells, has been found for several drugs, including nitrogen mustards, mitomycin C, nitrosoureas, cisplatin, and actinomycin D (Fig 17.7; Setlow, 1978). Recently, drug sensitivity of normal and mutant cells has been correlated directly with the development and repair of specific lesions in DNA as assessed by the method of alkaline elution.

Accumulation of sublethal damage may lead to the appearance of a shoulder on the survival curve following treatment of cells with some drugs, but this type of survival curve is found less commonly than after treatment with radiation. Differences in survival curves between DNA-repair-proficient and -deficient cells after treatment with drugs are in the slope as well as the shoulder of the curve (Fig 17.7). This result is to be expected if the amount of repair is proportional to the number of sites of damage on DNA, as opposed to a

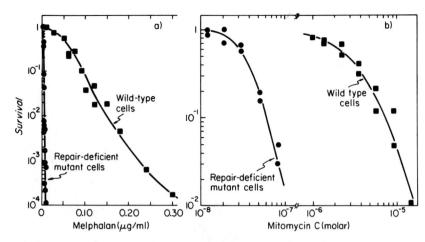

Figure 17.7. Survival of wild-type cells and DNA repair-deficient mutant cells following treatment with *a*, melphalan, and *b*, mitomycin C. Note the expanded logarithmic scale for dose of mitomycin C. (Adapted from Thompson, et al, 1980.)

constant amount of repair that occurs in many types of cells after treatment with radiation. A better understanding of repair of drug-induced damage is important in determining mechanisms of drug activity, and the wide variations in drug sensitivity among different cells.

17.4 EFFECTS OF DRUGS AGAINST TUMORS

17.4.1 IN SITU ASSESSMENT

The clonogenic assays described in the preceding sections have the advantage that they seek to assess directly reproductive death of cells after drug treatment. When used to study drug treatment in vivo, they require removal of tissue and production of a suspension of single cells, followed by study of colony formation in an environment that differs markedly from that in a tumor or normal tissue which is left in situ after treatment. These processes may add to cellular damage caused by drugs and may bias the results by assessment only of selected cells that can proliferate in the new environment. In situ assays avoid such problems, but do not provide a direct assessment of cell survival after drug treatment. Commonly used in situ assays are the time of animal survival after treatment or of drug-induced delay in tumor growth.

The influence of a drug on survival of animals (usually mice) bearing syngeneic transplanted tumors is used widely as the method for screening of new agents. In a typical experiment a number of mice are implanted with identical numbers of tumor cells; they are randomly assigned to drug treatment and control groups and their day of death is observed. Work by

Skipper and his colleagues (eg, 1964) has demonstrated a direct relationship between the proportion of cells killed by certain treatments and the observed increase in animal life span for the L1210 ascites tumor in mice; the method can then provide an indirect measure of cell survival. Other tumors do not always demonstrate this simple relationship, and the use of animal survival to predict cell lethality may be complicated by nonlethal effects of drugs that can delay tumor growth, and by toxic effects of drugs on normal tissues that tend to shorten animal survival. Assessment of relative effects of drugs on tumor and normal tissues in one experiment may, however, offer an advantage for drug screening. The method is technically simple, and perhaps appropriate for tumors that cause death by systemic effects, such as ascitic or widely metastasizing tumors. Duration of animal survival seems inappropriate, on both ethical and scientific grounds, for assessment of drug effects against most solid tumors.

Comparison of tumor growth in treated and untreated animals is the preferred in situ method for assessing drug effects against solid tumors in animals (Fig 17.8). The method of regrowth delay models the assessment of tumor remission, which is the major clinical endpoint for drug efficacy, since most chemotherapy is given with palliative rather than curative intent. It is humane, since animals can be killed painlessly before their tumors are sufficiently large to cause discomfort.

The effect of drugs to cause delay in tumor growth is usually studied in groups of animals that received different doses of drugs. A dose–response curve may then be generated which relates drug dose with some measure of growth delay (eg, the time for the tumor to grow to a fixed volume; Fig 17.8). Experiments with many

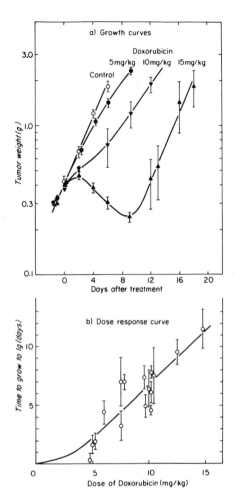

Figure 17.8. *a,* Illustration of tumor-growth curves for treatment of an experimental tumor with doxorubicin. Tumor weight was estimated by prior calibration with measurements of tumor diameter. Note that growth curves after drug treatment are not always parallel to the growth curve for controls, and that interanimal variation may lead to large standard errors. *b,* Dose–response curve, relates drug dose to the time for tumors to grow from size at treatment (0.4 g) to 1 g. The curve was obtained from multiple experiments similar to that shown in Figure 17.8a. (Adapted from Tannock, 1982.)

drugs and tumors lead to regrowth curves after treatment which are parallel to the growth curve for untreated controls, and the shape of the dose–response curve is then independent of the endpoint selected as a measure of growth delay. Other drug and tumor combinations lead to tumor regrowth that is slower than in controls, perhaps because of damage to blood vessels. Growth delay is due not only to lethal effects against tumor stem cells, but also includes the effects of drugs on other cells that may be present in the tumor, as well as nonlethal effects that may lead to slower proliferation of tumor cells. Likewise, partial remission of human

tumors after drug treatment does not necessarily imply major lethal effects of the drugs.

17.4.2 XENOGRAFTS

Human tumors may be implanted into immune-deficient mice and their responsiveness to drugs studied in vivo. Xenografts have the advantage that they may have similar characteristics to the human tumors from which they are derived. They also allow for in vivo drug pharmacology, although this may differ between mouse and man. They have been useful in assessing the activities of both new and established drugs against human tumors of varying origins and histological types. Usually, drug effects are assessed by delay in tumor growth.

The most widely used host for xenografting of human tumors is the congenitally athymic nude mouse (eg, Giovanella et al, 1978), but an alternative host is the immune-suppressed conventional mouse (Steel et al, 1978). Neither mouse is a perfect host, since nude mice produce antibodies and have large numbers of natural killer cells, while partial return of immunity occurs in immune-suppressed mice. These effects can cause problems when analyzing the response to treatment of slowly growing human tumor xenografts.

The success of xenografts in predicting clinical response has been reviewed by Steel et al (1983). The major use of xenografts has been to compare the drug response of a panel of human cell lines representative of a given histological type of human tumor. There is a correlation between response to drugs of such xenografts and the clinical response of human tumors of the same histological type. Attempts to individualize treatment through the use of xenografts have not been successful. Many tumors (especially breast cancer) produce a low proportion of successful xenografts, while others grow in only one or two of a group of immune-deficient mice. Assessment of drug sensitivity is usually performed on second- or third-generation transplants. This process may take several months and it is then too late to apply the results to an individual patient.

A different type of xenograft, involving transplantation of small pieces of human tumor under the capsule of the kidney of a normal mouse, has been proposed as a short-term predictive assay by Bogden et al (1981). Effectiveness of drugs is assessed by the relative change in size of the implant when drug-treated and control mice are killed a few days later. A major problem with this assay is that the immune response of the mouse will eventually lead to disappearance of tumors even in controls, so that only assays in which control tumors have not diminished in size are acceptable for assessment of

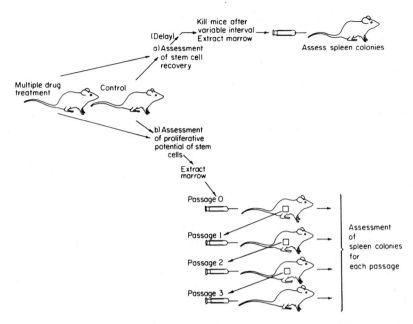

Figure 17.10. Experiments designed to study *a*, recovery of stem-cell function after chemotherapy, and *b*, repopulating ability of stem cells after chemotherapy. Methods were described by Botnick et al (1978, 1981).

17.5.2 OTHER PROLIFERATIVE TISSUES

Ulceration of the intestinal mucosa is a common dose-limiting toxicity when rodents are treated with anticancer drugs, and is due to interruption of the production of new cells which normally replace the mature cells that are continually sloughed into the lumen (section 9.5.2). Damage to bone marrow is more commonly dose limiting in man, but mucosal ulceration may occur after treatment with several drugs including methotrexate, 5-fluorouracil, bleomycin and cytosine arabinoside; other drugs such as cyclophosphamide and doxorubicin may increase the severity of ulceration when used in combination. Mucosal damage, with accompanying symptoms of soreness and diarrhea, usually begins about 5 days after treatment and its duration increases with its severity. Full recovery is usually possible if the patient can be supported through this period; recovery is analogous to that in bone marrow, with repopulation from slowly proliferating stem cells which are situated in the base of the intestinal crypts. As with bone marrow, some drugs (eg, cyclophosphamide, 5-fluorouracil and vincristine) seem to act only on proliferating cells in the crypts, whereas other agents (doxorubicin and radiation) appear to damage stem cells near the bases of the crypts as well (Ijiri and Potten, 1983). However, doxorubicin may have smaller effects against intestinal stem cells in man, since intestinal damage is usually dose limiting in mice but is rarely so in man.

Partial or complete hair loss is common after treatment with many anticancer drugs, and is due to lethal effects of drugs against proliferating cells in hair follicles; it usually begins about 2 weeks after treatment. Full recovery occurs after cessation of treatment, suggesting the presence of drug-resistant slowly proliferating precursor cells. In some patients hair begins to regrow despite continued treatment with the agent that initially caused its loss. Regrowth of hair might reflect a compensating proliferative process which increases the number of stem cells, or may represent the development of drug resistance in a normal tissue, akin to that which occurs in tumors.

Spermatogenesis in men, and formation of ovarian follicles in women, both involve rapid cellular proliferation, and are susceptible to the toxic effects of many anticancer drugs. Men who receive chemotherapy often have decreased production of sperm and infertility. Testicular biopsy usually demonstrates loss of germinal cells within the seminiferous tubules, presumably because of drug effects against these rapidly proliferating cells. Antispermatogenic effects may be reversible after lower doses of chemotherapy (Schilsky et al, 1980), but some men remain permanently infertile; it is now usual to recommend banking of sperm for young men who undergo intensive chemotherapy for potentially curable malignancies, such as Hodgkin's disease.

Chemotherapy given to premenopausal women often leads to temporary or permanent cessation of menstrual periods, and to menopausal symptoms. Reversibility of this effect depends on age, on the types of drug used, and on the duration and intensity of chemotherapy. Biopsies have been available less frequently from the relatively inaccessible ovaries than from testes, but the major finding has been failure of formation of ovarian follicles, sometimes with ovarian fibrosis. The pathological findings are consistent with a primary effect of drugs against the proliferating germinal epithelium.

17.5.3 NAUSEA AND VOMITING

Nausea and vomiting are frequent during the first few hours after treatment with many anticancer drugs, but are not due primarily to direct effects on intestinal mucosa. Drug-induced vomiting is thought to occur because of direct stimulation of chemoreceptors in the brain stem, which then emit signals via connecting nerves to the neighboring vomiting center, thus eliciting the vomiting reflex. Major evidence for this mechanism comes from studies in animals, where induction of vomiting by chemotherapy is prevented by removal of the chemoreceptor zone; additional mechanisms may be present in man since there are differences among species in mechanisms of drug-induced vomiting.

17.5.4 DRUGS AS CARCINOGENS

Many anticancer drugs cause toxic damage through effects on DNA, and also cause mutations and chromosomal damage. These properties are shared with known carcinogens (see chapter 6) and patients who are long-term survivors of chemotherapy may be at increased risk for developing a second malignancy. This effect has only become apparent where chemotherapy has resulted in long survival for some patients with drug-sensitive diseases (eg, lymphomas, myeloma and carcinoma of the ovary) or where it is used as an adjuvant to decrease the probability of recurrence of disease following local treatment. Most of the second malignancies are acute leukemias, and their most common time of presentation is 2–4 years after initiation of chemotherapy.

Drugs most commonly implicated in the cause of second malignancy include alkylating agents and procarbazine, and there is increased risk if patients also receive radiation. It is often difficult to separate an increase in probability of second malignancy that may be associated with the primary neoplasm (for example, in a patient with lymphoma) from that associated with its treatment. Comparisons of the incidences of leukemia and other malignancies in clinical trials which randomize patients to receive adjuvant chemotherapy, or no chemotherapy after primary treatment, have given

conclusive evidence of the carcinogenic potential of some drugs (eg, Boice et al, 1983). The relative risk of leukemia in drug-treated as compared to control patients may be substantial; for example, the relative risk of leukemia was 12.4 among 2000 patients receiving methyl-CCNU as adjuvant therapy for gastrointestinal cancer, in clinical trials reviewed by Boice et al (1983), although the absolute risk of second malignancy remained low. Care is needed in using alkylating agents as adjuvants where benefit may be minimal, but the risks of second malignancy are small compared to potential benefits in treating curable tumors such as Hodgkin's disease.

17.6 SUMMARY

Chemotherapy for cancer has evolved rapidly since the first patient was treated with nitrogen mustard in 1942, with about 30 drugs licensed for clinical use in North America. Major classes of drugs include alkylating agents, antimetabolites, and natural or synthetic compounds.

The most relevant endpoint for assessing lethal effects of drugs on cells is loss of reproductive potential as measured in a colony-forming assay. Attempts have been made to apply such assays following drug treatment of cells obtained by biopsy from human tumors with the aim of prediction of clinical response. At present, several problems should limit the use of such assays to a research setting.

Survival curves which relate colony-forming ability to drug concentration may be exponential, or may demonstrate no further killing above a certain concentration, if the drugs are cell-cycle-phase specific. Most drugs are more toxic to rapidly proliferating cells. Repair of drug-induced damage and the presence of resistant subpopulations may also influence the shape of cell-survival curves.

In situ assays of tumor response following drug treatment in animals include duration of animal survival and delay in tumor growth. Growth delay has been applied to the study of drug response of human tumor xenografts in immune-deficient mice. In situ assays are used in screening for activities of new drugs.

The toxicity of many drugs for bone marrow, intestine, hair follicles and gonads is probably due to depletion of rapidly proliferating cells in these tissues, with subsequent recovery from slowly proliferating stem cells. However, some drugs may cause permanent damage to stem cell function. Nausea and vomiting may occur through stimulation of chemoreceptors in the brainstem. Many drugs cause damage to DNA, which may result occasionally in the induction of a second malignancy.

REFERENCES

Boice JD Jr, Greene MH, Killen JY Jr et al: Leukemia and preleukemia after adjuvant treatment of gastrointestinal cancer with Semustine (Methyl-CCNU). *N Engl J Med* 1983; 309:1079–1084.

Bogden AE, Cobb WR, Lepage DJ et al: Chemotherapy responsiveness of human tumors as first transplant generation xenografts in the normal mouse: Six-day subrenal capsule assay. *Cancer* 1981; 48:10–20.

Botnick LE, Hannon EC, Hellman S: Multisystem stem cell failure after apparent recovery from alkylating agents. *Cancer Res* 1978; 38:1942–1947.

Botnick LE, Hannon EC, Vigneulle R, Hellman S: Differential effects of cytotoxic agents on hematopoietic progenitors. *Cancer Res* 1981; 41:2338–2342.

Bruce WR, Meeker BE, Valeriote FA: Comparison of the sensitivity of normal hematopoietic and transplanted lymphoma colony-forming cells to chemotherapeutic agents administered *in vivo. J Natl Cancer Inst* 1966; 37:233–245.

Bruce WR, Meeker BE, Powers WE, Valeriote FA: Comparison of the dose and time-survival curves for normal hematopoietic and lymphoma colony-forming cells exposed to vinblastine, vincristine, arabinosylcytosine, and amethopterin. *J Natl Cancer Inst* 1969; 42:1015–1023.

Burke PJ, Diggs CD, Owens AH Jr: Factors in human serum affecting the proliferation of normal and leukemic cells. *Cancer Res* 1973; 33:800–806.

Courtenay VD, Smith IE, Peckham MJ, Steel GG: *In vitro* and *in vivo* radiosensitivity of human tumour cells obtained from a pancreatic carcinoma xenograft. *Nature* 1976; 263: 771–772.

Driscoll JS: The preclinical new drug research program of the National Cancer Institute. *Cancer Treat Rep* 1984; 68:63–76.

Gilman A: The initial clinical trial of nitrogen mustard. *Am J Surg* 1963; 105:574–578.

Giovanella BC, Stehlin JS Jr, Williams LJ Jr et al: Heterotransplantation of human cancers into nude mice. A model system for human cancer chemotherapy. *Cancer* 1978; 42: 2269–2281.

Griffin TW, Bogden AE, Reich SD et al: Initial clinical trials of the subrenal capsule assay as a predictor of tumor response to chemotherapy. *Cancer* 1983; 52:2185–2192.

Hamburger AW, Salmon SE: Primary bioassay of human tumor stem cells. *Science* 1977; 197:461–463.

Ijiri K, Potten CS: Response of intestinal cells of differing topographical and hierarchical status to ten cytotoxic drugs and five sources of radiation. *Br J Cancer* 1983; 47:175–185.

Mauro F, Madoc-Jones H: Age response of cultured mammalian cells to cytotoxic drugs. *Cancer Res* 1970; 30:1397–1408.

Meistrich ML, Grdina DJ, Meyn RE, Barlogie B: Separation of cells from mouse solid tumors by centrifugal elutriation. *Cancer Res* 1977; 37:4291–4296.

Nias AH, Fox M: Synchronization of mammalian cells with respect to the mitotic cycle. *Cell Tissue Kinet* 1971; 4:375–398.

Nissen E, Tanneberger S, Projan A et al: Recent results in *in vitro* drug prediction in human tumour chemotherapy. *Arch Geschwulstforsch* 1978; 48:667–672.

Pallavicini MG, Lalande MG, Miller RG, Hill RP: Cell cycle distribution of chronically hypoxic cells and determination of the clonogenic potential of cells accumulated in $G_2 + M$ phases after irradiation of a solid tumor *in vivo. Cancer Res* 1979; 39:1891–1897.

Roper PR, Drewinko B: Comparison of *in vitro* methods to determine drug-induced cell lethality. *Cancer Res* 1976; 36:2182–2188.

Schilsky RL, Lewis BJ, Sherins RJ, Young RC: Gonadal dysfunction in patients receiving chemotherapy for cancer. *Ann Intern Med* 1980; 93:109–114.

Selby P, Buick RN, Tannock I: A critical appraisal of the "Human Tumor Stem Cell Assay." *N Engl J Med* 1983; 308:129–134.

Setlow RB: Repair deficient human disorders and cancer. *Nature* 1978; 271:713–717.

Skipper HE, Schabel FM Jr, Wilcox WS: Experimental evaluation of potential anticancer agents. XIII. On the criteria and kinetics associated with "curability" of experimental leukemia. *Cancer Chemother Rep* 1964; 35:1–111.

Steel GG, Courtenay VD, Peckham MJ: The response to chemotherapy of a variety of human tumour xenografts. *Br J Cancer* 1983; 47:1–13.

Steel GG, Courtenay VD, Rostom AY: Improved immunesuppression techniques for the xenografting of human tumours. *Br J Cancer* 1978; 37:224–230.

Tannock IF: Cell kinetics and chemotherapy: A critical review. *Cancer Treat Rep* 1978; 62:1117–1133.

Tannock IF: Response of aerobic and hypoxic cells in a solid tumor to Adriamycin and cyclophosphamide and interaction of the drugs with radiation. *Cancer Res* 1982; 42:4921–4926.

Tannock IF: Experimental chemotherapy and concepts related to the cell cycle. *Int J Radiat Biol* 1986; 49:335–355.

Thompson LH, Rubin JS, Cleaver JE et al: A screening method for isolating DNA repair-deficient mutants of CHO cells. *Somatic Cell Genet* 1980; 6:391–405.

Till JE, McCulloch EA: A direct measurement of the radiation sensitivity of normal mouse bone marrow cells. *Radiat Res* 1961; 14:213–222.

Tobey RA: Effects of cytosine arabinoside, daunomycin, mithramycin, azacytidine, adriamycin, and camptothecin on mammalian cell cycle traverse. *Cancer Res* 1972; 32: 2720–2725.

Twentyman PR, Bleehen NM: Changes in sensitivity to cytotoxic agents occurring during the life history of monolayer cultures of a mouse tumour cell line. *Br J Cancer* 1975; 31:417–423.

Van Putten LM, Lelieveld P, Kram-Idsenga LKJ: Cell cycle specificity and therapeutic effectiveness of cytostatic agents. *Cancer Chemother Rep* 1972; 56:691–700.

Von Hoff DD, Clark GM, Stogdill BJ et al: Prospective clinical trial of a human tumor cloning system. *Cancer Res* 1983; 43:1926–1931.

18

The Pharmacology of Anticancer Drugs

Charles Erlichman

18.1 INTRODUCTION

In this chapter some general principles of pharmacology which apply to anticancer drugs will be presented. Specific properties of anticancer drugs that are in clinical use will then be reviewed, with particular emphasis on their structure, mechanism of action, pharmacokinetics and host toxicity.

18.2 PHARMACOKINETICS

18.2.1 DRUG ABSORPTION, DISTRIBUTION AND EXCRETION

Pharmacokinetics is the study of the time course of drug and metabolite levels in different body fluids, tissues and excretions and includes drug absorption, distribution, metabolism and excretion (Gibaldi and Perrier, 1982).

A variable proportion of an administered drug may be delivered into the circulation and hence become available for a potential therapeutic effect (bioavailability). Absorption is assumed to be complete if a drug is administered intravenously, but may be partial if it is given by oral, intramuscular, subcutaneous or other routes. Absorption may be variable among patients receiving similar treatments, and may even vary from one course of treatment to another in the same patient. Several factors influence the bioavailability of a drug that is prescribed for oral administration (Fig 18.1). Compliance of the patient is an important but often neglected factor. Random tests of plasma concentration have disclosed poor compliance for many types of drugs, and this may be a major problem for anticancer drugs, which often produce unpleasant side effects. Second, dissolution of the capsule or tablet must occur to allow subsequent absorption. Third, the drug must pass through the gastrointestinal mucosa and into the intestinal capillaries, which drain into the portal vein. Finally, the drug must be transported through the liver, where it may undergo metabolism, and thence into the systemic circulation. Metabolism of a drug as it passes through the liver en route to the systemic circulation is referred to as the "first-pass effect"; this effect may decrease the bioavailability of a drug, and lead to large interpatient variation in drug efficacy (Pond and Tozer, 1984).

Metabolism of a drug in any organ (most commonly liver) will contribute to elimination of the parent compound from the plasma. However, for some drugs metabolites retain therapeutic activity, and for others (eg, cyclophosphamide) metabolism is required for activation. Many anticancer drugs have active metabolites, introducing a complex relationship between pharmacokinetics and antitumor effects (Houston, 1981).

Distribution of a drug or its metabolites in the body is governed by factors such as blood flow to different organs and diffusion of the drug from blood vessels, protein binding in plasma or elsewhere, and lipid solubility (Fig 18.1). In general, drugs with extensive binding to plasma proteins (eg, doxorubicin) or with high lipid solubility will tend to exhibit prolonged elimination phases because there is slow release of drug from these sites. However, this also depends on the rate of drug inactivation. For example, BCNU (bis-chloronitrosourea) is a lipid-soluble drug and penetrates into the central nervous system well, but it is rapidly inactivated resulting in a short exposure duration to body tissues.

Most drugs and their metabolites are eliminated from the body via the kidney, with excretion into the urine. For drugs which are potentially toxic to the kidney (eg, high-dose methotrexate and cisplatin) it may be important to stimulate drug excretion by maintaining the urine at an alkaline pH (methotrexate) or by maintaining a rapid urinary flow (cisplatin). Drugs excreted by the kidney may be poorly tolerated in patients with impairment of renal function, so that reduced doses must be given. A few drugs (eg, doxorubicin) are excreted predominantly via the liver and biliary tract and are eliminated in the feces. Therefore, the tolerated dose of doxorubicin is lower in patients with elevated levels of bilirubin secondary to liver disease because the elevated bilirubin indicates obstruction of the biliary tract or impairment of hepatic metabolism.

Cancer therapy often involves the administration of several anticancer drugs to patients during a short interval of time, in addition to medications for relief of pain, nausea and other symptoms. Interactions between drugs may influence each of the processes of absorption, metabolism, distribution and excretion. Although there are documented examples where administration of one drug has been found to influence the disposition of another (for example, excretion of methotrexate is inhibited by aspirin), interactions between anticancer drugs have not been investigated extensively.

Assays are available for many anticancer drugs which allow quantitation of the amount of drug in plasma or tissues of a patient. Measurement of drug levels aids in the understanding of drug pharmacokinetics and drug interaction with other medications. Such studies might also help to predict therapeutic and toxic effects in an

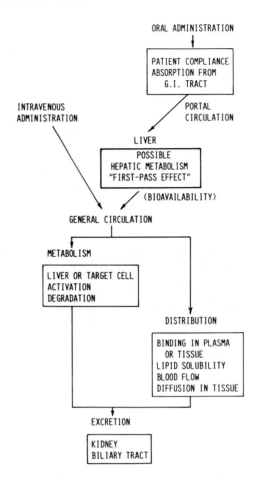

Figure 18.1. Factors influencing the pharmacokinetics of anticancer drugs following oral or intravenous administration.

individual patient. But the lack of simple and rapid assays, and the variability in drug concentration that leads to tumor response and normal tissue toxicity (Erlichman et al, 1980; Balis et al, 1983; Erlichman, 1986) has limited the practical utility of routine drug monitoring.

18.2.2 PHARMACOKINETIC ANALYSIS

The analysis of curves relating drug concentration to time in plasma and other body fluids may define simple theoretical models. Some terms which can be derived from such models are listed in Table 18.1. The terms and models are tools which can be used to predict a drug's behaviour in the body.

A drug's pharmacokinetics may be defined by either a linear or a nonlinear relationship between dose and plasma concentration. A linear relationship predicts that the elimination half-life ($t_{1/2}$) or clearance of a drug from plasma is independent of dose and is appli-

Table 18.1. Glossary of Terms Used Commonly in Pharmacokinetics*

Symbol	Definition
AUC	Area under the plasma concentration–time curve from zero to infinity (also referred to as $C \times T$) determined by integrating drug concentration in plasma over time
$C(t)$	Drug concentration in plasma at time t
$t_{1/2}$	Half-life. The time required for the drug concentration in plasma to decrease by one half. $t_{1/2}$ is constant if drug clearance is exponentially related to time
$t_{1/2}\alpha$	Half-life of the α or initial phase†
$t_{1/2}\beta$	Half-life of the β or second phase† in a two-compartment model
$t_{1/2}\gamma$	Half-life of the γ or third phase† in a three-compartment model
V_d	Apparent volume of distribution. This is a hypothetical volume of body fluid required to dissolve the total amount of drug at the same concentration found in blood
V_c	Volume of the central compartment
Cl	Clearance is the ratio of overall drug elimination rate to its concentration in the blood. It is the sum of all individual organ clearances and one of the most important pharmacokinetic parameters to consider in describing drug behavior

*See, for example, Balis et al (1983).

†It has been recommended recently that α, β, γ... be replaced by λ_i ($i = 1, 2 ...$) (Allen et al, 1982).

cable when means of drug disposition are not saturable. A nonlinear relationship may apply to drugs which are actively transported across membranes, which require enzyme-mediated metabolism, or which bind to plasma proteins or tissue. These mechanisms can be saturated at high concentration of drugs, and result in a nonlinear relationship between peak plasma concentration and drug dose as well as variable $t_{1/2}$ and clearance with dose. Although several anticancer drugs are handled by saturable mechanisms such as active transport, metabolism and protein or tissue binding, linear models may provide an adequate approximation to their pharmacokinetic behaviour if plasma concentrations are below levels which will saturate the above mechanisms (Ames et al, 1983).

Two common linear pharmacokinetic models which are applicable to many drugs are illustrated in Figure 18.2. The body is represented by compartments into which a drug or its metabolites are assumed to be distributed uniformly. The one-compartment model depicts the body as a single homogeneous volume for drug distribution. In the two-compartment model, the blood and all readily accessible fluids and tissues are represented as a common homogeneous unit of volume, referred to as the central compartment. Poorly perfused tissue such as muscle and fat are represented by a second homogeneous unit of different volume, referred to as the peripheral compartment. This type of modeling may be extended to include three or more compartments, which may be necessary to represent such additional factors as extensive binding in tissue or entero-hepatic circulation. The models are designed to explain experimental data relating drug concentration to time, but the compartments may have no anatomical or physiological reality. The volume of drug distribution (V_d) represents a *hypothetical* volume of body fluid that would be required to dissolve the total amount of drug at the same concentration as that found in plasma. The calculation of a value of V_d which is larger than the total volume of the body is possible, and may represent extensive binding of drug in extravascular tissues.

The one-compartment model (Fig 18.2a) assumes that any change which occurs in the drug concentration of plasma is matched by similar changes in drug concentration of tissue. The curve relating drug concentration in plasma (C) to time (t) is derived by assuming a linear model in which the rate of elimination of the drug is proportional to plasma concentration. Thus

$$-\frac{dC}{dt} = \alpha C , \qquad (18.1)$$

where α is a constant. Integration of this equation gives

$$C = C_0 e^{-\alpha t} \qquad (18.2)$$

Here C_0 is the concentration of drug in plasma at time $t = 0$, for an instantaneous intravenous administration.

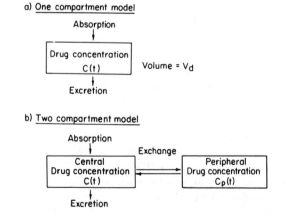

Figure 18.2. Examples of one- and two-compartment models used in analysis of pharmacokinetics.

The plasma half-life (ie, $t_{1/2} = [\log_e 2]/\alpha$) is a constant characterizing drug elimination in the one-compartment model.

In the two-compartment model (Fig 18.2b) both the rate of drug elimination and the rate of transfer between the compartments are assumed to be proportional to the drug concentration within them. Derivation of the equation which describes plasma concentration with time then leads to

$$C = C_1 e^{-\alpha t} + C_2 e^{-\beta t} \qquad (18.3)$$

Here α, β, C_1, and C_2 are constants, and the additional exponential term arises because of exchange of drug between the two compartments. This type of drug disposition curve which may be fitted by two exponentials is observed for many anticancer drugs, and is illustrated in Figure 18.3 by data for mitomycin C. One term of eq (18.3) (with a half-life designated usually as $t_{1/2}\alpha$) dominates at early times after drug administration, and the second term (with half-life $t_{1/2}\beta$) dominates at longer intervals. This leads to the familiar pattern of rapid early disappearance of drug followed by a later slow decline in plasma drug concentration (Fig 18.3). Study of the pharmacokinetics of some anticancer drugs may also reveal a third component of drug elimination with half-life designated $t_{1/2}\gamma$.

Pharmacokinetic modelling must take into consideration the method of administration (eg, intravenous bolus versus continuous infusion) and the frequency of drug administration. Whereas bolus injection will ensure high peak concentrations of drug in plasma, the duration of time between doses will define the lowest level or trough which is reached. Drugs with short $t_{1/2}$s will require frequent administration if a certain minimum or therapeutic range is to be maintained. Conversely, drugs with long $t_{1/2}$s will require less frequent administration of drug. Thus the $t_{1/2}$ is an important parameter which may predict the frequency of drug administration and give some insight into the time during which drug can be detected in the body. If the aim of drug treatment is to achieve a uniform exposure to the drug, continuous infusion of a stable drug may be appropriate. This can be achieved with mechanical pumps which are available for ambulatory patients as outpatient therapy.

These theoretical models have practical applications in the use of chemotherapeutic agents. Organ dysfunction (eg, renal or hepatic disease) may alter drug disposition in the body. Recommendations regarding drug dose in the face of such disease is one practical application of pharmacokinetic analysis of drug behavior. For example, hepatic dysfunction prolongs the clearance of doxorubicin, and hence tissue exposure to a cytotoxic compound. Therefore, the dose of doxorubicin should be decreased in the presence of an elevated bilirubin. The rational design and use of regional chemotherapy is another clinical application of pharmacokinetic modelling.

18.2.3 REGIONAL ADMINISTRATION OF DRUGS

Regional chemotherapy has been used in attempts to achieve high local concentration of a drug, and hence to obtain a therapeutic advantage when treating malignant disease localized to one region of the body. Many anticancer drugs have limited access to the central nervous system (CNS) and a widely used form of regional chemotherapy has involved injection of drugs into the cerebrospinal fluid (CSF), which flows around and through the CNS. Such intrathecal administration can be achieved by lumbar puncture (injection into the CSF in the space below the spinal cord in the lower back), or into an Ommaya reservoir, which is a small device that is implanted surgically just under the skin of the head, and through which CSF circulates via a catheter in contact with one of the ventricles (spaces containing CSF) of the brain. Other uses of regional chemotherapy involve instillation of drugs into the bladder through a cystoscope for treatment of superficial blad-

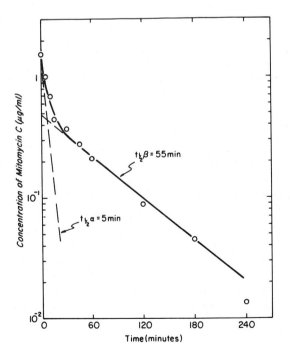

Figure 18.3. Plasma-clearance curve for the drug mitomycin C whose pharmacokinetics are described by a two-compartment model. Initial and final plasma half-lives are referred to as $t_{1/2}\alpha$ and $t_{1/2}\beta$, respectively. (C. Erlichman, unpublished results.)

der cancer, injection of drugs into the peritoneal cavity in patients with peritoneal seeding of malignant disease and ascites, or arterial infusion into limbs, liver or other organs of the body.

Regional administration of chemotherapy only offers a potential therapeutic advantage if the initial exposure due to regional administration is much higher than subsequent exposure due to recirculation of drug through the systemic circulation (Collins, 1984). One favourable circumstance for regional delivery is the administration of drug which will be removed rapidly from plasma by the region being perfused. Systemic exposure to drug will subsequently be lower. A low rate of drug exchange between site of perfusion and systemic circulation is responsible for the therapeutic advantage of intrathecal treatment for meningeal but not parenchymal CNS disease, and for intracystic therapy of bladder cancer, as compared to systemic administration of drug. Clear evidence for benefit of intra-arterial chemotherapy has yet to be established, but will depend on the use of drugs which are removed rapidly and effectively from blood and have a low regional rate of exchange. Intrahepatic administration of drugs such as methotrexate and cisplatin is unlikely to result in a major therapeutic benefit, since these drugs have low plasma clearance and a ready access to other organs when injected into the hepatic artery.

18.2.4 DRUG EFFECTS ON CELLS

The study of drug effects at the cellular level is known as pharmacodynamics. Important processes include uptake of the drug into cells, intracellular metabolism and binding to molecular targets, cellular mechanisms for overcoming of repair of drug-induced damage and cytotoxicity. Anticancer drugs may enter cells by passive diffusion, by facilitated diffusion, or by active transport. Passive diffusion is energy independent but concentration dependent, and is influenced by physicochemical characteristics of the drug such as lipid solubility and degree of ionization. Active transport is an energy-dependent process that involves a receptor molecule to which the drug is bound as it is transported across the cell membrane. This process is saturable, may be blocked by metabolic inhibitors and allows transport of drug against a concentration gradient. Active-transport systems have been demonstrated for methotrexate, doxorubicin, vinca alkaloids and several other drugs. Facilitated diffusion is also thought to involve a carrier molecule; drugs can therefore enter the cell more rapidly than by passive diffusion, but can only be transported down a concentration gradient. Some drugs are transported into cells by more than one mechanism, and the dominant process then depends on

the concentration gradient across the cell membrane, and the degree of saturation of available carrier sites.

Drug effects inside cells, and the mechanisms which cells use to try to circumvent or repair damage caused by them, vary widely among the different types of drugs (Chabner, 1982); these factors will be described for individual drugs in subsequent sections.

18.3 ALKYLATING AGENTS

18.3.1 GENERAL PROPERTIES

Alkylating agents are chemically diverse drugs which have the common property that they may undergo transformation to produce reactive intermediates which are electron deficient. These reactive groups can form covalent linkages with chemical groups on biological molecules which have an excess of electrons (ie, are "nucleophilic"), including amino, phosphate, sulfhydryl and hydroxyl groups (see also section 6.3). The process of covalent binding of alkyl groups (eg, CH_2Cl) to these groups is known as alkylation. Alkylating agents may contain either one or two reactive groups and are then referred to as monofunctional or bifunctional alkylating agents respectively. Bifunctional alkylating agents have the potential to form cross-links between biological molecules.

Nucleophilic chemical groups that are potential sites of alkylation occur on almost all biological molecules, but alkylation of bases in DNA appears to be the major cause of lethal toxicity. This is supported by a quantitative relationship between the concentration of drug which causes toxicity to cells and the production of lesions in DNA such as single-strand breaks and cross-links; these lesions can be quantitated by the technique of alkaline elution (Kohn, 1979). Also, increased toxicity of alkylating agents has been found in mutant cells which are deficient in enzymes that are required for repair of DNA (sections 7.4 and 17.3.5). Cross-linking of DNA strands seems to be the major mechanism of damage for bifunctional alkylating agents (which include most of those in common clinical usage), whereas toxicity of monofunctional alkylating agents may be related to single-strand breaks in DNA or damaged bases. Possible mechanisms underlying the development of resistance to alkylating agents include defects in their transport across the cell membrane, and increased ability to repair damage to DNA (section 19.2.1).

18.3.2 CYCLOPHOSPHAMIDE AND OTHER NITROGEN MUSTARDS

This family of drugs, derived from the prototype alkylating agent nitrogen mustard (or mechlorethamine), contains several drugs in common clinical use including cyclophosphamide, melphalan and chlorambucil. The structure of these drugs are shown in Figure 18.4: each of them is bifunctional with two chloroethyl groups which form the reactive electron-deficient groups responsible for alkylation of DNA.

The most common site of alkylation of DNA is the N-7 position on the base guanine. The reactions leading to alkylation of guanine are illustrated in Figure 18.5 for nitrogen mustard. First, one of the chloroethyl side chains of nitrogen mustard undergoes a first-order reaction leading to release of a chloride ion and to formation of a highly reactive positively charged intermediate. This intermediate may then bind covalently with the electro-negative N-7 group on a guanine base, resulting in alkylation. Alkylation of guanine may lead to mispairing with thymine or to strand breakage. The second chloroethyl side chain of nitrogen mustard may undergo a similar reaction leading to covalent binding with another base on the opposite strand of DNA, leading to formation of a cross-link.

Nitrogen mustard is still used clinically (eg, as part of the four-drug "MOPP" protocol for Hodgkin's disease) but its reactivity makes it unstable and liable to cause irritation at the injection site.

Addition of ring structures to the nitrogen mustard molecule conveys increased stability (Fig 18.4), and oral preparations of the more stable drugs chlorambucil, melphalan and cyclophosphamide are available. Chlorambucil is a well-tolerated drug with a narrow spectrum of activity that is used mainly in treatment of slowly progressive neoplasms such as chronic lymphocytic leukemia. Melphalan is used for treatment of multiple myeloma, breast and ovarian cancer and is usually given orally. Absorption of melphalan is variable after oral administration and 20–50% of an oral dose can be recovered in the feces; some patients with poor bioavailability after oral dosage have responded to intravenous drug. The pharmacokinetics of melphalan can best be fitted by a two-compartment model. Uptake of melphalan is mediated by an amino acid active transport system; resistance may occur because of mutation leading to change in this transport system (section 19.2). Both chlorambucil and melphalan have minimal specificity for cycling cells and may lead to delayed and/or cumulative toxicity to bone marrow because of their toxicity to bone marrow stem cells.

Cyclophosphamide is the alkylating agent in widest clinical use, and forms part of treatment protocols for many types of cancer. The parent compound is inactive. Cyclophosphamide was synthesized originally because tumor cells were known to contain phosphoramidase and phosphatase enzymes at high activity. It was thought that these enzymes might lead to selective

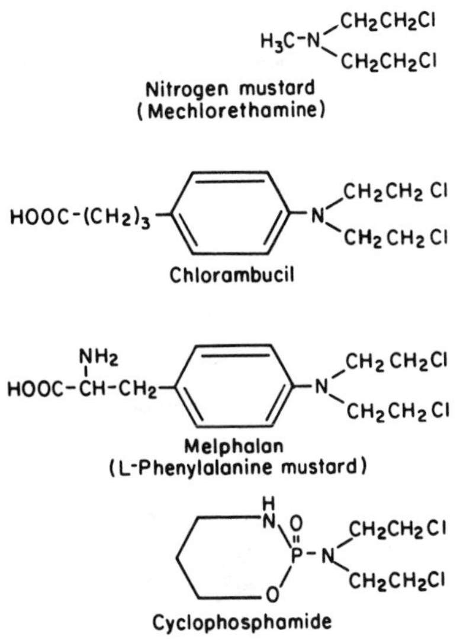

Figure 18.4. Structure of clinically used alkylating agents of the nitrogen mustard family.

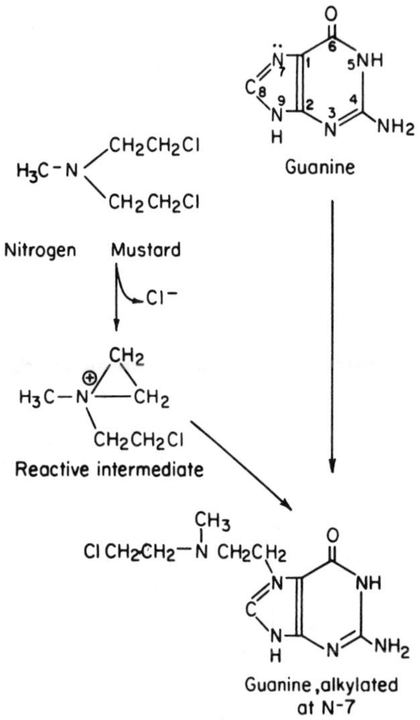

Figure 18.5. Reactions leading to alkylation at the N-7 position of guanine by nitrogen mustard.

activation of alkylating activity by cleavage of the ring structure within tumor cells; however, it is apparent that primary activation takes place in the liver. Microsomal enzymes in the liver metabolize cyclophosphamide to 4-hydroxycyclophosphamide, which exists in equilibrium with its acyclic isomer aldophosphamide

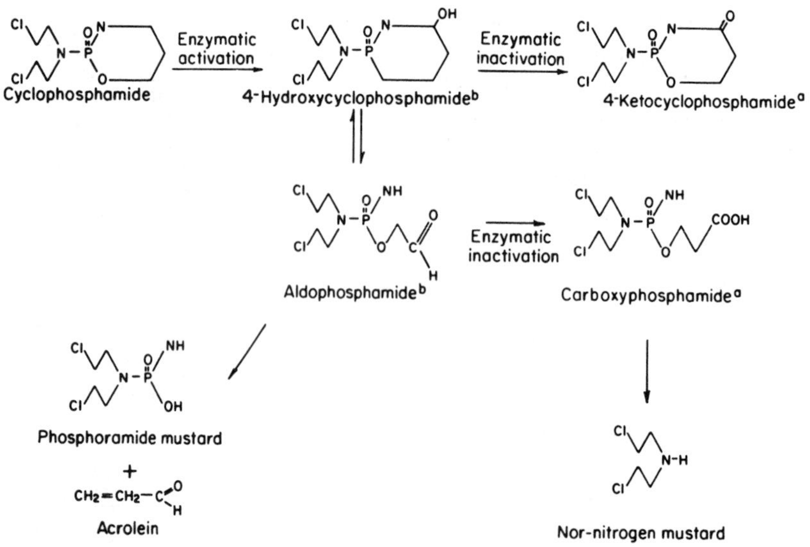

Figure 18.6. The metabolism of cyclophosphamide. a = Major urinary metabolites; b = transport forms. Phosphoramide mustard is an active alkylating agent, and acrolein is the probable cause of toxicity to bladder. (Adapted from Balis et al, 1983.)

(Fig 18.6; Grochow and Colvin, 1979). These metabolites are transported into cells and 4-hydroxycyclophosphamide probably decomposes within the cells to acrolein, and to phosphoramide mustard — an intermediate with direct alkylating activity. Other metabolites (Fig 18.6) account for most of the urinary excretion of cyclophosphamide. Acrolein appears to be the major cause of the bladder toxicity that may occur if a high urine output is not maintained after administration of cyclophosphamide (Brock et al, 1979; Cox, 1979).

The pharmacokinetics of cyclophosphamide have not been fully elucidated because of difficulty in detecting some of its metabolites in plasma. After intravenous administration of the parent compound, the plasma-disappearance curve is consistent with a two-compartment model (Grochow and Colvin, 1979) with a terminal half-life in the range of 3–10 hr. The drug is well absorbed after oral administration. Elimination occurs via renal excretion of both the parent compound and its metabolites. In spite of renal clearance, the use of cyclophosphamide in patients with renal failure has not been associated with increased toxicity, probably because renal clearance of the parent compound is quite low and can be maintained in patients with marginal renal function.

Metabolites of cyclophosphamide appear to be most active against cycling cells, and the drug causes a fall in granulocyte count with rapid recovery by 3–4 weeks after administration. Cumulative toxicity to bone marrow is rare. Cyclophosphamide toxicities which are common to many alkylating agents include nausea, vomiting, hair loss, gonadal damage and potential car-

cinogenicity (section 17.5). Very high doses, such as those used in preparation for bone marrow transplantation, may cause damage to the heart and lung.

18.3.3 NITROSOUREAS

The nitrosoureas BCNU, CCNU and methyl-CCNU (Fig 18.7; Prestayko et al, 1981) are lipid-soluble drugs which have the potential for penetration into the central nervous system for treatment of

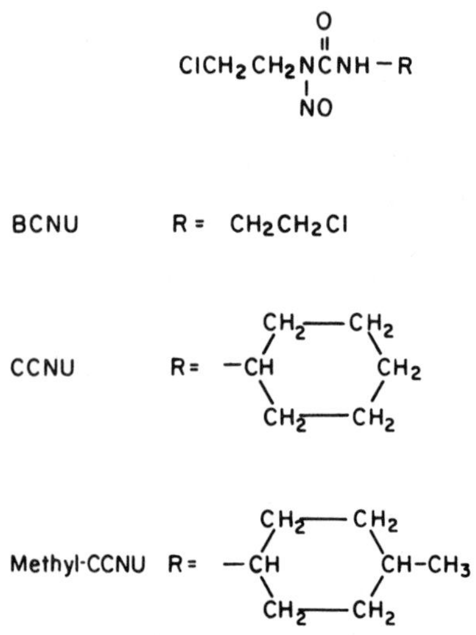

Figure 18.7. Structure of the nitrosoureas: BCNU = bis-chloroethylnitrosourea; CCNU = cyclohexyl-chloroethylnitrosourea; methyl-CCNU = methylcyclohexyl-chloroethylnitrosourea.

intracranial tumors. The drugs are effective for treatment of experimental tumors in mice, but have only limited clinical application. They tend to cause prolonged myelosuppression, probably because of direct effects on bone marrow stem cells.

BCNU resembles the nitrogen mustards in having two chloroethyl groups, whereas CCNU and methyl-CCNU are similar to monofunctional agents with a single chloroethyl group. BCNU forms DNA interstrand cross-links by chloroethylation of a nucleophilic site on one DNA strand and then displacement of the chloride to form an ethylene cross-link between two nucleophilic sites on opposite DNA strands (Prestayko et al, 1981). Both CCNU and methyl-CCNU are rapidly and completely absorbed after oral administration, but BCNU must be given intravenously. The parent drugs undergo rapid tissue uptake and metabolism and are not identified in plasma or urine. The extent to which metabolites contribute to toxicity of these agents is unknown.

18.3.4 OTHER ALKYLATING AGENTS

A large number of alkylating agents has been synthesized and several of them are used clinically.

Busulfan is used for treatment of chronic myelogenous leukemia and has the advantage of reducing the granulocyte count with relative sparing of platelets. Prolonged administration of busulfan may lead occasionally to irreversible and fatal fibrosis of the lung. The electron-deficient groups of busulfan are sulfonates (Fig 18.8) and these can form covalent bonds to alkylate DNA, and may form cross-links as described for the chloroethyl groups of nitrogen mustard.

Thio-TEPA is an example of the aziridine group of drugs (Fig 18.8) and is now used primarily for local instillation in the bladder for treatment of patients with superficial bladder cancer. A related drug, Trenimon, is used for systemic treatment of ovarian cancer in Europe.

Procarbazine is a synthetic derivative of hydrazine that is used in combination to treat lymphomas, including Hodgkin's disease. The drug undergoes extensive metabolism to produce alkylating species, and is probably activated by the cytochrome P-450 system in liver; however, details of its mechanism of action remain unclear.

Dacarbazine (DTIC) was originally synthesized as an antimetabolite which might be expected to inhibit purine biosynthesis. The drug has a narrow spectrum of activity and is used mainly for treatment of sarcomas, Hodgkin's disease and melanoma. The drug undergoes metabolism in vivo and is believed to cause damage by formation of a metabolite with alkylating properties.

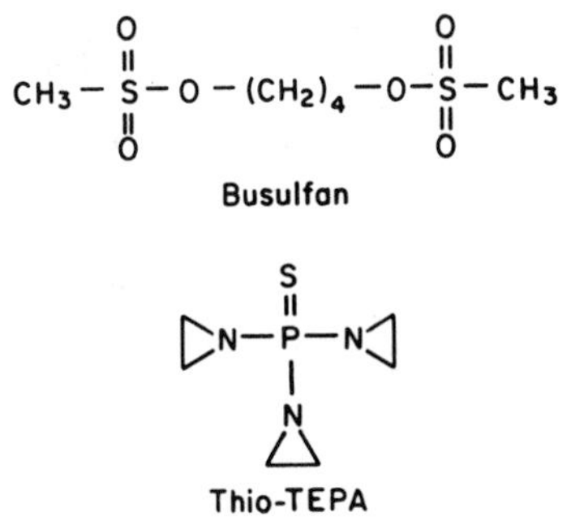

Figure 18.8. Structure of the alkylating agents busulfan and thio-TEPA (triethylenethiophosphoramide).

18.4 ANTIMETABOLITES

Antimetabolites are drugs which have been synthesized to inhibit critical biochemical pathways, usually leading to inhibition of DNA or RNA synthesis, and tend to be cell-cycle dependent. The most common clinical toxicities include myelosuppression and gastrointestinal effects (ie, inflammation of the mucosa and diarrhea).

18.4.1 METHOTREXATE

Methotrexate is an analog of the vitamin folic acid (Fig 18.9; Chabner, 1982; Schornagel, 1983). Reduced folate is required for transfer of methyl groups in the biosynthesis of purines, and in the conversion of deoxyuridine monophosphate (dUMP) to thymidine monophosphate (dTMP), a reaction which is catalyzed by thymidilate synthetase. Reduced folate becomes oxidized in the latter reaction, and its regeneration is dependent on the enzyme dihydrofolate reductase (DHFR) for further reduction to its active form.

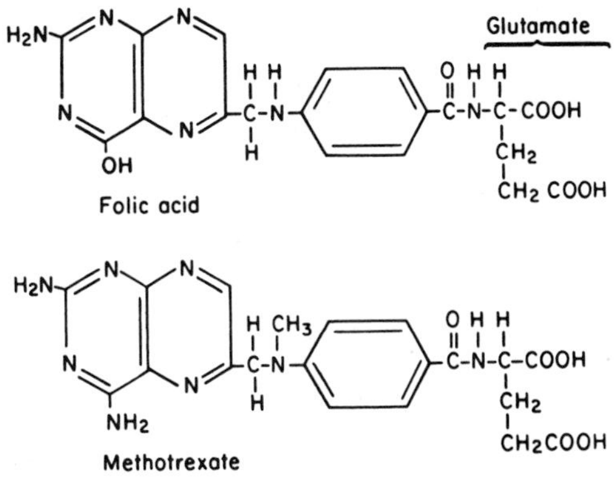

Figure 18.9. The structure of folic acid, and its analogue methotrexate. Note that glutamate forms one end of these molecules, and further glutamate molecules may be added to methotrexate within the cell.

Methotrexate is a competitive inhibitor of DHFR and thus prevents the formation of reduced folate (Fig 18.10). The result of this inhibition may be cessation of DNA synthesis due to nonavailability of dTMP and/or purines, leading to cell death.

Methotrexate enters the cell primarily by active transport. However, drug uptake may be by passive diffusion at high drug concentrations (>20 μM). Intracellular metabolism of methotrexate may lead to addition of glutamic acid residues to the initial glutamate residue of the drug (Fig 18.9), a process known as polyglutamation. Methotrexate polyglutamates cannot be transported across the cell membrane which prevents efflux of the drug, but they appear to be as effective as methotrexate in inhibiting the activity of DHFR.

The cytotoxic action of methotrexate depends critically on the duration of exposure of tissue to levels of drug above a certain threshold rather than on the peak levels of drug in the tissue. Methotrexate has selective toxicity for cells synthesizing DNA and prolonged treatment with the drug may expose more cells which enter this drug-sensitive phase of the cell cycle. For many tissues the threshold concentration for cytotoxicity appears to be in the range of 10^{-8}–10^{-7} M.

The toxicity of methotrexate may be reversed by administration of thymidine and exogeneous purines, or by a source of reduced folate (FH_4). These agents circumvent the effects of methotrexate by providing products of the interrupted metabolism (Fig 18.10); they have been used clinically to reverse the activity of methotrexate following a defined period of exposure (usually 24–36 hr) to methotrexate at high doses.

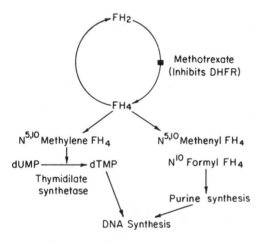

Figure 18.10. Influence of methotrexate on cellular metabolism. Through competitive inhibition of the enzyme dihydrofolate reductase (DHFR), the drug leads to depletion of the pool of reduced folates (FH_4). Derivatives of these reduced folates are required for synthesis of purines, and in the conversion of dUMP to dTMP. Interruption of these processes leads to inhibition of DNA synthesis.

Reduced folate in the form of 5-formyltetrahydrofolate, or leucovorin, has been used in many clinical protocols and has allowed the administration of doses of methotrexate that are increased by factors of 10–100 over conventional doses. The arguments put forward for such high-dose methotrexate treatment include (a) selective uptake by tumor cells, (b) better central nervous system penetration, and (c) lack of myelosuppression. This type of protocol may allow for frequent administration of methotrexate and retained therapeutic efficacy with little or no toxicity in many patients. However, responses to treatment are observed rarely in patients who are refractory to conventional doses of methotrexate given without leucovorin rescue. Although toxicity is often lower with the use of high doses of methotrexate and leucovorin, an occasional patient may experience life-threatening toxicity, usually mediated by damage to the kidney or sequestration into third spaces (eg, ascites, pleural effusions) and consequent delayed clearance of drug.

Resistance to methotrexate may be acquired through increased levels of DHFR, through variant forms of DHFR with reduced affinity for the drug, through decreased transport of methotrexate across the cell membrane, and through decreased production of polyglutamates. These mechanisms are discussed in detail in section 19.2.3.

Methotrexate can be given orally, intramuscularly, intravenously and intrathecally. It crosses the blood/brain barrier but achieves cytotoxic concentrations only with intrathecal or high-dose intravenous administration. It accumulates in fluid-filled spaces such as pleural effusions, from which it is released slowly. The parent compound and hepatic metabolites such as 7-hydroxymethotrexate are excreted by the kidney. This excretion can be inhibited by the presence of weak organic acids such as aspirin or penicillin. Aspirin may also displace methotrexate from its binding site on plasma albumin, and these two effects of aspirin can increase the toxicity of methotrexate. Most reports indicate that the pharmacokinetics of methotrexate can be described by a two-compartment model. The initial phase of drug disappearance from plasma has a half-life of 2–3 hr, whereas the final phase has a half-life of 8–10 hr. This terminal half-life may be prolonged in patients with poor kidney function. Entero-hepatic circulation of methotrexate (ie, circulation from liver to intestine to liver via the biliary tract and portal veins) which has been reported in some studies may contribute to a slow third phase of elimination from plasma.

Methotrexate has a wide spectrum of clinical activity, and may be curative for women with choriocarcinoma, a tumor derived from fetal elements. Its major toxicities are myelosuppression and inflammation of the oral and gastrointestinal mucosa; these toxicities are usually observed within 5–7 days of administration, earlier than for many other drugs. Damage to kidneys may occur after high doses of methotrexate due to precipitation of the drug in renal tubules; the risk of such toxicity may be minimized by maintaining a high output of alkaline urine to prevent precipitation. Rarer toxicities include damage to liver, lung, and brain, the latter occurring most frequently after intrathecal administration. In general, the drug is well tolerated compared to many other anticancer drugs.

18.4.2 5-FLUOROURACIL

5-Fluorouracil (5-FU) is a drug which resembles the pyrimidine bases uracil and thymine (Fig 18.11) that are components of RNA and DNA respectively (Myers, 1981). The drug penetrates rapidly into cells where it is metabolized to nucleoside forms by the addition of the sugars ribose or deoxyribose; these reactions are catalyzed by enzymes that normally act on uracil and thymine. Phosphorylation then leads to the active fluorinated nucleotides 5-FUTP and 5-FdUMP (Fig 18.12). 5-FUTP can be incorporated into RNA in place of UTP (uridine triphosphate); this leads to inhibition of the nuclear processing of ribosomal and messenger RNA, and may cause other errors of base pairing during transcription of RNA. 5-FdUMP inhibits irreversibly the enzyme thymidilate synthetase, leading to depletion of dTMP (thymidine monophosphate) that is required for DNA synthesis.

The relative importance of the above mechanisms for toxicity of 5-FU are disputed. Separation of these effects may be achieved by administration of (a) 5-fluorodeoxyuridine (5-FUdR), another agent that is available for clinical use and which seems to act solely (after phosphorylation) to inhibit thymidilate synthetase (Fig 18.12); or (b) 5-FU together with thymidine, which should prevent any toxic effects from inhibition of thymidilate synthetase. Both of these measures lead to toxicity on various types of cells. The relative importance of the two mechanisms underlying cytotoxicity of 5-FU probably varies for treatment of different tumors and normal tissues. In cells where toxicity is due to interruption of DNA synthesis through inhibition of thymidilate synthetase, the drug should have specificity for cells in the S phase of the cycle; when the major mechanism is incorporation of 5-FUTP into RNA the effects may be independent of cell-cycle phase.

Intrinsic or acquired resistance of cells to 5-FU occurs through a number of mechanisms, and their elucidation has been limited by technical difficulties associated with measurement of metabolites of the drug. Established mechanisms for some cells include decreased binding affinity of 5-FdUMP for the target enzyme thymidilate synthetase, and more rapid degra-

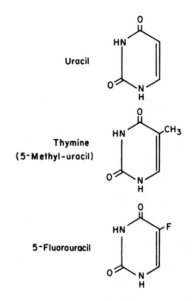

Figure 18.11. Structure of uracil, thymine, and the analogue 5-fluorouracil.

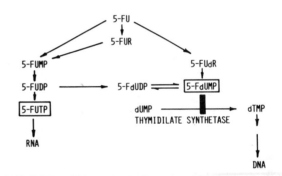

Figure 18.12. Metabolic activation of 5-fluorouracil (5-FU) leading to formation of 5-FdUMP (an inhibitor of the enzyme thymidilate synthetase) and 5-FUTP (which may be incorporated into RNA).

dation of 5-FdUMP. Several investigators have studied the interaction between 5-FU and methotrexate because they both inhibit DNA synthesis by affecting the reaction catalyzed by thymidilate synthetase, which converts uridine monophosphate to thymidine monophosphate. Mechanisms which may explain the sequence dependency of administration of methotrexate and 5-FU include: (a) Methotrexate given first may block purine synthesis, leading to elevation of phosphoribosyl-pyrophosphate (PRPP), which is necessary for activation of 5-FU, (b) 5-FU given first may block thymidilate synthesis, thus preventing consumption of reduced folates, and antagonizing the antipurine effects of methotrexate. Increased toxicity has been observed in tissue culture when methotrexate is given from 1 to 24 hr prior to 5-FU (Cadman et al, 1979). Although the in vitro results have not suggested a mechanism for tumor specificity, this "sequencing" has been studied recently in clinical trials, and little or no therapeutic advantage has been obtained in comparison with simultaneous administration.

5-Fluorouracil is usually given intravenously, because bioavailability after oral administration is variable. The drug is eliminated rapidly from plasma with a half-life of a few minutes. This agent demonstrates nonlinear pharmacokinetics when given by bolus injection but not when given by infusion. This difference in pharmacokinetic behaviour under the two conditions of administration may explain why higher doses of drug can be given during infusion and why the dose-limiting toxicity differs for bolus and infusion. 5-Fluorouracil has modest activity and is used most commonly for treatment of breast and gastrointestinal cancer. Major toxicity is to bone marrow and mucous membranes, and the latter becomes dominant if the drug is given over 4–5 days by continuous infusion. Rarer toxicity includes skin rashes, conjunctivitis, and ataxia (loss of balance) due to effects on the cerebellum.

18.4.3 CYTOSINE ARABINOSIDE

Cytosine arabinoside (Ara-C) differs from the nucleoside deoxycytidine only by the presence of a beta-hydroxyl group on the 2-position of the sugar (Fig 18.13), so that the sugar moiety is arabinose instead of deoxyribose. Ara-C penetrates cells rapidly by a carrier-mediated process shared with deoxycytidine, and is phosphorylated to Ara-CTP (Fig 18.14; Chabner, 1982). Ara-CTP is a competitive inhibitor of DNA polymerase, an enzyme necessary for DNA synthesis, and has similar affinity for this enzyme to the normal substrate dCTP. When Ara-CTP binds to this enzyme, DNA synthesis is arrested; replicating cells may die. Incorporation of Ara-C into DNA also occurs and may contribute to its cytotoxic effects, possibly because of defective ligation or incomplete synthesis of DNA fragments.

The availability of Ara-CTP for cytotoxic activity depends critically on the balance between the kinases which activate the drug, and the deaminases which degrade it (Fig 18.14). The activity of these enzymes varies greatly among different types of cells, leading to different rates of generation of Ara-CTP. Resistance to the action of Ara-C may occur by mutations which lead to deficiency in deoxycytidine kinase, or to cells with an expanded pool of dCTP which competes with the active metabolite Ara-CTP, and regulates enzymes involved in activation and degradation of the drug. Ara-C is specific in its activity for cells synthesizing DNA. Since it is rapidly degraded in plasma with a half-life of 7–20 min, it must be given intravenously by frequent injec-

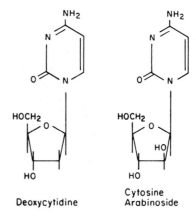

Figure 18.13. Structure of deoxycytidine and its analogue cytosine arabinoside.

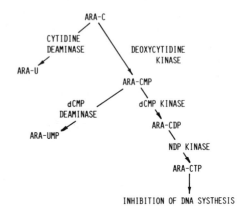

Figure 18.14. Metabolic activation and degradation of cytosine arabinoside (Ara-C). Formation of the active metabolite Ara-CTP depends on the balance between activity of the kinases which activate the drug, and deaminases which degrade it. (Adapted from Chabner, 1982.)

tions or by continuous infusion to kill cells as they pass from G_1 to S phase of the cycle. Myelosuppression and gastrointestinal toxicity are the major side effects, but abnormal behaviour and thought processes may also occur following high doses.

18.4.4 PURINE ANTIMETABOLITES

A large number of purine analogues have been synthesized, and a few of these have found application as antiviral agents (eg, adenosine arabinoside, Ara-A), immunosuppressive agents used in preservation of kidney and other organ grafts (eg, azathioprine), and as anticancer drugs (eg, 6-mercaptopurine and 6-thioguanine, 6-MP and 6-TG; Fig 18.15). The use of these latter two drugs is limited to treatment of leukemia and they are rarely employed in the management of solid tumors.

Various mechanisms of action may account for toxicity of 6-MP and 6-TG. Like guanine these drugs are metabolized to deoxynucleotides by addition of the sugar–phosphate moiety, and are incorporated into DNA. This mechanism presumably accounts for the selective toxicity of 6-TG for cells in DNA synthesis. Metabolites of the drug may also inhibit purine and RNA synthesis, and the relative importance of these mechanisms is unclear. Cross-resistance is usually observed between 6-MP and 6-TG, and drug-resistant mutant cells may lack the enzyme HGPRT (hypoxanthine–guanine phosphoribosyltransferase) which is necessary for their activation. Alternative mechanisms which convey resistance probably involve increased degradation of the drugs and their metabolites.

Recent studies of the clinical pharmacology of 6-MP have revealed a low bioavailability of drug when administered orally because of first-pass hepatic metabolism and a wide patient-to-patient variability. The clinical toxicities of this agent which are encountered most commonly include myelosuppression as demonstrated by leukopenia and thrombocytopenia, and gastrointestinal toxicity manifested by mucositis, diarrhea, nausea and vomiting. Hepatic toxicity is a less common problem associated with jaundice and rarely necrosis.

18.5 NATURAL PRODUCTS

18.5.1 DOXORUBICIN

Doxorubicin (Adriamycin) is a planar four-ring anthracycline molecule linked to the sugar daunosamine (Fig 18.16); it is produced by a species of *Streptomyces*. Doxorubicin has a wide range of clinical activity for many types of solid tumors and leukemia, but differs only by the presence of a hydroxyl group as compared to daunorubicin, a drug used almost exclusively for treatment of acute leukemia.

A number of mechanisms appear to contribute to the cytocidal effect of doxorubicin and related drugs. Most data relate cytotoxicity to binding of the drug with DNA: doxorubicin can intercalate between base pairs perpendicular to the long axis of the double helix, leading to partial unwinding of the DNA helix. However, much of the DNA is organized and folded into chromatin and may be protected from this type of drug interaction. Doxorubicin may also cause single- and double-strand breaks in DNA. The drug inhibits both DNA and RNA synthesis and has preferential toxicity for cells in the S phase of the cell cycle.

Doxorubicin may undergo metabolism of its quinone ring to a semiquinone radical (ie, a group containing an unpaired electron) which in turn reacts rapidly with oxygen to yield superoxide, O_2^- (Bachur et al, 1977). The superoxide radical is known to undergo several

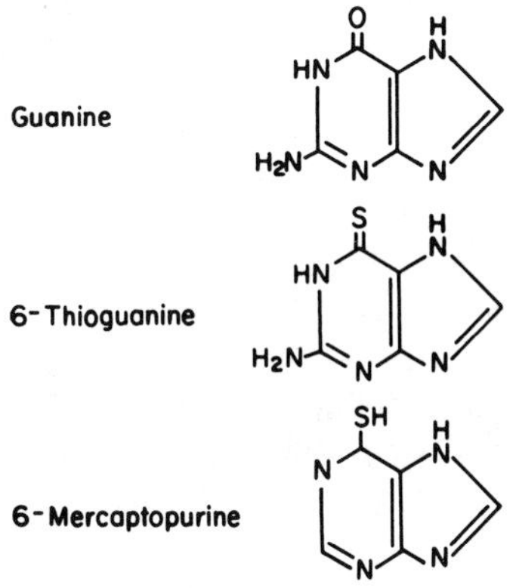

Figure 18.15. Structure of guanine and the analogues 6-thioguanine and 6-mercaptopurine.

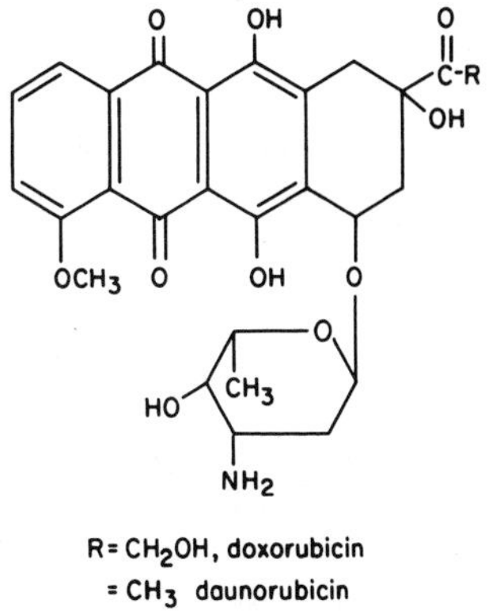

reactions which can lead to cell death, including oxidative damage of cell membranes and DNA. Although this mechanism may contribute to cell death, doxorubicin retains toxicity under hypoxic conditions when superoxide radicals cannot be formed (eg, Tannock and Guttman, 1981). There is evidence that free radical formation contributes to cardiac toxicity in animals through peroxidation of mitochondrial lipids, and this damage is reduced in the presence of scavengers of free radicals such as alpha-tocopherol.

Doxorubicin and related drugs also bind to cell membranes and may kill cells through membrane-related effects. Tritton and Yee (1982) studied the effects of doxorubicin in vitro when linked to beads, and demonstrated that the drug could cause cell death without its transport into the cell. However, transport of doxorubicin into other cells is important for toxicity since decrease in membrane transport is an important mechanism relating to acquired drug resistance of some mutant cells (section 19.2.4). Thus, the mechanisms underlying toxicity of doxorubicin are variable, complex and as yet only partly understood.

R = CH₂OH, doxorubicin
= CH₃ daunorubicin

Figure 18.16. The structure of doxorubicin (Adriamycin) and daunorubicin.

Doxorubicin is administered intravenously because oral absorption is poor. It is widely distributed in the body with significant binding to plasma proteins and tissue. Plasma clearance after intravenous administration may be described by three exponential components with half-lives in the ranges of 8–25 min, 1.5–10 hr and 24–48 hr. The second phase is attributed to metabolism of the drug in liver, and the final phase to release of drug from tissue binding sites. Doxorubicin is metabolized in the liver to doxorubicinol, which retains some cytotoxic activity, and to several other metabolites, and the drug and its metabolites are excreted via the bile. Thus dosage reduction is required for patients with biliary obstruction.

The acute toxicities of doxorubicin include myelosuppression, total loss of hair, nausea, vomiting, mucositis and local tissue necrosis following leakage of drug at the injection site. Damage to heart muscle is a major chronic toxicity of doxorubicin whose incidence increases with increasing cumulative dose of drug (Unverferth et al, 1982). This toxicity is a cardiomyopathy manifested by a decrease in the ability of the heart to pump and often is irreversible. A large number of drugs is being developed and tested in efforts to retain or increase the antitumor therapeutic effects of doxorubicin, but to reduce toxicity. These include anthracyclines with various chemical groups added or substituted, and naturally occurring or synthetic three-ring anthracenediones such as mitoxantrone and bisantrene. The former drug is being used as an alternative to doxorubicin in the treatment of breast cancer. It causes less nausea, vomiting and hair loss and may have comparable antitumor activity.

18.5.2 ACTINOMYCIN D

Actinomycin D is produced by *Streptomyces* species and is used mainly in the treatment of childhood tumors. Structurally the molecule consists of two polypeptide chains linked to a planar three-ring (phenoxazone) structure. Actinomycin D is known to bind to guanosine residues of DNA, and the planar rings probably intercalate between adjacent base pairs of the DNA helix. The major effect is inhibition of transcription of RNA, and the drug has had wide use in research as a relatively specific inhibitor of RNA synthesis.

Plasma clearance of actinomycin D after intravenous injection shows a rapid initial component due to tissue distribution, and a prolonged second component with a half-life of about 36 hr. Most of the drug is excreted in the parent form, and excretion occurs both in urine and in feces. Myelosuppression, gastrointestinal toxicity, and hair loss are the common toxicities, and the drug may also cause skin rashes; like doxorubicin, actinomycin D causes severe necrosis if it escapes into tissue from infusion sites and both drugs may also cause dramatic increases in tissue reactions to radiation therapy when both modalities are used (section 19.4.4).

18.5.3 BLEOMYCIN

Bleomycin consists of a family of molecules with a complex structure that have been derived from fungal culture, the dominant active component being known as bleomycin A2 (Chabner, 1982). Bleomycin causes DNA strand breaks through a complex sequence of reactions that involves the binding of a bleomycin-ferrous iron complex to DNA. This binding leads to insertion of the drug between base pairs (intercalation) and unwinding of the double helix. A second step in the formation of DNA strand breaks may involve the reduction of molecular oxygen to superoxide or hydroxyl radicals, catalyzed by the bleomycin–ferrous iron complex. However, like doxorubicin, bleomycin retains some of its lethal activity under hypoxic conditions, so that oxygen is not an absolute requirement for killing of cells by the drug. Bleomycin may exert preferential toxicity in the G_2 phase of the cell cycle, but also has toxicity for slowly proliferating cells in plateau-phase cell culture. Bleomycin-resistant cells have been obtained following treatment with a mutagen, and this resistance seems to be due to decreased cellular uptake of the drug.

Bleomycin may be given by intravenous, intramuscular or subcutaneous injections, and most of the administered drug is eliminated unchanged in the urine. Plasma-clearance curves have two components with half-lives of about 0.5 hr and 2–24 hr respectively. The major use of bleomycin is with other drugs to treat testicular cancer and lymphomas, and the drug also has minor activity for head and neck cancer. Bleomycin has little toxicity to bone marrow, but may cause fever, chills, and damage to skin and mucous membranes. The dose-limiting toxicity is interstitial fibrosis of lung, and the incidence is related to cumulative dose, age of the patient and use of other agents which may damage lung such as oxygen or radiation therapy. The mechanism of pulmonary toxicity has not been well defined, but experiments in rats suggest that lung damage might be diminished through the use of an analogue of proline which inhibits enzymes involved in synthesis of collagen (Kelley et al, 1980).

18.5.4 VINCA ALKALOIDS

The vinca alkaloids, vinblastine, vincristine, and vindesine, are chemically similar, multiring compounds derived from the periwinkle plant (Fig 18.17). These

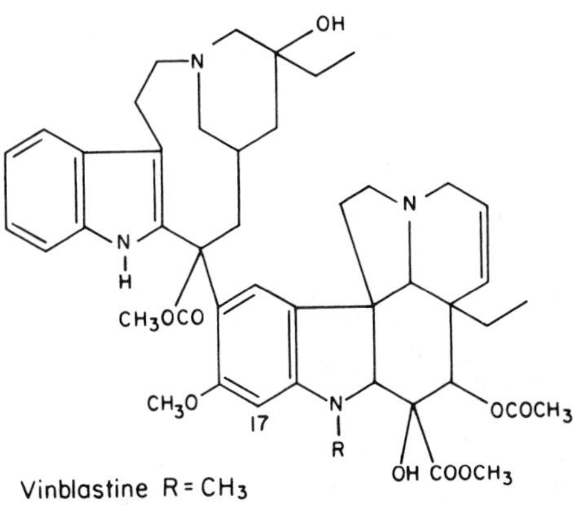

Vinblastine R = CH₃
Vincristine R = CHO

Figure 18.17. Structure of vinblastine and vincristine.

compounds act by binding to the protein tubulin, thus inhibiting its polymerization to form microtubules (Chabner, 1982). Microtubules have several important cellular functions including formation of the mitotic spindle responsible for separation of chromosomes, and structural and transport functions in axons of nerves. Microtubules are in a state of dynamic equilibrium with continuous formation and degradation from cytoplasmic tubulin. This process is interrupted by treatment with vinca alkaloids, and lethally damaged cells may be observed to enter an abortive metaphase and then lyse. However, experiments with synchronized cells have demonstrated maximum lethal toxicity for vinblastine and vincristine when cells are exposed during the period of DNA synthesis and it is presumably the morphological expression of that damage which is observed in attempted mitosis. Resistance to these drugs has been reported due to decreased membrane transport, and cross-resistance occurs with other naturally derived compounds such as doxorubicin (section 19.2.4).

Vinca alkaloids are given intravenously and are excreted mainly through the biliary tract. Their plasma clearance is described by triphasic curves with terminal half-lives of about 20 hr and 30 hr for vinblastine and vincristine respectively.

Despite similarities in their structures, vinblastine and vincristine differ in both their clinical spectra of activity and in their toxicities. Vinblastine is an important drug in combination chemotherapy of testicular cancer, while vincristine is a mainstay of treatment for childhood leukemia. Both drugs have been combined with other cytotoxic agents to treat lymphomas or various solid tumors. Vinblastine causes major toxicity to bone marrow, whereas vincristine has greater and dose-limiting toxicity for nerves. This neurotoxicity probably occurs because of damage to the microtubules. Vindesine is a metabolite of vinblastine and seems to

offer little therapeutic advantage as compared to the parent drug.

18.5.5 VP-16 AND VM-26

Podophyllotoxin is an antimitotic agent derived from the mandrake plant which binds to tubulin at a site different from the vinca alkaloids. VP-16 (etoposide) and VM-26 (teniposide) are semisynthetic glycoside derivatives of podophyllotoxin which have shown clinical activity. VP-16 is being used increasingly for treatment of small-cell lung cancer, testicular cancer and lymphomas (Issell et al, 1984). This family of drugs shares a common multiringed structure (epipodophyllotoxin) from which is derived the family name for these compounds. Although podophyllotoxin binds to tubulin and inhibits its polymerization, VP-16 and VM-26 seem to have little effect on microtubule assembly or degradation. The drugs can inhibit nucleoside transport into cells, inhibit nucleoside incorporation into RNA and DNA, and cause single-strand breaks in DNA. The major mechanism underlying their lethal toxicity is unknown, but they appear to exert maximum activity in the late S or G_2 phase of the cell cycle and prevent cells from entering mitosis.

VP-16 is administered by intravenous injection and its disposition in plasma can be described by a two-compartment model with initial and terminal half-lives for plasma clearance of about 3 and 15 hr respectively. About 45% of the administered drug is excreted unchanged in urine and an additional 15% is excreted in feces. The dose-limiting toxicity is to bone marrow, and hair loss is also common. An acute fall in blood pressure after rapid intravenous administration may be prevented by infusing VP-16 over 30 min or longer.

18.5.6 MITOMYCIN C

Mitomycin C is derived from a *Streptomyces* species and requires activation to an alkylating metabolite by reductive metabolism (Carter and Crooke, 1979). The drug is more active against hypoxic than against aerobic cells in tissue culture, but it does not show preferential toxicity for hypoxic cells in vivo, perhaps because of limited penetration from tumor blood vessels (Rauth et al, 1983). The drug causes mild nausea, but gives rather unpredictable myelosuppression and occasionally an unusual and potentially fatal disorder involving thrombus formation in small vessels of multiple organs. Nephrotoxicity and pulmonary toxicity are two other rare and unpredictable toxicities of this drug which are potentially lethal. Availability of equally active drugs with lower toxicities limits the clinical utility of mitomycin C, but the drug is being tested in combination for a variety of solid tumors.

18.6 MISCELLANEOUS DRUGS

18.6.1 CISPLATIN

Cisplatin (cis-diamminedichloroplatinum II, Fig 18.18) is an important anticancer drug whose discovery followed an observation that an electric current delivered to bacterial culture via platinum electrodes led to inhibition of bacterial growth. The active compound was found to be cisplatin, and this compound was shown subsequently to exert major activity against several tumors in mice (Rosenberg et al, 1969). The trans-isomer (Fig 18.18) is inactive.

Cisplatin acts by a mechanism that is similar to that of classical alkylating agents (Prestayko et al, 1980). The chlorine atoms are leaving groups which may be compared to those of nitrogen mustards (Fig 18.5); these atoms may be displaced directly by nucleophilic groups of DNA, or indirectly after chloride ions are replaced by hydroxyl groups through reactions of the drug with water. As for classical alkylating agents, the preferred site for binding of cisplatin to DNA is the N-7 position of guanine bases. Most cisplatin binds to only one site on DNA with the other active ligand bound to nucleophils (eg, $-NH_2$ or $-SH$ groups) of smaller molecules or proteins. However, lethal effects against cells seem to correlate with the number of cross-links formed between the DNA strands. Studies of the kinetics of formation and removal of cross-links (Kohn, 1979) have shown that both cisplatin and its trans-isomer lead to formation of DNA protein cross-links, but only cisplatin produces DNA interstrand cross-links at clinically achievable concentration in vivo. These cross-links are formed for several hours after removal of the drug, and are then repaired. Intrinsic and acquired resistance to cisplatin appears to depend on a decreased ability to form interstrand cross-links in drug-treated cells or on more rapid and efficient mechanisms of DNA repair.

The pharmacokinetics of cisplatin are complicated by the techniques required to analyze the drug, and by its high protein binding. Following administration, cisplatin is rapidly and tightly bound to proteins with greater than 90% of free cisplatin lost in the first 2 hr. The plasma-disappearance curve for free cisplatin conforms to a two-compartment model. Total platinum (free and bound drug) disappears more slowly from plasma than free platinum; this disposition may be described by a three-component curve with a prolonged terminal half-life of 2–3 days. Cisplatin is excreted mainly via the urine, and 15–30% of the administered dose is excreted during the first 24 hr.

Cisplatin is used as part of drug combinations which can cure testicular cancer, and in combination with other drugs for palliation of a variety of solid tumors. It causes little toxicity to bone marrow, but has major dose-limiting toxicities of severe nausea and vomiting,

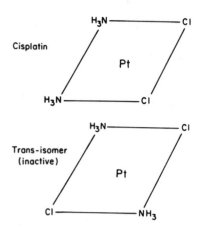

Figure 18.18. Structure of cisplatin and its inactive isomer trans-diamminedichloroplatinum (II).

and damage to the kidney. The latter effect may be minimized by maintaining a rapid urine output during and after drug administration. A large number of analogues of cisplatin have been synthesized and are being tested in experimental animals and in man.

18.6.2 OTHER DRUGS

Drugs with limited clinical use that are not described in preceding sections include hydroxyurea and L-asparaginase. Hydroxyurea is a simple structural analogue of urea that was synthesized more than a century ago. The drug inhibits ribonucleotide reductase enzymes, which catalyze the conversion of ribose nucleotides (eg, CDP) to deoxyribose nucleotides (dCDP) that are necessary for DNA synthesis. Currently it has only occasional clinical use, for example as an alternative to busulfan in treatment of chronic myelocytic leukemia. Hydroxyurea is used experimentally as a specific inhibitor of DNA synthesis.

L-asparaginase is an enzyme purified from bacterial sources, which causes degradation of the amino acid L-asparagine. Asparagine is synthesized from aspartic acid and glutamine, through the enzyme L-asparagine synthetase. However, this enzyme appears to be lacking in some tumors, particularly acute leukemia in children. L-asparaginase may then lead to death of these leukemic cells since their viability depends on the availability of asparagine in the circulation. Major toxicity of the drug is due to hypersensitivity reactions, and to inhibition of synthesis of important proteins such as clotting factors.

18.7 SUMMARY

The efficacy of anticancer drugs depends on drug concentration and time of exposure, which in turn depend on absorption, metabolism, distribution, and excretion. Analysis of these pharmacokinetic properties is aided by the use of models in which the body is considered as a number of compartments into each of which a drug is uniformly distributed. For most anticancer drugs, drug disappearance from plasma may be described by two- or three-compartment models, so that clearance curves have two or three exponential components, each with their corresponding half-lives.

Anticancer drugs are grouped conveniently into alkylating agents, antimetabolites, naturally derived compounds and miscellaneous drugs such as cisplatin. Alkylating agents and cisplatin appear to cause major damage to cells through cross-linking of strands of DNA. Most antimetabolites inhibit DNA or RNA synthesis either directly or due to inhibition of the formation of essential precursors. Anthracyclines such as doxorubicin also cause damage to DNA, but may exert additional toxicity by damaging cell membranes.

Many anticancer drugs undergo extensive metabolism with the formation of both active and inactive products. Many of these metabolites cannot easily be detected and quantified. Thus theories about the mechanisms of action for many drugs are frequently revised in the light of new experimental data.

REFERENCES

Allen L, Kimura K, MacKichan J, Ritschel WA: Manual of symbols, equations and definitions in pharmacokinetics. *J Clin Pharmacol* 1982; 22:1S–23S.

Ames MM, Powis G, Kovach JS: *Pharmacokinetics of Anticancer Agents in Humans.* Elsevier, Amsterdam, 1983.

Bachur NR, Gordon SL, Gee MV: Anthracycline antibiotic augmentation of microsomal electron transport and free radical formation. *Mol Pharmacol* 1977; 13:901–910.

Balis FM, Holcenberg JS, Bleyer WA: Clinical pharmacokinetics of commonly used anticancer drugs. *Clin Pharmacokinet* 1983; 8:202–232.

Brock N, Stekar J, Pohl J et al: Acrolein, the causative factor of urotoxic side-effects of cyclophosphamide, ifosfamide, trofosfamide and sulfosfamide. *Arzneimittel-Forschung* 1979; 29:659–661.

Cadman E, Heimer R, Davis L: Enhanced 5-fluorouracil nucleotide formation after methotrexate administration: Explanation for drug synergism. *Science* 1979; 205:1135–1137.

Carter SK, Crooke ST: *Mitomycin C: Current Status and New Developments.* Academic Press, New York, 1979.

Chabner BA: *Pharmacologic Principles of Cancer Treatment.* W. B. Saunders, Philadelphia, 1982.

Collins JM: Pharmacologic rationale for regional drug delivery. *J Clin Oncol* 1984; 2:498–504.

Cox PJ: Cyclophosphamide cystitis—identification of acrolein as the causative agent. *Biochem Pharmacol* 1979; 28:2045–2049.

Erlichman C: Potential applications of therapeutic drug monitoring in treatment of neoplastic disease by antineoplastic agents. *Clin Biochem* 1986; 19:101–106.

Erlichman C, Donehower RC, Chabner BA: The practical benefits of pharmacokinetics in the use of antineoplastic agents. *Cancer Chemother Pharmacol* 1980; 4:139–145.

Gibaldi M, Perrier D: *Pharmacokinetics.* Marcel Dekker, New York, 1982.

Grochow LB, Colvin M: Clinical pharmacokinetics of cyclophosphamide. *Clin Pharmacokinet* 1979; 4:380–394.

Houston JB: Drug metabolite kinetics. *Pharmacol Ther* 1981; 15:521–552.

Issell BF, Muggia FM, Carter SK: *Etoposide (VP-16): Current Status and New Developments.* Academic Press, New York, 1984.

Kelley J, Newman RA, Evans JN: Bleomycin-induced pulmonary fibrosis in the rat: Prevention with an inhibitor of collagen synthesis. *J Lab Clin Med* 1980; 96:954–964.

Kohn KW: DNA as a target in cancer chemotherapy: Measurement of macromolecular DNA damage produced in mammalian cells by anticancer agents and carcinogens. *Methods Cancer Res* 1979; 16:291–345.

Myers CE: The pharmacology of the fluoropyrimidines. *Pharmacol Rev* 1981; 33:1–15.

Pond SM, Tozer TN: First-pass elimination: Basic concepts and clinical consequences. *Clin Pharmacokinet* 1984; 9:1–25.

Prestayko AW, Crooke ST, Carter SK: *Cisplatin: Current Status and New Developments.* Academic Press, New York, 1980.

Prestayko AW, Crooke ST, Baker LM et al: *Nitrosoureas: Current Status and New Developments.* Academic Press, New York, 1981.

Rauth AM, Mohindra JK, Tannock IF: Activity of mitomycin C for aerobic and hypoxic cells *in vitro* and *in vivo. Cancer Res* 1983; 43:4154–4158.

Rosenberg B, VanCamp L, Trosko JE et al: Platinum compounds: A new class of potent antitumour agents. *Nature* 1969; 222:385–386.

Schornagel JH, McVie JG: The clinical pharmacology of methotrexate. *Cancer Treat Rev* 1983; 10:53–75.

Tannock I, Guttman P: Response of chinese hamster ovary cells to anticancer drugs under aerobic and hypoxic conditions. *Br J Cancer* 1981; 43:245–248.

Tritton TR, Yee G: The anticancer agent adriamycin can be actively cytotoxic without entering cells. *Science* 1982; 217:248–250.

Unverferth DV, Magorien RD, Leier CV, Balcerzak SP: Doxorubicin cardiotoxicity. *Cancer Treat Rev* 1982; 9:149–164.

BIBLIOGRAPHY

Ames MM, Powis G, Kovach JS: *Pharmacokinetics of Anticancer Agents in Humans.* Elsevier, Amsterdam, 1983.

Chabner BA: *Pharmacologic Principles of Cancer Treatment.* W. B. Saunders, Philadelphia, 1982.

19

Experimental Chemotherapy

Ian F. Tannock

19.1 INTRODUCTION

19.1.1 CURRENT STATUS OF CHEMOTHERAPY

In current clinical practice chemotherapy is used in the following ways: (a) as the major curative modality for a few rare types of malignancies, such as acute leukemia in children or testicular cancer in men; (b) as palliative treatment for many types of advanced cancers; (c) as adjuvant treatment before or after local treatment (usually surgery) for primary disease, with the aim of eradicating occult micrometastases; and (d) in combination with other modalities (usually radiotherapy) in an attempt to improve their therapeutic effects.

Improvements in clinical chemotherapy have depended largely on the use of drugs in combination. Some drugs have been combined because there is a theoretical or experimental basis for expecting synergistic interaction through their known mechanisms of action either at the molecular level, or because of their complementary effects on cell-cycle kinetics. Synergy does not, however, lead to therapeutic benefit unless the interaction between drugs is tumor specific (section 19.4.1). The most important factors underlying the successful use of drugs in combination are (a) the ability to combine drugs at close to full dosage with additive effects against tumors and less than additive toxicities to normal tissues, and (b) the expectation that drug combinations will include at least one drug to which the tumor is sensitive.

19.1.2 THERAPEUTIC INDEX

All anticancer drugs have toxicity as well as antitumor effects, and toxicity to normal tissues limits the dose of drugs that can be given to patients. The relationship between probability of a biological effect of a drug and administered dose is usually described by a sigmoid curve (Fig 19.1). If the drug is to be useful, the curve describing probability of antitumor effect (eg, complete clinical remission) must be displaced toward lower doses as compared to the curve describing probability of major toxicity to normal tissues (eg, myelosuppression leading to infection). Therapeutic index (or therapeutic ratio) may be defined from such curves as the ratio of the doses required to produce a given probability of toxicity and antitumor effect. Therapeutic index in Figure 19.1 is the ratio of 50% levels of probability for toxicity (sometimes referred to as toxic dose 50 or TD-50) and antitumor effect (ie, effective dose 50 or ED-50). Any stated levels of probability might be

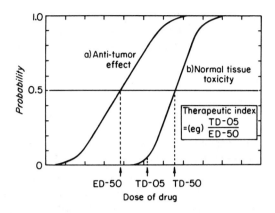

Figure 19.1. Schematic relationship between dose of a drug and *a*, the probability of a given measure of antitumor effect, and *b*, the probability of a given measure of normal-tissue toxicity. The therapeutic index might be defined as the ratio of doses to give 50% probabilities of normal-tissue damage and antitumor effects. However, if the endpoint for toxicity is severe (eg, lethality), it would be more appropriate to define the therapeutic index at a lower probability of toxicity (eg, TD-05/ED-50).

used, and the appropriate endpoints of tumor response and toxicity will depend on the limiting toxicity of the drug, the intent of treatment (ie, cure versus palliation), and on whether treatment is given to a patient or an experimental animal. Unfortunately, dose–response curves similar to those of Figure 19.1 have been defined rarely for drug effects in man.

Improvement in the therapeutic index is the goal of experimental chemotherapy. The concept emphasizes that any modification in treatment which leads to increased killing of tumor cells in tissue culture or animals must be assessed for its effects on critical normal tissues prior to therapeutic trials.

19.1.3 RELATIONSHIP BETWEEN TUMOR REMISSION AND CURE

For most tumors the limit of clinical and/or radiologic detection is about 1 g of tissue ($\sim 10^9$ cells). If therapy can reduce the number of malignant cells below this limit of detection, the patient will be described as being in complete clinical remission. Surgical biopsy of sites that were known to be previously involved with tumor may lower the limit of detection, but a pathologist is unlikely to detect sporadic tumor cells present at a frequency of less than 1 in 1000 normal cells, so that even a "surgically confirmed complete remission" may be compatible with the presence of a large number of tumor cells. Tumor cure requires eradication of all tumor cells that have the capacity for tumor regeneration. The proportion of such stem cells among those of

the tumor population is unknown (see section 8.2), but clinical and even surgical remissions are compatible with the presence of a substantial residual population of tumor stem cells. Attainment of complete remission is but a small step on the road to tumor cure.

For many drugs the relationship between cell survival and dose is close to exponential, so that a constant *fraction* of the cells (rather than a constant *number*) is killed by a given dose of drug (section 17.3). Drugs are usually given in sequential courses, with dosage and schedule limited by normal tissue tolerance. Some repopulation of tumor cells may take place between courses, so that the number of tumor cells in a drug-sensitive tumor may change with time during a course of chemotherapy, as illustrated in Figure 19.2. In this example, each course of drug kills 90% of the tumor cells, and starting from a large (100 g) tumor, complete clinical remission is achieved after three courses. Note that a further six to ten courses (depending on the prevalence of tumor stem cells) would be required to achieve cure. Realization of the need to continue aggressive treatment during complete remission, demonstrated originally by the experimental work of Skipper and his colleagues (1964), led to success in the treatment of acute lymphoblastic leukemia in children, and subsequently to cures in other tumors such as lymphomas. Unfortunately, for most solid tumors, a drug-resistant subpopulation emerges and leads to relapse, as shown in Figure 19.2.

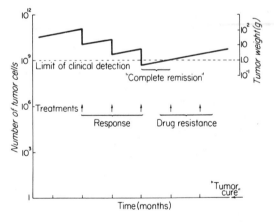

Figure 19.2. Illustration of the relationship between tumor remission and cure. In this hypothetical example, treatment of a human tumor starts when it has 10^{11} cells (~ 100 g), and each treatment, given at monthly intervals, kills 90% of the cells present. This course of therapy leads to complete disappearance of clinical tumor. Drug resistance then develops, and the tumor grows despite continued treatment. Note that despite the attainment of a complete clinical response there are always at least 10^8 viable cells present, and that the reduction in cell numbers is small compared to that required for cure.

19.2 DRUG RESISTANCE

19.2.1 MECHANISMS OF DRUG RESISTANCE

Many types of cancer that occur commonly in man (eg, colon cancer, lung cancer other than small-cell type) show only infrequent responses to treatment with anticancer drugs. This resistance to chemotherapy may be influenced by such factors as the proliferative state of the cells (section 17.3) and by vascular access and penetration of drugs into tissue (section 19.3.6), but the most important factor is the *intrinsic resistance* of the tumor cells to available anticancer drugs. Other human tumors (eg, breast cancer or small-cell cancer of the lung) often respond to initial treatment, but *acquired resistance* to further therapy usually prevents drug treatment from being curative. Thus intrinsic and acquired drug resistance are the major factors which limit the successful use of chemotherapy. A wide range of metabolic or structural properties of cells may lead to drug resistance (for review, see Fox and Fox, 1984), and some of the mechanisms underlying intrinsic or acquired drug resistance are summarized in Table 19.1.

Alkylating agents and cisplatin cause cellular damage by binding with DNA, leading to cross-linkages and breaks in DNA strands (section 18.3). Cells may be resistant to these drugs through a number of mechanisms, including decreased cellular uptake, reduced

activation, and increased inactivation of alkylating species, but a major determinant of resistance appears to be the capacity for repair of lesions in DNA. There is current interest in drugs (eg, aphidicolin) which might overcome resistance by inhibiting the repair of DNA, but it seems unlikely that this approach will be tumor specific and lead to large improvements in the therapeutic index.

A number of mechanisms may also lead to resistance to antimetabolite drugs. These mechanisms include impaired drug transport into cells, overproduction or reduced affinity of the molecular target, stimulation of alternative biochemical pathways, and impaired activation or increased catabolism of the drug. The most widely studied of the antimetabolites is methotrexate, and the varied mechanisms of resistance to this agent will be described as an example for other antimetabolites in section 19.2.3.

19.2.2 GENETIC BASIS OF DRUG RESISTANCE

The following evidence suggests that many types of drug resistance are genetic in origin (Ling, 1982; Goldie and Coldman, 1984).

1. Characteristics of drug-resistant cells (ie, their phenotypes) are often stably inherited in the absence of the selecting drug.
2. Drug-resistant cells are spontaneously generated with a rate that is consistent with known rates of genetic mutation.
3. Generation of drug-resistant cells is increased by exposure to compounds (eg, ethyl methane sulfonate) which induce mutation. This property has been used to generate and select a large number of drug-resistant mutants that have been used to study drug-resistant phenotypes (Fig 19.3).
4. Altered gene products have been identified in some drug-resistant cells.
5. Some drug-resistant phenotypes have been transferred to drug-sensitive cells by transfer of DNA in vitro. An example is the transfection of DNA from cells that are drug resistant to induce resistance in normal bone marrow cells of experimental animals (Cline et al, 1980).

At least two types of genetic lesion may convey drug resistance: point mutation and gene amplification. Drug resistance due to point mutation may be expected to occur in a single step that is not critically dependent on the concentration of drug used to select for resistance, and the degree of resistance should be quite stable. One of many well-characterized examples is mutation in the gene which codes for the enzyme

Table 19.1. Probable Mechanisms Associated with Resistance to Commonly Used Anticancer Drugs

Mechanism	Drugs
Increase in proficiency of repair of DNA	cisplatin, cyclophosphamide, melphalan, mitomycin C, nitrogen mustard, nitrosoureas
Decrease in cellular uptake or increase in efflux of drugs	actinomycin D, daunorubicin, doxorubicin, melphalan, 6-mercaptopurine, methotrexate, nitrogen mustard, vincristine, vinblastine
Increase in levels of "target" enzyme	methotrexate
Alterations in "target" enzyme	5-fluorouracil, 6-mercaptopurine, methotrexate, 6-thioguanine
Decrease in drug activation	cytosine arabinoside, doxorubicin, 5-fluorouracil, 6-mercaptopurine, 6-thioguanine
Increase in drug degradation	bleomycin, cytosine arabinoside, 6-mercaptopurine
Alternative biochemical pathways	cytosine arabinoside

Note:: Adapted from Fox and Fox (1984).

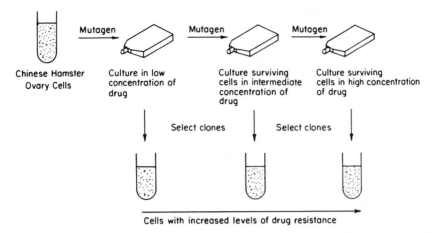

Figure 19.3. General method used for stepwise selection of drug-resistance mutant cells.

HGPRT (hypoxanthine guanine phosphoribosyl transferase) which is necessary for activation of the drug 6-thioguanine. In contrast to point mutation, gene amplification occurs in a stepwise manner, and drug-resistant cells are selected more rapidly by exposing cells to graded increases in the concentration of the selecting drug. The best-characterized example (Schimke, 1984) is amplification of the gene encoding dihydrofolate reductase (DHFR), the target enzyme of methotrexate (section 19.2.3).

The frequency of occurrence of drug-resistant cells in a cell culture or tumor population may be estimated by plating the cells after exposure to the drug at a pharmacologically achievable concentration and counting the resultant colonies. Typical spontaneous frequencies for the incidence of a variety of stable drug-resistant phenotypes are in the range 10^{-7}–10^{-5}. These frequencies are consistent with origin by spontaneous mutation,

and definitive evidence for this origin has been obtained for a few drugs by performing a fluctuation test — a test devised by Luria and Delbruck (1943) to distinguish between (a) mutation and selection and (b) induction by a drug, as the major cause of bacteriophage resistance in bacteria. It may also be applied to mammalian cells and involves generation of subclones from a parent population of cells (Fig 19.4). When these subclones have grown to a predetermined size the number of drug-resistant cells is estimated in each of them by plating each subpopulation in the presence of the drug, and counting the number of colonies that form from surviving cells. If drug resistance occurs by spontaneous mutation, the random nature of this process causes the variance in the number of drug-resistant mutants in the different subclones to be much greater than the mean. The fluctuation test has been performed using only a few drugs (eg ouabain, L-asparaginase and hydrox-

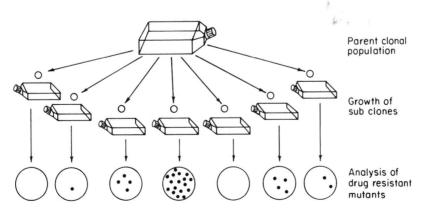

Figure 19.4. The Luria–Delbruck fluctuation test to demonstrate the spontaneous generation of drug-resistant cells. (Figures 19.4 and 19.7 are from Ling, 1982, with permission.)

yurea), but has established mutation and selection as a major mechanism for generation of drug-resistant mutants.

At least two other mechanisms might contribute to the generation of genetically based drug resistance. Many anticancer drugs (especially alkylating agents) are themselves mutagenic: treatment with such drugs may be expected to increase the rate of generation of mutant cells and to accelerate the development of resistance to themselves and to other drugs. Also, drugs which cause cell-cycle progression delay during DNA synthesis may allow an increased rate of gene amplification. Thus treatment with some drugs may stimulate the development of drug resistance.

Second, there is increasing evidence that different populations of cells may interact to influence the drug sensitivities of each other (Heppner, 1984; Tofilon et al, 1984). This influence may involve sharing of drug metabolites, or increased activation of a drug by one of the cell populations. Cell fusion, the transfer of DNA between cells, or the uptake of DNA from dead cells are also potential mechanisms which could lead to horizontal transmission of drug resistance between mammalian cells. The importance of these mechanisms in contributing to the increase in drug resistance in tumor populations is currently unknown.

Generation of drug-resistant mutants among cells in human tumors has implications for planning optimal chemotherapy. Goldie and Coldman (eg, 1984) have demonstrated that the probability of there being at least one drug-resistant cell in a tumor population is dependent on tumor size (Fig 19.5). This probability increases from near zero to near unity over a small range of tumor sizes (~6 doublings) with the critical size depending on the rate of mutation to drug resistance. This effect, and others, imply a greater chance of cure if therapy is begun early, when the total burden of tumor cells is low. The Goldie–Coldman model also predicts a better therapeutic effect when different schedules of two equally effective and non-cross-resistant drugs are alternated, rather than given sequentially, since this minimizes the emergence of cell populations that are resistant to both drugs. A number of clinical trials are in progress which seek to test this hypothesis, but these trials may be limited for many types of human tumors by the lack of equally effective and non-cross-resistant drugs or drug combinations.

19.2.3 RESISTANCE TO METHOTREXATE

Resistance to methotrexate may occur by several mechanisms (Bertino et al, 1981; Fig 19.6). Methotrexate is transported across cell membranes both by passive diffusion and by an energy-dependent active transport system. Drug-resistant cells may arise which have impaired transport of methotrexate into the cell, probably due to point mutation (eg, Flintoff et al, 1976). Transport-deficient cells also show a decrease in polyglutamation of intracellular methotrexate (Frei et al, 1984); primary defects in polyglutamation or in intracellular binding could lead to decreased uptake of methotrexate in the drug-resistant mutants.

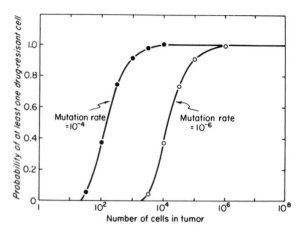

Figure 19.5. Probability that there will be at least one drug-resistant cell in a tumor containing varying numbers of cells, based on rates of mutation of 10^{-6} (open symbols) and 10^{-4} (closed symbols) per cell per generation. Note that this probability increases from low to high values over a relatively short period in the life history of the tumor and that drug-resistant cells are likely to be established prior to clinical detection. (Adapted from Goldie and Coldman, 1984.)

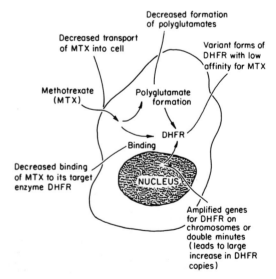

Figure 19.6. Probable mechanisms underlying cellular resistance to methotrexate.

A second type of mutation may lead to production of variant forms of DHFR, the target enzyme for methotrexate. Variant enzymes have been found to retain adequate function for reduction of their normal substrate (dihydrofolate), but to have a greatly decreased affinity for methotrexate (eg, Goldie et al, 1980).

The most common mechanism leading to methotrexate resistance in cell lines and experimental tumors that are exposed to increasing concentrations of the drug is overproduction of DHFR from amplified genes. This process has been extensively characterized by Schimke and his colleagues (eg, Schimke, 1984) and their major findings are:

1. Selection for methotrexate resistance in mammalian cells by stepwise increase in drug concentration in the medium may lead to as many as 100–1000 copies of the DHFR gene, and to high levels of drug resistance.

2. High levels of resistance to methotrexate cannot be obtained in a single-step selection process. Gene amplification occurs in small steps.

3. Resistance occurs from overproduction of the normal enzyme (although overproduction of variant forms of DHFR has also been observed).

4. Drug resistance and amplified genes may be either stable or unstable when cells are passaged in the absence of the drug. Stable amplification is usually associated with chromosomal location of the genes, seen as homogeneously staining regions in stained chromosome preparations (section 3.3.1). Unstable amplification is usually associated with location of the genes in extrachromosomal chromatin structures known as double minutes. Both locations may be evident during selection for drug resistance.

5. Gene amplification appears to take place by multiple replication of the DHFR gene (and flanking sequences) during the S phase of the cell cycle. Interruption of DNA synthesis in synchronized cells by drugs such as hydroxyurea, or by transient exposure to hypoxic conditions (Rice et al, 1986), leads to an increase in the rate of gene amplification. Other anticancer drugs may increase drug resistance by gene amplification.

6. Gene amplification and overproduction of DHFR have been observed in cells from human tumors treated with methotrexate so that the process probably has clinical relevance.

Although gene amplification has been studied most extensively in relation to methotrexate, there is increasing evidence for the importance of this mechanism in determining resistance to several other drugs, includ-

ing 5-fluorouracil and the multiple drug resistance phenotype described below.

19.2.4 MULTIPLE DRUG RESISTANCE

Several investigators have observed that cells which are selected for resistance to one of a group of drugs (Table 19.2) may show cross-resistance to each of the other drugs in the group (for review, see Riordan and Ling, 1985). Thus, Chinese hamster ovary cells selected for resistance to colchicine after prior treatment with a mutagen were found subsequently to be cross-resistant to several anticancer drugs including anthracyclines (eg, doxorubicin), vinca alkaloids (eg, vinblastine) and to other types of drug such as puromycin, an inhibitor of protein synthesis. Many of these drugs have quite different chemical structures, but most of them are derived from natural products. Cells that are selected for resistance to an individual drug of the group are cross-resistant to other members of the group, but usually show the highest degree of resistance to the drug that was used for selection. Thus, the mechanism of drug resistance shows some degree of specificity. Multidrug-resistant cells do not usually show major cross-resistance to antimetabolites or to alkylating agents, with the exception of melphalan, and increased sensitivity has been reported to a few drugs, including cyclophosphamide.

When membrane proteins from multidrug-resistant cells are separated by electrophoresis, they are found to contain a glycoprotein whose molecular weight is about 170 kd, and which has been termed the P-glycoprotein (Fig 19.7). The degree of resistance correlates with the amount of P-glycoprotein expressed in the cell membrane. There is evidence from monoclonal antibody studies that the P-glycoprotein is similar in several different species, including hamster and mouse (Kartner et al, 1983). Since quantitative levels of drug resistance (and drug transport) depend on the drug used for selection of resistance, it seems likely that P-glycoprotein

Table 19.2. Family of Drugs Associated with Cross-Resistance and Expression of P-glycoprotein

Actinomycin D	Podophyllotoxin
Colchicine	Puromycin
Daunorubicin	Vinblastine
Doxorubicin	Vincristine
(Adriamycin)	Vindesine
Emetine	Melphalan
Etoposide (VP-16)	(weaker association)

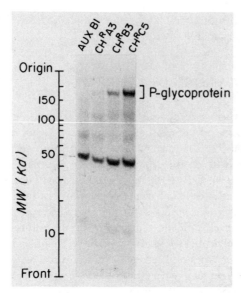

Figure 19.7. Increased levels of P-glycoprotein in mutant Chinese hamster ovary cells derived from wild type (Aux B1 cells) by stepwise selection (as indicated in Fig. 19.3). Membrane components were separated by SDS gel electrophoresis, transferred to nitrocellulose paper, and stained using a radiolabeled hetero-antiserum.

may display some heterogeneity, although with common determinants recognized by monoclonal antibodies. Recent work has shown that P-glycoproteins are encoded by a family of related genes.

Multiple-drug-resistant cells have decreased uptake and increased efflux of drugs to which they are resis-

tant (Fig 19.8), and this change in membrane transport has recently been associated with the expression of P-glycoprotein.

It is also unknown whether P-glycoprotein is expressed at low levels in drug-sensitive cells or if it is an abnormal product of a mutant gene. Increased levels of P-glycoprotein appear to be associated with gene amplification and in some cells also with double minutes. Definitive evidence of genetic origin has been obtained by transfer of drug resistance to sensitive cells using DNA transfection (Riordan and Ling, 1985). Molecular cloning of the gene which codes for P-glycoprotein is underway in several laboratories and will probably allow a more definitive study of mechanisms which underlie this important phenomenon.

Recent evidence has shown that cells from drug-resistant human ovarian cancer may express P-glycoprotein (Fig 19.9; Bell et al, 1985), so that the multidrug-resistance phenotype is probably relevant to the development of drug resistance in patients. If so, it will be important to seek methods which might reverse the phenomenon. Of particular interest is the finding that drugs which inhibit calcium influx into cells (eg, verapamil), drugs which inhibit the calcium-binding protein calmodulin, and other drugs which tend to stabilize cell membranes (eg, quinidine) all tend to restore partial sensitivity to drug-resistant cells (eg, Tsuruo et al, 1983). It is encouraging that these agents appear to have little effect on drug activity for sensitive cells in normal tissues.

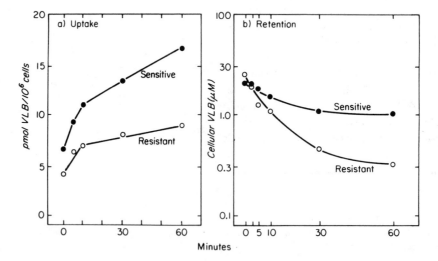

Figure 19.8. *a*, Uptake of ^{3}H-vinblastine (VLB) in drug-sensitive human leukemic cells (CEM) and drug-resistant cells (CEM/VLB$_{100}$). *b*, Retention of ^{3}H-vinblastine in drug-sensitive and resistant cells following their transfer into drug-free medium. Initial loading of resistant cells was achieved by placing them in 100-fold-higher concentration than sensitive cells. Drug-resistant cells show decreased uptake and retention of drug. (Adapted from Beck, 1983.)

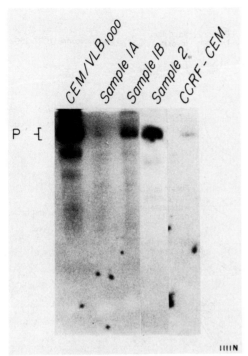

Figure 19.9. Levels of P-glycoprotein in ascites tumor cells from two patients with ovarian cancer. Patient 1 received three courses of chemotherapy with cyclophosphamide, doxorubicin and cisplatin between the time that samples 1A and 1B were obtained. Drug-sensitive (CCRF-CEM) and resistant (CEM/VLB$_{100}$) cultured cells are shown for comparison. Technique is the same as for Figure 19.7, except that a radiolabeled monoclonal antibody was used to detect P-glycoprotein. (From Bell *et al*, 1985, with permission.)

19.3 EXPERIMENTAL APPROACHES TO IMPROVEMENT OF CHEMOTHERAPY

19.3.1 ADJUVANT CHEMOTHERAPY

Chemotherapy may be given to patients who have no overt evidence of residual cancer after local treatment such as surgery or radiation, but where past experience with similar patients has shown a high chance of subsequent relapse from the presence of undetectable micrometastatic disease. Adjuvant chemotherapy is used widely in the clinic although increases in the probability of cure have been recorded only for malignancies which show a high chance of palliative response when chemotherapy is used to treat overt metastatic disease.

Experiments in animals have provided a sound basis for the use of adjuvant chemotherapy. Chemotherapy which causes shrinkage (but not cure) of established tumors in mice may lead to cure if treatment is commenced after transplantation but before the tumor has grown to a detectable size (Fig 19.10). This result has been confirmed using several types of drugs and tumors, and for treatment given after local implantation

or after intravenous injection to produce experimental metastases (eg, Schabel, 1975).

Several mechanisms may allow for increased curability of smaller tumors. Eradication of a smaller number of cells will require less drug. Smaller tumors may have better perfusion of blood than larger tumors, allowing both better access of drug to the tumor cells and also a higher rate of cell proliferation due to better nutrition; rapidly proliferating cells are more sensitive to most anticancer drugs (section 17.3). Finally, emergence of drug-resistant cells may occur in larger tumors, thus preventing curative treatment (section 19.2.2). In view of the multiple mechanisms which support the use of adjuvant treatment, and the definitive evidence of benefit for transplanted tumors in mice, it is disappointing that adjuvant chemotherapy has not been more beneficial to patients. A major limitation of the animal experiments is that rapidly growing, homogeneous and extensively passaged transplanted tumors in mice may be poor models for slowly growing and heterogeneous tumors in man.

Adjuvant chemotherapy is sometimes started in patients before treatment of the primary tumor with surgery or radiation, a strategy that has been termed "neo-adjuvant chemotherapy." Experiments in animals suggest that this approach should be used with caution, since many drugs have been found to increase the chance of metastasis to the lungs from circulating tumor cells that are introduced by intravenous injection (eg, Van Putten et al, 1975). This effect is largest after treatment with cyclophosphamide, when the frequency of metastasis may be increased by a factor of 100–1000, but smaller effects have been observed following treatment with several other anticancer drugs. There is also some evidence that drug treatment may increase spontaneous metastasis from transplanted tumors, although

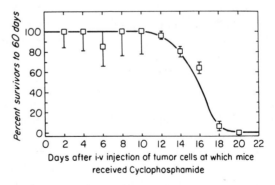

Figure 19.10. Result of an experiment in which mice were treated at different times after intravenous injection of Lewis lung tumor cells. Therapy is only curative if it is started early when the number of tumor cells is low. (Adapted from Hill and Stanley, 1977.)

this is not a universal finding. The mechanisms under-lying these effects are unknown but probably involve drug-induced damage to organs such as the lung, resulting in increased retention of tumor cells.

19.3.2 ANTIMETASTATIC DRUGS

The term "antimetastatic drug" is reserved ideally for a compound which may inhibit the process of tumor dissemination through mechanisms other than direct toxicity to tumor cells. The process of metastasis involves several steps (section 10.2) which include vascular invasion from the primary tumor, circulation through the blood, and arrest, invasion and growth at the secondary site. Several types of drug may influence this process, and have led to reduction in metastases in experimental animals (Fig 19.11).

Razoxane (ICRF 159) is a drug which has little direct cytotoxicity but which was found to inhibit lung metastases from some transplantable tumors in mice, perhaps by inhibiting release of cells from the primary tumor (eg, Hellmann, 1984). The drug has been used as an adjuvant to surgery for colon cancer, but despite a trend to decreased metastases in patients receiving the drug, its use has been abandoned because of evidence for the induction of leukemia.

Metastasis depends on the arrest of circulating tumor cells, and many anticoagulant and antiplatelet drugs have therefore been assessed for their ability to inhibit metastases (eg, Hilgard, 1984). Heparin administration tends to decrease the formation of lung colonies after IV injection, but to increase the number of colonies in other organs; it has little effect on spontaneous metastasis from transplanted tumors. The coumarin family of drugs (eg, warfarin), which cause anticoagulation by inhibiting synthesis of clotting factors, appear to have moderate but consistent effects in reducing metastases, including those from established tumors. Warfarin has been reported to inhibit metastases in patients, but a large trial of its use in patients with lung, colon, head and neck, and prostate cancer led to little or no improvement in survival (Zacharski et al, 1984).

Aggregation of platelets appears to play an important role in the arrest and retention of circulating tumor cells. Aspirin and dipyridamole, which have long been known to inhibit platelet aggregation, have only minor effects on formation of metastases. Recently, more potent inhibitors of platelet aggregation have been tested including calcium-channel blockers, antiplatelet antibodies, the prostaglandin PG-I$_2$ (also known as prostacyclin), nafazatrom, forskolin, and the protease inhibitor leupeptide, which inhibits thrombus formation. Each of these agents may lead to a large decrease in lung metastases after intravenous injection of tumor

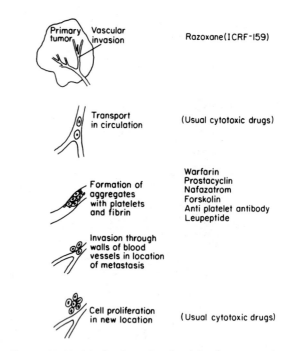

Figure 19.11. Mechanisms involved in the generation of metastases and their potential inhibition by drugs.

cells (eg, Honn et al, 1984), or to a decrease in metastases from transplanted tumors, although this is not a universal finding.

Manipulation of the immune system may be effective in decreasing metastases, as least in experimental animals, and is discussed in chapter 20.

A major limitation to the clinical use of antimetastatic therapy is the establishment of microscopic metastases prior to detection and treatment of the primary tumor. Prevention of secondary metastases (ie, metastases from metastases) might be useful in palliation, but the potential for increased cure through the use of antimetastatic agents is limited to patients in whom metastases are seeded after diagnosis and prior to eradication of the primary tumor. While tumor cells are know to enter the circulation at the time of surgery, this process is probably the sole source of metastatic failure for only a small proportion of patients who subsequently die from overt metastatic disease.

19.3.3 DIRECTED DRUG DELIVERY

A major limitation to the use of chemotherapy is lack of selectivity of anticancer drugs for tumor cells. A potential method of increasing the therapeutic index is to direct drugs to tumor cells by linking them to some form of carrier. Among the approaches that have been subjected to experimental research are (Fig 19.12) (a) linkage of drugs to large molecules such as DNA, (b)

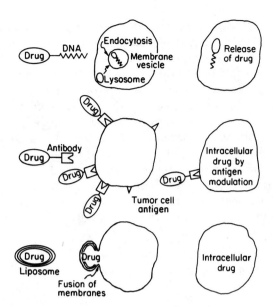

Figure 19.12. Different methods of delivery of anticancer drugs to tumor cells. *a*, Drug linked to a large molecule such as DNA; *b*, drug linked to an antibody that is specific for tumor-associated cell antigens; *c*, drug encapsulated in liposomes.

linkage of drugs to antibodies which recognize antigens on tumor cells, and (c) entrapment of drugs in lipid vesicles known as liposomes (for review see Gregoriadis, 1984). Each of these methods has led to improvement in the therapeutic index for selected tumors in animals, but several problems have prevented their widespread clinical use.

Linkage of drugs with DNA leads to their uptake into cells by endocytosis, and the drug is thought to be released intracellularly following digestion of the linkage by lysosomal enzymes after fusion of the membrane vesicle with lysosomes. Tumor specificity may result because tumor cells have a high capacity for endocytosis. Increased therapeutic effects have been reported for some experimental tumors after injection of doxorubicin or daunorubicin complexed to DNA, as compared to injection of the free drug. Major problems with this approach are stability of the complex in blood and the low probability of its penetration into solid tumors.

Several drugs have been linked to antibodies directed against tumor-associated antigens, but evidence for selectivity as compared to free drug has been limited. Problems associated with this technique include the rarity of antibodies specific for tumor cells, and low numbers of antibody binding sites which make it difficult to deliver sufficient molecules of the drug to kill a tumor cell. Also, linkage of an antibody to a drug may mask the antigen recognition site or diminish drug activity. The complex will itself be foreign and immunogenic, so that it may, after repeated administration, be inacti-

vated by the immune response of the host, or cause anaphylaxis. Research is in progress to try to overcome these problems, particularly involving the use of monoclonal antibodies (see section 20.3). There is current interest in the therapeutic potential of monoclonal antibodies bound to nonspecific toxins such as the A chain of ricin; this toxin is so potent that delivery of one molecule to a tumor cell may lead to its death.

A large body of research relates to the entrapment of anticancer drugs in lipid vesicles, known as liposomes (Weinstein and Leserman, 1984). Liposomes may be constructed of varying size and with positive, neutral or negative charge; they may be single or multilayered, and the lipid composition may be varied to provide solid or fluid forms of the lipid membrane. In general, liposomes are taken up by reticuloendothelial cells in liver, spleen and lungs; their site of localization depends on the size of the liposomes and their membrane composition. Subsequent release of drug may mimic the effect of chronic low-dose administration of free drug. This mechanism alone might sometimes result in increased therapeutic effects. Liposomes may change the relative availability of drug to different tissues; an example is the administration of doxorubicin within charged liposomes, which may lead to a decrease in drug uptake and toxicity in the heart, but with retention of antitumor activity (eg, Rahman et al, 1980). Liposomes might also overcome drug resistance that is due to decreased membrane transport; thus Poste and Papahadjopoulos (1976) could overcome membrane-based resistance of mutant cells to actinomycin D by trapping the drug in liposomes. The liposomes fused with the cell membrane of drug-resistant cells, leading to intracellular release of the drug (Fig 19.12c). A further mechanism which might convey selectivity for drugs within liposomes is local heating of a tumor following administration of drug-containing liposomes with a transition temperature between 37 °C and the temperature (~42 °C) of the heated tumor (Yatvin et al, 1981). This method could lead to lysis of liposomes and release of drug within a tumor, but is limited to tumors that are localized in a region of the body that can be effectively heated.

Treatment of experimental animals with liposome-encapsulated drugs has been associated with therapeutic benefit for treatment of several leukemias and ascites tumors, and for a few solid tumors. The outcome of drug therapy may depend critically on dose and schedule, however, and many investigators have not conducted experiments to demonstrate whether administration of a drug entrapped in liposomes is superior to more chronic administration of free drug. If selectivity were based merely on a change in pharmacokinetics, similar effects might be obtained in man by using prolonged infusions at lower dosage in place of bolus injections. All carrier-mediated drug delivery systems face a major problem in delivering drug to cells within a solid tumor. Even free drugs may have difficulty in diffusing from blood vessels to tumor cells (see section 19.3.6); this problem will probably be much greater for drugs that are linked to large molecules or entrapped within liposomes.

19.3.4 DRUGS THAT CAUSE DIFFERENTIATION

Some drugs are not cytotoxic per se but may cause morphological differentiation of cells in tissue culture, resulting in cessation of growth. Thus, embryonal carcinoma and other undifferentiated cells may differentiate to form glial cells, muscle cells or other functional cells under the influence of agents such as retinoic acid, dimethylsulfoxide, or 5-azacytidine (eg, Strickland and Mahdavi, 1978). Many of the involved mechanisms are poorly understood, but treatment with 5-azacytidine leads to its incorporation into DNA in place of cytosine; the consequent inhibition of DNA methylation may lead to changes in the expression of genes (eg, Taylor et al, 1984). The development of cancer in epithelial tissues appears to involve a decrease in the normal process of cellular differentiation and an increase in the self-renewal of tumor stem cells (see section 8.2.2). The observation that some malignant stem cells may respond to agents which induce differentiation has led to the proposal that cancer might be treated with such agents; thus the aim would be to induce differentiation rather than death of tumor stem cells (eg, Bloch, 1984).

At present there have been few successful reports of the in vivo use of drugs which induce cell differentiation, although retinoids have been used to obtain remission of skin tumors and papillary tumors in the bladder. A large amount of work is in progress which is defining a relationship between growth factors, expression of oncogenes and differentiation (see section 8.4.5). Continued development of drugs which perturb these relationships is likely to lead to in vivo testing for anticancer effects of new agents that promote differentiation.

19.3.5 ANTI-ANGIOGENESIS

Solid tumors can grow only if they induce proliferation of blood vessels, and this process appears to be stimulated by release of a factor (tumor angiogenesis factor, TAF) from tumor cells (see section 9.6.2). Agents which inhibit the release or activity of TAF might therefore have potential in cancer therapy. Inhibitors of angiogenesis include protamine, and a substance that may be obtained from cartilage (Langer et

al, 1980). Recent interest in this concept has been stimulated by the report of Folkman et al (1983) that a heparin fragment could cause dramatic regression of several experimental tumors, and inhibition of metastases, when used in the presence of hydrocortisone. This combination had no direct toxicity for tumor cells, but was a specific inhibitor of capillary proliferation. It is important to determine whether this is a general observation, especially as it appeared to depend critically on the type of heparin that was used. Current efforts to purify angiogenesis factors (eg, Shing et al, 1984) should allow the development of further inhibitors that might be tested therapeutically.

19.3.6 DRUGS FOR HYPOXIC AND NUTRIENT-DEPRIVED CELLS

Many tumors are known to have a poorly organized vascular system, so that some cells within them may be deficient in the supply of oxygen and other nutrients. Hypoxic cells are known to be resistant to radiation (section 15.6), and they may also be protected from the activity of several anticancer drugs. This protection may occur because of limited penetration of drugs from tumor blood vessels, and because nutrient-deprived cells tend to be slowly proliferating (Fig 19.13; section 9.6.2). The nutritional state of the cells might also influence the cellular uptake and metabolism of some anticancer drugs.

Penetration of drugs into tissue can be studied conveniently using spheroids (Sutherland et al, 1979). Spheroids are spherical aggregates of tumor cells which will grow in suspension culture, and which resemble tumor nodules (section 9.6.2). Drugs may be placed in the medium and their penetration into the spheroids can be followed as a function of time using fluorescence microscopy (eg, doxorubicin) or autoradiography (eg,

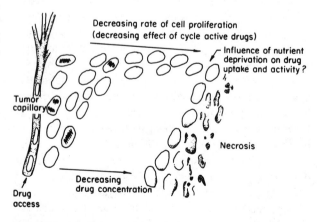

Figure 19.13. Influence of drug diffusion and nutrient environment on drug activity for cells within solid tumors.

radiolabeled drugs). A spheroid showing limited penetration of doxorubicin is shown in Figure 19.14. Other drugs which have poor penetration into spheroids or tumor nodules include methotrexate, vinblastine and vincristine.

Assessment of the toxicity of an anticancer drug for aerobic and hypoxic cells in tumors in vivo has been derived from study of effects of the drug used alone, or after a dose of radiation which will preferentially kill the oxygenated cells (Hill and Stanley, 1975; Tannock, 1982). Recently the fluorescent dye Hoechst 33342 has been injected intravenously to establish a concentration gradient with distance from a blood vessel, thus allowing separation of cells at different distances from functional capillaries by flow cytometry after subsequent tumor dissociation (Chaplin et al, 1985). A similar technique was used previously to study drug effects at different depths in spheroids (Durand, 1982). Experimental results obtained by one or both of the above methods suggest preferential toxicity of doxorubicin, nitrogen mustard and BCNU for aerobic perivascular cells; probable mechanisms include avid uptake of doxorubicin by well-nourished cells close to blood vessels, and rapid breakdown of nitrogen mustard and BCNU, leading to poor penetration of these drugs. Cyclophosphamide and 5-fluorouracil do not appear to exert selective toxicity for subpopulations of aerobic or hypoxic cells in solid tumors, and these drugs or their active metabolites presumably have a uniform distribution.

Since nutrient-deprived cells in solid tumors may be spared by both radiation and some forms of conventional chemotherapy, there is potential for therapeutic benefit by combining these agents with drugs that have good distribution in tissue and which show selectivity for hypoxic or nutrient-deprived cells. Several classes of drug show a high degree of selective toxicity for hypoxic cells in tissue culture. These include nitroimidazole radiosensitizers such as misonidazole (section 16.5), and analogues of glucose such as 5-thio-D-glucose. Unfortunately, these drugs exert toxic effects against hypoxic cells in vivo only at or above their limit of tolerance. Mitomycin C is a drug that requires reductive metabolism for activity, and is more active in tissue culture against hypoxic than against aerobic cells. Limited distribution of the drug from blood vessels appears to prevent selective toxicity of mitomycin C against hypoxic cells of solid tumors in vivo.

It may be possible to select drugs which are active against nutrient-deprived cells for reasons other than hypoxia; for example, poorly nourished cells produce lactic acid, so that drugs which inhibit transport of lactate out of the cell, or which diminish the ability of a tumor cell to tolerate a low extracellular pH, could achieve selective toxicity. Screening for activities of

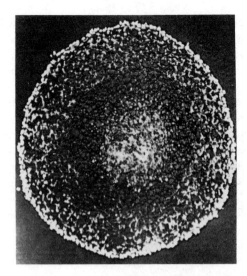

Figure 19.14. Fluorescence photomicrograph of a spheroid showing limited penetration of doxorubicin. (Reprinted with permission from *Int J Radiat Oncol Biol Phys*, vol 5, Sutherland RM et al, © 1979 Pergamon Press Ltd.)

drugs that are selectively toxic for a subpopulation of nutrient-deprived cells in tumors will require the use of prior treatment with agents such as radiation or doxorubicin to reveal effects against this subpopulation.

19.4 TREATMENT WITH MULTIPLE AGENTS

19.4.1 INFLUENCE ON THERAPEUTIC INDEX

It has become common practice to treat patients with multiple anticancer agents; examples are the use of multiple drugs in combination chemotherapy or the use of drugs in combination with radiation therapy.

When two or more agents are combined to give an improvement in the therapeutic index, this implies that the increase in toxicity to critical normal tissues is less than the increase in damage to tumor cells (section 19.1.2). Since the dose-limiting toxicity to normal tissues may vary widely for different drugs and for radiation, two agents may often be combined with only minimal reduction in doses as compared to those that would be used if either agent were given alone. Additive effects against a tumor with less than additive toxicity for normal tissue may then lead to therapeutic advantage.

Mechanisms by which drugs or other modalities may give therapeutic benefit when used in combination have been classified by Steel and Peckham (1979) as follows: (a) independent toxicity, which may, for example, allow combined use of anticancer drugs at full dosage; (b) spatial cooperation, whereby disease that is missed by one agent (eg, local radiotherapy) may be treated by another (eg, chemotherapy); (c) protection of normal tissues; and (d) enhancement of tumor response.

The above factors suggest guidelines for choosing drugs which might be given in combination. Most drugs exert dose-limiting toxicity for the bone marrow, but this is not the case for vincristine (dose-limiting neurotoxicity), cisplatin (nephrotoxicity) or bleomycin (mucositis and lung toxicity). These and some other drugs can be combined with myelosuppressive agents at full dosage, and have contributed to therapeutic success of drug combinations used to treat lymphoma and testicular cancer. Research on drug resistance (section 19.2) has defined drugs which commonly (eg, doxorubicin and vincristine) or rarely (eg, doxorubicin and cyclophosphamide) demonstrate cross-resistance. Combination of non-cross-resistant drugs may contribute to therapeutic benefit as, for example, in the combined use of doxorubicin and cyclophosphamide to treat many types of tumors. Nevertheless, most drug combinations in clinical use have evolved empirically through the combination of drugs which demonstrate some antitumor effects when used singly.

19.4.2 SYNERGY AND ADDITIVITY

Claims are made frequently that two agents are "synergistic," implying that the two agents given together are more effective than would be expected from their individual activities. A large amount of confusion has arisen because different investigators have disagreed as to what constitutes an "expected" level of effect when two noninteracting agents are combined (Berenbaum, 1981). While it may be impossible to obtain consensus as to what constitutes an expected or additive effect, an appropriate definition must take into account the dose–effect relationship for each agent used alone, rather than a simple summation or multiplication of individual effects. The use of multiple agents may lead to an increase in the therapeutic index, but it is rare that a claim for synergy of effects against a single population of cells can be substantiated.

The concepts of synergy and additivity between two agents can be most conveniently understood by discussing damage caused by the agents to a single population of cells, either in a tumor or in normal tissue. Suppose a given dose of agent A gives a surviving fraction of cells (S_A), that a surviving fraction (S_B) follows treatment with a given dose of agent B, and a combination of the agents gives a surviving fraction (S_{A+B}) (Fig 19.15). Claims for synergy are often made if S_{A+B} is less than the product $S_A \times S_B$. This conclusion is correct only if cell survival is exponentially related to dose for both agents. However, if the survival curves have an initial "shoulder" (Fig 19.15), then the combined effects of the two agents may be expected to lead to an upper limit of survival equal to $S_A \times S_B$ if they act independently of each other, so that the shoulder of the

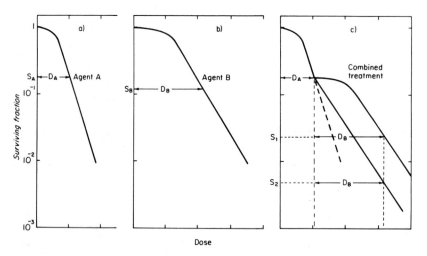

Figure 19.15. *a* and *b*: Cell survival (S_A or S_B) is indicated following treatment with either of two agents, A, and B, each of which has a survival curve characterized by an initial shoulder followed by an exponential fall with increasing dose. *c*: Survival (S_{A+B}) after combined use of dose D_A of agent A and dose D_B of agent B will be equal to S_1 (= $S_A \times S_B$) if there is no overlap of damage, and the "shoulder" representing accumulation of sublethal damage is retained for the second agent. Survival after combined treatment (S_{A+B}) will be equal to S_2 if cells have accumulated maximum sublethal damage from the first agent A, and the "shoulder" of the curve is lost for the second agent B.

survival curve is retained for both agents. Combined treatment will lead to a lower level of survival if, after treatment with one agent A, the survival falls exponentially with dose (in the absence of a "shoulder" effect) for the second agent B (Fig 19.15c). The fallacy of defining this lower level of survival as a "synergistic effect" can be illustrated by replacing agent B with a second, equal dose of agent A. If agent A has a survival curve with an initial shoulder one would then conclude erroneously that the second dose of agent A was synergistic with the first (ie, that agent A is synergistic with itself).

The above discussion suggests that there is a range over which two agents can produce additive effects. A method for formalizing this definition of additivity analyzes the interaction between two agents whose doses are individually varied to produce a constant level of biological effect (Steel and Peckham, 1979). Appropriate biological endpoints would include a constant level of cell survival, or a constant level of normal tissue damage. First, dose-response curves must be determined which describe a range of values of this biological effect for varying doses of each agent alone. These dose-response curves are used to generate isoeffect plots (known as "isobolograms") which relate the dose of agent A to the dose of agent B that would be predicted, when used in combination, to give a constant level of biological effect for the assumptions of (a) independent damage and (b) overlapping damage (Fig 19.16). These curves defined an envelope of additivity. If when the two agents are given together the doses required to give the same constant level of biological effect lie within the envelope, the interaction is said to be additive. If they lie between the lower isobologram and the axes (ie, the combined effect is caused by lower doses of the two agents than predicted) the interaction is "supra-additive" or synergistic. If the required doses of the two agents in combination lie above the envelope of additivity (ie, the effect is caused by higher doses than predicted), the interaction is "sub-additive" or antagonistic (Fig 19.16). Although the concept of an envelope of additivity implies some assumptions about what is meant by an expected or additive interaction, and is therefore not universally accepted, it is a useful concept which emphasizes that an understanding of interactions between agents requires consideration of dose-response relationships for each of the agents given alone.

19.4.3 MODIFIERS OF DRUG ACTIVITY

Some drugs with little or no toxicity for tumor cells may modify the action of anticancer drugs to produce increased toxicity. This effect is only useful if it leads to greater killing of cells in tumors as compared to normal tissues (ie, to an improvement in the therapeutic index).

A variety of drugs may influence the toxicities of anticancer agents. Changes in pharmacokinetics may be caused by inducers of hepatic microsomal enzymes (eg, phenobarbitol) or by drugs which compete for plasma binding or renal excretion, as is the case for aspirin and methotrexate. Other drugs are being studied which inhibit the repair of lesions in DNA caused by alkylating agents, cisplatin and other anticancer drugs.

A direct influence on cellular toxicity of several drugs has been observed recently for the polyamine biosynthesis inhibitor difluoromethylornithine (DFMO), but these effects are modest and variable in direction. There is little evidence to suggest potential for selective effects against tumors for drug combinations of this type.

There is current interest in the modification of the activity of anticancer drugs through the use of radiosensitizing drugs such as misonidazole. Misonidazole led to an increase in both antitumor effects and normal-tissue toxicity when used with many anticancer drugs in experimental animals (eg, Tannock, 1980). Some investigators have reported a larger influence of misonidazole and related compounds on antitumor effects of drugs than on their normal tissue toxicity, and this has led to recent clinical trials for this type of drug combination. There is, as yet, insufficient information to judge whether this will lead to improvement in the therapeutic index for patients. Several mechanisms contribute to the effects of misonidazole on the toxicity of

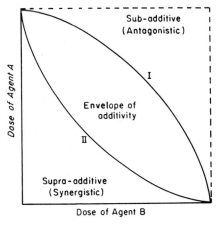

Figure 19.16. Isobolograms relate the doses of two agents that would be expected to give a constant level of biological effect when used together. They are generated from dose-response curves for each agent separately. Assumptions about overlap or nonoverlap of damage lead to generation of two isobologram curves (I and II) (cf Fig. 19.15) which describe an envelope of additive interaction. Experimental data falling outside this envelope may indicate synergistic or antagonistic interactions as shown. (Adapted from Steel and Peckham, 1979.)

anticancer drugs (eg, Siemann, 1984) and these mechanisms are summarized in Figure 19.17.

An alternative approach to modification of drug activity involves the use of agents that may offer selective protection against toxicity of normal tissue. The drug WR 2721 protects normal tissue against damage from radiation and from several anticancer drugs, including cisplatin and alkylating agents (Yuhas et al, 1980). The mechanism of action of WR 2721 probably involves greater deposition in well-vascularized normal tissue than in tumors, and activity as a scavenger for reactive groups including those responsible for alkylation. Unfortunately this mechanism may lead to protection of small, well-vascularized tumors from drug toxicity, but potential benefits are being tested in clinical trials.

19.4.4 RADIATION AND DRUGS

Patients frequently receive both radiation and anticancer drugs, and many investigators have studied the interaction between these modalities in tissue culture and experimental animals. In general these experiments have sought to define an optimal sequence and schedule for radiation and drugs used in combination, and to detect any severe and unpredictable damage to normal tissue.

Study of mechanisms of interaction between drugs and radiation at the cellular level may be evaluated from cell-survival curves for radiation obtained in the presence or absence of the drug (Fig 19.18). Drugs may influence the survival curve in at least three ways: (a) the curve may be displaced downwards by the amount of cell kill caused by the drug alone; (b) the "shoulder" on the survival curve may be lost, suggesting an inability to repair radiation damage in the presence of the drug; and (c) the slope of the exponential part of the survival curve may be changed (Fig 19.18). Most drugs influence survival curves according to the first two patterns described above; this corresponds to the limits of additivity defined in section 19.4.2, where sublethal damage may be independent or overlapping, and the interaction is described as dose additive. An example is loss of the "shoulder" on the radiation-survival curve in the presence of doxorubicin (eg, Belli and Piro, 1977). The third pattern, leading to a change in slope of the dose–response curve, defines agents that are radiation sensitizers or protectors (section 16.5); it is observed when drugs such as misonidazole are used to treat hypoxic cells, but rarely for anticancer drugs. Sensitization of this type has been reported for cisplatin and for prolonged exposure to 5-fluorouracil after radiation.

The interaction of drugs and radiation assessed against tumors and normal tissues is often dependent

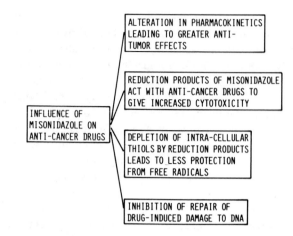

Figure 19.17. Potential mechanisms that may lead to an increase in antitumor effects, or to an increase in toxicity to normal tissues, when misonidazole is combined with anticancer drugs.

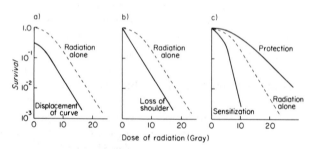

Figure 19.18. Possible influences of drug treatment on the relationship between radiation dose and cell survival: *a*, displacement of curve; *b*, loss of shoulder, indicating effects of drug on the repair of sublethal damage; *c*, change in slope of the curve indicating sensitization or protection.

on sequence and schedule. Schedule dependence may be explained in part by selectivity of the agents for cells in different phases of the cell cycle, and by their ability to cause differing durations of cell-cycle arrest in surviving cells; however, the influence of cell-cycle effects on cell killing by different schedules is rarely predictable. Drugs such as doxorubicin, where limited tissue penetration gives selective effects against perivascular and hence aerobic cells, give less cell killing in tumors when used simultaneously with radiation because both agents are then selective for the same (aerobic) cell population; an interval of a few hours between the agents may allow for spatial redistribution of the cell population which survives the first agent (Tannock, 1982). An unusual and schedule-dependent effect is the observation that cytosine arabinoside and several other drugs may protect against the lethal effects of whole-body radiation given to mice about 48 hr later. This effect has been useful in immunosuppression of thymectomized mice since mice treated in this way provide an alternative to nude mice as hosts for xenografts (see section 17.4.2).

If combined effects of drugs and radiation on tumors and normal tissues are analyzed with the aid of isoeffect curves (ie, isobolograms, section 19.4.2) most of them fall within the range of additivity. Thus, if therapeutic benefit is achieved, it is most likely due to additive effects against the tumor, with different and nonadditive types of normal tissue damage caused by drug and radiation. Localized radiation usually adds little or no toxicity to bone marrow suppression by a drug, and some drugs do not appear to increase the probability of normal tissue damage within the radiation field. However, both clinical experience and studies in animals have shown that several drugs can increase the incidence of toxicity from radiation, sometimes in organs (eg, the kidney) where the drugs alone rarely cause overt toxicity (Phillips and Fu, 1976). Some of the important interactions that have been documented in clinical experience are indicated in Table 19.3; these interactions may lead to a reduction in the maximally tolerated dose of radiation by factors of 10–50% as compared to treatment with radiation alone, when radiation is used in combination with drugs.

Table 19.3. Combined Effects of Radiation and Anticancer Drugs That Have Led to Increased Toxicity for Normal Tissues of Patients*

Tissue	Drugs Used with Radiation
Central nervous system	methotrexate
Peripheral nerves	vincristine
Lung	actinomycin D, doxorubicin, bleomycin
Heart	doxorubicin
Esophagus	actinomycin D, doxorubicin, bleomycin
Lower gastrointestinal tract	actinomycin D, 5-fluorouracil
Kidney	actinomycin D, doxorubicin
Bladder	cyclophosphamide
Skin and mucous membranes	actinomycin D, doxorubicin, bleomycin, 5-fluorouracil, cisplatin, methotrexate

*See also Phillips and Fu (1976).

19.5 SUMMARY

Experimental chemotherapy is directed towards improvement of the therapeutic index, which requires greater selectivity of drugs for tumors as compared to critical normal tissues. The most important limitation to this aim is intrinsic or acquired resistance to drugs of tumor cell populations. Drug resistance occurs through a variety of mechanisms, and usually results from mutation or amplification of genes (or both). Common mechanisms such as a decrease in intracellular transport may lead to cross-resistance between chemically unrelated drugs, providing a plausible explanation for clinical resistance to multiple agents.

Experiments in animals have demonstrated that drug administration may lead to cure of microscopic tumors; but not larger tumors; these experiments provide a model for adjuvant chemotherapy. Drugs which inhibit metastasis without causing direct toxicity to tumor cells are under investigation, but are likely to have limited clinical application.

Attempts have been made to increase delivery of drugs to tumor cells by the use of carriers such as antibodies or liposomes. These methods have shown limited benefit for treatment of solid tumors, and a major problem may be penetration of these complexes into tumor tissue. Some drugs have limited tissue penetration when used alone, suggesting a therapeutic role for other drugs that are active against nutrient-deprived or hypoxic cells, which may be protected from the action of conventional agents.

Anticancer drugs are used frequently in combination with each other and with radiation. Agents that modify drug toxicity are also undergoing clinical trial. The major potential for benefit of combined treatment is from additive effects against tumors with less than additive toxicity for critical normal tissues.

REFERENCES

Beck WT: Vinca alkaloid-resistant phenotype in cultured human leukemic lymphoblasts. *Cancer Treat Rep* 1983; 67:875–882.

Bell DR, Gerlach JH, Kartner N et al: Detection of P-glycoprotein in ovarian cancer: A molecular marker associated with multidrug resistance. *J Clin Oncol* 1985; 3:311–315.

Belli JA, Piro AJ: The interaction between radiation and adriamycin damage in mammalian cells. *Cancer Res* 1977; 37:1624–1630.

Berenbaum MC: Criteria for analyzing interactions between biologically active agents. *Adv Cancer Res* 1981; 35:269–335.

Bertino JR, Dolnick BJ, Berenson RJ et al: Cellular mechanisms of resistance to methotrexate, in Sartorelli AC, Lazo JS, Bertino JR (eds): *Molecular Actions and Targets for Cancer Chemotherapeutic Agents*. Academic Press, New York, 1981, pp 385–397.

Bloch A: Induced cell differentiation in cancer therapy. *Cancer Treat Rep* 1984; 68:199–205.

Chaplin DJ, Durand RE, Olive PL: Cell selection from a murine tumour using the fluorescent probe Hoechst 33342. *Br J Cancer* 1985; 51:569–572.

Cline MJ, Stang H, Mercola K et al: Gene transfer in intact animals. *Nature* 1980; 284:422–425.

Durand RE: Use of Hoechst 33342 for cell selection from multicell systems. *J Histochem Cytochem* 1982; 30:117–122.

Flintoff WF, Spindler SM, Siminovitch L: Genetic characterization of methotrexate-resistant Chinese hamster ovary cells. *In Vitro* 1976; 12:749–757.

Folkman J, Langer R, Linhardt RJ et al: Angiogenesis inhibition and tumor regression caused by heparin or a heparin fragment in the presence of cortisone. *Science* 1983; 221:719–725.

Fox BW, Fox M (eds): *Antitumor Drug Resistance.* Springer Verlag, Berlin, 1984.

Frei E III, Rosowsky A, Wright JE et al: Development of methotrexate resistance in a human squamous cell carcinoma of the head and neck in culture. *Proc Natl Acad Sci USA* 1984; 81:2873–2877.

Goldie JH, Coldman AJ: The genetic origin of drug resistance in neoplasms: Implications for systemic therapy. *Cancer Res* 1984; 44:3643–3653.

Goldie JH, Krystal G, Hartley D et al: A methotrexate insensitive variant of folate reductase present in two lines of methotrexate-resistant L5178Y cells. *Eur J Cancer* 1980; 16:1539–1546.

Gregoriadis G (ed): Targeted drug delivery and biological interaction, in *Liposome Technology.* CRC Press, Boca Raton, FL, 1984, Vol III, pp 263–282.

Hellmann K: Antimetastatic drugs: Laboratory to clinic. *Clin Exp Metastasis* 1984; 2:1–4.

Heppner GH: Tumor heterogeneity. *Cancer Res* 1984; 44:2259–2265.

Hilgard P: Anticoagulants and tumor growth: pharmacological considerations, in Nicolson GL, Milas L (eds): *Cancer Invasion and Metastasis: Biologic and Therapeutic Aspects*, Raven Press, New York, 1984, pp 353–360.

Hill RP, Stanley JA: The response of hypoxic B16 melanoma cells to *in vivo* treatment with chemotherapeutic agents. *Cancer Res* 1975; 35:1147–1153.

Hill RP, Stanley JA: Pulmonary metastases of the Lewis lung tumor—cell kinetics and response to cyclophosphamide at different sizes. *Cancer Treat Rep* 1977; 61:29–36.

Honn KV, Menter DG, Onoda JM et al: Role of prostacyclin as a natural deterrent to hematogenous tumor metastasis, in Nicolson GL, Milas L (eds): *Cancer Invasion and Metastasis: Biologic and Therapeutic Aspects.* Raven Press, New York, 1984, pp 361–388.

Kartner N, Riordan JR, Ling V: Cell surface P-Glycoprotein associated with multidrug resistance in mammalian cell lines. *Science* 1983; 221:1285–1288.

Langer R, Conn H, Vacanti J et al: Control of tumor growth in animals by infusion of an angiogenesis inhibitor. *Proc Natl Acad Sci USA* 1980; 77:4331–4335.

Ling V: Genetic basis of drug resistance in mammalian cells, in Bruchovsky N, Goldie JH (eds): *Drug and Hormone Resistance in Neoplasia.* CRC Press, Boca Raton, FL, 1982, vol 1, pp 1–19.

Luria SE, Delbruck M: Mutations of bacteria from virus sensitivity to virus resistance. *Genetics* 1943; 28:491–511.

Phillips TL, Fu KK: Quantification of combined radiation therapy and chemotherapy effects on critical normal tissues. *Cancer* 1976; 37:1186–1200.

Poste G, Papahadjopoulos D: Drug-containing lipid vesicles render drug-resistant tumour cells sensitive to Actinomycin D. *Nature* 1976; 261:699–701.

Rahman A, Kessler A, More N et al: Liposomal protection of Adriamycin-induced cardiotoxicity in mice. *Cancer Res* 1980; 40:1532–1537.

Rice GC, Hoy C, Schimke RT: Transient hypoxia enhances the frequency of dihydrofolate reductase gene amplification in Chinese hamster ovary cells. *Proc Natl Acad Sci USA* 1986: 83:5978–5982.

Riordan JR, Ling V: Genetic and biochemical characterization of multidrug resistance. *Pharmacol Ther* 1985; 28:51–75.

Schabel FM Jr: Concepts for systemic treatment of micrometastases. *Cancer* 1975; 35:15–24.

Schimke RT: Gene amplification, drug resistance, and cancer. *Cancer Res* 1984; 44:1735–1742.

Shing Y, Folkman J, Sullivan R et al: Heparin affinity: Purification of a tumor-derived capillary endothelial cell growth factor. *Science* 1984; 223:1296–1299.

Siemann DW: Modification of chemotherapy by nitroimidazoles. *Int J Radiat Oncol Biol Phys* 1984; 10:1585–1594.

Skipper HE, Schabel FM Jr, Wilcox WS: Experimental evaluation of potential anticancer agents. XIII. On the criteria and kinetics associated with "curability" of experimental leukemia. *Cancer Chemother Rep* 1964; 35:1–111.

Steel GG, Peckham MJ: Exploitable mechanisms in combined radiotherapy–chemotherapy: The concept of additivity. *Int J Radiat Oncol Biol Phys* 1979; 5:85–91.

Strickland S, Mahdavi V: The induction of differentiation in teratocarcinoma stem cells by retinoic acid. *Cell* 1978; 15:393–403.

Sutherland RM, Eddy HA, Bareham B et al: Resistance to Adriamycin in multicellular spheroids. *Int J Radiat Oncol Biol Phys* 1979; 5:1225–1230.

Tannock IF: *In vivo* interaction of anti-cancer drugs with misonidazole or metronidazole: Cyclophosphamide and BCNU. *Br J Cancer* 1980; 42:871–880.

Tannock I: Response of aerobic and hypoxic cells in a solid tumor to Adriamycin and cyclophosphamide and interaction of the drugs with radiation. *Cancer Res* 1982; 42: 4921–4926.

Taylor SM, Constantinides PA, Jones PA: 5-Azacytidine, DNA methylation, and differentiation. *Curr Top Microbiol Immunol* 1984; 108:115–127.

Tofilon PJ, Buckley N, Deen DF: Effect of cell–cell interactions on drug sensitivity and growth of drug-sensitive and -resistant tumor cells in spheroids. *Science* 1984; 226:862–864.

Tsuruo T, Iida H, Tsukagoshi S, Sakurai Y: Potentiation of Vincristine and Adriamycin effects in human hemopoietic tumor cell lines by calcium antagonists and calmodulin inhibitors. *Cancer Res* 1983; 43:2267–2272.

Weinstein JN, Leserman LD: Liposomes as drug carriers in cancer chemotherapy. *Pharmacol Ther* 1984; 24:207–233.

Yatvin MB, Muhlensiepen H, Porschen W et al: Selective delivery of liposome-associated cis-dichlorodiammine-platinum (II) by heat and its influence on tumor drug uptake and growth. *Cancer Res* 1981; 41:1602–1607.

Yuhas JM, Spellman JM, Jordan SW et al: Treatment of tumours with the combination of WR-2721 and cis-dichlorodiammineplatinum (II) or cyclophosphamide. *Br J Cancer* 1980; 42:574–585.

Zacharski LR, Henderson WG, Rickles FR et al: Effect of warfarin anticoagulation on survival in carcinoma of the lung, colon, head and neck, and prostate. Final Report of VA Cooperative Study #75. *Cancer* 1984; 53:2046–2052.

BIBLIOGRAPHY

Fox BW, Fox M (eds): *Antitumor Drug Resistance*. Springer Verlag, Berlin, 1984.

20

Immunotherapy and the Potential Applications of Monoclonal Antibodies

Ian F. Tannock

20.1 INTRODUCTION

Experimentally induced tumors in animals can often stimulate an immune response against the tumor (chapter 14). This finding has led to many experiments in animals, and subsequently in patients, in which attempts were made to stimulate the immune response of the host to induce shrinkage or rejection of the tumor. Manipulation of the immune response in an attempt to induce tumor regression is known as immunotherapy. Multiple methods have been used to stimulate anti-tumor immunity, but the impact of immunotherapy on the treatment of human cancer so far has been minimal. This chapter will review the problems associated with immunotherapy, and will discuss the potential for new approaches that have arisen from an increased understanding of the biology of the immune response. It includes also an assessment of the potential role of monoclonal antibodies in diagnosis and therapy of cancer.

20.1.1 TUMOR ANTIGENS

Immunotherapy requires the presence of target molecules on tumor cells that can be recognized by anti-

bodies or by cells which participate in the immune response. It is not always necessary that these target molecules be immunogenic in the original host (ie, capable of eliciting an immune response) since immune effectors (antibodies or cells) can be obtained if they are antigenic in other animals. The target molecules must, however, have some degree of specificity for the tumor in order to obtain a differential effect against tumor as compared to normal tissue. Evidence for the existence of tumor-associated antigens, and a review of some of their properties, have been discussed in section 14.3. In brief, the following has been found to pertain.

1. Immunization of animals followed by attempts at tumor transplantation have demonstrated unique tumor-specific antigens on cells of rapidly growing chemically induced tumors of mice, and common tumor antigens on cells from experimental tumors induced by the same type of virus.

2. Antigens can be detected on cells of many spontaneous tumors, including human tumors, by antisera or monoclonal antibodies; these antigens are not expressed by most tissues of the adult host. Antibodies with specificity for these tumor-associated antigens will often react with some cells from normal

tissues, with embryonic tissue, and/or with tumors from other patients of the same or different histologic origin. Expression of these antigens may be heterogeneous among the cells of a tumor population, and may relate to the state of differentiation of the cells.

3. Unique tumor-associated antigens in animal systems were demonstrated in experiments involving transplantation, and these cannot be duplicated in man. With the exception of some lymphoid malignancies, the use of antisera or monoclonal antibodies has failed to demonstrate unique antigens on the surface of cells from spontaneous tumors in mice or man.

4. Most tumors that are clinically evident continue to grow, and there is little evidence that they elicit an effective immune rejection response in their host. Some tumors, notably melanoma and renal-cell carcinoma, may regress spontaneously, while others are diagnosed by the presence of metastases, with no evidence of a primary tumor. These less frequent events may represent the presence of an effective immune rejection response. It should be kept in mind that for a tumor to become clinically detectable, it must usually contain at least 10^9 cells. Tumors reaching this size have obviously not been destroyed by the immune system. Many other tumors could well have been destroyed before reaching this size.

The above results imply the presence of surface antigens on cells of some human tumors that differ from those on many normal tissues, and these antigens might be used as targets for immunotherapy. The weak expression of some of these antigens, their heterogeneity, their failure to stimulate recognizable immunity against most tumors, and their possible expression on some normal cells are some of the problems associated with induction of an effective antitumor immune response against established tumors.

20.1.2 ANIMAL MODELS

A high proportion of experimental tumors used as models for immunotherapy have been transplanted through many generations in "syngeneic" mice. Many of these tumors have been exchanged between laboratories. Unfortunately, inbred mice of the same nominal strain show genetic drift between laboratories, and during prolonged maintenance in single institutions. In addition, after multiple passages either in vivo or in vitro, transplantable tumors can undergo extensive change involving both gain and loss of antigens. Thus multiply transplanted tumors may not be truly syngeneic with their host animal. Experiments with such

tumors may provide useful information about transplantation immunity, but probably are not valid models for induction of tumor-specific immunity (Fig 20.1).

Experimental tumors that are strongly immunogenic in the syngeneic animal include those induced by chemical carcinogens. For convenience, chemically induced tumors are usually induced by administering high doses of carcinogen to a strain of animal that produces a high yield of tumors. However, use of lower doses of carcinogen leads to a lower incidence of tumors, and those that do occur are less likely to be immunogenic (Fig 20.1; Prehn, 1975). Many human tumors are probably caused by prolonged exposure to low levels of carcinogens (chapter 2) and experimental tumors induced by high doses of carcinogens may therefore provide inappropriate models for studying their immunity. Hewitt et al (1976) found no evidence for any host immune response in a careful study of 27 tumors that arose spontaneously in mice, and suggested that spontaneous tumors in animals would be more appropriate models for immunotherapy of human tumors. Few investigators have attempted to stimulate an immune response in rodents bearing spontaneous tumors.

In animals, many forms of immunotherapy have been effective in eradicating small numbers of cells from transplanted or induced tumors or in causing shrinkage of localized tumor masses. Usually, the immune stimulation has been commenced before, or soon after, tumor implantation. Immunotherapy has usually been ineffective against large tumors, even when tumors can be demonstrated to be strongly immunogenic.

The limitations of many of the animal models suggest that results obtained following direct stimulation of host immunity against rodent tumors will not necessarily apply to man. This does not, however, invalidate the use of animal models for study of monoclonal antibodies or of immune cells which have been generated in

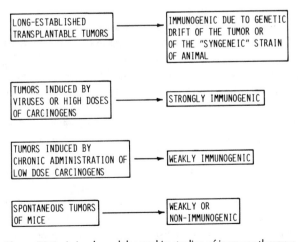

Figure 20.1. Animal models used in studies of immunotherapy.

other animals, and which may recognize antigens on tumor cells to which the host is tolerant. Such agents might be directly toxic, or might cause loss of tolerance in the host.

20.2 METHODS OF IMMUNOTHERAPY

20.2.1 TUMOR-SPECIFIC ACTIVE IMMUNIZATION

Active immunization of the tumor-bearing host is termed specific if immunization is performed with preparations containing tumor antigens (Fig 20.2). Immunization of rodents with tumor cells that have been inactivated by treatment with drugs or radiation may inhibit growth of the same type of tumor. In general, this effect is observed only when immunization is carried out prior to, or immediately after, tumor transplantation, when the total number of live tumor cells is small. The development of metastases following eradication of a primary transplant with radiation or surgery may also be prevented. Various approaches have been shown to increase the effectiveness of immunization, including the admixture of immunological adjuvants to tumor preparations and treatment of cells with surface-active agents such as neuraminidase, which may reveal more antigenic sites (Prager, 1978; Lutz, 1983). However, results obtained with animal models have demonstrated that some forms of active immunization might specifically suppress rather than stimulate any immune rejection response, leading to enhancement of tumor growth.

Active immunization of patients with their own killed tumor cells, or with killed cells from patients bearing tumors of a similar histological type, has been attempted for several different malignancies. The aim of such treatment has been palliation for patients with established metastases, or to prevent recurrence of disease following removal of the primary tumor. Although well-documented regression of metastatic lesions is observed for some tumors (eg, carcinoma of the kidney) these effects are usually transient.

There are a number of possible reasons why tumor-specific active immunization has not had a major impact on human cancer. The tumor-bearing host has been exposed to tumor antigens during the period of tumor growth, and although immunization may change the site and manner in which any tumor antigens are presented to the immune system, it seems unlikely that this would stimulate a marked rejection response that has remained dormant during tumor growth. Antigens may be demonstrated on the surfaces of cells of many types of human tumors using monoclonal antibodies or other methods (see section 20.3). A major question is

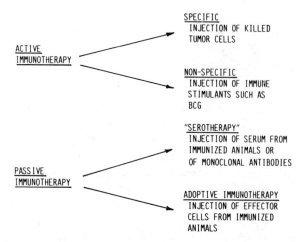

Figure 20.2. Terminology used in different approaches to immunotherapy.

whether the host fails to respond to such antigens or whether tumor immunity is actively suppressed by T-suppressor cells (section 14.2.2). Patients with far advanced tumors tend to be immune deficient, but this is not generally true in earlier stages. If the antitumor response is actively suppressed, there may be a future role for stimulating tumor-specific immunity through treatment aimed at killing T-suppressor cells. This can be achieved by the use of cyclophosphamide, but agents with higher specificity will probably be required to test this hypothesis. In the case where a tumor has antigens but the host fails to respond because of absence of effector-cell precursors of appropriate specificity, it would appear that the tumor has somehow had its antigens treated as self-antigens. To circumvent this, it will be necessary to develop a better understanding of the mechanisms responsible for self–nonself discrimination, an understanding only now being developed (see section 14.2.3).

20.2.2 NONSPECIFIC IMMUNE STIMULATION

BCG (bacillus Calmette Guérin), an attenuated live strain of mycobacteria, and nonviable fractions such as the methanol extract residue (MER), are potent stimulators of several arms of the immune response; they have been used in numerous attempts to control experimental and clinical cancer (Bast et al, 1974).

Experiments in animals have demonstrated that immunization with BCG can protect mice against subsequent transplantation of immunogenic tumors. In one study, about 45% of antigenically distinct chemically induced fibrosarcomas were rejected, there was no effect in 45%, and there was possible stimulation of growth in about 10% (Old et al, 1961). Established tumors are usually unaffected by BCG treatment of their host animal, although regression of small solid tumors can be achieved by direct injection of BCG into the tumor. Critical limitations on the effectiveness of BCG in the treatment of experimental tumors are the following (Bast et al, 1974): (a) tumor size; (b) ability to develop an immune response to mycobacterial antigens; (c) the presence of adequate numbers of BCG organisms ($>\sim10^8$); (d) close contact between BCG and tumor cells; and in many cases (e) the ability of the host to develop an immune response to tumor-associated antigens. Probable mechanisms for the activity of BCG are indicated in Figure 20.3.

The initial encouraging results of clinical trials using BCG as a systemic agent in the treatment of acute leukemia, melanoma and other human malignancies have not been confirmed in large randomized controlled studies. For example, there was minimal benefit recorded from a review of 24 trials using BCG or similar agents to treat more than 1400 patients with acute myelogenous leukemia (Foon et al, 1983). Injection of BCG into cutaneous tumor nodules of patients with melanoma may lead to shrinkage of both the injected and neighboring nodules, but there is no effect on more distant sites. Thus the treatment has a limited role in palliation of the disease. These clinical results are consistent with the experience using animal tumors.

Other nonspecific stimulants of the immune response that have been used in trials of immunotherapy include an inactive vaccine of *Corynebacterium parvum*, other bacterial products, and the orally administered adjuvant levamisole. None of these agents has shown consistent beneficial effects.

20.2.3 PASSIVE IMMUNOTHERAPY

Passive immunotherapy involves the injection of immune mediators, obtained by immunization of other subjects, into tumor-bearing hosts (Fig 20.2). Prior to the development of monoclonal antibodies, most attempts at passive immunotherapy involved the injection of heterologous serum. This type of serotherapy has given disappointing results (Rosenberg and Terry, 1977); therapeutic effects in animals have been minimal, except for strongly antigenic tumors induced by viruses, and there is no convincing evidence that immune serum from any source has been beneficial in man. These negative findings are probably due to (a) the limited role of most antibodies in cytotoxic responses against tumor cells; (b) the lack of tumor specificity and relatively low titers of most of the antisera that were used; (c) limited diffusion of immune antibodies from blood vessels to tumor cells; and (d) the foreign nature of the antiserum itself, which will induce an im-

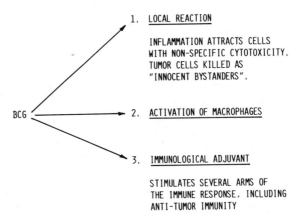

Figure 20.3. Probable mechanisms which may lead to antitumor effects of BCG.

mune reaction against it in the tumor-bearing host. Some, but not all, of these problems may be overcome by the use of monoclonal antibodies (section 20.3).

Since rejection of tissue depends mainly on a cellular rather than a humoral response (section 14.2.4), several investigators have passively transferred immune cells from an animal or patient, a procedure known as adoptive immunotherapy (Fig 20.2; Rosenberg, 1984). Effector cells from genetically dissimilar (ie, allogeneic) animals or patients are rejected rapidly, but those obtained by immunization of syngeneic animals have demonstrated some therapeutic effects against small tumors in rodents. The requirement for large numbers of effector cells has stimulated current interest in the possibility of expanding clones of immune lymphocytes in tissue culture to provide adequate cells for therapeutic effects (section 20.4.1).

20.3 MONOCLONAL ANTIBODIES

20.3.1 PRODUCTION OF MONOCLONAL ANTIBODIES

Antiserum derived by immunization of an animal with foreign cells has a range of different specificities (ie, is heterologous) because many different lymphoid cells are stimulated, each of which has a defined but slightly different specificity. Köhler and Milstein (1975) showed that it was possible to stimulate hybridization between malignant plasma cells (ie, cells capable of making immunoglobulin) maintained in continuous culture and immune lymphoid cells. Hybrid cells which grew in culture and which produced antibodies with the single defined specificity of an immune lymphoid cell could then be selected by cloning.

The basic technique for production of monoclonal antibodies is shown in Figure 20.4. Spleen cells from an

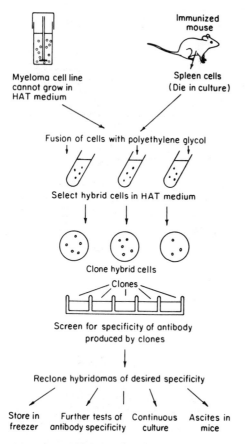

Figure 20.4. Schematic diagram indicating major steps in the production of monoclonal antibodies.

animal that has been immunized with foreign antigens are placed in culture with a continuously growing myeloma cell line in the presence of polyethylene glycol to stimulate cell fusion. The myeloma line used in the experiments is a mutant which does not secrete immunoglobulin, and has been selected for an enzyme deficiency that prevents its growth in medium containing hypoxanthine, aminopterin and thymidine (HAT medium). The normal spleen cells cannot grow in culture; thus only hybrid cells, formed by fusion, will grow in HAT medium since the missing enzyme is provided by the fused lymphoid cell.

After selection in HAT medium, hybrid cells are cloned by placing individual cells into single wells of a multiwell tissue-culture plate. Antibodies secreted by each clone of hybrid cells (hybridoma) can then be tested for specificity, for example, by reactivity to tumor cells but not to normal cells (Fig 20.5). Large quantities of monoclonal antibodies may be obtained from supernatants of "hybridoma" cell cultures, or by growing the hybridoma as an ascites tumor in mice. Hybrid cells can also be frozen and stored.

The most difficult aspect of making monoclonal antibodies is selecting the hybrid clone with the desired specificity since a very large number of clones may need to be screened. When the aim is to produce monoclonal antibodies specific for human tumors of a given histological type it is usual to test the antibody products of hybrid clones against the index tumor, against estab-

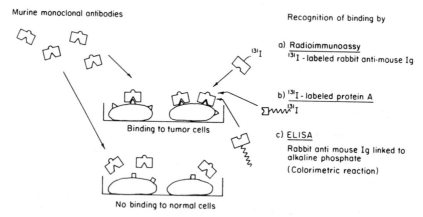

Figure 20.5. Assays which allow the detection of monoclonal antibodies bound to tumor cells. *a*, In the radioimmunoassay, antibodies to mouse immunoglobulin are labeled with ^{131}I, and their binding to monoclonal antibodies on washed cells is detected by gamma-counting. *b*, ^{131}I-linked staphylococcal protein A also binds to mouse immunoglobulins on cells. *c*, In the enzyme-linked immunoadsorbent assay (ELISA), alkaline phosphatase is linked to antibodies against mouse immunoglobulin, and binding is recognized by a colorimetric reaction. Specificity in each assay is indicated by lack of binding to normal cells, and by failure of monoclonal antibodies with other specificity to bind to tumor cells.

lished cell lines and cells from primary human tumors of the same and different histological types, and against a variety of normal tissues. Several methods are available to test for reactivity of antibodies to different cells based usually on binding of monoclonal antibodies to the cells or their membrane preparations (Fig 20.5). A rapid screening test is performed first and is followed by more detailed studies of those monoclonal antibodies with some degree of specificity; these studies include tests of their cytotoxicity and attempts to characterize the antigen to which they bind.

Monoclonal antibodies which recognize antigenic determinants on cells of human tumors of a given histological type (eg, melanoma-associated antigens) are now available for many types of tumors. Most of these antibodies show some cross-reactivity with the cells of a few normal tissues. Many of these monoclonal antibodies probably recognize antigens that are related to cell differentiation, such as carcinoembryonic antigen (CEA), which is expressed at high frequency on cells from tumors of the colon.

20.3.2 HUMAN MONOCLONAL ANTIBODIES

Most monoclonal antibodies have been made using rodent cell lines. This is a problem when they are to be used for diagnosis or treatment of human cancer because they are recognized as foreign proteins and elicit an immune response which leads to their rapid clearance and loss of activity, or to anaphylactic reactions. The strength of such a reaction might be decreased by using monoclonal antibodies of human origin, and if a patient's own lymphoid cells were used as a fusion partner, syngeneic monoclonal antibodies could be obtained. Attempts to obtain stable hybridoma cultures by fusion of human lymphoid and mouse myeloma cells have been frustrated by selective loss of human chromosomes from the hybrid cells, with consequent failure to continue secretion of antibody.

Monoclonal antibodies have been produced by fusion of human lymphoid cells with a human myeloma cell line (Olsson and Kaplan, 1980); however, this approach has been limited by the lack of established human myeloma cell lines, and the difficulty of obtaining mutant cells that are sensitive to HAT medium. Also, available human myeloma cell lines have continued to produce immunoglobulins or their heavy or light chains so that hybridomas formed with them secrete antibody molecules which may contain components of *both* parent cells, rather than antibodies of single, uniform specificity. Another problem is access to sufficient human immune lymphoid cells as fusion partners, but this might be overcome partly by stimulating

human lymphoid cells which react to a specific antigen by exposure to that antigen in vitro.

An alternative approach has been to expose human lymphoid cells obtained from immunized individuals to Epstein–Barr virus, since viral infection may allow continuous passage of cells in culture. The method may allow production of antibodies with defined specificity over several generations in culture, but is limited by difficulties in cloning of the cell lines, and by progressive loss of antibody production with time (eg, Zurawski et al, 1978).

For the above reasons, only a few human monoclonal antibodies are available for potential use in tumor diagnosis or therapy. A new approach to this problem is the production of chimeric antibodies which have a constant region of human origin and a variable region of murine origin. Such antibodies have now been produced by genetic engineering (see section A3.3) where DNA sequences specific for murine and human components are linked in a plasmid vector and transfected into bacteria which produce the chimeric antibody (eg, Boulianne et al, 1984). The variable region of murine origin in such antibodies should not be more immunogenic than that of monoclonal antibodies of human origin.

20.3.3 MONOCLONAL ANTIBODIES IN DIAGNOSIS AND IMAGING

Monoclonal antibodies which recognize antigens that are associated with several types of cancer (eg, melanoma, ovarian and colon cancer) have been used in radioimmunoassays to detect antigens in serum or other body fluids of patients who are suspected of having cancer. They provide sensitive assays for detection of tumor markers such as CEA, human chorionic gonadotropin (hCG) or α-fetoprotein (see section 12.2). The limitation of such monoclonal antibodies in diagnosis is set by the specificity of the production of the marker antigen by the tumor cells, and by the association of detectable levels of many antigens only with advanced tumors that are no longer curable.

Monoclonal antibodies (eg, conjugated with fluorescein) may allow recognition of a small number of tumor cells in bone marrow or biopsies of tissue that would not be recognized by conventional histological techniques. For example, involvement of bone marrow by small-cell lung cancer was detected at diagnosis in 69% of samples with the aid of a monoclonal antibody, but in only 16% by usual histochemical stains (Stahel et al, 1985). Use of monoclonal antibodies as an aid to staging of malignant disease is likely to become routine.

Monoclonal antibodies may be tagged with isotopic

labels (eg, ^{131}I) and used as an aid to tumor imaging. Imaging of human tumor xenografts implanted into immunosuppressed mice has provided a useful preclinical model (Fig 20.6). The tumor image is obtained by subtracting images formed with a nonspecific antibody (representing background due to the blood pool and nonspecific binding) from that obtained using the monoclonal antibody directed against tumor-associated antigens.

Many studies of the use of monoclonal antibodies for imaging in patients have used radiolabeled CEA to detect tumors of the colon and rectum, ovary, cervix or lung (eg, Goldenberg et al, 1980). Large tumors have been detected readily by this method, but it could not visualize tumors less than about 2 cm in diameter. Thus monoclonal antibodies given intravenously do not as yet offer an improvement in sensitivity as compared with conventional procedures used to detect metastases

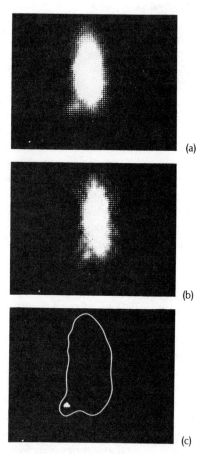

(a)

(b)

(c)

Figure 20.6. Nuclear images obtained after the injection of *a*, ^{125}I-labeled anti-colon-cancer monoclonal antibody, and *b*, nonspecific ^{131}I-labeled antibody into a nude mouse bearing a human colorectal tumor xenograft in the left thigh. The image in *c* was obtained by computer-assisted subtraction of the blood-pool radioactivity. (Reproduced by permission of J. Zalcberg.)

in liver, bone or brain. There may be considerable potential for detection of small metastases in lymph nodes following subcutaneous injection of radiolabeled monoclonal antibodies (Weinstein et al, 1982; Thompson et al, 1984). In this application tumor cells are exposed to a high concentration of antibodies, and there are fewer problems with background that occurs in the blood pool after IV injection.

The current use of monoclonal antibodies in imaging is limited by the following difficulties: (a) incomplete specificity for antigens on tumor cells; (b) heterogeneity in expression of tumor-associated antigens among individual tumor cells or among metastatic nodules; (c) limited diffusion of monoclonal antibodies from tumor blood vessels (although diffusion might be improved by use of monovalent antibody fragments obtained by partial enzymatic digestion of monoclonal antibodies prior to labeling); (d) binding of antibodies to antigens that are secreted from tumor cells (which can lead to loss of specific localization and to toxic reactions from immune-complex disease); (e) loss of the radiolabel into the circulation with consequent increase in background; and (f) the poor physical characteristics for imaging of easily attachable radiolabels such as [131]I. More suitable isotopes such as technetium-99 or indium-111 are difficult to link to antibodies without an adverse effect on their binding affinity. It seems likely that most of these difficulties will be overcome by further research and that monoclonal antibodies will come to play an important role in the detection of human tumors.

20.3.4 MONOCLONAL ANTIBODIES IN IMMUNOTHERAPY

Monoclonal antibodies have the potential to cause lysis of cells to which they bind through interaction with complement, or through antibody-dependent cellular cytotoxicity (ADCC; Fig 20.7). Also, circulating tumor cells could be coated with immunoglobulin and cleared by the reticuloendothelial system. Major advantages in therapeutic potential for monoclonal as opposed to heterologous antibodies (section 20.2.3) are their greater specificity for tumor-associated antigens, and the large quantity of monospecific antibodies that may be produced by growing hybridomas as ascites tumors in mice.

Several investigators have used monoclonal antibodies directed against tumor-associated antigens to treat experimental tumors in mice (eg, Bernstein et al, 1980; Foon et al, 1982). It was found that large quantities of monoclonal antibodies could cause inhibition of tumor growth or cure if they were injected shortly after tumor implantation when the tumor burden was small. The antibodies were toxic to tumor cells in the circulation

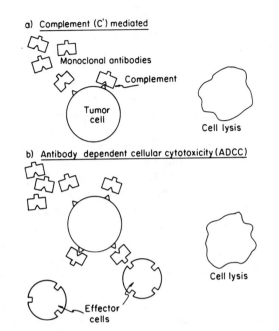

a) Complement (C') mediated

Monoclonal antibodies

Complement

Tumor cell

Cell lysis

b) Antibody dependent cellular cytotoxicity (ADCC)

Cell lysis

Effector cells

Figure 20.7. Schematic diagram indicating potential mechanisms by which antibodies may induce lysis of tumor cells.

but were less effective against established tumors. The administration of complement increased the therapeutic effect against some tumors in animals, but cell killing by ADCC appeared to be the more important mechanism leading to cell lysis (Fig 20.7).

Rare examples of the successful use of monoclonal antibodies to treat human malignancy have been reported; one example is the report of a durable complete remission in a patient with B-cell lymphoma (Miller et al, 1982). Malignant B cells express a monoclonal immunoglobulin on their cell surface, and monoclonal antibodies were raised to the variable part of the molecule (ie, to its "idiotype"). Since each immunoglobulin produced by a clone of B cells has a different idiotype, this situation afforded a unique opportunity to direct a monoclonal antibody against a tumor-specific antigen. This type of therapy is limited to B-cell lymphomas, although analogous methods might apply to T-cell lymphomas, which often appear to have unique rearrangements of the genes coding for the T-cell receptor. Successful therapy also requires that the disease be controlled by conventional methods during the often lengthy production and isolation of anti-idiotype antibodies.

The problems associated with the use of monoclonal antibodies in therapy are similar to those described in the previous section and include diffusion to tumor cells, heterogeneity of antigen expression on tumor cells, absorption of antibodies by antigens secreted into serum, and the induction of an immune response

against the antibody. In addition, tumor cells may escape damage by redistribution and release of antigen–antibody complexes from the cell surface. This process of antigenic modulation appears to require bivalent antibodies, however, and monovalent antibodies produced by limited proteolytic digestion might prevent the process (Cobbold and Waldmann, 1984). The use of pooled monoclonal antibodies against several antigenic determinants also has the potential to minimize the effects of both antigenic modulation and heterogeneity of antigenic expression. A more serious limitation may be the number of ADCC effector cells that are available in the tumor-bearing host to eliminate antibody-coated target cells (Mastrangelo et al, 1984).

20.3.5 MONOCLONAL ANTIBODY DIRECTED THERAPY

Monoclonal antibodies have therapeutic potential as carriers of anticancer drugs, toxins or radioisotopes to the surfaces of tumor cells (see also section 19.3.3). Specific cytotoxicity may then occur through local release or activity of the toxic ligand.

Radioimmunotherapy by injection of high-specific-activity ^{131}I linked to monoclonal antibodies against tumor-associated antigens has led to regression of some tumors in experimental animals, and clinical trials have been initiated. Ligation of monoclonal antibodies with a variety of anticancer drugs has also led to increased antitumor effects in animals as compared to free drug and monoclonal antibodies. Most of the therapeutic effects observed with the above techniques were against experimental leukemias or ascites tumors, although regression of a few solid tumors has been observed (for review, see Foon et al, 1982).

The linking of agents to monoclonal antibodies is analogous to the linking of isotopes used in imaging (section 20.3.3) except that the agent should have a short range of action. Similar problems arise, and in particular, the ligation of monoclonal antibodies to anticancer drugs may be difficult to achieve without change in drug activity or affinity of the monoclonal antibody for its binding site. The use of monoclonal-antibody-directed therapy is likely to be limited by the number of binding sites on tumor cells, which may not allow delivery of sufficient radioactivity or drug to kill the cell. Nonspecific uptake of the complexes by the reticuloendothelial system or by the kidney may also lead to toxicity for these normal tissues.

Directing adequate dosage of a toxic agent may be less of a problem when monoclonal antibodies are linked to potent toxins such as the A chain of ricin or diptheria toxin, since one molecule of these toxins can be sufficient to kill the cell (Blythman et al, 1981; Foon et al, 1982). Injection of toxin–antibody conjugates has led to antitumor effects against several types of experimental tumors. Heterogeneity of antigen expression, the presence of tumor-associated antigens on some cells of normal tissues, and the requirement for penetration of antibody complexes from blood vessels of solid tumors present remaining obstacles to the successful use of such complexes in man. Despite these problems, treatment directed by monoclonal antibodies is likely to achieve a useful but limited role in therapy of human cancer.

20.4 NEW POSSIBILITIES IN IMMUNOTHERAPY

20.4.1 CELL-MEDIATED IMMUNOTHERAPY

The approaches to immunotherapy described in previous sections have had limited success, but recent research suggests that several different types of cell-mediated immunity might have greater potential for use in immunotherapy. Three different types of cells have been discussed in section 14.4, each of which might be involved in mediation of antitumor immunity: cytotoxic T lymphocytes, natural killer (NK) cells, and activated macrophages. Each of these appears to recognize different kinds of "foreignness," and all three respond to determinants other than those recognized by antibodies.

Cytotoxic T lymphocytes (CTLs, sections 14.2.8 and 14.4.2) recognize antigens on foreign tissue in conjunction with a product of the major histocompatibility complex (MHC). CTLs are thought to be involved in the elimination of viruses, and probably recognize tumor-associated antigens. Cloned lines of CTLs may be established and expanded in vitro using a medium containing T-cell growth factor (also known as interleukin 2) and these cloned cells can be injected into patients (Rosenberg, 1984). The ability of a tumor-bearing host to reject foreign cells, and the dependency of cytotoxic activity on MHC determinants common to the tumor-bearing host are likely to restrict the utility of this approach to infusion of the patient's own cloned CTLs. This method could convey therapeutic benefit if the patient's tumor was able to be controlled by conventional therapy while cloned cell lines of CTLs were established and expanded in vitro.

The activity of the antibody-directed immune response (and probably also of CTLs) is controlled by T-helper and T-suppressor cells (section 14.2.2); thus a possible approach to stimulating such immunity is through manipulation of the ratio of T-helper to T-suppressor cells. This might be achieved by isolation, expansion and injection of T-helper cells, or through the use of cytotoxic monoclonal antibodies that recognize determinants unique to T-suppressor cells.

Natural killer (NK) cells are lymphocytes which recognize and kill some types of tumor cells without prior sensitization (section 14.4.3). NK cells may be stimulated to a modest degree by interferons (section 20.4.2) and cloned NK cell lines have been established in culture. As for CTLs, injection of NK cells cloned from the patient to be treated might have a limited future role in immunotherapy.

Macrophages, like NK cells, have poorly understood mechanisms for distinguishing tumor cells from normal cells (section 14.4.4). Macrophages can be "activated" to kill tumor cells. Activation may occur following exposure to a lymphokine called MAF (macrophage-activating factor) or to muramyl dipeptide (MDP), a component of bacterial cell walls. MAF is produced by T cells when they interact with their appropriate antigen. Production of MAF is antigen specific, but once activated the macrophages are not specific for cells carrying the antigen. Perhaps the principal antitumor effect of BCG following injection into a tumor is via activation of macrophages.

A major problem in the use of activated macrophages in therapy is to get them to the tumor. Activated macrophages do not move freely from place to place. Tumors normally contain quiescent macrophages which could be activated if one could give them MAF or MDP, but these substances may cause adverse reactions and are rapidly cleared after parenteral injection. One approach to this problem is to inject MAF or MDP in lipid vesicles (liposomes) which can be constructed to allow preferential trapping and phagocytosis by macrophages in the lung (Fidler, 1985). This method has been used in the successful treatment of lung metastases from experimental tumors in mice. Although this treatment is only effective against small metastases ($<10^7$ cells), attempts to develop tumor cell lines that are resistant to killing by activated macrophages have not be successful.

20.4.2 BIOLOGICAL RESPONSE MODIFIERS

A large number of molecules may act to regulate various components of the immune response. Most of these molecules are polypeptides; the techniques of molecular genetics (section A3.3) are being used to purify them and to synthesize them by cloning their genes in bacteria. These techniques allow the large-scale production of pure molecules, some of which have been proposed as agents that may be useful in cancer therapy. These molecules are known collectively as biological response modifiers (Oldham, 1984) since any potential for therapeutic benefit is likely to occur through modification of immunological or other defense mechanisms that are present in the patient. Some of the factors which might have therapeutic potential are listed in Table 20.1.

Therapeutic experience with biological response modifiers is most extensive for interferons. These molecules are produced normally by leukocytes (IFN-α) or fibroblasts (IFN-β) in response to viral infection, or by lymphoid cells in culture that are stimulated by a mitogen (IFN-γ). Each of these types of interferon can now be produced by gene-cloning methods. As well as antiviral activity, the interferons inhibit cell proliferation and can cause direct cytotoxicity at high concentration in tissue culture; at lower doses interferons have a variety of effects on the immune response, including stimulation of NK-cell and macrophage activity. Interferons have been used to treat various types of human cancer, and well-documented but uncommon regressions of advanced cancers have been observed, especially for patients with lymphoma, myeloma and renal-cell cancer. However, treatment has involved daily injections of interferon for prolonged periods and may therefore have been mediated by direct cytotoxic effects rather than through modification of the host response. Treatment is associated with considerable toxicity which may include fever, chills, myelosuppression, and a general feeling of malaise, but toxicity seems to be lower for recombinant interferons produced by gene cloning than for natural products of mammalian cells, many of which are quite impure.

Several other agents listed in Table 20.1 have been shown to cause regression of tumors in animals and will be tested for clinical activity. Agents which may activate macrophages were described in the previous section. Another interesting agent is tumor necrosis factor (TNF), which is a glycoprotein produced in response to endotoxin, probably by macrophages (Carswell et al, 1975). TNF leads to hemorrhagic necrosis of a wide variety of experimental tumors, including xenografts of human cancer (Haranaka et al, 1984) but appears to have little effect on normal cells. The structure of TNF has recently been determined, and it was found to have homology with lymphotoxin (Pennica et al, 1984). Pure TNF is now being produced in bacteria by recombinant DNA technology, and is available for use in clinical trials.

20.5 SUMMARY

There is evidence that some tumors have antigenic determinants that are not shared by most normal tissues of the same host. There have been numerous attempts to stimulate an immune response against such antigens by using immune sera, active immunization with preparations of tumor cells, and nonspecific stimulants such

Table 20.1. Biological Response Modifiers with Therapeutic Potential

Agent	Major Mechanism(s) of Action
Interferons	antiviral agents
	increased NK-cell and macrophage activity
	antiproliferative effects and direct cytotoxicity
Poly I-C	inducer of interferon
Thymosins (eg, thymosin-1)	augment T-cell responses
Interleukin 1 (lymphocyte activating factor, IL-1)	stimulates production of IL-2 activation of T cells
Interleukin 2 (T-cell growth factor, IL-2)	stimulates T-cell proliferation activates lymphocytes to produce nonspecific killing
Lymphotoxins	effectors in delayed hypersensitivity reactions
Macrophage activating factor (MAF) Muramyl dipeptide	activate macrophages
Tumor necrosis factor (TNF)	causes hemorrhagic necrosis of tumors

as BCG. These measures may cause regression of small and localized tumors in animals, but have not produced major benefit in patients.

The development of monoclonal antibodies has allowed production of large quantities of immunoglobulin with specificity for tumor-associated antigens of some tumors. Monoclonal antibodies are already in use to improve the detection of malignant cells in biopsies of tissue, and show promise for improvement of tumor imaging; they may also find limited application in tumor therapy.

Approaches to immunotherapy that are under investigation include the infusion of tumor-specific cytotoxic T lymphocytes that have been cultured in medium containing T-cell growth factor and the stimulation of antitumor effects by NK cells or macrophages. Biological response modifiers that stimulate T cells (interleukin 2), NK cells (interferons), macrophages or other components of the immune response are also undergoing therapeutic trials. The large-scale production by genetic engineering of pure mediator substances such as tumor necrosis factor holds promise for improvements in immunologically based cancer therapy. Such therapy is likely to be most applicable in the adjuvant setting following eradication of the primary tumor by surgery or radiation.

REFERENCES

Bast RC Jr, Zbar B, Borsos T, Rapp HJ: BCG and cancer. *N Engl J Med* 1974; 290:1413–1420, 1458–1466.

Blythman HE, Casellas P, Gros O et al: Immunotoxins: Hybrid molecules of monoclonal antibodies and a toxin subunit specifically kill tumor cells. *Nature* 1981; 290:145–146.

Bernstein ID, Tamm MR, Nowinski RC: Mouse leukemia: Therapy with monoclonal antibodies against a thymus differentiation antigen. *Science* 1980; 207:68–71.

Boulianne GL, Hozumi N, Shulman MJ: Production of functional chimaeric mouse/human antibody. *Nature* 1984; 312:643–646.

Carswell EA, Old LJ, Kassel RL et al: An endotoxin-induced serum factor that causes necrosis of tumors. *Proc Nat Acad Sci USA* 1975; 72:3666–3670.

Cobbold SPK, Waldmann H: Therapeutic potential of monovalent monoclonal antibodies. *Nature* 1984; 308:460–462.

Fidler IJ: Macrophages and metastasis—A biological approach to cancer therapy: Presidential Address. *Cancer Res* 1985; 45:4717–4726.

Foon KA, Bernhardt MI, Oldham RK: Monoclonal antibody therapy: Assessment by animal tumor models. *J Biol Resp Modif* 1982; 1:277–304.

Foon KA, Smalley RV, Riggs CW, Gale RP: The role of immunotherapy in acute myelogenous leukemia. *Arch Int Med* 1983; 143:1726–1731.

Goldenberg DM, Kimm EE, Delano FH et al: Radioimmunodetection of cancer with radioactive antibodies to carcinoembryonic antigen. *Cancer Res* 1980; 40:2984–2992.

Haranaka K, Satomi N, Sakurai A: Antitumor activity of murine tumor necrosis factor (TNF) against transplanted murine tumors and heterotransplanted human tumors in nude mice. *Int J Cancer* 1984; 34:263–267.

Hewitt HB, Blake ER, Walder AS: A critique of the evidence for active host defence against cancer, based on personal studies of 27 murine tumours of spontaneous origin. *Br J Cancer* 1976; 33:241–259.

Köhler G, Milstein C: Continuous cultures of fused cells secreting antibody of predefined specificity. *Nature* 1975; 256:495–497.

Lutz D: Immunotherapy of cancer: a critical review. *Int J Clin Pharm Ther Toxicol* 1983; 21:118–129.

Mastrangelo MJ, Berd D, Maguire HC Jr: Current condi-

tion and prognosis of tumor immunotherapy: a second opinion. *Cancer Treat Rep* 1984; 65:207–219.

Miller RA, Maloney DG, Warnke R, Levy R: Treatment of B-cell lymphoma with monoclonal anti-idiotype antibody. *N Engl J Med* 1982; 306:517–522.

Old LJ, Benacerraf B, Clarke DA et al: The role of the reticuloendothelial system in the host reaction to neoplasia. *Cancer Res* 1961; 21:1281–1300.

Oldham RK: Biologicals and biological response modifiers: fourth modality of cancer treatment. *Cancer Treat Rep* 1984; 68:221–232.

Olsson L, Kaplan HS: Human–human hybridomas producing monoclonal antibodies of predefined antigenic specificity. *Proc Natl Acad Sci USA* 1980; 77:5429–5431.

Pennica D, Nedwin GE, Hayflick JS et al: Human tumour necrosis factor: Precursor structure, expression and homology to lymphotoxin. *Nature* 1984; 312:724–729.

Prager MD: Specific cancer immunotherapy. *Cancer Immunol Immunother* 1978; 3:157–161.

Prehn RT: Relation of tumor immunogenicity to concentration of the oncogen. *J Natl Cancer Inst* 1975; 55:189–190.

Rosenberg SA: Adoptive immunotherapy of cancer: Accomplishments and prospects. *Cancer Treat Rep* 1984; 68:233–255.

Rosenberg SA, Terry WD: Passive immunotherapy of cancer in animals and man. *Adv Cancer Res* 1977; 25:323–388.

Stahel RA, Mabry M, Skarin AT et al: Detection of bone marrow metastasis in small-cell lung cancer by monoclonal antibody. *J Clin Oncol* 1985; 3:455–461.

Thompson CH, Lichtenstein M, Stacker SA et al: Immunoscintigraphy for detection of lymph node metastasis from breast cancer. *Lancet* 1984; ii:1245–1247.

Weinstein JN, Parker RJ, Keenan AM et al: Monoclonal antibodies in the lymphatics: Towards the diagnosis and therapy of tumor metastases. *Science* 1982; 218:1334–1337.

Zurawski VR Jr, Haber E, Black PH: Production of antibody to tetanus toxoid by continuous human lymphoblastoid cell lines. *Science* 1978: 199:1439–1441.

BIBLIOGRAPHY

Lutz D: Immunotherapy of cancer: A critical review. *Int J Clin Pharm Ther Toxicol* 1983; 21:118–129.

Mastrangelo MJ, Berd D, Maguire HC Jr: Current condition and prognosis of tumor immunotherapy: a second opinion. *Cancer Treat Rep* 1984; 65:207–219.

21

Hyperthermia

Richard P. Hill and John W. Hunt

21.1 INTRODUCTION

Hyperthermia as a treatment for cancer extends back to antiquity. Hippocrates recommended heat for treatment of tumors. More recently, Coley, in the latter part of the last century, investigated treatment of advanced tumors by inducing severe fever in patients with bacterial toxins. He reported encouraging results but was hampered by variability in both fever induction and tumor response, and other clinicians had difficulty repeating his results. These two factors, together with the introduction of radiation for treatment of cancer, prevented extensive application of the modality, although a number of workers continued to study the effects of hyperthermia both experimentally and clinically (see Hornback, 1984 for historical review).

There has been renewed interest over the last 15 years in the treatment of cancer by hyperthermia. This interest is partially due to the fact that, for many patients, the existing modalities fail to control the disease effectively, either locally or at distant sites. In addition, there are reports that malignant cells may be intrinsically more sensitive to heat treatment than normal cells, although this is controversial. Recent biological studies have, however, established a rationale for hyperthermic treatment of cancer which is independent of any such intrinsic property of malignant cells.

Potential mechanisms which favor hyperthermia are the greater sensitivity to heat of cells treated under acidic conditions, which are known to occur in tumors, and the fact that it may be possible to heat tumors to higher temperatures than surrounding normal tissue. This is because blood flow is the major cooling mechanism in tissue and tumors often have a poorly formed and inadequate blood supply. Studies with animal tumors and in patients have demonstrated that tumor regression can be induced by heat treatment alone without causing severe damage to surrounding normal tissue, although in patients there is presently little evidence for long-term control.

There are major difficulties in the application of hyperthermia, particularly regional hyperthermia, since, despite advances in the technology of heating, it is almost impossible to obtain a uniform regional rise in temperature which is reproducible from treatment to treatment or from tumor to tumor. Whole-body heating or regional perfusion with heated blood can provide greater temperature uniformity, but these procedures are limited in their applicability. Thus the current use of hyperthermia in the clinic is largely experimental, although a few controlled trials are in progress.

This chapter first discusses the response of cells and tissues to heat treatment, both alone and in combination with radiation or chemotherapy, to elucidate the biological basis for hyperthermia as a potential modality of cancer treatment. Methods for delivering heat to the body, and techniques available for measuring tissue temperature, will then be described. Finally some of the recent clinical results will be reviewed.

21.2 HYPERTHERMIA ALONE

21.2.1 CELL SURVIVAL

Cells in tissue culture can easily be maintained at a uniform temperature, and it has been shown that raising the temperature above normal influences a wide range of biochemical functions including DNA, RNA, and protein synthesis, respiration, and glycolysis. For treatment of cancer the most important property of cells is their reproductive integrity, as measured by a colony-forming assay (cell survival), since this parameter relates directly to the ability of a cancer to maintain growth (sections 15.4 and 17.3). Results from experiments in which a number of different types of cells have been exposed to heat treatment are illustrated by the survival

curves shown schematically in Figure 21.1. These curves illustrate a number of important characteristics of heat treatment.

1. Significant cytotoxicity occurs at temperatures above 41°C, but both time and temperature are important when determining heat dose.
2. At higher temperatures, cell survival decreases exponentially with heat dose after an initial shoulder, as is observed following radiation treatment (section 15.4.4). At lower temperatures there is a resistant tail to the curve. This resistance is due to the development of thermotolerance (section 21.2.3) and does not reflect the presence of a subpopulation of cells which is intrinsically resistant.
3. Small changes in time or temperature can result in large differences in cell survival.

The third point has major implications for the potential use of hyperthermia in cancer treatment. Its importance is illustrated by in vivo studies of heat treatments required to give tissue damage. An example is shown in Figure 21.2, where the sensitivity of the tissue to small increases in time or temperature is readily apparent.

Morphological studies of heat-treated tissues, particularly tumors, have found that heat damage to cells is often observable within a few hours of treatment. This observation is consistent with in vitro cell studies which demonstrate that heat-killed cells often express their damage and disintegrate during interphase. This response is in contrast to cells killed by ionizing radiation, which usually attempt cell division before expressing their damage.

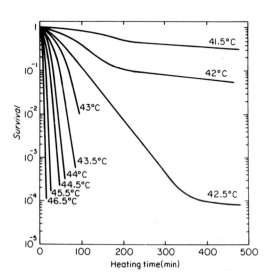

Figure 21.1. Survival of cells plotted as a function of time of heating for a number of different temperatures. (Adapted from Dewey et al, 1977.)

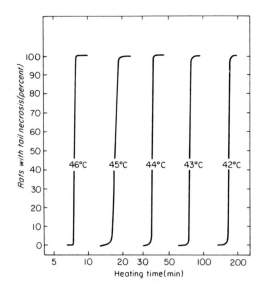

Figure 21.2. Percentage of baby rats developing tail necrosis following heating of the distal part of the tail for various times at different temperatures. (Adapted from Morris et al, 1977.)

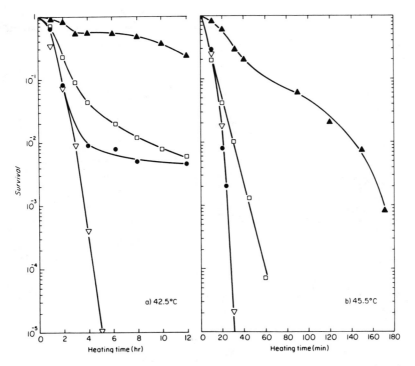

Figure 21.3. Survival curves for four different types of cells heated for various lengths of time at either *a*, 42.5 °C or *b*, 45.5 °C. The different symbols in the two parts of the figure are for the same cell type. The cells were all treated under identical conditions. Data derived from Raaphorst et al (1979) to illustrate range of sensitivity observed.

21.2.2 FACTORS INFLUENCING CELL SURVIVAL

Studies of cells in culture have identified several factors which can influence the effect of heat on cell survival.

1. *Cell line.* Different types of cells vary widely in their intrinsic sensitivities to heat, in contrast to results for ionizing radiation (see Fig 21.3). Early studies, particularly those using biochemical functions as endpoints, suggested that tumor cells were more sensitive to heating than normal cells. More recent studies using the endpoint of cell survival have not shown consistent differences between tumor cells and normal cells.

2. *Cell-cycle effects.* Sensitivity of cells to heat varies with position in the cell cycle, and cells in S phase and mitosis seem to be the most sensitive (Fig 21.4). This pattern is different than that for radiation treatment (section 15.6.2).

3. *pH and nutrient deprivation.* Cells at acid pH and/or in a deprived nutritional environment (such as a balanced salt solution or a medium containing a low concentration of glucose) are found to be much more sensitive to heat treatment (see Figs 21.5 and

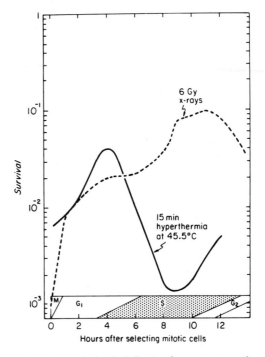

Figure 21.4. Survival of cells following heat treatment (15 min at 45.5 °C) or X-irradiation (6 Gy) delivered at various times after the selection of cells synchronised in mitosis. (Adapted from Dewey et al, 1977.)

21.6). Initially it was thought that cells treated under hypoxic conditions were also more sensitive to heat. It now seems likely that these findings were the result of concomitant changes in pH and that acute exposure to hypoxia does not affect sensitivity to heat if other conditions are normal (see Fig 21.6). Chronic exposure of cells to hypoxia increases sensitivity to heat but it is not clear whether this is due to the hypoxia itself, or to changes in the cell population (eg, cell-cycle distribution) induced by the hypoxic exposure.

Some of the above results obtained using cells in culture provide a rationale for hyperthermic therapy. Tumors, because of their poorly organised vasculature, often have regions where the cells are poorly supplied

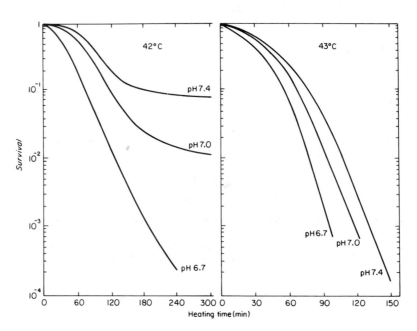

Figure 21.5. Survival of cells following heating for various times at two different temperatures while the cells were in growth medium at different pH. (Modified from Gerweck, 1977.)

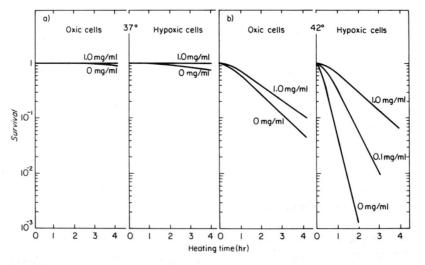

Figure 21.6. Survival of cells following exposure for various periods of time to *a*, 37°C or *b*, 42°C under oxic or hypoxic conditions while the cells were in growth medium containing different concentrations of glucose. (Modified from Kim et al, 1980.)

with nutrients, including glucose, and where the pH is acid due to anaerobic glycolysis (Wike–Hooley et al, 1984). Cells in these regions of tumors should be more sensitive to heat treatment than those in normal tissues, which usually have better nutrition and maintain pH above 7.0. Furthermore, these regions in tumors may achieve higher temperatures during heating because their poor blood supply will provide less cooling. Hypoxia might be expected to be present in these same regions, so cells that are resistant to ionizing radiation may be sensitive to heat.

21.2.3 FRACTIONATION OF HEAT TREATMENT AND THERMOTOLERANCE

Cells have the capacity to develop resistance to heat treatment, a phenomenon known as thermotolerance. The resistant tail on the survival curves for lower temperatures shown in Figure 21.1. is a manifestation of this effect. Thermotolerance can also be induced at higher temperatures, but its effect is not seen in Figure 21.1 because it requires a few hours to develop. From in vitro studies, thermotolerance leads to a high level of resistance 12–48 hr after heat exposure as is illustrated in Figure 21.7, but its effect decays by about 72 hr. Cells at lower pH (6.0–6.5) are less able to develop thermotolerance than cells at normal pH (see Fig 21.5). Thermotolerance develops in vivo in both tumors and normal tissues, giving a large amount of protection against a second heat dose (Law, 1982). It appears to take longer (>5 days) to decay in vivo and both the time of the peak effect and the time for decay can be dependent on the initial treatment.

The presence of an initial shoulder on survival curves for heat treatment suggests that cells may be able to accumulate and repair sublethal damage, as is observed for ionizing radiation. The recovery of the shoulder during a short interval between treatments suggests that repair can occur but that the induction of thermotolerance is a much bigger effect and is largely responsible for the relative resistance of cells to a second treatment (Fig 21.7).

Because of thermotolerance, the efficacy of fractionated heat treatment is critically dependent on the interval between the fractions. The effect in tumors is well demonstrated in work by Overgaard (eg, Overgaard and Nielson, 1983). They found that two heat treatments (at 43.5 °C), with a 16–48 hr interval, were less effective than a single treatment with the same total heating time, but when the interval between the treatments was extended to 120 hr, the treatments were as effective as a single dose. This result is consistent with the development and decay of thermotolerance and suggests little repair capacity. When multiple treatments

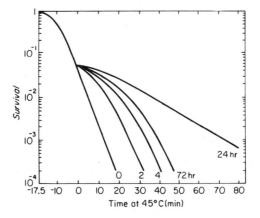

Figure 21.7. Survival of cells following exposure to heating for various times at 45°C either as a single treatment (0-hr line) or as two treatments separated by 2, 4, 24 or 72 hr as indicated. The initial treatment was 17.5 min at 45°C. (Modified from Henle and Dethlefsen, 1978.)

(five) were given with daily intervals they were substantially less effective than a single treatment with the same total heating time. In fact, for a heat-resistant tumor there was no difference in effect on the tumor when a single treatment (60 min at 42.5 °C) was compared with five such treatments given at daily intervals. Thus the last four treatments had no measurable effect on the tumor, consistent with the induction of a high degree of thermotolerance. If the intervals between the exposures were increased to 5 days, the thermotolerance had decayed and the tumor was found to have regained its sensitivity. No recovery was demonstrated. These studies suggest that daily treatments, as used widely in radiotherapy, are unlikely to be optimal for the administration of hyperthermia.

21.2.4 MECHANISMS OF HEAT-INDUCED CELL DEATH

The nature of the critical lesion(s) which lead to death of cells following heat treatment remains unknown. There is evidence to implicate membrane damage, protein denaturation, chromosome damage and the inhibition or stimulation of a variety of cellular biochemical pathways. The primacy of one particular type of lesion has not been established, although the weight of opinion favors membrane damage. A plausible hypothesis is that damage to membrane proteins affects the function of surface receptors, that heat-induced changes in the "second messengers" (Ca^{++}, cAMP) disrupts the flow of information in the cell, and that these together disrupt regulation of the cytoskeleton, protein synthesis and DNA replication (see Leeper, 1985, for review).

Cellular response to heat treatment is associated with the production of a small number of well-defined proteins, the so-called "heat-shock" proteins, which are produced even though protein synthesis is reduced to a few percent of normal. These proteins are synthesized by a wide range of organisms in response to heat (or exposure to other stresses, eg, treatment with ethanol or arsenite) and their appearance and disappearance is often correlated with the development and loss of thermotolerance (Landry et al, 1982). The function of these proteins in the cell is not known but some or all of them can be found associated with DNA.

21.2.5 THE INFLUENCE OF TIME AND TEMPERATURE

The biological effects of heat are dependent on both the temperature and the duration of heating. If results such as those shown in Figure 21.1 are presented as an isoeffect plot of times and temperatures which give the same level of cell killing, then a relationship of the form shown in Figure 21.8a is obtained. Here the heating time is plotted on a logarithmic scale and temperature on a linear scale. The relationship has two linear components with a change in slope in the temperature range 42–43 °C, which probably reflects the development of thermotolerance during the longer heating times required at lower temperatures. Isoeffect relationships have been derived for a variety of both normal tissues and tumors treated in vivo using specific biological-response endpoints appropriate for the particular tissue (Field and Morris, 1983). Some of these results are shown in Figure 21.8b. Most of the relationships are similar to that shown in Figure 21.8a. At tem-

peratures above 42.5 °C, the lines are all approximately parallel to one another, indicating that a change of 1 °C is equivalent to a change of heating time by a factor of 2. Below this temperature there is more variability, but a change of 1 °C is equivalent to changing the heating time by a factor of about 4–6.

Although the isoeffect relationships shown in Figure 21.8b are similar in shape, the absolute sensitivity of tissues to heat varies widely. Mouse testis shows great sensitivity, while human and pig skin is much more resistant, although it must be recognised that different endpoints have been used to assess damage to the two tissues. The displacement between the isoeffect curves for these two tissues is a factor of about 200 in terms of heating time or about 6 °C in terms of critical temperature.

Experimental tumors show an equal or greater range of sensitivity (Suit, 1977). The difference in the response of two tumors to heating is illustrated by the experiments described by Hahn (1982), who addressed the issue of whether tumor cure by heat treatment was due to direct killing of the tumor cells by heat. A heat treatment of 44 °C for 30 min was found to cure the transplantable EMT-6 tumor in mice, but such a treatment had little effect on the growth of the heat-resistant transplantable RIF-1 tumor in mice. If the tumors were immediately excised after the heating, it was found that greater than 1% of the tumor cells in both tumors retained clonogenic capacity, implying that extensive extra cell death occurred when the EMT-6 tumors were left in situ after the heating. Further studies implicated vascular damage leading to ischemia as the likely reason for this extra cell death, although the EMT-6 tumor is also found to be more immunogenic than the

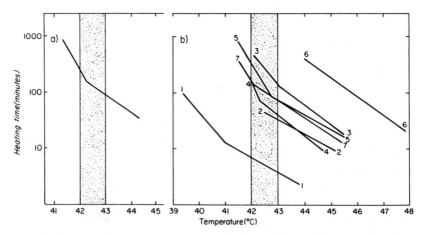

Figure 21.8. Relationship between temperature and heating time required to give a constant level of biological damage, *a*, for a given level of cell survival; *b*, for different types of tumor or normal tissue: (1) mouse testis, (2) 9L rat tumor, (3) mouse foot skin, (4) mouse jejunum, (5) mouse mammary tumor, (6) pig and human skin, (7) mouse ear skin. (Modified from Field and Morris, 1983.)

RIF-1 tumor. Thus differences in sensitivities of tumors may result from differences in host response and tumor physiology, as well as from intrinsic differences in sensitivity to heat of the tumor cells.

21.2.6 EQUIVALENT HEAT DOSE

The similarity of the isoeffect relationships shown in Figure 21.8b has suggested (Field and Morris, 1983; Sapareto and Dewey, 1984) that different heat doses (times and temperatures) can be expressed in terms of the equivalent amount of time at a reference temperature (eg, 42.5 °C) which would be expected to induce the same level of biological damage. This concept of equivalent heat dose potentially allows estimation of an effective dose of heat for treatments during which the temperature varies (at a minimum this occurs at the beginning and end of a treatment). It could also allow the conversion of a measured temperature distribution into a distribution of equivalent heat doses, analogous to isodose lines in radiotherapy. Equivalent heat dose is not universally accepted but has been applied in the clinical use of hyperthermia. The desirability of a valid unifying unit for heat dose is obvious, but at present the biological information on which such calculations would be based is limited to only a few normal tissues (eg, skin, gut, cartilage) and tumors. More information on a wider range of tissues is required.

21.2.7 BLOOD FLOW

Blood flow is of major importance when tissue is heated. It is the principal route by which heat is removed from tissue and heat-induced changes in blood flow may lead to nutrient deprivation and cell death. Several investigators have studied the effect of heating on blood flow in animal tumors and normal tissues (Song 1984; Reinhold and Endrich 1986). A combination of their results is shown in Figure 21.9. Important findings are:

1. A large increase (five- to tenfold) in blood flow can occur in normal tissue (skin or muscle) during heating but only a small, if any, increase occurs in large tumors.
2. Heating to high temperatures can lead to a reduction in blood flow due to collapse of the microcirculation. This can occur after the end of the heat treatment itself. There is some evidence that blood vessels in tumors may be more sensitive to heat (particularly high temperatures) than those in surrounding normal tissue. Such an effect could lead to reduced removal of heat from tumors and hence to the possibility of obtaining a wide temperature differential between tumor and surrounding normal tissue.

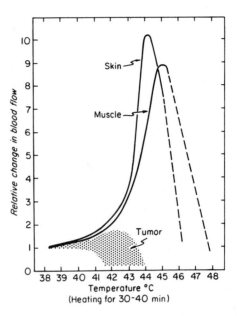

Figure 21.9. Relative changes in blood flow induced by heat treatment plotted as a function of the temperature of heating (for 30–40 min). A compilation of results largely from studies on mice or rats. (Modified from Song, 1984.)

In Figure 21.9 the measurements of blood flow have been normalised to their pretreatment values. This is potentially misleading because blood flow in tumors is quite variable and average blood flow declines substantially with increase in tumor size. There is also a wide range in the blood flow of different normal tissues. Thus, in some locations, tumor blood flow prior to heating may be higher than that of the surrounding normal tissue so that, even if heat has a differential effect on blood flow, there may not be a large difference in ability to remove heat energy. Also, tumor vasculature is heterogeneous and may respond differently to heat in different regions of a tumor; it is often possible to heat the central region of a large tumor to a higher temperature than the peripheral regions. The vasculature in large and rapidly growing rodent tumors may not, however, be an appropriate model for that in more slowly growing human tumors, and further studies are required to establish the generality of any differential effect of heating on tumor and normal tissue blood flow.

21.3 HYPERTHERMIA AND RADIATION

21.3.1 CELLULAR RESPONSES

The resistance to ionizing radiation of hypoxic cells (section 15.6), and the possibility that such cells exist in regions of tumors where the pH is low and hence will be sensitive to heat treatment, provide a rationale for combining hyperthermia with radiation. It has also been demonstrated that hyperthermia will sensitize cells to radiation treatment (Fig 21.10). Heating of cells during irradiation can reduce both the shoulder and slope of the radiation survival curve. The magnitude of the sensitization depends on both the temperature and the duration of heating, but an effect can occur at lower

temperatures (~40 °C) than are generally required to cause significant killing of cells. Heat treatments (different times and temperatures) which give equivalent levels of cell killing alone also give similar degrees of radiosensitization.

Radiosensitization by heat can be expressed in terms of a thermal enhancement ratio (TER), which is defined as the ratio of the radiation dose required to give the same level of cell killing at normal temperature to that at the elevated temperature. Most studies in which simultaneous heat and radiation treatments were given to cells in culture have obtained TER values which range up to a maximum of about 2, if the results are normalized to allow for the toxic effects of the heat treatment alone (Hahn, 1982).

Heat also enhances the cytotoxic effect of radiation in vivo. The thermal enhancement ratio (TER) has been estimated for several tumors and a few normal tissues, and values of the TER for simultaneous or closely sequenced heat and radiation treatments are summarized in Figure 21.11. The TER increases with heat dose (in this case increase in temperature) as has been observed in vitro. Observed values of the TER may be higher than those recorded in vitro, but this is probably due to the effect of direct killing by the heat alone. It is probable that there was considerable temperature variation within the tumors or normal tissues which would account for some of the variability seen in Figure 21.11. There is, however, no obvious difference between the TER values for tumors and normal tissues, despite the rationale discussed above for expecting such a difference.

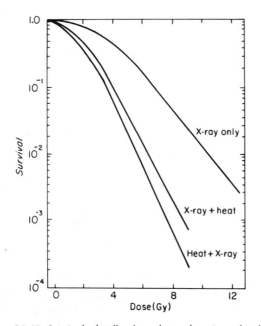

Figure 21.10. Survival of cells plotted as a function of radiation dose. Heat treatment (60 min at 43 °C) was given immediately before or after the radiation treatment. (Modified from Li and Kal, 1977.)

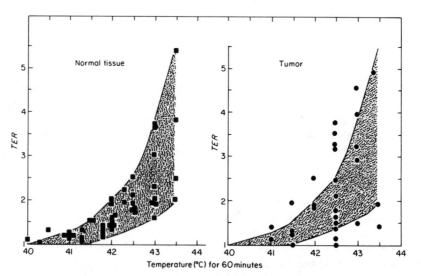

Figure 21.11. Thermal enhancement ratios (TERs), obtained for a number of different normal tissues or tumors (of rodents), plotted as a function of the temperature of the heat treatment (for 60 min). The radiation and heat treatments were given simultaneously or closely sequenced. (Modified from Law, 1982.)

21.3.2 MECHANISMS OF INTERACTION

The mechanisms by which heat and radiation interact to cause cell death are not clearly understood. Most studies have focussed on DNA damage since there is strong evidence that this is responsible for radiation-induced cell death (see section 15.3). Dewey and his colleagues (1980) have observed that radiosensitization by heat is associated with an increase in chromosome aberrations in CHO cells and suggest that this is a result of thermal inhibition of DNA repair processes. It has also been demonstrated that heat treatment both before and after irradiation reduces the ability of cells to repair sublethal radiation damage, an effect which is dependent on heat dose. Repair of potentially lethal damage is inhibited by heat treatment after irradiation.

21.3.3 SEQUENCING OF HEAT AND RADIATION

The cell-cycle dependence of cell killing by heat is different from that due to radiation (see Fig 21.4) and appears to be complementary in the cell lines so far studied. The S-phase cells tend to be more resistant to radiation, but more sensitive to heating than G_1- or G_2-phase cells. This difference should minimize the phase dependency for combined treatment as compared to that for either modality alone. This factor might improve the therapeutic ratio for combined treatment if there were differences in the cycle distribution of cells in the tumor and in critical normal tissue.

Therapeutic gain might also be achieved by appropriate sequencing of the heat and radiation treatments. Combined heat and radiation treatments have their maximum effect when the two treatments are given simultaneously or, more usually, one immediately after the other. As the time interval between the two treatments is increased, regardless of which modality is given first, the TER declines, both for cells in vitro and for tumors and normal tissues in vivo (Fig 21.12). This decline is probably due to the repair of potentially lethal damage, induced by one modality, which can be prevented by the other. When heat is given before irradiation, thermal enhancement is observed for intervals of up to 12 hr or more, depending on the heat dose and, in vivo, possibly also on the tissue. If heat is given after irradiation, the thermal enhancement of the radiation effect on normal tissues decays over a period of about 4 hr, with quite similar kinetics for a number of different tissues. The decay of thermal enhancement appears to be much more variable for tumors, and thermal enhancement can still be demonstrated after 4 hr (Overgaard, 1980; Stewart and Denekamp, 1978): A possible reason is slower repair of radiation damage in tumors than in normal tissues, particularly in hypoxic, poorly nourished cells. These results suggest that it might be possible to achieve a therapeutic gain by judicious sequencing of heat and radiation, such that there is no thermal enhancement for normal tissue but that enhancement still exists for the tumor. Initial studies with murine and human tumors have sometimes, but not always, supported this concept. An important caveat

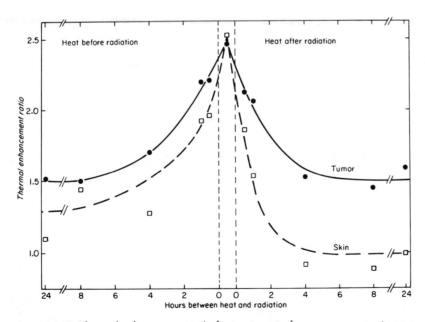

Figure 21.12. Thermal enhancement ratio for treatment of mouse mammary tumors or foot skin with radiation and heating (42.5°C for 1 hour) given with various time intervals. (Adapted from Overgaard, 1980.)

concerning combination treatments is that, if the heat treatment is sufficient to damage the tumor vasculature, an increase in radiation-resistant hypoxic cells may occur, which would reduce tumor response to subsequent radiation treatments.

21.3.4 FRACTIONATION

As with heat treatment alone, a difficulty associated with multifraction treatments with heat and radiation is the development of thermotolerance. Tolerance to the interactive effect of heat and radiation may develop but it is probably a smaller effect than thermotolerance itself. Thermotolerance is substantial by 24 hr after an initial treatment with heat, so the administration of heat with daily fractions of radiation may not be optimal. Relatively little is known about the effect of heat combined with radiation on subsequent treatments. In contrast to results obtained with single treatments of heat plus radiation, studies of the response of a mouse tumor and normal skin by Stewart and Denekamp (1980) found no therapeutic gain with two or five daily fractions of heat plus radiation. Further studies are required to examine this issue in more detail. It may be necessary to give daily radiation fractions with heat treatments at intervals sufficient (about 1 week) for thermotolerance to have decayed between the treatments.

21.4 HEAT AND DRUGS

21.4.1 CELLULAR STUDIES

Many, but not all, cytotoxic drugs have enhanced cytotoxicity at elevated temperatures. The combined use of heat and drugs might therefore be used to increase the efficacy of chemotherapy or possibly to target an increased drug effect to a heated tumor, with no increase in toxicity to critical normal tissues such as the bone marrow.

The most extensive studies of the interaction between heat and drugs have been carried out by Hahn (1982), who has classified drugs into four general categories in relation to this interaction (Fig 21.13). For alkylating agents and cisplatin, there is a continuous increase in drug sensitivity as the temperature is raised, demonstrated by an increasing slope of the cell-survival curve (Fig 21.14a). Other drugs, such as the antibiotics doxorubicin and bleomycin, demonstrate a threshold effect and their cytotoxicity is not enhanced unless the temperature is raised above 42–43 °C (Fig 21.14b). There is a group of miscellaneous agents, such as SH-containing compounds, ethanol, polyamines and lidocaine, which have relatively little toxicity at 37 °C but demonstrate significant toxicity at higher temperatures (Fig 21.14c). Finally, the cytotoxicity of antimetabolites, such as methotrexate, 5-fluorouracil and the vinca alkaloids, seems to be affected little by increased temperature.

Drugs such as misonidazole, which sensitize hypoxic cells to radiation, have also been examined for their cytotoxicity under hyperthermic conditions. These drugs show selective toxicity for hypoxic cells and this toxicity is significantly enhanced at elevated temperatures.

21.4.2 MECHANISMS OF INTERACTION

The mechanisms by which heat acts to enhance drug toxicity are likely to be different for different drugs. Studies of the interaction of heat and alkylating agents have demonstrated an increase in the number of DNA breaks and cross-links, and inhibition of repair of these lesions. Changes in drug pharmacokinetics, includ-

GROUP 1	ENHANCED TOXICITY WITH ELEVATED TEMPERATURE	GROUP 3	MISCELLANEOUS - THERMAL SENSITIZERS
	CISPLATIN		AMPHOTERICIN B
	CYCLOPHOSPHAMIDE (IN VIVO)		CYSTEAMINE + OTHER-SH COMPOUNDS
	MELPHALAN		ETHANOL
	MITOMYCIN C		LIDOCAINE + OTHER LOCAL ANAESTHETICS
	NITROSOUREAS		POLYAMINES
	THIO-TEPA		MISONIDAZOLE
GROUP 2	ENHANCED TOXICITY ABOVE A THRESHOLD TEMPERATURE	GROUP 4	NO INTERACTION
	ACTINOMYCIN D		5-FLUOROURACIL
	BLEOMYCIN		METHOTREXATE
	DOXORUBICIN		VINBLASTINE
			VINCRISTINE

Figure 21.13. Groups of drugs whose cytotoxic action on cells may be enhanced by heating. The different groups display characteristic differences in the mode of interaction as is further illustrated in Figure 21.14.

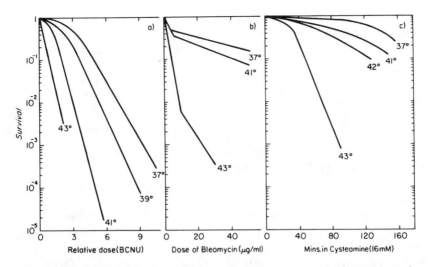

Figure 21.14. Survival of cells treated with cytotoxic drugs, from the groups indicated in Figure 21.13, and heated to different temperatures. The survival values are all normalised to remove killing by heat alone. *a,* Cells treated with group 1 drug BCNU for 1 hr at various temperatures and effective concentrations; *b,* cells treated with group 2 drug bleomycin for 1 hr at various temperatures and concentrations; *c,* cells treated with group 3 drug cysteamine (16 mM) for the times and temperatures indicated. (Modified from Hahn, 1982.)

ing increased drug activation, may also be involved. For the antibiotics, mechanisms probably include inhibition of repair of potentially lethal damage and changes in the membrane permeability to the drug. Many of the drugs in the miscellaneous category (Fig 21.13) probably also interact to cause damage to the cell membrane.

21.4.3 IN VIVO EFFECTS

Combined use of heat and cytotoxic drugs to treat tumors in experimental animals has, in general, confirmed the in vitro findings. The effects of alkylating agents such as cyclophosphamide and the nitrosoureas have been shown to be enhanced at higher temperatures. Results with the antibiotics doxorubicin and bleomycin have been more varied, possibly because these drugs have only shown thermal enhancement above a threshold temperature and the temperatures achieved in heated tumors may be quite heterogeneous. Normal-tissue toxicity is also enhanced by increased temperature, which may be a problem when drugs are combined with whole-body hyperthermia. This should be of little consequence for localised heating of human tumors, since the critical normal tissues (ie, bone marrow and intestine) usually remain at normal temperature.

Heat and drugs must be administered in close sequence or simultaneously for maximum interactive effects to be observed. Most studies have not been

detailed enough, however, to assess whether or not such interactions are greater than additive (see section 19.4.2). Optimum sequencing of the two modalities in vivo will depend on drug pharmacokinetics, which may itself be influenced by hyperthermia, especially if organs involved in drug metabolism (eg, liver) are heated. Induction of thermotolerance may also cause resistance of cells to drugs such as doxorubicin or actinomycin D (Hahn, 1982). However, the usual intervals of 1–3 weeks between courses of chemotherapy should make the development of thermotolerance less of a problem in combined heat and drug treatment.

21.5 HEATING TECHNIQUES AND THERMOMETRY

Two general approaches are being used for hyperthermia treatments. Whole-body or regional perfusion heating can provide fairly uniform temperature elevation, but is limited in its temperature range and its applicability. Localized or regional heating, applied by different surface or deep-heating techniques, has a wider range of both temperature and applicability, but the production of reliable well-controlled temperatures throughout a defined region of the body is very difficult. Although considerable efforts have been expended by many research and commercial groups, no heating systems are yet available which can provide the desired level of temperature control. The development of such heating systems, with associated thermal monitoring and treatment planning, is not trivial and requires sophisticated physical and engineering equipment.

21.5.1 SYSTEMIC HEATING

Fevers of 40.0–40.8 °C, induced using bacterial toxins, provided one early approach to systemic heating. This method was later replaced by heating cabinets ("electropyrexia therapy"). A more recent method is to apply heat to most parts of the skin using, for example, a heated wax bath in which the liquid/solid mixture of paraffin wax maintains a temperature of approximately 42.0 °C. Other approaches include "warm blankets," water-heated suits or radiant heating, which are used to heat the patient to about 42.0 °C. The maximum temperature is limited to this value by the tolerance of liver and brain. At the present time, these procedures are being investigated largely as palliative treatments in combination with drugs for widely disseminated disease (Robins, 1984). A number of investigators have also tried regional perfusion using heated blood or other suitable fluid. Such procedures are limited to the treatment of extremities, but higher temperatures can be reached than are possible with whole-body heating.

21.5.2 LOCAL AND REGIONAL HEATING

Ideally, a local heating technique should produce a uniform and predictable temperature distribution throughout the tumor, with lower temperatures in the surrounding normal tissues. A number of different sources have been developed to generate local heating. Radiofrequency (RF) and microwave systems produce heating due to the resistive losses induced by electrical currents or electromagnetic waves passing through parts of the body, while ultrasound beams produce heating as a result of the mechanical friction between vibrating molecules. Each technique has its characteristic strengths and weaknesses, as summarized in Table 21.1, and is described in more detail in the subsequent sections.

In traditional radiotherapy, each treatment is planned by calculating the energy absorbed in the body using the known properties of radiation beams and the tissues involved. Thermal dosimetry is controlled by two major factors that determine the temperature reached during the treatment. One is the power absorbed from the heating source at a specific point in the body, which is generally called the specific absorption rate (SAR). The second is the cooling rate, which is mainly a result of blood flow, but is affected to a lesser extent by thermal conductivity and size of the heated region. An ideal heating system should be able to adapt for the different absorption rates in the tissues in the body, and for blood flow which may vary during the treatment. The sensitivity of biological effect to small changes in temperature (see section 21.2.1) makes it very important that a well-controlled thermal distribution is generated. This is particularly true at the tumor margins (interfaces with normal tissue). Somewhat higher temperatures can be accepted deep within a tumor.

21.5.3 ELECTRICAL (RF) HEATING

When an electrical current passes through a resistance, the absorbed power is converted into heat as a result of ohmic losses. If an alternating RF voltage is applied across part of the body, the amplitudes of the currents generated are related to the specific resistivity of the tissue and the dielectric constant, which in turn depend on the frequency of the RF voltage and the temperature of the tissue. In the simplest arrangement a voltage is applied to a pair of conducting plates placed on opposite sides of the body in line with the tumor; this arrangement is a capacitor. As shown in Figure 21.15, when a high-powered RF transmitter (usual frequencies between 8 and 27 MHz) is connected across the electrodes, strong RF currents are generated. The advantage of capacitive heating is that these currents, shown as dashed lines, pass completely through the body; thus heating at depth is possible. Due to the spreading of the currents away from the electrodes, however, there is no focusing and the power absorbed is reduced at the center of the body. If the conducting plates are of different sizes, then some focusing near the

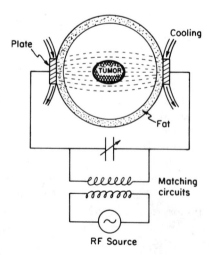

Figure 21.15. Schematic diagram illustrating the principles of RF capacitive heating. The conducting plates connected to the RF sources can be cooled by a flow of water or suitable liquid.

Table 21.1. Summary of Deep-Heating Techniques

Sources	Frequencies (MHz)	Depth–Dose Distribution*		Focusing	Flexible Heating Distribution	Common Thermometry Systems	Comments
		single or pair applicator(s)	multiple or array				
RF Heating							
Capacitive	8–27	excellent	excellent	some	fair	nonperturbing probes	Excess heating of fat.
Inductive	2–150	fair	good	no	poor	nonperturbing probes	Difficult to obtain maximum absorption in the tumor.
Microwave							
Surface	300–2450	fair	good	some	fair	nonperturbing probes	Requires shielded rooms. Difficult to focus and control.
Deep heating	27–915	fair	excellent	some	fair	nonperturbing probes	For large fields only.
Ultrasound							
Planar sources	0.3–3	good to fair	excellent	no	good	thermocouples: read following beam interruption	Field is limited due to air cavities and bone with potential high temperatures and pain near bone.
Focused source	0.5–1.5	excellent if scanned	excellent	yes	good to excellent		
Interstitial							Only useful when the lesion is accessible.
RF currents	0.1–1	poor	good	some	good	thermocouples or nonperturbing probes	Depth and field size are limited only by the implant distribution.
Microwave: antennae	500–2450	fair	good	yes	fair	thermocouples or nonperturbing probes	Large intensity changes along the axis.
Inductive: hysteresis seeds	0.5–1	poor	good	no	excellent	thermocouples or nonperturbing probes	The seed separation and distributions are crucial.
Magnetic wires	0.1–2	poor	good	no	excellent	thermocouples or nonperturbing probes	The seed separation and distributions are crucial.
Self-regulating wires	0.1–2	poor	good	no	excellent	thermocouples or nonperturbing probes	Temperature gradients and number of temperature sensors are reduced.

*Depth–dose distribution: depth in which the power drops to half (poor <2 cm, fair 2–4 cm, good 4–8 cm, excellent >8 cm).

smaller plate can be achieved, since the current density will be greater in this region.

When the electrodes are placed parallel to the body surface all of the current must pass through the various tissue layers. In this arrangement, a large amount of heating occurs in the layer of subcutaneous fat due to its high resistivity. Despite this excess absorption of power in subcutaneous fat, a number of clinical applicators have been fabricated using the capacitive technique. These heaters usually incorporate systems to cool the skin, in order to minimize the excess subcutaneous heating. Differential heating of large tumors has been reported, but it is likely that this difference was the result of poor blood flow in such tumors.

The excess heating of subcutaneous fat can be eliminated using an inductive heating technique. When an

RF current passes through a coil, rapidly changing magnetic fields are produced. These fields, passing through a conducting medium such as the body, induce eddy currents which generate ohmic heating. The size of the eddy currents induced depends mainly on the resistivity of the various tissues. Thus at similar positions in a magnetic field, high-water-content (low-resistivity) tissues, such as muscles or tumors, will have a higher current density (and hence there will be greater heating) than in low-water-content (high-resistivity) tissues, such as fat or bone.

For pancake coils (see Fig 21.16) the penetration of the magnetic fields and hence the depth of the effective heating is poor (a few cm) and is strongly dependent upon the diameter of the coil. Considerable surface cooling is necessary to improve the heat distribution. Some improvement of the heat distribution can be obtained by using a pair of concentric coils on opposite sides of the body (Fig 21.16), or by placing the patient in a large, inductive solenoid. The power distribution (SAR) is not constant through the body in such a solenoid, but is reduced towards zero at the center of the

coil. Some tumors have been heated effectively in such devices but it appears likely that these successes are linked to poor blood flow in large lesions.

21.5.4 MICROWAVE HEATING

The most extensive clinical experience in local and regional heating has been obtained using microwave beams with frequencies between 27 and 2450 MHz. Microwaves are an electromagnetic (EM) radiation and they follow the general physical laws of waves as they propagate through the body. The electric field of the radiation induces displacement currents in the tissue and heating is the result of the ohmic resistive losses discussed earlier. The penetration of planar electromagnetic waves into tissue is given for two different frequencies in Table 21.2. Absorption increases rapidly with frequency. One particular advantage of microwaves is a large absorption in water-containing tissues such as muscle (or tumor), smaller absorption in fat or bone, and almost no absorption in air. Thus lower-frequency microwaves can penetrate most regions of the body. Unfortunately, the wavelength of electromagnetic radiation in the microwave frequencies is quite long; for example, a 915-MHz beam has a wavelength of about 33 cm in air and 4.7 cm in muscle. These wavelengths are similar in magnitude to the width of a practical surface applicator; consequently the beam cannot be easily focused and tends to spread rapidly in the body, so that the effective beam penetration is less than that given in Table 21.2.

Numerous microwave sources have been developed to produce local heating and, with surface cooling, have been used to treat superficial tumors with thicknesses of up to 3 cm. A waveguide applicator and a stripline spiral applicator are illustrated in Figure 21.17. The spiral applicators give a better distribution of the electric field and effective penetration depths of up to about 4 cm (Tanabe et al, 1984). Lower frequencies and/or arrays of microwave applicators can be used to obtain

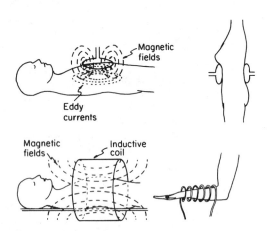

Figure 21.16. Various possible arrangements for use in an RF inductive-heating technique. The magnetic field lines and induced eddy currents are illustrated.

Table 21.2. Penetration of Microwave and Ultrasound for Planar Beams

| | Microwaves (MHz) | | | | | | Ultrasound (MHz) | | | | | |
| | 100 | | | 1000 | | | 0.5 | | | 3.0 | | |
Tissue	d_{80}	d_{37}	λ	d_{80}	d_{37}	λ	d_{80}	d_{37}	λ	d_{80}	d_{37}	λ
Fat	5.8	26	106	1.6	7.4	12	4.5	20	0.3	1.2	5.5	0.05
Muscle	0.6	2.9	27	0.3	1.4	3.9	2-3	~13	0.3	~0.5	~2.5	0.05
Bone	~5.8	26	~100	~1.6	~9	~12	0.3	1.5	0.7	0.02	0.1	0.12

Penetration d (cm) is the depth at which the power drops to 80% (d_{80}) and 37% (d_{37}) of the initial power, at the skin surface. λ is wavelength (cm) in the tissue.

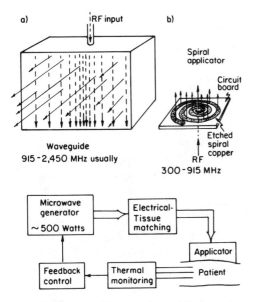

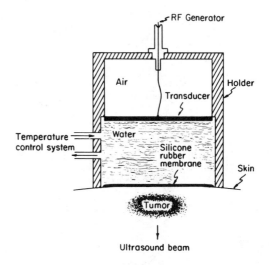

Figure 21.17. Schematic diagram of two different microwave applicators, *a*, waveguide, *b*, copper spiral, and outline of circuit for treating patients. The electric field associated with the applicators is shown as the full lines with arrows. The broken lines on the waveguide represent the magnetic field.

Figure 21.18. Schematic diagrams of planar ultrasound source designed for surface heating. The water "cuff" couples the ultrasound to the body and can be used for surface cooling if required. (Adapted from Hunt, 1982.)

deeper heating. These arrays use two or more microwave sources directed towards the tumor and, by suitable phasing of the excitation of the sources, some focusing can be achieved, so that the maximum power is obtained at the tumor. One system, which consists of an annular array of up to 16 low-frequency (approximately 50 MHz) microwave sources that encircle the body, can give an absorbed power distribution which is fairly homogeneous (Turner, 1984).

21.5.5 ULTRASOUND HEATING

Ultrasound, which is produced by transducers driven by high-powered RF amplifiers, is also propagated through the body as a wave motion and is thus subject to the same physical laws as microwaves. However, it is a mechanical motion and results in vibration of individual tissue elements causing heating by friction. As for EM radiations, the penetration of ultrasound into the body is dependent on frequency and is different for different tissues in the body (see Table 21.2). Typically, frequencies of 0.3–3 MHz are used to penetrate tissues up to 15 cm. For a frequency of 0.5 MHz the wave length in the tissue is short (~0.3 cm), thus ultrasound beams can be focused within the body using transducers of practical size. This property allows for the possibility that deep-seated tumors can be heated without excess heating of the overlying structures. A major

problem with ultrasound, however, is that there is essentially no transmission of ultrasound through air cavities in the body (such as lung) and large reflections occur in and around bones, giving rise to elevated temperatures.

A simple ultrasound source designed for surface heating is shown in Figure 21.18, where the transducer is coupled to the patient through a temperature-controlled water jacket or "cuff." Reasonably flat temperature profiles across the width of the beam can be produced with careful design of the transducer. The depth–dose relationship achieved with such a heater is comparable to the best surface microwave or inductive pancake sources.

Several ultrasound devices have been developed to produce heating at a depth in the body by focusing the ultrasound beam (Lele, 1985). One such device is based on the concept that if a focused beam is scanned around the periphery of the tumor, then the blood flow will help to heat the whole tumor volume homogeneously. A beam is scanned rapidly in a circular trajectory (see Fig 21.19) near the periphery of the treatment field, and a second one is scanned closer to the center to heat the central region. With this device, an excess temperature of 6 °C was obtained in a dog throughout a region of 6 cm × 7 cm with rapid decrease outside this region. Temperatures measured in deep-seated human tumors such as a pelvic chondrosarcoma, transitional-cell carcinoma in urinary bladder, and rectal carcinoma appeared to confirm the potential of this scanning ultrasound technique although complete heating distributions could not be obtained.

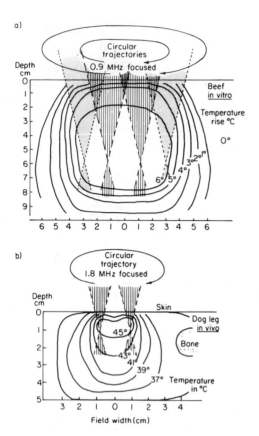

Figure 21.19. Illustration of heating with focused ultrasound. *a,* Two beams were scanned in circular trajectories with different radii to produce deep heating in a beef phantom *in vitro* as indicated. *b,* A single beam was scanned in a circular trajectory to produce deep heating in the muscle of a dog leg *in vivo* as indicated. (Adapted from Lele, 1985.)

21.5.6 INTERSTITIAL HEATING

Although considerable improvements have been achieved with noninvasive heating techniques, direct heating of a tumor with little heating outside can be done most effectively by an interstitial technique. Interstitial hyperthermia treatments often use an array of needles excited by RF sources (at frequencies from approximately 0.1 to 1 MHz) to produce a localised current throughout the treatment field. Usually, pairs of needles are excited and switched rapidly in sequence so that all parts of the tumor are heated. In many ways, this technique is similar to capacitive heating, and the relevant tissue parameters are similar. An advantage of this technique is that combination with interstitial radiotherapy (brachytherapy) is easily achieved by inserting radioactive wires inside the needles.

An alternative approach is to use either a single or an array of needle microwave antennae. A single implanted antenna generates an approximately ellipsoid-shaped microwave field, and the power drops markedly away

from the axis. An array of antennae placed 1–2 cm apart yields an improved microwave field and heating distribution. By using variable excitation voltages on the separate antennae, the electrical field can be altered to compensate for the shape of the tumor or for variable cooling due to blood flow.

The use of ferromagnetic implants excited by strong RF magnetic fields also appears to have considerable potential for local heating, and a number of approaches are being studied. At frequencies as low as 50 kHz, the inductive field produces little heating through eddy currents in the tissue but magnetic interactions induce eddy currents in the ferromagnetic sources, which dissipate energy through resistive losses. A recent promising approach is the fabrication of self-regulating ferromagnetic materials. These materials change from a magnetic to a nonmagnetic state above a critical temperature (the Curie point) and can be made with a defined Curie point so that the final temperature reached in a treatment will be less sensitive to the intensity of the inductive field, to tissue losses and to cooling by blood flow.

21.5.7 THERMOMETRY

Thermal dosimetry is critical for hyperthermia treatments. There are three general ways of obtaining detailed information concerning temperature distributions and thermal dose. One is to measure accurate temperatures at multiple points in the field during the treatment by using invasive probes. The second, called thermal modelling, uses a few selective temperature readings and by making several measurements, such as the rates of heating and cooling, calculates the thermal dose. The third method is to use appropriate information concerning the heating source, the absorptive characteristics of tissue and cooling due to blood flow, etc, to calculate an expected thermal-dose distribution similar to the procedure carried out to calculate radiation dose during planning of radiation therapy. At the present time this latter approach is conceptual only and the second approach, which is just being developed, cannot be carried out accurately. Thus invasive probes must be used.

Appropriate features of a thermometry system suitable for hyperthermia are (Cetas, 1982): (a) the sensitivity, accuracy and stability of the system should be within 0.1 °C; (b) the response time should be no more than 1 s; (c) the detector should not significantly perturb the heating distribution; and (d) the size of the detector must be much smaller than the region being examined. In general, multiple thermal detectors must be used and should be read at regular intervals. The thermometry system must include a good visual monitor and a good recording system to store (and display as required) the multiple readings being obtained.

A large range of invasive probes is available for measuring temperature. The most common sensor is the thermocouple, in which the sensitive region is the junction of two different metals. A small voltage, which is proportional to temperature, is generated at the junction and the circuit is completed with a reference junction at a standard temperature. The most common thermocouple is made of fine copper–constantan wires that are fixed inside a stainless steel hypodermic needle (see Fig 21.20). However, because of the thermal conductivity along the needles, more precise measurements in large thermal gradients can be obtained using very fine thermocouples without the needles (see Fig 21.20).

A major difficulty with most conducting thermodetectors is that they perturb and absorb the heating field, thereby leading to inaccuracies. Such probes must usually be read with the heating source turned off, even when carefully aligned with the field to minimize the effects. Almost complete elimination of EM interference with temperature readings can be obtained using temperature-sensitive solid-state devices (thermistors) interconnected in a balance circuit with high-resistance leads (Bowman, 1976).

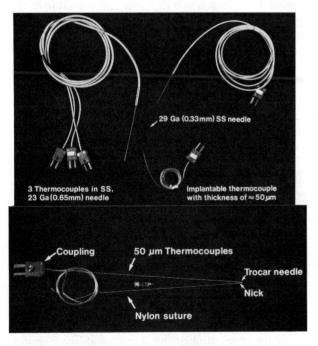

Figure 21.20. Photographs of thermocouples of different thicknesses which are typical of those used for thermal monitoring in tissue. The very fine thermocouple is inserted with a trocar needle which is then withdrawn. (This thermocouple was obtained from Dr. F.W. Hetzel, Henry Ford Hospital, Detroit Michigan; photograph by Dr. J.W. Hunt.)

Several probes have been developed which use nonconducting materials. These probes monitor the changes in the fluorescent bands in materials (such as gallium arsenide) which occur at characteristic temperatures. Fine optical fibers are used to conduct light to and from the probe so there is little perturbation of the heating field from EM sources. At the present time such thermometers cannot be used for ultrasound because of the large acoustic absorption in the probe.

A more satisfactory system of thermometry than using invasive probes would be to accurately map the temperatures in any region of the body by noninvasive means. Such a noninvasive system would have to be able to penetrate effectively into the body, and have a spatial resolution of at least 1 cm. Possible approaches such as microwave radiometry, ultrasound tomography, X-ray tomography, and NMR scanning are being investigated, but at the present time no practical systems for noninvasive thermometry are available.

21.6 CLINICAL APPLICATION OF HYPERTHERMIA

21.6.1 HYPERTHERMIA ALONE

Many different approaches have been used for applying hyperthermia to human tumors. The results of these investigations (reviewed by Meyer, 1984) have shown that about 50% of spontaneous tumors in both humans and domestic animal pets will regress after heat treatments which cause minimal acute normal tissue complications. Some of these results are summarized in Table 21.3. Most of the treated tumors were superficial, because it was only technically possible to heat such lesions and the temperature distributions achieved were almost certainly nonuniform. Often the patients had late-stage disease which had received extensive prior treatment. Most tumor responses were partial, recurrence was usually fairly rapid (within a few months) and long-term tumor control was rarely documented. The various tumor types responded similarly and the different heating modalities show no obvious differences in efficacy. The studies included both single and multiple treatments with hyperthermia. There was little evidence to suggest that multiple treatments were more effective than a single treatment.

21.6.2 HYPERTHERMIA WITH RADIATION OR DRUGS

The encouraging tumor responses achieved by hyperthermia alone have led to recent emphasis on the use of hyperthermia in combination with radiation or drugs in attempts to achieve improved clinical efficacy.

Table 21.3. Different Studies of Tumor Response to Hyperthermia Alone

	Tumor Response		
	Complete	Partial	Response (%)
Heating method			
Radiofrequency* (capac. or induc.)	4/25	7/25	44
Microwaves*	5/34	10/34	44
Ultrasound*	10/72	25/72	49
Bladder perfusion†	19/104	47/104	63
Totals	38/235 (16%)	89/235 (38%)	54
Histology			
Squamous-cell Ca*	7/36	12/36	53
Adeno Ca*	2/32	10/32	38
Melanoma*	4/21	7/21	52
Miscellaneous*	6/42	13/42	45
Bladder Ca†	19/104	47/104	63
Totals	38/235 (16%)	89/235 (38%)	54

*Derived from references given in Table 1 in Meyer (1984).

†Derived from Hall et al (1974) and Okada et al (1977).

Studies with spontaneous tumors in dogs and cats have demonstrated increased control of tumors using heat and radiation with tolerable effects in normal tissue. Gillette (1984) obtained dose–response curves for tumor control and for late bone necrosis in the mandible for radiation given alone or combined with heat; they documented thermal enhancement by a factor of 1.1–1.2 for tumor control with no increase in bone necrosis. Dewhirst and Sim (1984) monitored the temperature distribution, using up to seven probes, in tumors heated with microwaves or RF current. They found that there was a variation in temperature by as much as 5 °C between different points in the tumor. The lowest temperature recorded in the tumor correlated best with tumor control, and improved long-term control was only achieved in tumors which received radiation combined with larger equivalent heat doses. The combined treatment also led to an increased level of tissue fibrosis, but the time course of its development indicated that the increase was due to heat damage alone (fibrosis occurring at the site of a burn) and was not due to the enhancement of late radiation fibrosis.

The documentation of a nonuniform temperature distribution in tumors highlights an important caveat when examining reported studies. Many investigators have used only one or two probes, often placed in the center of the tumor, and thus the reported temperature will not necessarily be representative. The most uniform heating distributions are obtained using implanted arrays for either RF electrical or microwave heating. The results of clinical studies done using such systems, in which hyperthermia was given in combination with interstitial radiotherapy, have been very good although such procedures are limited to accessible tumors (eg, tumors of the skin, head and neck, breast, cervix and extremities).

Many human tumors have been treated with combinations of externally applied heat and radiation. Most reports have been anecdotal so that claims for increased efficacy are hard to assess. In a few studies, matched superficial lesions have been treated with radiation alone or radiation plus hyperthermia. The results of these studies (Table 21.4) indicate that the combined treatment gives a superior level of complete regression for a range of different tumors. There is some evidence for improved long-term control, but most patients have not been followed for a sufficient period of time to assess the long-term benefits of combined treatment. In the study of dog tumors by Dewhirst and Sim (1984), an increased rate of regression did not necessarily translate into increased long-term control. In the studies reviewed in Table 21.4, in which radiation doses were high enough, there was evidence of some enhancement

Table 21.4. Hyperthermia Plus Radiation—Response of Matched Lesions*

Histology	Heating Method†	No of tumors giving complete response		Reference
		rad alone	rad & heat	
Melanoma	radiofrequency	3/8	10/16	Overgaard (1981)
Mixed	microwaves	1/7	6/7	U et al (1980)
Melanoma	radiofrequency	25/54	31/45	Kim et al (1982)
Mixed (mostly squam. cell or adeno Ca.)	microwaves	22/57	50/66	Arcangeli et al (1983)
Mixed (mostly squam. cell or adeno Ca.)	microwaves	12/31	27/31	Scott et al (1984)
Totals		63/157 (40%)	124/165 (75%)	

*Same radiation dose both treatments; various fractionation schedules.

†Various numbers of heat treatments and schedules.

of acute reactions in skin, but the extent of any enhancement of late damage remains largely unknown.

The optimum sequencing for the combined use of heat and radiation in the clinic is also unknown. The best approach will likely depend on whether an increased temperature can be achieved in the tumor relative to surrounding normal tissue. If so, simultaneous heating can be used to take advantage of greater thermal enhancement in the tumor than in the normal tissue. If not, sequential heating may be better, since animal studies have suggested more rapid loss of thermal enhancement in normal tissues (see section 21.3.3).

Clinical studies of the combination of heat and drugs have been confined largely to the use of whole-body heating or regional perfusion with heated blood. The reports from most of such studies have been anecdotal, but some studies using regional perfusion (Stehlin 1980) or radiant heating (Robins et al, 1985) have been sufficiently encouraging to warrant further investigation. Controlled studies are clearly required to delineate any therapeutic advantage which might be obtained with the addition of hyperthermia to chemotherapy.

21.7 SUMMARY

Heating to temperatures above about 40 °C results in cell killing by mechanisms which are not well understood but which probably involve membrane damage. Both temperature and duration of heating are important, and small changes in either can have large biological effects. Although different cell types and tissues can have different sensitivities, within any one cell line sensitivity to heating is influenced by position in the cell cycle and by the cell's environment. Cells are more sensitive to heat under conditions of acid pH and nutritional deprivation. A major effect of heating a cell population or tissue is that the surviving cells rapidly (within 1 day) develop a state of thermotolerance in which they are much more resistant to subsequent heat treatments. This thermotolerance decays over a period of days.

Hyperthermia sensitizes cells and tissues to treatment with ionizing radiation, probably by interfering with DNA repair mechanisms. It also interacts with many cytotoxic drugs for reasons which probably depend both on the particular drug action and on heat effects such as membrane damage. The maximum interactive effect of heat with radiation or drugs occurs when the two treatments are given close together and is small or absent if more than a few hours elapse between the treatments.

Blood flow is the major cooling mechanism for tissue and consequently it plays an important role during the heat treatment. In normal tissues blood flow can increase substantially during heating but in large tumors it appears that only small increases occur. There is some evidence that tumor microvasculature is more sensitive to heating than microvasculature in normal tissue. Furthermore, tumor vasculature is often poorly formed and inadequate to supply nutritional needs of the cells. All these factors give a rationale for hyperthermia treatment, since it should be possible to heat tumors to higher temperatures than surrounding normal tissue and both acidic pH and nutrient deprivation sensitize cells to heat treatment. Nutrient-deprived regions in tumors are also likely to contain radiation-resistant hypoxic cells and to be inaccessible to some chemotherapeutic drugs, which suggests a possible gain from the use of combined treatments.

A major difficulty in the introduction of hyperthermia as a cancer treatment modality is that it is difficult to produce uniform well-controlled heating of tissue, particularly of deep-seated tumors. Whole-body or regional perfusion heating can provide reasonable uniformity, but these methods are limited in the temperature which can be achieved (tolerated) or in their applicability. Localised heating methods, which include radiofrequency (RF) electrical capacitive or inductive techniques as well as microwaves and ultrasound, have difficulty achieving reliable heating at depths of more than a few centimeters. This is due both to poor penetration of the energy involved and to variable blood flow within the regions to be heated. These difficulties are further confounded by the fact that monitoring of hyperthermia treatments involves the use of invasive temperature probes, which limits the extent to which the distribution of temperatures can be mapped. The best heating distributions are currently being achieved by interstitial RF electrical or microwave procedures. Despite the present inadequacies of heating methods and the probable variability in the heating distributions obtained, initial studies with tumors in domestic pets and in patients have demonstrated significant effects. Hyperthermia treatment alone has given measurable responses in about 50% of treated tumors, although long-term control has not been documented. Combination of heat with radiation has also led to improvement in tumor regression, but there is, as yet, limited evidence of improved long-term control. Assessment of the role of hyperthermia in cancer treatment awaits the long-term results of controlled trials and particularly the development of more adequate methods of heating and thermometry.

REFERENCES

Arcangeli G, Cividalli A, Nervi C et al: Tumor control and therapeutic gain with different schedules of combined radiotherapy and local external hyperthermia in human cancer. *Int J Radiat Oncol Biol Phys* 1983; 9:1125–1134.

Bowman RR: A probe for measuring temperature in radiofrequency heated material. *IEEE Trans Microwave Theory and Techniques* 1976; MTT-24:43–45.

Cetas TC: Invasive thermometry in physical aspects of hyperthermia, in Nussbaum GH (ed): *Medical Physics Monograph, No. 8*, American Institute of Physics, 1982, pp 231–265.

Dewey WC, Freeman ML, Raaphorst GP et al: Cell biology of hyperthermia and radiation, in Meyn RE, Withers HR (eds): *Radiation Biology in Cancer Research*. Raven Press, New York, 1980, pp 589–620.

Dewey WC, Hopwood LE, Sapareto SA, Gerweck LE: Cellular responses to combinations of hyperthermia and radiation. *Radiology* 1977; 123:463–474.

Dewhirst MW, Sim DA: The utility of thermal dose as a predictor of tumor and normal tissue responses to combined radiation and hyperthermia. *Cancer Res (Suppl)* 1984; 44:4772s–4780s.

Field SB, Morris CC: The relationship between heating time and temperature: Its relevance to clinical hyperthermia. *Radiother Oncol* 1983; 1:179–186.

Gerweck LE: Modification of cell lethality at elevated temperatures: The pH effect. *Radiat Res* 1977; 70:224–235.

Gillette EL: Clinical use of thermal enhancement and therapeutic gain for hyperthermia combined with radiation or drugs. *Cancer Res (Suppl)* 1984; 44:4836s–4841s.

Hahn GM: *Hyperthermia and Cancer*. Plenum Press, New York, 1982.

Hall RR, Schade ROK, Swinney J: Effects of hyperthermia on bladder cancer. *Br Med J* 1974; 2:593–594.

Henle KJ, Dethlefsen LA: Heat fractionation and thermotolerance: A review. *Cancer Res* 1978; 38:1843–1851.

Hornback NB: *Hyperthermia and Cancer: Human Clinical Trial Experience*, CRC Press, Boca Raton, FL, 1984, vol 1.

Hunt JW: Applications of microwave, ultrasound and radiofrequency heating in cancer therapy by hyperthermia, drugs and radiation, in Dethlefsen LA, Dewey WC (eds): *NCI Monograph* 61. National Cancer Institute, Bethesda, MD, 1982.

Kim JH, Hahn EW, Ahmed SA: Combination hyperthermia and radiation therapy for malignant melanoma. *Cancer* 1982; 50:478–482.

Kim SH, Kim JH, Hahn EW, Ensign NA: Selective killing of glucose and oxygen-deprived HeLa cells by hyperthermia. *Cancer Res* 1980; 40:3459–3462.

Landry J, Bernier D, Chretien P et al: Synthesis and degradation of heat shock proteins during development and decay of thermotolerance. *Cancer Res* 1982; 42:2457–2461.

Law MP: Prospects for hyperthermia in cancer therapy. *Radiography* 1982; 48:209–218.

Leeper D: Molecular and cellular mechanisms of hyperthermia alone or combined with other modalities, in Overgaard J (ed): *Hyperthermia Oncology*, 1984. Taylor and Francis, 1985, vol 2, pp 9–40.

Lele PP: Ultrasound: Is it the modality of choice for controlled, localized heating of deep tumors? in Overgaard J (ed): *Hyperthermic Oncology*, 1984. Taylor and Francis, 1985, vol 2, pp 129–154.

Li GC, Kal HB: Effect of hyperthermia on the radiation response of two mammalian cell lines. *Eur J Cancer* 1977; 13:65–69.

Meyer JL: The clinical efficacy of localised hyperthermia. *Cancer Res (Suppl)* 1984; 44:4745s–4751s.

Morris CC, Myers R, Field SB: The response of the rat tail to hyperthermia. *Br J Radiol* 1977; 50:576–580.

Okada K, Kiyotake S, Kawazoe K et al: II. Hyperthermic treatment for the bladder tumor. *Jpn J Urol* 1977; 68:128–135.

Overgaard J: Simultaneous and sequential hyperthermia and radiation treatment of an experimental tumor and its surrounding normal tissue in vivo. *Int J Radiat Oncol Biol Phys* 1980; 6:1507–1517.

Overgaard J: Fractionated radiation and hyperthermia: Experimental and clinical studies. *Cancer* 1981; 48:1116–1123.

Overgaard J, Nielsen OS: The importance of thermotolerance for the clinical treatment with hyperthermia. *Radiother Oncol* 1983; 1:167–178.

Raaphorst GP, Romano SL, Mitchell JB et al: Intrinsic differences in heat and/or x-ray sensitivity of seven mammalian cell lines cultured and treated under identical conditions. *Cancer Res* 1979; 39:396–401.

Reinhold HS, and Endrich B: Tumor microcirculation as a target for hyperthermia. *Int J Hyperthermia* 1986; 2:111–137.

Robins HI: Role of whole-body hyperthermia in the treatment of neoplastic disease: Its current status and future prospects. *Cancer Res (Suppl)* 1984; 44:4878s–4883s.

Robins HI, Dennis WH, Neville AJ et al: A non-toxic system for 41.8°C whole-body hyperthermia: Results of a phase I study using a radiant heat device. *Cancer Res* 1985; 45:3937–3944.

Sapareto SA, Dewey WC: Thermal dose determination in cancer therapy. *Int J Radiat Oncol Biol Phys* 1984; 10:787–800.

Scott RS, Johnson RJR, Story KV, Clay L: Local hyperthermia in combination with definitive radiotherapy: Increased tumor clearance, reduced recurrence rate in extended follow-up. *Int J Radiat Oncol Biol Phys* 1984; 10:2119–2123.

Song CW: Effect of local hyperthermia on blood flow and microenvironment: A review. *Cancer Res (Suppl)* 1984; 44: 4721s–4730s.

Stehlin JS, Jr: Hyperthermic perfusion for melanoma of the extremities: Experience with 165 patients, 1967–1979. *Ann NY Acad Sci* 1980; 335:352–355.

Stewart FA, Denekamp J: The therapeutic advantage of combined heat and x-rays on a mouse fibrosarcoma. *Br J Radiol* 1978; 51:307–316.

Stewart FA, Denekamp J: Fractionation studies with combined x-rays and hyperthermia in vivo. *Br J Radiol* 1980; 53:346–356.

Suit HD: Hyperthermic effects on animal tissues. *Radiology* 1977; 123:483–487.

Tanabe E, McEuen AH, Caslow S et al: Microstrip spiral antenna for local hyperthermia, in *IEEE MMTT-S International Microwave Symposium Digest, Expanding Microwave Horizons*. IEEE, New York, 1984, pp 133–134.

Turner PF: Regional hyperthermia with an annular phased array. *IEEE Trans Biomed Eng* 1984; BME-31: 106–114.

U R, Noell KT, Woodward KT et al: Microwave-induced local hyperthermia in combination with radiotherapy of human malignant tumors. *Cancer* 1980; 45:638–646.

Wike-Hooley JL, Haveman J, Reinhold HS: The relevance of tumour pH to the treatment of malignant disease. *Radiother Oncol* 1984; 2:343–366.

BIBLIOGRAPHY

Hahn GM: *Hyperthermia and Cancer*. Plenum Press, New York, 1982.

Lowanthal JP (ed): Hyperthermia in cancer treatment. *Cancer Res (Suppl)* 1984; 44:4703s–4908s.

Nussbaum GH (ed): *Physical Aspects of Hyperthermia*. Amer. Inst. of Physics, New York, 1982.

Overgaard J (ed): *Hyperthermic Oncology, 1984: Review Lectures, Symposium Summaries and Workshop Summaries*. Taylor and Francis, London, 1985, Vol 2.

Stewart JR, Bagshaw MA, Corry PM, et al: Hyperthermia as a treatment of cancer. *Cancer Treatment Symposia* 1984; 1: 135–145.

Strohbehn JW, Cetas TC, Hahn GM (ed): Hyperthermia and cancer therapy. Special Issue, *IEEE Trans Biomed Eng* 1984; BME-31:1–172.

22

A Guide to Studies of Diagnostic Tests, Prognosis and Treatment

Norman F. Boyd

22.1 INTRODUCTION

Clinical oncologists are expected to be experts in the application of diagnostic tests, the estimation of prognosis, and in the selection of therapy. Despite the importance of these subjects to all forms of medical practice it is uncommon for medical schools to give formal instruction in their theoretical bases. This omission is unfortunate because practicing clinicians are expected to be able to evaluate critically the results of clinical studies; from this literature they must decide which new diagnostic tests to adopt, which new therapies to recommend, and what advice to give to patients about the expected course of their illness.

This chapter will provide a brief overview of the methods used to evaluate diagnostic tests, to estimate prognosis, and to evaluate therapy, indicating some of the pitfalls that studies in these areas can encounter. Guidelines for the formal critical appraisal of papers, and a fuller discussion of the issues raised in connection with clinical trials, can be found in the Bibliography.

22.2 DIAGNOSTIC TESTS

Diagnostic tests are used to establish the existence or extent of cancer among people suspected of having the disease, to screen for cancer among people who are symptom-free, and to follow changes in the extent and severity of the disease during therapy. Less obvious consequences of using diagnostic tests are the effects they have on the deployment of other diagnostic tests, the effects that they have upon the selection of treatment, and most important, the effects they may have upon the health outcomes of the individuals to whom they are applied, in terms either of the quality or duration of survival. For example, diagnostic tests can influence health by affecting the time in its clinical course at which disease is detected or by the effect they have on a clinician's choice of treatment.

The impact of diagnostic tests upon the health of the tested individuals is often estimated when screening procedures are applied to individuals who are presumed to be healthy, but their impact usually remains unknown when tests are used in the management of patients who are known to be diseased. It is, however, the *outcome* of testing, in terms of the health of the individuals to whom tests are given, that ultimately determines the clinical usefulness of any test procedure.

22.2.1 TESTS AS DISCRIMINATORS

Diagnostic tests are used to distinguish patients with and without a particular attribute of disease. Test results can be displayed on a scale that may be continuous, as, for example, it would be for carcinoembryonic antigen (CEA) or alkaline phosphatase, or dichotomous, as it would be for an X-ray that is interpreted as normal or abnormal (Fig 22.1).

In order to assess how well a diagnostic test performs in discriminating between patients with and without disease, it is necessary to have another, independent, method of determining who among the individuals tested has disease. This independent standard might be the findings of surgery, the results of a biopsy or autopsy, or the clinical outcome of patients after follow-up. If direct anatomical confirmation of the presence of disease is not possible, the results of another diagnostic test, whose properties are known from previous studies, may be the only standard available.

After independent classification of disease status, a cut-off point must be selected for the diagnostic test that separates negative from positive results. The choice of a cut-off point, above which values will be regarded as abnormal and below which they will be regarded as normal, can be made in several ways. For example, alkaline phosphatase can be described as having a "normal range," which is simply a statistical term that means that 95% of apparently healthy people have values falling within the limits defined by the normal range, and 5% of healthy people have values that lie outside this range. This definition of normality is not the same as the one a clinician is likely to use when interpreting the results of an alkaline phosphatase measurement. Values within the normal range are then

usually regarded as indicating the absence of disease, and results lying above the upper limit of the range are interpreted as indicating that disease may be present and that further investigations are required. (See Murphy, 1972, for a discussion of the several meanings of normality.)

The effects of choosing different cut-off points for a diagnostic test are shown in Figure 22.1. A cut-off point placed initially at location A in Figure 22.1 provides some separation of diseased and nondiseased individuals, but because of the overlap between diseased and nondiseased subjects there is inevitably some misclassification. If the cut-off point is moved to location C, fewer nondiseased subjects are misclassified, but more diseased people fall below the cut-off and will be incorrectly classified as nondiseased. A cut-off point at location B has the opposite effect; more diseased subjects are correctly classified, but at the cost of misclassifying larger numbers of nondiseased people. This trade-off between the ability of a test to correctly identify diseased and nondiseased people is a feature of all diagnostic tests.

The application of an independent standard to identify diseased and nondiseased subjects and the selection of a cut-off point for a diagnostic test define four subpopulations (Fig 22.2). These are true-positives (people with the disease in whom the test is positive), true negatives (people without the disease in whom the test is negative), false positives (people without the disease in whom the test is positive), and false negative (people with the disease in whom the test is negative).

Test performance can be described by several indices which can be calculated from the 2 × 2 array shown in Figure 22.3. "Vertical" indices are calculated from the columns in the table and describe the ability of a test to classify people whose disease status is known. These

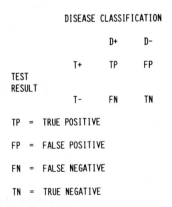

DISEASE CLASSIFICATION

		D+	D−
	T+	TP	FP
TEST RESULT			
	T−	FN	TN

TP = TRUE POSITIVE

FP = FALSE POSITIVE

FN = FALSE NEGATIVE

TN = TRUE NEGATIVE

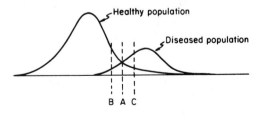

Figure 22.1. Interpretation of a diagnostic test requires the selection of a cut-off point that separates negative from positive results. The position of the cut-off point influences the proportion of patients who are incorrectly classified as being healthy or diseased.

Figure 22.2. Selection of a cut-off point for a diagnostic test defines four subpopulations as shown. D+ and D− indicate presence or absence of disease; T+ and − indicate positive or negative tests.

	D+	D-
T+	TP	FP
T-	FN	TN

CALCULATED FROM COLUMNS ("VERTICAL PROPERTIES")

SENSITIVITY = TP/TP + FN

SPECIFICITY = TN/FP + TN

FALSE NEGATIVE RATIO = FN/TP + FN

FALSE POSITIVE RATIO = FP/FP + TN

CALCULATED FROM ROWS ("HORIZONTAL PROPERTIES")

PREVALENCE = TP + FN/TP + FN + FP + TN

PREDICTIVE VALUE (+) = TP/TP + FP

PREDICTIVE VALUE (-) = TN/TN + FN

Figure 22.3. Indices that are used to describe the performance of a diagnostic test. Predictive values (but not sensitivity and specificity) depend on the prevalence of disease in the population that is tested.

indices include sensitivity (the ability of the test to correctly identify diseased subjects) and specificity (the ability of the test to correctly identify nondiseased subjects). These indices do not depend on the prevalence of disease in the sample.

"Horizontal" indices describe the ability of the test as it will be used in clinical practice. These indices are calculated from the rows of the table and describe the frequency with which individuals turn out to have disease when the test is positive (the predictive value of a positive test), or conversely, prove not to have disease when the test is negative (the predictive value of a negative

A) HIGH PREVALENCE (50%)

	D+	D-		
T+	80	10	SENS.	80%
			SPEC.	90%
T-	20	90	PRED. VALUE (+)	89%

B) INTERMEDIATE PREVALENCE (10%)

	D+	D-		
T+	80	100	SENS.	80%
			SPEC.	90%
T-	20	900	PRED. VALUE (+)	44%

C) LOW PREVALENCE (1%)

	D+	D-		
T+	80	1000	SENS.	80%
			SPEC.	90%
T-	20	9000	PRED. VALUE (+)	4%

Figure 22.4. A diagnostic test is applied to populations in which disease has high, intermediate or low prevalence. The predictive value of the test decreases when there is a low prevalence of disease.

test). The prevalence of disease among the sample tested is calculated as indicated in Figure 22.3. If three of these indices are known, the sensitivity, specificity, and disease prevalence, all other indices of test performance can be calculated.

Figure 22.4 illustrates the influence of prevalence of disease in the population to which a test is applied. Examples are shown for three levels of prevalence for a hypothetical test, and in each example the sensitivity and specificity are kept the same. As the prevalence of disease declines, as it would, for example, if subjects in the general population were studied instead of patients in a hospital, the positive predictive value of the test falls progressively. This fall occurs because, although the percentage of nondiseased subjects who give positive test results remains the same regardless of disease prevalence, the absolute number of nondiseased subjects with a positive test increases with the number of patients tested.

22.2.2 EVALUATION OF TEST PERFORMANCE

The 2 × 2 table is a simple and convenient method of describing test performance, but it gives no information about the effect of using a different cut-off point, and is not ideal for comparing different diagnostic tests. These problems can be overcome by describing test performance using the receiver-operating-characteristics (ROC) curve. As indicated in Figure 22.3 the true-positive ratio (or sensitivity) plus the false-negative ratio of a test equals 1, and the true-negative ratio (or specificity) plus the false-positive ratio equals 1. Thus two terms, for example the true-positive ratio and the false-positive ratio, may be used to describe test performance completely. An ROC curve describes the way in which these two test properties change with respect to each other as the cut-off criterion is varied.

An example of an ROC curve is shown in Figure 22.5. The figure also shows two hypothetical curves, one describing a perfect test and the other a useless test. In the perfect test (curve A) all diseased and nondiseased subjects are correctly identified with the cut-off criterion plotted at point X. In the useless test (curve C) diseased and nondiseased subjects are not separated at any cut-off point. Curve B shows the performance of an actual test which is intermediate between these two extremes.

Variation of the cut-off point for a continuous variable like CEA is straightforward, but different tactics have to be used for procedures like X-rays whose results are not expressed in numerical terms. Figure 22.6 shows a portion of a reporting form for a radiologic procedure (computed tomography of the abdomen in

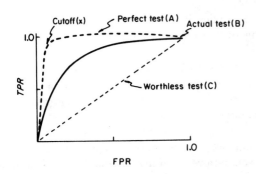

Figure 22.5. Receiver operating curves (ROCs) plot the true-positive rate (TPR) against the false-positive rate (FPR) of a diagnostic test as the cut-off criterion is varied. The performance of the test is indicated by departures from the diagonal, as shown.

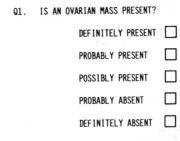

Q1. IS AN OVARIAN MASS PRESENT?

- DEFINITELY PRESENT ☐
- PROBABLY PRESENT ☐
- POSSIBLY PRESENT ☐
- PROBABLY ABSENT ☐
- DEFINITELY ABSENT ☐

Figure 22.6. Part of a reporting form for a computed tomographic (CT) scan of the abdomen in patients suspected of having ovarian cancer. Different levels of certainty can be used to generate an ROC curve.

patients with ovarian cancer) that generates results suitable for ROC analysis. The radiologist reporting the films records findings according to his or her level of certainty. Different levels of certainty can then be used as cut-off points and their associated true-positive ratios and false-positive ratios plotted to generate an ROC curve.

ROC analysis is now an accepted and commonly reported method of evaluating diagnostic tests. To date, most of the published literature deals with radiology, but it can be applied to all forms of diagnostic technology.

22.2.3 SPECTRUM OF PATIENTS TESTED

The performance of a diagnostic test can be distorted by several factors (Table 22.1). These include the way in which subjects to whom the test will be applied are selected, and the way in which those subjects are subsequently investigated (Ransohoff and Feinstein, 1978).

Diagnostic tests are used in clinical practice to iden-

tify patients most likely to have disease from among a larger group of patients who are suspected of having disease. The suspicion of disease that prompts application of a test may arise because patients have symptoms or signs suggesting the presence of disease, because of identified conditions with which disease may be associated, or because the patient is a member of a high-risk group. To adequately examine the performance of a diagnostic test the patients selected for testing should challenge the test in as many of these respects as possible.

If the test is to be used to identify patients with colon cancer it should be applied to patients with as wide as possible a spectrum of disease extent (clinical spectrum), to demonstrate the ability of the test to detect both localized and advanced disease. Similarly it should be applied to patients with a wide range of clinical conditions affecting the colon and other digestive organs whose manifestations may resemble colon cancer and to whom the test might be applied in the clinical setting (comorbid spectrum). Furthermore, where different histologic forms of a cancer exist, the test should be challenged by including as wide a variety of histologic types as possible.

Table 22.1. Factors Which May Distort the Performance of a Diagnostic Test

Spectrum of patients used for evaluation of the test

1. *Clinical spectrum:* Should include patients with all stages of the disease for which the test is to be used
2. *Comorbid spectrum:* Should include patients with a wide range of other diseases
3. *Pathologic spectrum:* Should include patients with a range of histological types of disease

Potential sources of bias in test evaluation

1. *Exclusion of equivocal cases*
2. *Work-up bias:* Results of the test influence the choice of subsequent tests which confirm or refute diagnosis
3. *Test review bias:* Results of the test influence the interpretation of subsequent measures to establish diagnosis
4. *Diagnostic review bias:* Knowledge of the disease influences the interpretation of the test
5. *Incorporation bias:* Test information is used as a criterion to establish diagnosis

22.2.4 POTENTIAL SOURCES OF BIAS IN ASSOCIATING TEST RESULTS WITH A STANDARD

If conclusions about the association between the results of a diagnostic test and classification of the patient's disease status are to truly describe the performance of the test, then the two acts of classifying the patient must be carried out independently. If the classification of the patient's disease status is influenced by the test result, or if interpretation of the test result is influenced by the patient's disease status, then the tests are not performed independently and a biased view of test performance is likely to result. Bias in associating the test result with the standard can arise in several ways (Table 22.1).

Work-up bias arises if the results of the diagnostic test under evaluation influence the choice of subsequent tests that are used to confirm or refute the diagnosis of disease. For example, investigation of patients with ovarian cancer using computed tomographic (CT) scanning might influence the selection of patients who have subsequent laparotomy to definitively classify patients' disease status. Work-up bias has then occurred, and comparison of the results of CT scan and the findings at laparotomy will give a distorted view of the diagnostic accuracy of CT scanning.

Diagnostic review bias and test review bias arise in circumstances where the subjective review of information, as for example might occur in a review of histology or radiologic images, is influenced either by knowledge of the test result or of the diagnosis. For example, a radiologist reviewing CT scans of the abdomen might be influenced in his interpretation by knowledge of the findings at laparotomy (test review bias); alternatively, a surgeon carrying out a laparotomy might be influenced either in his search for disease or in his interpretation of findings by knowledge of the results of a preoperative scan.

Incorporation bias is the most flagrant violation of the principle that independent classification of test results and disease status is required. It arises when test information is itself incorporated into the decision as to whether or not a patient has disease.

22.2.5 SOURCES OF BIAS IN ASSESSING THE IMPACT OF DIAGNOSTIC TESTS

The influence of diagnostic tests on the health outcomes of patients with cancer is usually assessed by considering their impact on the probability of death from the disease. Other health outcomes that might be influenced by diagnostic tests include quality of life and the avoidance of morbidity or reduction of disability,

but few studies have used these endpoints and the following discussion will consider only the outcome of death.

Several types of bias may confound assessment of a diagnostic test on the survival of patients. For example, if the survival of patients with breast cancer diagnosed by mammography while they had occult disease is superior to that of patients diagnosed in other ways, it does not necessarily establish that survival has been improved as a result of mammography. Survival might be better in patients diagnosed by mammography even if the test does nothing to influence the clinical course of patients with breast cancer. This seemingly paradoxical state of affairs arises from two possible sources of bias, length bias and lead-time bias.

The concept of length bias is illustrated in Figure 22.7. The horizontal lines in the figure represent the length of time that a disease, such as breast cancer, is present in a patient from its inception until the death of the patient. Long lines thus describe slowly growing disease, and short lines rapidly growing disease. A single examination, such as screening with mammography (represented in the figure by the dotted vertical line), will intersect a larger number of long lines than short lines. In fact, the probability that a line will be intersected by the vertical line is proportional to its length. A single screening examination will thus identify selectively patients who have disease which is growing slowly. Because of this, a comparison of the survival time of patients identified by screening is likely to show that their survival is better than that of other patients simply because slowly growing variants of the disease have been identified by screening.

Lead-time bias is illustrated in Figure 22.8. The purpose of many diagnostic tests, and of all tests that are used to screen healthy subjects, is to allow clinicians to identify disease at an earlier point in its clinical

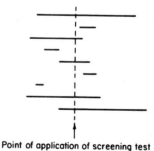

Point of application of screening test

Horizontal lines represent the length of time that disease is present

Figure 22.7. Illustration of length bias in a screening test. The test is more likely to detect disease that is present for a long time (ie, slowly progressive disease).

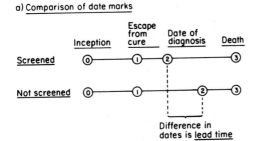

a) Comparison of date marks

b) Comparison of survival

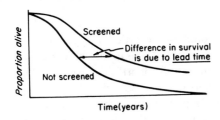

Figure 22.8. Illustration of lead-time bias. *a*, Application of a test may lead to earlier diagnosis without changing the course of disease. *b*, There is an improvement in survival when measured from time of diagnosis.

course than would be possible without the test. Four critical time points in the clinical course of the disease are indicated in Figure 22.8: the time of inception of the disease, the date of diagnosis under ordinary circumstances, the date at which the disease becomes incurable, and the date of death.

The date at which the disease becomes incurable may occur after the usual date of diagnosis for some tumors (eg, this is generally the case for patients with basal-cell carcinoma of the skin). For many common cancers, however, escape from curability occurs before the date of customary diagnosis. The purpose of screening tests is to advance the date of diagnosis to a point where it occurs before the date of escape from cure. Even if this objective is not achieved, the length of time by which the date of diagnosis has been advanced by screening (added to the time that the patient is observed before

death) will make it appear that survival time has been increased by screening (Fig 22.8). This additional time is called lead time, and it may be several years in length. In breast cancer it is estimated to average about two years when screening with mammography is carried out. The effect of adding this lead time to the patients' survival time is called lead-time bias. Simply advancing the date of diagnosis may not be beneficial to patients. Indeed, if advancing the date of diagnosis does not increase a patient's chance of cure, early diagnosis may be undesirable because patients spend a longer time with the knowledge that they have incurable disease.

To determine whether or not a diagnostic test influences the number of patients who are cured of cancer, a measure must be used that is not influenced by either length bias or lead time. The disease-specific mortality of a population is such a measure. It differs from the case fatality rate in that its denominator is formed by the total population of individuals to whom the test was applied, as opposed to the number of individuals in whom disease was diagnosed (Table 22.2).

There is now evidence that, at least in postmenopausal women, screening for breast cancer with mammography does reduce the disease-specific mortality of the population (Shapiro, 1977). It must therefore allow detection of curable disease in some patients who would have been incurable by the time their disease would have been detected by other methods.

22.3 PROGNOSIS

22.3.1 IMPORTANCE OF PROGNOSTIC FACTORS

There are several variables, such as tumor size and extent of disease, as well as characteristics of patients that influence the outcome of all forms of cancer. Knowledge of these factors that influence the outcome of disease is important for several reasons, but particularly in planning and analyzing clinical trials of cancer therapy. Prognostic factors in cancer often have an

Table 22.2. Possible Measures for Evaluating Diagnostic Tests

Measure	Numerator	Denominator	Affected by Length Bias	Affected by Lead-Time Bias
Case fatality rate	number dying of cancer	number found to have cancer by screening	yes	yes
Population mortality rate	number dying of cancer	number of subjects to whom screening test was applied	no	no

enormous influence upon the outcome of disease and many treatments have a much weaker effect. An example of this phenomenon is illustrated in Figure 22.9, which shows that the prognostic influence of lymph-node status in a clinical trial of tamoxifen as adjuvant therapy in patients with stage II breast cancer is much greater than the effect of treatment. If the influence of strong prognostic factors is ignored in the conduct and analysis of clinical trials, small but important effects of treatment may be concealed. Alternatively, if prognostic factors are not equally distributed between treatment groups, a difference in outcome may be mistakenly attributed to therapy. Furthermore, several clinical trials in cancer have shown that treatments may have different effects in patients with different prognostic characteristics.

Although it is commonplace to speak of the "natural history of disease," the clinical course of untreated patients is seldom known adequately, since there are few opportunities for the observation of untreated patients. Even if no therapy is available to treat an underlying disease such as cancer, the administration of treatment for complications such as pain or infection may influence favorably the patients' survival, even though the primary disease remains unaffected. A clinician's knowledge about prognosis thus comes from personal recollections about similar patients, and from reports in the literature.

There are several ways in which a clinician's recollections of past patients may either impair or distort his ability to use past experience as a guide to making predictions about present patients. These include a sharply limited capacity to retain items of quantitative information, a predilection to generalize from patients who have been seen recently, and the undue influence exerted by the recollection of unusual or atypical cases. Reports in the literature are therefore likely to be more reliable sources of information about clinical course or prognosis. Such reports examine the association between characteristics of patients or their diseases, and health outcomes which in cancer usually means recurrence of disease or death.

22.3.2 DESIGN OF PROGNOSTIC STUDIES

Study of the clinical course of a particular group of patients requires selection of a specified time in their disease history (called zero time), at which the patients will be characterized and from which their subsequent survival will be measured. Thus in a study of the influence of estrogen receptors on the survival of patients with breast cancer the zero time might be specified as the time of the diagnosis of breast cancer; receptor status would be characterized at that time, and survival

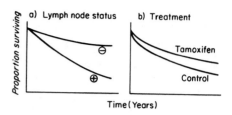

Figure 22.9. Factors which influence survival of postmenopausal patients with primary breast cancer. a, Involvement of axillary nodes by disease; b, treatment with tamoxifen. Note that the prognostic influence of nodal involvement is much greater than the effect of treatment.

time would be recorded for patients with different receptor values. A group of such patients is referred to as "an inception cohort" (Feinstein, 1985a). An inception cohort refers to any group of patients assembled at a common point in their clinical course. This time point often is the time of diagnosis, but it could be some other suitable point in time. For example, for the study of prognosis of patients with metastatic breast cancer, zero time might be the date at which metastases were first identified.

Prognostic variables cannot be evaluated in isolation. For example, suppose that patients with positive receptors were found to survive on average longer than patients with negative receptors. In order to conclude that estrogen receptors are prognostic factors in breast cancer, it would be necessary to demonstrate that estrogen receptors do not influence survival because of their association with some other prognostic factors (ie, that these factors are independent). If estrogen receptors were associated with lymph-node involvement, or with the degree of differentiation of the tumor, one would expect to find that they were also associated with survival. Evaluation of the influence of a prognostic factor therefore requires examination of the influence of other known variables on its association with survival. Multivariate statistical procedures are used for making such assessments.

Complete follow-up is important in prognostic studies. Patients who are lost to follow-up are unlikely to have experienced the same outcomes as those who remain. Patients are often lost to follow-up because they die or because they are well enough to move away from the environment of the investigator. Incomplete follow-up may therefore introduce bias.

Assessment of outcome in prognostic studies requires objective criteria for the recognition of disease recurrence or for attributing death to a particular cause such as cancer. The assessment of outcome can be influenced by knowledge of the patients' initial prognostic characteristics. For example, a follow-up bone scan in patients with breast cancer that is equivocal may be more likely to be read as positive if it is known that the patient initially had extensive lymph-node involvement. To avoid such possible sources of bias all patients in the inception cohort should be assessed with the same frequency, using the same set of tests, and test results should be interpreted using explicit criteria without knowledge of the patient's initial characteristics.

22.3.3 PROGNOSTIC INFORMATION IN CANCER STUDIES: USES AND LIMITATIONS

Clinicians have long recognized the important influence of prognostic factors on the outcome of patients with cancer and the need to take account of prognostic factors when reporting the results of treatment. This recognition has led to the development of methods of classifying cancer that are based on factors that are known to influence prognosis.

The methods used to classify most malignant diseases are based upon descriptions of the histology and anatomic extent of the tumour. Thus the widely used TNM system of classifying or staging cancers is based on the size of the primary tumour (T), the presence or absence of regional lymph node involvement (N) and the presence or absence of distant metastases (M). Leukemia cannot be classified according to anatomical extent and is instead classified according to cellular morphology.

More recently, other attributes of the tumor, such as the estrogen-receptor concentration in breast cancer or the phenotype of lymphocytes in lymphomas as defined by surface markers, have been found to have an important influence on the outcome of disease and increasingly are included as prognostic factors in the analysis and reporting of therapeutic trials in these disorders.

Prognostic classifications based on tumor morphology have been used in several ways. Clinicians use them to describe the characteristics of patients entering clinical trials; tumor registries use them to report the outcome of patients in different countries; and they are the benchmark against which the importance and independence of new prognostic factors are assessed.

Because the attributes of the tumor that are used in these classifications do, in general, exert a major influence on prognosis, their use does facilitate comparisons of the results of therapy and the assessment of other factors that may influence outcome.

Classifications of cancer that are based solely upon attributes of the tumor omit, however, many other factors that are known to affect prognosis. These include the "performance status" of patients (in the few instances where comparison with other prognostic factors has been made, performance status has been found to

exert the greatest influence on outcome), the presence or absence of symptoms, the severity of the illness and the presence or absence of other disease. Prognostic distinctions due to these or other related attributes, that are independent of tumor morphology and extent, have now been shown for several diseases (see Feinstein, 1985b).

The result of the omission of these factors from systems of classifying cancer is that patients who are alike with respect to the morphology and extent of their cancer may differ in their prognosis because of differences in these other features.

Not only are patients with similar tumors likely to be heterogeneous with respect to prognosis but the ability of clinicians to determine the anatomical extent of cancer is likely to change with improvements in diagnostic technology. Thus the introduction of new and more sensitive methods of imaging is likely to result in patients being recognized as having disseminated disease who would formerly have been classified as having more localized disease.

The influence of these changes in the classification of patients, on the survival of patients within each category of anatomical extent, may be similar to the effects of "lead time" discussed in section 22.2.5; that is, the survival of each category of patient defined by anatomical stage may improve without there having been any prolongation of the patients' life span. This state of affairs arises because before the introduction of the new technology each anatomical stage contained both patients who truly belonged to that stage and patients who had more advanced disease that was unrecognized and who were therefore misclassified. Because the prognosis of the patients with unrecognized more advanced disease can always be expected to be worse than that of patients who in reality have more localized disease, their recognition and correct classification will "improve" the survival of patients in the stage to which they were formerly assigned (see Feinstein et al, 1985 for a detailed discussion of this phenomenon).

An example of differences in survival that may be due to this phenomenon of "stage migration" is shown in Table 22.3. The results shown are the five-year survival rates, according to anatomical stage, for patients with ovarian cancer in Saskatchewan and Toronto. Within each anatomical stage, except the most extensive (stage IV), the survival of patients in Toronto is superior and the difference in survival is particularly striking in the more localized stages.

The overall survival of patients in the two regions is, however, virtually identical, indicating that the differences in survival according to stage are due to differences in the composition of the stages in the two regions and are not due to differences in the effectiveness of

Table 22.3. Five-Year Survival Rates in Ovarian Cancer in Toronto and Saskatchewan According to Anatomic Stage

| Region | Stage | | | | | | Overall Survival |
	Ia	Ib + c	IIa	IIb + c	III	IV	
Toronto	44/54 (87)	10/15 (67)	2/6 (33)	52/103 (51)	40/200 (20)	4/82 (5)	152/459 (33%)
Saskatchewan	34/53 (64)	5/16 (31)	3/10 (30)	0/7 (0)	4/49 (8)	1/20 (5)	47/155 (30%)

Note: From the *Annual Report on the Results of Treatment in Gynecologic Cancer*; vol 19. Stockholm: International Federation of Gynecology and Obstetrics, 1985.

treatment. The reason for this difference in the composition of the stages cannot be determined from the data available but it could arise from differences in prognostically important characteristics of patients referred to above, or from differences in the diagnostic technology that is used to classify patients. In either event, despite the undeniable usefulness of anatomical methods of classifying cancer, their limitations should be kept in mind.

22.3.4 GENERALIZATION OF PROGNOSTIC INFORMATION

Patients who are referred to centers that conduct prognostic studies may differ systematically from those who are not referred. As a result people who enter the inception cohort may, by virtue of self-selection or referral, differ systematically from the population to whom the results of the study will be applied. It is thus necessary that the route by which the patients entered the study should be described. They may come from a primary care center, they may be selected from many hospitals in a geographically defined region, or they may be assembled in highly specialized tertiary-care centers. Each of these locations is likely to have different types of patients. For example, tertiary-referral centers are likely to attract sicker patients, patients with unusual manifestations of disease, or patients with rare diseases. For these reasons the prognosis of a given disease, as described by a special center, may be different from that in less highly selected groups of patients. The qualitative influence of prognostic factors on outcome is, however, less likely to be affected by referral bias than is survival. For example, if estrogen-receptor status influences survival, it is likely to do so in all centres, although the actual survival of patients classified according to receptor status may differ somewhat between centres. Ideally, an inception cohort should be formed by all identified cases within a large geographically defined area.

22.4 CLINICAL TRIALS OF TREATMENT

22.4.1 THE PURPOSE OF A CLINICAL TRIAL

Therapeutic trials in patients with cancer can be classified according to the sequence that is usually followed when a new potential treatment for cancer is first identified. First, the tolerance of human subjects for the new treatment is established and its toxicity described (phase 1 trials), next the biologic activity of the treatment in various diseases is examined (phase 2 trials), and finally the place of a new treatment in the management of patients (phase 3 trials) is determined.

Decisions about which patients to include, how to compare treatments, and which patients to include in the analysis are determined by the purpose of the trial. These decisions are aided by a useful classification that has been proposed by Schwartz et al (1980). This classification distinguishes between trials that are designed to detect the biological effects of treatment (referred to as explanatory trials), and trials that are designed to determine whether patients benefit from receiving treatment (called pragmatic trials). The existence of a biological effect, say for example in the case of a drug that possesses antitumor properties, does not mean that the drug will necessarily benefit patients. Drugs that have strong antitumor properties may be so toxic that patients cannot tolerate them, and so cannot derive benefit from them.

The major differences between explanatory and pragmatic trials are listed in Table 22.4. Phase 1 and 2 trials conducted on new therapeutic agents are explanatory, whereas phase 3 trials are usually pragmatic in intent. The literature, is however, often confusing because trials that are conducted and reported with the intention of describing a benefit to patients from treatment (ie, are pragmatic in their intention) are carried out in a manner that is more appropriate for explanatory trials. Such trials frequently use highly selected groups of patients, do not incorporate randomization to a control group of patients, exclude patients from analysis on

Table 22.4. Classification of Clinical Trials

	Explanatory	Pragmatic
Purpose	The results will be used to guide further research, and not to formulate treatment policy. The purpose of the work is to contribute new knowledge.	The results will be used to select future treatment policy
	Idealized conditions	"Real-life" conditions
Treatment	Choose treatment most likely to demonstrate the phenomenon under study.	Choose treatment with tolerance of the target population in mind.
	Select a control so as to isolate treatment effect in the analysis.	Select controls according to practical considerations.
Assessment criteria	Choose criterion that gives biologic information such as tumor response.	Choose information of practical importance such as functional capacity or survival.
	Use single or a small number of criteria.	Take account of all practically important criteria, but require a *single* decision at the stage of analysis.
Choice of patients	Choose patients most likely to demonstrate an effect.	Choose patients who are representative of the population to whom the results of the research will be applied.
	Patients are used as a "means to an end" in the research.	The effect of treatment in the patients is the end product of the research.

the grounds that they are "nonevaluable," and cite tumor response as the only measure of benefit, without consideration of quality or duration of survival. Trials of this type, often referred to as "phase 2," are suitable only for making inferences about the antineoplastic properties of treatments and are not suitable for drawing broader conclusions about issues of patient benefit.

The following discussion will emphasize pragmatic phase 3 trials, and the remainder of the chapter will focus primarily on the randomized control trial as a means of establishing the place of new treatments in patient management.

22.4.2 THE GENERAL ARCHITECTURE OF CLINICAL TRIALS

Thinking about clinical trials is assisted greatly by a general formulation proposed by Feinstein (1985a), which requires that three components of a trial be specified. These three components are (a) the initial state, which describes the patient population to which treatment is applied; (b) the manoeuvre, which describes the treatment that is the subject of the trial; and (c) the subsequent state, which describes the outcome events, such as survival, that will be used to determine the effectiveness of the treatment.

For example, clinical trials of adjuvant therapy in patients with breast cancer often involve patients who have had mastectomy and have tumor deposits in axil-

lary nodes (the initial state), who are randomly allocated to receive chemotherapy or no chemotherapy (the manoeuvre), and whose survival (the subsequent state) is then compared. It is possible to describe the objectives of any clinical trial by specifying these three components.

22.4.3 CHARACTERISTICS OF THE INITIAL STATE

The patient population entered into a clinical trial must be described in terms of its salient features. These include demographic (ie, age, gender, and race composition), and clinical (the type of disease, its extent, and the methods used to characterize it) characteristics. Further criteria must be given for the way in which patients are selected according to these features. Sufficient details should be given that a reader can determine the resemblance of the treated patients to those seen in practice. Unless such information is given the extent to which the results of this trial can be generalized will be in doubt.

The presence of disease unrelated to cancer (comorbidity) may contraindicate some treatments for cancer or make modifications of treatment necessary, and may also influence the outcome of treatment. The inclusion or exclusion of patients with comorbid disease, and the types of comorbid disease present, should be specified in a description of the initial state.

The baseline prognostic characteristics of the patients

also need to be described. As described in the section on prognosis, prognostic factors in cancer often have effects upon patient outcome that are much greater than the effects of treatment. Before we can conclude that a difference in outcome in a trial is due to treatment, we must therefore take whatever steps are possible to assure that the observed difference is not due to differences in prognostic factors between the groups compared. This is done in part by employing randomization (see section 22.4.5), and by in addition taking prognostic factors into account. This may be carried out in conjunction with randomization, by "stratifying" for prognostic factors at the time of randomization, or it may be done in the analysis by "adjusting" for the effects of prognostic variables on outcome. In "stratification," patients entering the trial are first grouped according to their prognostic characteristics, and then randomly assigned to treatment within these groups.

Stratification does ensure that the groups compared are indeed comparable with respect to the known prognostic factors concerned, but it is only practical to stratify for a small number of prognostic variables. Adjustment in analysis can, in principle, be carried out with any number of prognostic variables, and has the additional advantage that the data acquired in the trial can itself be used to identify the major prognostic influences in the trial. The effects of these variables can then be incorporated into the analysis. Stratification can of course only be carried out on factors that are known before the trial has begun to influence prognosis. Stratification and adjustment in the analysis are of course not mutually exclusive activities and both can be carried out on the same trial.

22.4.4 THE THERAPEUTIC MANOEUVRE

The therapeutic manoeuvre is the treatment whose effect is being assessed in the clinical trial. The effects of the manoeuvre may be contrasted with an untreated control group or with the effects of standard treatment, where one exists, for the disease under study. A trial must contain a description of how the manoeuvre was allocated (see section 22.4.5), and details of its route of administration, dose, frequency, and criteria provided for any modifications in dose that might be made. Sufficient detail should be present to allow another investigator to give the manoeuvre exactly as it was administered in the trial.

These details are usually provided in trials of drug or radiation therapy, but are more difficult to specify in treatments involving surgical intervention, where the expertise of a surgeon may influence the way the therapeutic manoeuvre is delivered.

The effect of treatment on outcome may be influ-

enced by three additional factors: compliance, contamination, and co-intervention.

Compliance refers to the extent to which the therapeutic manoeuvre is delivered as intended. It is influenced by the willingness of patients to receive treatments in the manner prescribed, as well as the willingness of physicians to deliver treatments as specified in the trial protocol. Physicians often assume that compliance with drug therapy for cancer is good, but there has been little systematic assessment of this issue. In many other fields of medicine compliance is a major barrier to the delivery of treatments of known efficacy, and the little work done in the cancer field suggests that this may also apply to cancer therapy.

Although poor compliance with an effective treatment can certainly reduce the influence of treatment on outcome, the practice of assessing whether or not treatment is effective by analyzing results only in patients who do comply is likely to be misleading. In many clinical trials, patients who comply with therapy have been found to have a better outcome than patients who do not comply, even when the treatment involved is a placebo. This effect is called "compliance bias" (Feinstein, 1985a). The observation that the therapeutic outcome following adjuvant chemotherapy for breast cancer is better among patients who receive full doses of chemotherapy may, as the investigator suggests, indicate a "dose–response relationship" (Bonnadonna and Valagussa, 1981); or it may be an example of compliance bias.

Contamination refers to circumstances in which the principal manoeuvre in a trial is received not only by the experimental group, but also to some extent by the control group. Contamination is rarely a problem in clinical trials of chemotherapeutic agents or radiation therapy, but may create difficulties in clinical trials involving dietary treatments, vitamin supplementations, or the use of other generally available agents. Interpretation of the much publicized MRFIT trial in which the manoeuvre involved intervention on risk factors for coronary heart disease such as weight reduction, blood pressure control, and stopping smoking, was made much more difficult by contamination. Both controls and experimental subjects showed evidence of substantial modification of risk factors.

Co-intervention describes treatments other than the principal maneuvre that may be given in a clinical trial and may influence outcome. Examples are blood products and antibiotics in drug trials for acute leukemia, or radiation therapy in trials of systemic adjuvant therapy for breast cancer. Because co-interventions are not involved in the random allocation that should be applied to the principal maneuvre (see section 22.4.5) they may be distributed unequally between the groups being compared and so may contribute to a difference in outcome that might otherwise be incorrectly assigned to the principal manoeuvre.

22.4.5 RANDOMIZATION

Clinicians are accustomed to selecting therapy for patients, and the idea of having a treatment allocated to a patient by a chance mechanism in clinical trials often causes great difficulty, much of which cannot be easily justified. If it is indeed ethical to compare the treatments to which patients may be randomly assigned, then there must be considerable doubt about which treatment is better. A randomized trial comparing two treatments gives the patient a 50/50 chance of receiving the better treatment. It is unlikely that allocation of treatment by clinical judgment can improve on these odds, but the difficulties involved in randomization have prompted attempts to find alternative methods of allocating treatment.

Allocation by clinical judgment alone is likely to generate treatment groups that differ in their prognostic characteristics (eg, patients who are selected to receive postoperative radiotherapy for breast cancer are likely to have worse prognostic features than patients not so selected). In the face of such *systematic differences* it is usually impossible to draw conclusions about the different effects of treatment.

Historical controls are used often for comparative purposes. Diseases, criteria for patient selection, diagnostic methods, referral patterns, and hospital facilities may change with time and invalidate the comparison of treatment in one time with treatment in another time. In addition, the act of carrying out a new treatment in a trial may introduce changes, and may attract (or repel) patients and so change the spectrum of disease admitted to a hospital.

Allocation of treatment by other methods, such as the patient's registration number or date of birth have been proposed, but it is difficult to see how they differ ethically from randomization. These methods all have the major limitation that the physician *knows the treatment allocated before he sees the patient*. This introduces an undesirable opportunity for biased selection, and will always provide an alternative explanation for any difference that is found in a trial. Clinical trials are sufficiently laborious, time consuming and expensive that they should be conducted in such a way that interpretation of the results is as unambiguous as possible. This can only be achieved through randomization.

22.4.6 ANALYSIS OF SURVIVAL

Several methods might be used to compare the effects of different treatments upon survival.

1. The trial could be analyzed after all the patients have died, allowing a comparison of the mean survival times of all the patients. This is usually far too time consuming.

2. The proportions of deaths (the number dead divided by the total number of patients) may be compared in each treatment group. However, since patients enter the trial over a period of time, and the proportion dead is calculated at a particular point in time, patients will have been observed for different lengths of time.

3. The proportions of deaths may be compared at a fixed point in time after treatment, for example, by specifying a survival rate at five years. This method has the disadvantage that it fails to use information about patients who have been followed for less than five years, and for deaths that have occurred after five years.

4. The survival experience of the two treatment groups can be compared over the entire period of time since randomization by constructing actuarial survival curves. This method is preferred because it uses all of the available information. A method of constructing an actuarial survival curve is illustrated in Table 22.5. The period of follow-up after treatment is divided into convenient short intervals of duration Δt (intervals of one month are often used in trials of cancer therapy). The probability of dying in an interval from time t to time $t + \Delta t$ after treatment is calculated as the ratio of the number of patients who have died within this time interval Δt to the number of patients who have been followed for at least time t and who were therefore at risk of death during the interval. The probability of surviving is of course the complement of the probability of dying. The actuarial survival curve is constructed by cumulative multiplication of the probability of surviving as shown in Table 22.5. During early analysis when only small numbers of patients have long follow-up, the latter part of the curve is subject to a high degree of uncertainty, and may change as further patients are followed.

The method described for calculating survival without taking into account the cause of death gives a *crude survival curve*. If the cause of death is known for each patient, a survival curve can be drawn considering death only from the disease of interest. In making these calculations patients dying from other causes are treated as "withdrawn alive" at the time of their death. This is known as *corrected survival*. *Relative survival* expresses the survival of the group in relation to that of the general population of the same age and sex. Because the survival of a group of patients may, for a variety of socio-

Table 22.5. Calculation of Actuarial Survival

Follow-up Interval (A)	Number at Risk (B)	Number Dying (C)	Number Withdrawn Alive (D)	Probability of Dying (E)	Probability of Survival (F)	Overall Probability of Surviving (G)
0	100	–	–	–	–	1
1	100	8	2	.080	.920	.920
2	90	3	2	.033	.967	.890
3	85	1	0	.012	.988	.879
4	84	3	1	.036	.964	.847
5	80	7	3	.087	.913	.774
6	70	6	4	.086	.914	.707
7	60	5	5	.083	.917	.648
8	50	1	4	.020	.980	.635
9	45	1	2	.022	.978	.621
10	42	1	1	.024	.976	.606

(A) Follow-up interval may be of any convenient size; usually days, weeks or months.

(B) Number at risk means number alive at the start of the interval.

(C) Number dying is number dying during each interval.

(D) Number withdrawn refers to patients alive who have not been followed longer than the interval after randomisation.

(E) Probability of dying is number dying (C) ÷ number at risk.

(F) Probability of survival is the complement (1-E) of the probability of dying.

(G) Overall probability of survival is product of probabilities in (F). The numbers in this column may be plotted as a survival curve.

economic or other reasons, be at times better than that of the general population relative survival may actually rise with the passage of time.

22.4.7 COMPARISON OF SURVIVAL CURVES

Survival curves may differ because of inherent variability among patients, because of differences in patients' baseline prognoses, or because of true differences in treatment effects. Even if groups of patients could be assembled who were all identical with respect to their clinical and biological characteristics, and they were then treated in exactly the same way, the survival of a series of such groups would *not* be identical. Some groups would survive better than average, and others worse. Thus, a decision has to be made as to whether observed differences in survival are real differences due to different treatments or are those that might be expected as a result of underlying variability.

Comparison of treatments is undertaken by first postulating that the treatments are associated with the same survival (this is the statistician's null hypothesis). A calculation is then made of the probability (referred to as the *p* value) that a difference in survival, equal to or larger than the one observed, would arise by chance (ie, as a result of underlying variability in survival). This probability or *p* value is then used to make a *decision* about the validity of the original assertion that the treatments are the same. This process of deciding is analo-

gous to that used in diagnostic tests (section 22.2.1) and will also generate false positives and false negatives as well as true positives and true negatives.

The decision criterion that is most often adopted is to abandon the idea that the treatments are the same when *p* is less than .05. This criterion is arbitrary, but entrenched in our thinking. It implies that treatments will not be regarded as identical when there is a 1 in 20 or less chance that variability has created the observed differences in survival.

A number of statistical tests are available for calculating the *p* value for observed differences in survival. The log rank test is used widely to compare actuarial survival curves (Peto et al, 1976, 1977). It is based on a comparison of the *observed* probabilities of dying within time intervals Δt after each treatment with the probability of death that would be *expected* if the actuarial survival curves for the two treatments were the same. Differences in these observed and expected numbers are then analyzed by using the χ^2 (chi-squared) test. There are other statistical techniques for comparing survival curves. These include the Wilcoxan–Gehan method (Gehan, 1965), which can be used to compare two survival curves, as well as more complex multivariate methods such as Cox's proportional hazards model (Tibshirani, 1982). This method, like the log rank test, can be used to adjust the comparison of survival for prognostic factors, but unlike the log rank test it can analyze continuous variables, such as weight or blood pressure, without first forcing them into categories.

22.4.8 HOW MANY PATIENTS ARE REQUIRED?

Clinical trials are carried out in order to obtain as accurate as possible an estimate of the true effects of treatment. Because of the variability inherent in any comparison of treatments, described in the preceding section, the result actually observed in a trial may not correctly describe the effects of treatment.

The observed results may be misleading either by describing a difference between treatments where in fact no difference exists (a false-positive result), or by showing no difference between treatments where in reality a difference does exist (a false-negative result).

Although chance variability plays a role in the generation of false results, either positive or negative, the magnitude of the role played by chance is influenced by decisions that are made by the investigator before the trial is begun. These decisions are made when the number of patients required for the trial is selected.

The number of patients required for a clinical trial depends upon the following variables:

1. The number of events (eg, deaths) that are likely to occur.
2. Willingness to risk a false-positive result (type 1 or alpha error).
3. Willingness to risk a false-negative result (type 2 or beta error).
4. The magnitude of the difference that is considered worthwhile to detect.
5. The period of time during which patients are accrued and the duration of follow-up.

Note that items 2, 3, and 4 are subjective and matters of opinion. Willingness to accept a false-positive result is expressed by the p value that is used to decide about "statistical significance." Custom dictates $p < .05$, but it can be set at any level. There are good arguments for setting it at a lower value (see Peto et al, 1976, 1977).

The magnitude of the risk that is accepted for a false-negative result is a major determinant of the number of patients required for a clinical trial. *Power* refers to the ability of the trial to detect the difference between treatments when in fact they do differ. If beta is the probability of a false-negative result in a trial then 1 minus beta is the power of the trial. The relationship between power, expected differences between treatments, and the number of patients required is shown in Table 22.6. Note that a randomized clinical trial which seeks to detect an improvement in survival of 20%, compared to a control group receiving standard treatment whose expected survival is 40%, will require 130 patients in each arm at alpha = 0.05 and a power of 0.9. This means that a clinical trial of this size has about a 90%

chance of detecting an improvement in survival of this magnitude. Detection of a smaller difference between treatments, for example a 10% increase in survival, will require larger numbers, in this case ≈500 patients in each arm. A substantial proportion of clinical trials have been published which are too small to give even a 50% chance of detecting large treatment differences (Freiman et al, 1978).

Although the selection of beta is subjective, in practice it will be influenced by the number of patients that are available to enter the trial. If, however, there are insufficient patients to have an 80–90% chance of detecting a worthwhile difference in survival, the trial should probably not be undertaken.

The decision as to what constitutes a worthwhile difference between treatments can be subjected to an attempt at quantitation, particularly when a new treatment is being compared to an existing one. Practitioners who would be expected to make decisions based on the results of the trial can be asked what magnitude of improvement would be sufficient for them to change practice and adopt the new treatment. Based on such information the number of patients required can be estimated from tables similar to Table 22.6 (Freedman, 1982). Estimates of the difference in the outcome that would influence clinicians in their choice of treatment define differences that are clinically significant. It should be borne in mind that while all clinically significant differences in outcome must also be statistically significant, not all differences that are statistically significant will be clinically important.

22.4.9 THE SUBSEQUENT STATE: ASSESSMENT OF OUTCOME

The outcome of a clinical trial may be assessed in terms of survival, as described above, or in terms of disease response rate, disease-free survival or other mea-

Table 22.6. Number of Patients Required to Detect an Improvement in Survival ($\alpha = .05$; $1 - \beta = .90$)*

	$P_2 - P_1$				
P_1	0.10	0.20	0.30	0.40	0.50
.10	395	135	76	53	41
.20	676	200	103	66	48
.30	879	243	118	74	51
.40	995	262	123	73	50
.50	1020	259	116	67	—

*The total number of patients required to detect or rule out an improvement in survival when two treatments are compared in a clinical trial. P_1 = proportion of controls expected to survive; $P_2 - P_1$ = expected difference in probability of survival between experimental and control groups. (Adapted from Freedman, 1982.)

sures. Whatever outcome is employed it is essential to know what happened to all patients who entered the trial. It is common in cancer trials to exclude patients from the analysis of outcome on the grounds that they are not "evaluable." Reasons for nonevaluability vary, but may be because patients died soon after treatment was started, or failed to receive the full course of treatment for other reasons. It may in some circumstances be permissible to exclude patients from analysis in explanatory trials, which are seeking to describe the biological effects of treatment, but full reasons should be given for any such exclusions. It is seldom if ever permissible to exclude patients in pragmatic trials, which should imitate as far as is possible the circumstances in which treatment would be applied in the "real world." Patients who die before treatment has been completed should therefore be included in the analysis of pragmatic trials.

For some events (eg, death) there may be no doubt as to whether the event has occurred, but assignment of a particular cause of death (eg, whether or not it was cancer related) is a subjective matter, as is the assessment of tumor response, recognition of tumor recurrence, and the determination of disease-free survival. "Blinding" of observers may be necessary to avoid bias if the detection of outcome could be influenced by knowledge of the treatment received by patients.

The compared groups should be followed with similar types of evaluation so that they are equally susceptible to the detection of outcome events such as the detection of disease recurrence. Whenever the detection of outcome is subjective (ie, cannot be assumed to be independent of the person making the assessments) variation between different observers in the assessment of outcome should be examined.

In clinical trials where tumor response is the outcome variable, there is a particular need for rigorous criteria and careful attention to measurement error. It has been found that reports of clinical trials frequently lack the criteria needed to determine whether a meaningful response to treatment has occurred, and that measurement error itself can contribute substantially to the spurious identification of response (Warr et al, 1984; Tonkin et al, 1985).

22.5 SUMMARY

Diagnostic tests are used to distinguish patients with and without disease, or to evaluate the extent of disease. Their performance may be described by their sensitivity and specificity, which are independent of the prevalence of disease, or by the more clinically relevant properties of predictive values for positive and negative tests, which depend on prevalence. ROC curves pro-

vide an optimal method for assessing the performance of a diagnostic test. Evaluation of tests depends on the spectrum of patients that is included, and on the availability of an independent standard which indicates the true state. It is important to assess the effects of diagnostic tests on health outcomes, such as survival, but several types of bias must be avoided if this assessment is to be valid.

Knowledge of prognostic factors is important for planning and analyzing clinical trials. Prognostic factors are often interdependent.

Evaluation of prognosis in referral centers may introduce bias since the patients may not be representative of a larger population with the same disease.

Clinical trials of treatment may be grouped into those that seek to detect the biological effects of treatment (explanatory trials, including phase 1 and 2 trials of new agents) and those that seek to determine whether patients benefit from receiving treatment (pragmatic trials, including most phase 3 trials). These trials require major differences in design and analysis. Pragmatic trials of cancer treatment usually require randomization to prevent bias in the allocation of treatment. Analysis of such trials should compare actuarial survival curves. The number of patients required in trials may be determined from the difference between treatments that is sought, the level of significance required (ie, α or the p value, usually set at $<.05$) and the power to detect the specified difference (usually 0.8 or 0.9).

Critical appraisal of clinical trials requires consideration of their relevance and the validity of their results. As well as an adequate number of patients, the trial should satisfy methodologic criteria which apply to the initial state of the patients, their treatment, and the description of outcome. Adherence to these criteria should ensure that the results of a clinical trial are valid.

REFERENCES

Bonadonna G, Valagussa P: Dose–response effect of adjuvant chemotherapy in breast cancer. *N Engl J Med* 1981; 304:10–15.

Feinstein AR: *Clinical Epidemiology: The Architecture of Clinical Research.* W. B. Saunders, Philadelphia, 1985a.

Feinstein AR: On classifying cancers while treating patients. *Arch Intern Med* 1985b; 145:1780–1791.

Feinstein AR, Sosin DM, Wells CK: The Will Rogers Phenomenon: Stage migration and new diagnostic techniques as a source of misleading statistics for survival in cancer. *N Engl J Med* 1985; 312:1504–1608.

Freedman LS: Tables of the number of patients required in clinical trials using the logrank test. *Stat Med* 1982; 1:121–129.

Freiman JA, Chalmers TC, Smith H Jr et al: The importance of beta, the type II error and sample size in the design and interpretation of the randomized control trial. Survey of 71 "negative" trials. *N Engl J Med* 1978; 299:690–694.

Gehan EA: A generalized two-sample Wilcoxon test for doubly censored data. *Biometrika* 1965; 52:650–653.

Murphy EA: The normal, and the perils of the sylleptic argument. *Perspect Biol Med* 1972; 15:566–582.

Peto R, Pike MC, Armitage P. et al: Design and analysis of randomized clinical trials requiring prolonged observation of each patient. I. Introduction and design. *Br J Cancer* 1976; 34:585–612.

Peto R, Pike MC, Armitage P et al: Design and analysis of randomized clinical trials requiring prolonged observation of each patient. II. Analysis and examples. *Br J Cancer* 1977; 35:1–39.

Ransohoff DF, Feinstein AR: Problems of spectrum and bias in evaluating the efficacy of diagnostic tests. *N Engl J Med* 1978; 299:926–930.

Shapiro S: Evidence on screening for breast cancer from a randomized trial. *Cancer (Suppl)* 1977; 39:2772–2782.

Schwartz D, Flamant R, Lellouch J: *Clinical Trials.* Academic Press, London, 1980.

Tibshirani R: A plain man's guide to the proportional hazards model. *Clin Invest Med* 1982; 5:63–68.

Tonkin K, Tritchler D, Tannock I: Criteria of tumor response used in clinical trials of chemotherapy. *J Clin Oncol* 1985; 3:870–875.

Warr D, McKinney S, Tannock I: Influence of measurement error on assessment of response to anticancer chemotherapy: Proposal for new criteria of tumor response. *J Clin Oncol* 1984; 2:1040–1046.

BIBLIOGRAPHY

Department of Clinical Epidemiology and Biostatistics, McMaster Health Sciences Centre: How to read clinical journals: I. Why to read them and how to start reading them critically. *Can Med Assoc J* 1981; 124:555–558.

Department of Clinical Epidemiology and Biostatistics, McMaster Health Sciences Centre: How to read clinical journals. II. To learn about a diagnostic test. *Can Med Assoc J* 1981; 124:703–710.

Department of Clinical Epidemiology and Biostatistics, McMaster Health Sciences Centre: How to read clinical journals. III. To learn about the clinical course and prognosis of disease. *Can Med Assoc J* 1981; 124:869–872.

Department of Clinical Epidemiology and Biostatistics, McMaster Health Sciences Centre: How to read clinical journals. IV. To determine etiology or causation. *Can Med Assoc J* 1981; 124:985–990.

Department of Clinical Epidemiology and Biostatistics, McMaster Health Sciences Centre: How to read clinical journals. V. To distinguish useful from useless or even harmful therapy. *Can Med Assoc J* 1981; 124:1156–1162.

Feinstein AR: *Clinical Epidemiology: The Architecture of Clinical Research.* W.B. Saunders, Philadelphia, 1985

Osborn JF, Armitage P: *Statistical Methods in Medical Research.* Blackwell, Oxford, 1977.

Peto R, Pike MC, Armitage P et al: Design and analysis of randomized clinical trials requiring prolonged observation of each patient. I. Introduction and design. *Br J Cancer* 1976; 34:585–612.

Peto R, Pike MC, Armitage P et al: Design and analysis of randomized clinical trials requiring prolonged observation of each patient. II. Analysis and examples. *Br J Cancer* 1977; 35:1–39.

Sackett L, Haynes RB, Tugwell P: *Clinical Epidemiology. A Basic Science for Clinical Medicine.* Little, Brown and Company, Boston, 1985.

Schwartz D, Flamant R, Lellouch J: *Clinical Trials.* Academic Press, London, 1980.

Symposium on Methodology and Quality Assurance in Cancer Clinical Trials. *Cancer Treat Rep* 1985; 69:1039–1129.

Glossary

Italicized terms are defined in the glossary.

Adjuvant Chemotherapy: Drug treatment given to patients following surgical removal of or radiotherapy to their primary tumor, when there is known to be a high risk of occult micrometastases but no clinical or radiologic evidence of metastatic disease. If chemotherapy is given prior to treatment of the primary tumor, this therapy is referred to as neo-adjuvant chemotherapy. (See section 19.3.)

Alkylating Agent: A compound which has positively charged (ie, electron-deficient) groups, or which may be metabolized to form such groups. These reactive groups can form covalent linkages with negatively charged chemical groups on biological molecules such as those on the bases of DNA. A monofunctional alkylating agent can form a single adduct, whereas bifunctional alkylating agents can form two adducts leading to inter- or intra-strand DNA-DNA cross-links or to DNA-protein cross-links. Alkylating agents include commonly used anti-cancer drugs such as cyclophosphamide. (See section 18.3.) They may also have mutagenic and carcinogenic properties.

Anaplasia: Histopathological appearance of a tumor which lacks features allowing easy identification with the tissue of origin. Anaplastic tumors are usually rapidly growing and have a large number of cells in mitosis. (A synonym is undifferentiated.)

Angiogenesis: Formation of new blood vessels. This process is essential for tumor growth and appears to be stimulated by endothelial cell growth factor(s) which have been referred to as "tumor angiogenesis factor(s)." (See section 9.6.2.)

Antibody: A soluble protein molecule produced by plasma cells in response to an antigen and capable of specifically binding to that antigen. (See section 14.2.)

Antigen: An agent that is foreign (ie "non-self") to an animal and that is recognised by the immune system. (See section 14.2.)

Antimetabolite: A type of anticancer drug which is an analog of a normal metabolite. Antimetabolites may inhibit metabolic pathways or may be mistaken for normal metabolites during the synthesis of macromolecules such as DNA or RNA. Examples are methotrexate and 5-fluorouracil. (See section 18.4.)

Autocrine: Refers to the production of substances (ie, growth factors or hormones) which can influence the metabolism of the cell which produces them. (See sections 8.4 and 13.1.)

Autoradiography: A technique to identify where a radioactive isotope is localised in cells or subcellular components. The process involves covering biological material with photographic film or emulsion. The radioactivity produced by the isotope then causes local exposure of the overlying film or emulsion. (See section 9.3.)

Bias: Systematic departure from the true state (as compared to error, which is random departure from the true state). Faulty design may lead to the presence of many types of bias in trials of cancer causation and cancer treatment. (See sections 2.2 and 22.2.)

Bioassay: Quantitation of an agent by measuring the extent of its interaction with living organisms whose dose response has been predetermined. An example would be the assessment of the quantity of active metabolites of a drug in human serum by the toxicity of that serum for cells of known sensitivity.

Bioavailability: The proportion of an administered drug which is delivered to its site of action. For most agents, this is the proportion of drug entering the circulation. Bioavailability may be low if the drug is given orally. (See section 18.2.)

Biological Response Modifier: A therapeutic agent which influences the host's own defence mechanisms to act against cancer cells. Examples of such agents are Interferons and Interleukin 2. (See section 20.4.)

Cancer: A disease characterised by proliferation of cells leading to local growth (ie, a tumor), to local invasion, and to metastasis.

Carcinoembryonic Antigen (CEA): A glycoprotein produced in the embryo, and in smaller concentrations in the adult colon. It may also be produced in higher concentration by certain types of tumor cells such as those originating in the colon or rectum. CEA is one example of substances that are known generally as oncofetal antigens and which are used as tumor markers. (See chapter 12.)

Carcinogen: A substance which causes cancer. Some chemical carcinogens can act directly, but others require metabolism in vivo before becoming effective. Most carcinogens are mutagens. (See chapter 6.)

Carcinoma: Type of cancer arising from epithelial tissue (ie, tissue lining internal or external organs, or glandular tissue, etc). Most human cancers are carcinomas.

cDNA: A DNA copy complementary to m-RNA sequences transcribed from a given gene or genes. cDNA will therefore hybridize with these genes and, if radiolabeled, will allow their detection in chromosomes ("in situ hybridization") or in DNA extracted from cells and separated by electrophoresis (as in "Southern blots") or in RNA (Northern blots).

Cell Survival: A major determinant of the efficacy of anticancer drugs or radiation. Cell survival is determined by the ability of treated cells to proliferate to form a colony or clone. A cell survival curve relates cell survival (usually plotted on a logarithmic scale) to dose of radiation or anticancer drug. (See chapters 15 and 17.)

Cellular Immunity: Immunological defence against foreign agents which is mediated by cells (eg, various types of lymphocytes) rather than by antibodies. (See chapter 14.)

Chromosome: The structural unit containing the genetic material (DNA) within a cell. Human cells usually have 46 chromosomes consisting of 22 pairs of autosomes plus the sex chromosomes (XX in females, XY in males). Different chromosomes may be recognised in metaphase cells by their shape and by the application of various stains which leads to the production of characteristic bands. Each chromosome contains a pair of chromatids joined at the centromere. Alterations in the structure of chromosomes (aberrations) may pre-exist in cells or may be induced by treatment with drugs or radiation. (See sections 3.3 and A3.2, p. 39.)

Clone: A family of cells all derived from one parent cell. A clonal marker (eg, an abnormal chromosome or protein product) may identify all of the cells within a given clone. Most human tumors appear to arise from a single cell and hence are clonal. (See section 8.2.)

Cloned Gene: A gene that has been isolated and inserted into a "vector," usually a plasmid or bacterial virus. The vector containing the gene can be produced in large amounts, thereby providing genetic material suitable for assays and studies of the function of the gene. Cloned genes can be used to produce large quantities of pure protein products of cells (eg, insulin, interferons). (See section A3.3, p. 41.)

Clonogenic Cell: A cell which has the ability to generate progeny which form a colony of predetermined minimum size. Such a cell is also referred to as a Colony Forming Unit (CFU). Clonogenic cells may be identified in assays of cell survival. The term CFU is most often applied to progenitor cells in the bone marrow which may produce clones of cells in one or more pathways of differentiation. (See sections 8.2 and 9.5.)

Coding Region: The coding region is that part of the DNA which actually codes for a protein. The part of the DNA mol-

ecule which is initially transcribed into messenger RNA (m-RNA) contains both *introns* and *exons*. The introns are regions of m-RNA which are spliced out during post-transcriptional processing. The exons are the regions in the m-RNA which comprise the processed message; they contain the coding regions and are, therefore, the "expressed" portion of the gene. The final processed m-RNA may still contain untranslated regions both 5' and 3' to the region which actually codes the protein being made; some of these untranslated regions contain important regulatory signals.

Codon: A group of three DNA bases which code for a given amino acid. Codons thus form the "alphabet" of the genetic code.

Deletion: Loss of DNA. Deletions can be small, affecting only a small part of a single gene, or large, resulting in a chromosomal deletion involving many genes.

DNA Repair: The process whereby damaged DNA acts as a substrate for enzymes that attempt to restore the original base sequence. It is a complex process involving several enzymes and may lead to repair of damage in one or both strands. Repair may lead to complete restoration of the DNA (error-free repair) or may result in alteration or deletion of bases (error-prone repair). (See section 7.4.)

Differentiation: The development by cells of specific characteristics which allow the normal function of tissues. Tumors may show varying degrees of differentiation depending upon their similarity to the structure of the organ from which the tumor was derived.

Diurnal Rhythm: Variation throughout the day in biological properties of an organism. Many properties such as the concentrations of hormones or the activity of certain enzymes may show diurnal variation.

Double Minute: A small amount of genetic material that is seen in some cells as a paired body resembling a very small chromosome without a centromere. Because they lack a centromere, double minutes distribute themselves randomly at mitosis and are easily lost during cell growth. Double minutes have often been shown to contain amplified genes. (See section 3.3.)

Doubling Time: The time taken for an exponentially growing tumor (or cell population) to double its volume (or number of cells).

Ectopic Hormone: A hormone produced by cells that do not usually produce it. The cells of several types of tumor may produce ectopic hormones. (See section 13.4.)

Endocrine: Hormone production by a gland at one site in the body which releases the hormone into the blood stream to act on tissues which are distant to that site. An example of an endocrine gland is the thyroid. (See chapter 13.)

Enhancer: A DNA sequence which increases the activity of promoter sequences which are initiators of transcription (ie, production of messenger RNA). Enhancers can be located anywhere in the noncoding regions of a gene.

Enzyme Linked Immuno Adsorbant Assay (ELISA): A sensitive method for measuring the amount of a substance. The method requires the availability of an antibody to the substance and depends upon measuring the activity of an enzyme (eg, alkaline phosphatase) bound to the antibody.

Episome: A circular form of DNA which replicates in cells independent of the chromosomes. Viral DNA may form episomes in cells. Plasmids used for gene cloning grow as episomes in bacteria. (See section 4.3.)

Exocrine: Hormone production by a gland which releases the hormone to act locally through a duct. An example of an exocrine gland is the sweat gland. (See section 13.1.)

Exons: The regions of a gene found in the processed m-RNA.

Flow Cytometry: A technique in which cells are tagged with a fluorescent dye and then directed in single file through a laser beam. The intensity of fluorescence induced by the laser light is detected and the number of cells exhibiting different levels of fluorescence is recorded. The method is used frequently to study cell cycle properties since several dyes are available whose binding and hence fluorescence intensity is proportional to DNA content. Cells may also be separated according to the intensity of their fluorescence in a process known as fluorescence-activated cell sorting. (See section 9.4.)

Gene: A sequence of DNA that codes for a single polypeptide. This sequence includes coding and noncoding regions as well as regulatory regions. Genes may sometimes be overlapping so that the same sequence contributes to two different proteins. Gene amplification may occur through multiplication of the sequences in the gene; a large amount of amplification may often be recognized by the presence of either *homogeneously staining regions* (HSRs) on chromosomes or by the presence of *double minutes*.

Glycoprotein: A protein to which various types of sugar molecule have been attached. Glycoproteins form an important component of the cell surface. (See section 11.5.)

Grade: The histopathological appearance of a tumor in terms of its degree of differentiation. A low grade tumor is well differentiated, and a high grade tumor tends to be anaplastic.

Growth Factor: A polypeptide produced by cells which stimulates either the same cell or other cells to proliferate. Several types of growth factor have been isolated and some of these may be associated with abnormal regulation of growth in transformed cells. Growth factors interact with cells through specific receptors in the cell membrane. (See section 8.4.)

Growth Fraction: The proportion of cells within a tumor which is actively proliferating (ie, progressing through the cell cycle; see section 9.3).

Heterogeneity: Variability in the properties of cells within an individual tumor. Wide heterogeneity of many properties is found among cancer cells. (See section 8.3.)

Histocompatibility Antigen: Rejection of foreign tissue is determined by differences in histocompatibility antigens on cells of the donor and host tissues. One locus (which includes several genes) is associated with strong rejection, and is known as the major histocompatibility complex (MHC). (See section 14.2.)

Homeostasis: The maintenance of a normal physiological state. Homeostasis is often maintained through feedback systems employing signals (eg, hormones) which have opposite effects.

Homogeneously Staining Region (HSR): A region which appears uniform on chromosomes stained to examine their banding pattern. It often represents amplification of genes. HSRs tend to be stably inherited by daughter cells. (See section 3.3.)

Humoral Immunity: Immunological defences that are determined by antibodies. (See section 14.2.)

Hybridization: (a) The fusion of two cells to form a single cell. (b) The binding of complementary (homologous) sequences of DNA or RNA. Hybridization may take place under different conditions (degree of stringency) which dictate the extent of homology required for binding to occur. Radiolabeled pieces of DNA or RNA can be used as *probes* to identify the presence of specific DNA sequences by hybridization. The technique may localize genes to specific chromosomes in a process known as in situ hybridization. (See sections A3.3, p. 41, and A3.4, p. 46.)

Hybridoma: The term is most commonly used to describe a population of hybrid cells which produces *monoclonal antibodies*. Such a cell is produced by fusing an antibody-producing normal cell and a non-antibody-secreting myeloma tumor cell. (See section 20.3.)

Hypoxic Cell: A cell, usually within a tumor, that lacks oxygen. Such cells are important because they are resistant to the effects of radiation therapy, and are usually in regions with poor vascular supply. (See section 15.6.)

Immortalization: The process which may allow cells to form a continuous cell line (ie, proliferate indefinitely) in culture. Normal cells will proliferate for only a limited number of passages in culture and immortalization appears to be a necessary but not a sufficient step in transformation to a malignant state. (See section 8.4.)

Immune Surveillance: A proposed mechanism whereby the immune response recognises the development of malignant cells at an early stage and inactivates them before they can develop into tumors. (See section 14.3.)

Immunoglobulin: An antibody molecule. (See section 14.2.)

Incidence: A term used in epidemiology to describe the number of new cases (of cancer) observed in a population in a given unit of time, usually one year. (See section 2.1.)

Induction: The process by which a virus whose genetic material is integrated into the cellular DNA is caused to be released from the cell as a mature virus. (See section 4.3.)

Initiation: The first stage in the process of carcinogenesis. It involves interaction of the carcinogen with the DNA of the target cells to produce, after DNA replication, a permanent lesion. Subsequent steps include promotion and *progression*. (See section 6.3.)

Integration: The process by which viral DNA, or DNA copies of the RNA of a retrovirus, are incorporated into the chromosomal DNA of a cell. (See sections 4.3 and 4.4.)

Interferon: A protein produced by cells in response to viral infection. Several types of interferon have been identified and they have multiple effects on the host immune response, as well as more general effects on cell growth and differentiation. Interferons are examples of *biological response modifiers*. (See section 20.4.)

Intron: A noncoding region in the internal portion of a gene. These regions are spliced out during processing of the initial m-RNA transcript. (See *Coding Region*.)

Invasion: Infiltration by cancer cells into neighboring normal tissues. It is one of the distinguishing features of malignancy. (See sections 10.1 and 10.2.)

Ionizing Radiation: Radiation (eg, X- or γ-rays) which is sufficiently energetic that it can cause formation of ions during its passage through matter (tissue).

Isobologram: A diagram in the format of a graph whose axes are doses of two cytotoxic agents A and B. The isobologram joins points at which the combination of different doses of A and B give an equal level of biological damage. The diagram is useful in determining whether the effects of two agents may be additive, sub-additive (or antagonistic), or supra-additive (or synergistic). (See section 19.4.)

Isoeffect Curve: An isoeffect curve indicates graphically the relationship between different dose schedules of a treatment which give the same biological effect. The curve is used mainly to represent the effects of radiation treatments given as different numbers of fractions or in different overall times of treatment. The total radiation dose is plotted as a function of the fraction number, of the fraction size or of the treatment time. (See section 16.4.)

Isozyme (Isoenzyme): One of several chemical forms of an enzyme which have the same biological function. Tumors often produce one particular isozyme, frequently that which is associated with fetal tissue. (See section 11.3.)

Karyotype: The chromosome content of a particular cell. The karyotype is usually displayed by photographing the chromosomes in a metaphase cell, cutting the individual chromosomes out of the photograph and ordering them according to a standard notation. (See section A3.2, p. 39.)

Labeling Index: The proportion of cells in any tissue that are synthesizing DNA, and which therefore are recognized as labeled in autoradiographs following administration of ^{3}H-thymidine. (See section 9.3.)

Lethal Dose 50% (LD-50): The dose of radiation or of a drug which will, on average, cause 50% of animals receiving it to die.

Linkage: A description of the proximity of two genes on a chromosome. The more closely linked the two genes are, the less likely they are to be separated by crossing over of chromosomes during meiosis and hence the more likely they are to be inherited together. (See section A3.4, p. 46.)

Liposome: A small vesicle containing fluid surrounded by a lipid membrane. Liposomes may be constructed to have varying lipid content in their membrane and to contain various types of drug. (See section 19.3.)

Lymphokine: A substance produced by lymphocytes (or monocytes) having an effect on other lymphocytes. An example is interleukin 2 (IL-2), also known as T-cell growth factor, which is required for the growth of T-lymphocytes. Lymphokines are examples of *biological response modifiers*. (See section 20.4.)

Malignancy: The essential property of cancer cells which is demonstrated by their ability to proliferate indefinitely, to invade surrounding tissue and to metastasize to other organs.

Marker: A substance produced by tumor cells and released into the blood such that the concentration in blood may be related to the bulk of tumor present in the individual. (See chapter 12.)

Metastasis: The spread of cells from a primary tumor to a noncontiguous site, usually via the blood stream or lymphatics, and the establishment of a secondary growth. (See chapter 10.)

Mitotic Delay: Delay in passage of a cell through its growth cycle that is induced by radiation or some anticancer drugs.

Mitotic Index: The proportion of cells in a tissue which are in mitosis at any given time.

Monoclonal Antibody: An antibody of a single defined specificity, most commonly obtained from a single clone of antibody-producing cells or from a *hybridoma*. (See section 20.3.)

Mucositis: Inflammation of the mucous membranes, especially in the mouth, which may occur after treatment with radiation or anticancer drugs.

Mutation: A change in one or more of the DNA bases in a gene. Changes can include insertion of extra bases or deletion of a base(s). Mutations in coding exons lead to altered protein products; mutations in noncoding regions can lead to altered amounts of protein.

Myelosuppression: A reduction in mature blood cells in the peripheral circulation, particularly granulocytes, which may occur after treatment with anticancer drugs. (See section 17.5.)

Natural Killer Cell: A lymphocyte that can kill certain types of malignant cell without prior specific sensitization. (See section 14.4.)

Necrosis: Death of cells which often occurs in solid tumors leading to areas containing degenerating or pyknotic cells.

Neoplasm: Literally a new growth or tumor. Often used to describe a malignant tumor or cancer.

Northern Blot Analysis: A technique for determining the presence of specific messenger RNA sequences in cells. Messenger RNA molecules are separated by electrophoresis and then blotted onto nitrocellulose paper. A radiolabeled probe, containing DNA sequences (cDNA) complementary to the RNA which is to be detected, is applied to the blot and allowed to hybridize. The labeled cDNA is then detected by autoradiography. (See section A3.3, p. 41.)

Nude Mouse: A mouse which congenitally lacks a thymus and hence mature T-cells. Xenografts of human tumors will often grow in such animals. For unknown reasons these mice are also hairless, hence the term "nude." (See section 17.4.)

Oncofetal Antigen: A protein produced by fetal tissue which is usually present at very low levels in the adult. Many tumors produce onco-fetal antigens (eg, *carcinoembryonic antigen*) which have been used as *markers* of tumor bulk. (See section 12.2.)

Oncogene: A gene whose protein product may be involved in processes leading to transformation of a normal cell to a malignant state. (See chapter 5.) Classically, it is a normal cellular gene (or part of a normal gene) which has been incorporated into a (RNA) virus, and is responsible for transformation when the virus infects a cell.

Paraneoplastic Syndrome: Signs or symptoms that may occur in a patient with cancer but which are not due directly to the local effects of the tumor cells. Examples include the effects of ectopic production of hormones by cancer cells. (See section 13.4.)

Pharmacodynamics: The interaction of drugs with cells. It includes such factors as binding to cells, uptake, intracellular metabolism, and cytotoxicity. (See chapter 18.)

Pharmacokinetics: The time course of drug disposition within the body. This may include absorption, distribution, metabolism and excretion. (See section 18.2.)

Phenotype: Characteristics of a cell or tissue resulting from the expression of specific genes.

Plasmid: A circular piece of DNA which may reproduce separately from chromosomal DNA within cells, bacteria, or other organisms. (See *episome.*)

Pleiotropic Drug Resistance: Resistance which develops in cells to a group of chemically unrelated drugs and which may be induced or selected for by exposure of the cells to any one of the drugs. Also referred to as Multidrug resistance. (See section 19.2.)

Ploidy: A description of the chromosome content of the cell. Normal mammalian cells contain two copies of each chromosome (except for the sex chromosomes in males) and are diploid. Germ cells contain only one copy and are haploid. Cells in tumors often have missing or additional chromosomes (Aneuploidy), and/or may have one or more chromosome aberrations.

Potentially Lethal Damage: Damage to a cell which may be caused by radiation or drugs and which may or may not be repaired depending upon the environment of the cell following treatment. (See section 15.6.)

Prevalence: The frequency of disease in a population at a given time. (See section 2.1.)

Probe: A cloned gene or fragment of a cloned gene which can be made radioactive and used to detect homologous DNA (Southern blot or in situ hybridization) or RNA (Northern blot).

Prognosis: The expected outcome (eg, chance of survival) for a patient with a particular type and stage of disease. (See section 22.3.)

Progression: The tendency of tumors to become more malignant as they grow. (See section 8.3.)

Promoter: (a), A compound that may not itself be carcinogenic, but which stimulates the proliferation of initiated cells to form a cancer. Promotion is reversible and is normally a slow process. (See section 6.4.) (b), A DNA sequence where the transcription initiates. Promoters, in contrast to enhancers, have direction and are always located near the beginning of the first exon.

Protein Kinase: An enzyme that catalyses the phosphorylation of proteins. Phosphorylation and dephosphorylation of proteins appear to be major mechanisms which control their function. Many oncogenes code for protein kinases. (See sections 5.4 and 11.4.)

Proto-oncogene: A gene, in a normal cell, homologous to a viral transforming gene. Some proto-oncogenes encode proteins that influence the control of cellular proliferation and differentiation. Mutations, amplifications, rearrangements, etc, of proto-oncogenes may allow them to function as *oncogenes*, ie, genes whose products are involved in cell transformation. (See chapter 5.)

Provirus: The DNA copy of the RNA of a retrovirus which is integrated into the chromosomal DNA of a cell. (See section 4.4.)

Radioimmunoassay: A sensitive method that may be used for the quantitation of any substance which can be recognized by an antibody. It depends on the binding of radiolabeled antibodies to the substance. (See section 12.2.)

Radiosensitizer: A compound which increases the sensitivity of cells to radiation. (See section 16.5.)

Rearrangement: Changes in the sequence of genes or of DNA sequences within genes that lead to alteration in their protein products. Rearrangement of genes is important in such processes as the generation of diversity of antibody molecules. Abnormal rearrangements between different genes appear to be important in malignant transformation, eg, the Philadelphia chromosome in chronic myelogenous leukemia. (See sections 3.3 and A3.2, p. 39.)

Receptor: A molecule inside or on the surface of cells which recognizes a specific hormone, growth factor, or other biologically active molecule. The receptor also mediates transfer of signals within the cell.

Relative Risk: The ratio of disease frequency in exposed and nonexposed members of a population. (Exposure implies any attribute, personal, environmental or genetic, that may cause or protect against disease.)

Remission: Decrease in tumor volume (or cell number) following treatment. Complete remission indicates that disease cannot be detected by physical examination or clinical tests, but does not necessarily imply that the disease has been cured. Partial remission is usually defined as shrinkage by at least 50% of the cross-sectional area of measurable tumors. (See section 19.1.)

Restriction Enzymes: Enzymes obtained from bacteria which make cuts at specific sequences of 4-8 bases in double-stranded DNA. (See section A3.3, p. 41.)

Restriction Fragment Length Polymorphism (RFLP) Analysis: A method which may be used to identify unique DNA sequences on two homologous chromosomes within a cell. (See section A3.3, p. 41.)

Retrovirus: A virus in which the genome comprises RNA. (See section 4.4.)

Reverse Transcriptase: An enzyme found mostly in retroviruses which catalyses the production of a complementary DNA strand from an RNA strand. (See section 4.4.)

Sarcoma: A malignant tumor derived from mesenchymal cells (eg, connective tissue, vascular tissue, bone, etc).

Screening: The application of a test (eg, mammography) which may detect disease in a population of individuals who have no symptoms of the disease.

Second Messenger: A substance involved in transmission of information between the surface of the cell and its interior, often leading to changes in the expression of specific genes. Nonsteroidal hormones stimulate second messengers such as cyclic AMP or phosphoinositides to influence the behaviour of cells. (See sections 11.4 and 13.3.2.)

Segregation: The process by which the chromosomes are separated during meiosis.

Southern Blot Analysis: A technique used for detecting specific DNA sequences in cells. DNA is extracted from cells and cut with one or more restriction enzymes. The DNA fragments are separated by electrophoresis and blotted onto nitrocellulose paper. The DNA is then hybridized using a radiolabeled DNA probe with a sequence complementary to the specific sequence to be detected. The DNA fragments which hybridize with the probe are detected by autoradiography. (See section A3.3, p. 41.)

Stem Cell: A cell which has the capacity to repopulate functional units within a tissue. The term is most aptly applied to renewal tissue such as the bone marrow where it is possible to demonstrate the presence of a cell which can regenerate all the various differentiated cells in blood. It is also used to describe a cell in tumors that has the capacity to produce a very large number of progeny and which, if it survives, can regenerate the tumor after treatment. (See section 8.2.)

Sublethal Damage: Damage to a cell which may be caused by radiation or drugs and which can be repaired in a few hours after the treatment. Classically, repair of sublethal damage is revealed by giving two treatments separated by a variable time interval. (See section 15.6.)

Synchronized Cells: A population of cells in which most of them are at a given stage of the growth cycle at any one time and move through the cell cycle as a cohort. Drugs which kill cells at a given phase of the cell cycle lead to partial synchrony among the survivors. (See sections 15.6 and 17.3.)

Synergy: An interaction between two agents which is greater than would be predicted from the activity of either alone. This word is commonly misused in describing the interaction between drugs or between drugs and radiation, since there is a range of effects that would be predicted as being additive. (See section 19.4.)

Therapeutic Index (Therapeutic Ratio): The ratio of the dose of a therapeutic agent, that is required to produce a given level of damage to a critical normal tissue, to the dose of the agent required to produce a defined level of antitumor effect. Therapeutic index is therefore a measure of the relative efficacy of therapy against tumors as compared to the normal tissue damage caused. (See sections 16.2 and 19.1.)

Thymidine: One of the bases of DNA. Tritiated thymidine contains radioactive tritium (an isotope of hydrogen) and is used widely in studies of cell kinetics since it is either degraded rapidly to tritiated water or taken up into cells and incorporated into newly synthesized DNA. High specific activity (highly labeled) tritiated thymidine can be used to suicide cells since the cells that are engaged in DNA synthesis incorporate sufficient radioactivity to kill themselves. (See section 9.3.)

Tolerance: (a), A term used in immunology to indicate the process whereby specific antigens fail to elicit an immunological response. Tolerance is required to prevent a response against "self-antigens," and can also be induced against foreign antigens. (See section 14.2.) (b), Thermo-tolerance is the development of resistance to the effects of further heating induced by initial heating of cells or tissues. (See section 21.2.)

Transcription: The synthesis of messenger RNA from a DNA template.

Transduction: Excision of viral sequences in cells from chromatin together with cellular sequences and their packaging as mature viral particles. This process provides a method by which DNA sequences may be transferred from one cell to another with the virus acting as an intermediary. (See section 4.3.)

Transfection: The direct transfer of DNA molecules into a cell. Transfection of specific genes is a powerful tool for determining their function. (See sections A3.3, p. 41, and 5.2.)

Transformation: Commonly used to describe the conversion of normal cells to those with abnormalities in cellular appearance and growth regulation in tissue culture (morphologic transformation). Malignant transformation requires in addition the demonstration that cells can produce an invasive tumor in an appropriate animal. (See section 8.4.)

Translation: The process by which messenger RNA directs the synthesis of protein.

Translocation: The displacement of one part of a chromosome to a different chromosome or to a different part of the same chromosome. An example is the translocation between chromosomes 9 and 22 that leads to the appearance of the Philadelphia chromosome in chronic myelogenous leukemia. (See sections 3.3 and A3.2, p. 39.)

Tumor: A swelling or growth. It usually implies a collection of cells rather than, for example, an abscess. A tumor may be benign (ie, the cells do not invade or metastasize) or malignant.

Western Blot Analysis: A procedure analogous to Southern and Northern blot analysis which allows the detection of specific proteins. Proteins are separated by electrophoresis and blotted on to nitrocellulose paper. They are usually identified by autoradiography following binding of radiolabeled antibodies. (See section A3.3, p. 41.)

Xenograft: Tissue that is transplanted from one species of animal into another. Most commonly this refers to the transplantation of a human tumor into a nude or immune-deficient mouse. (See section 17.4.)

Index

and malignant disease, 28
and poxviruses, 63
Metronidazole, 272
Microtubules, and vinca alkaloids, 305
Microwave heating, 350–351
Mineralocorticoids, 208
Misonidazole
  and chemotherapy, 321, f322
  hyperthermia effects, 346
  and hypoxic cells, 319
  in radiotherapy, 271–273
Mithramycin, DNA flow cytometry, 147
Mitomycin C
  biological properties, 284
  and hypoxic cells, 319
  pharmacology, 305
Mitosis, thymidine autoradiography, 143–147
Mitoxantrone, 304
Molecular analysis
  cloned genes, 43–44
  gene placement into cells, 46
  restriction enzymes, 43
  restriction-fragment-length polymorphisms, 45–46
  Southern blots, 44–45
Molecular correlation concept, 179–181
MOPP protocol, 297
Mormon population, cancer studies, 27, 28
Morris hepatomas
  biochemical properties, 177–178
  and molecular correlation concept, 180
Mouth cancer, 103
Multiple endocrine neoplasias, 212, t213
Multiple myeloma
  melphalan treatment, 297
  tumor markers, 195–196
Multiple sclerosis, recognition of self, 226
Multitarget mathematical model, 245–246
Muramyl dipeptide, 334
Muscle
  cell renewal in normal tissue, 127
  radiation dose response, 260
Mutagenicity assay, 102
Mutations
  point, oncogene activation, 78–79
  and radiation damage, 113
Myeloma
  antibody production, 224
  drug-induced damage, 290
  immunotherapy, 335

Nafazatrom, 316
Nasopharyngeal carcinoma
  and herpes viruses, 63–64
  and wood furniture manufacture, 9

Natural killer cells, 163, 232, 334
Natural products, pharmacology of, 303–305
Nausea and vomiting, with anticancer drugs, 290
Nerve cell renewal in normal tissue, 127
Nerve growth factor, and oncogenes, 84
Neuroblastoma cells
  chromosome abnormalities, 34
  cyclic nucleotides, 182
Neutrons, in energy-loss processes, 108
N-glycosidic linkage, in glycoproteins, 187, f188
Nitrites, and cancer epidemiology, 19–20
Nitrogen mustard
  biological properties of, 278, 284 288
  and hypoxic cells, 319
  pharmacology of, 296–298
Nitroimidazoles, 271–273
Nitrosamines
  metabolic activation, 97
  in tobacco, 103
Nitrosodiethylamine, dose-response study, 90
Nitrosodimethylamine, metabolic activation, 97
Nitrosomethylurea
  and oncogenes, 93
  point mutations, 79
Nitrosoureas
  and cell survival, 283, 284
  hyperthermia effects, 347
  pharmacology of, 298–299
Nomenclature
  of chromosomes, 40–41
  families of tumor viruses, 55, t56
Nominal Standard Dose (NSD), 269–270
Nucleosides, as tumor markers, 196
Nulliparity, and endometrial carcinoma, 214

Obesity
  and endometrial carcinoma, 214
  steroid hormone action, 209–210
Occupational exposure, and cancer risk, t20, 22, t103
Odds ratio, 11, f12
O-glycosidic linkage, in glycoproteins, 187, f188
Ommaya reservoir, 295
Oncogenes, 72–88
  activation
    chemical carcinogens, 78–79
    chromosome translocations, 80–82
    complementation, 83
    gene dosage, 79
    point mutation, 78

cellular origin of, 73–74
growth factor effects, 138
in human cancer cells
  critique of transfection assay, 77–78
  DNA transfection, 75–77
  genetic basis of malignancy, 75
  viral oncogenes and transfected DNA, 78
and phosphoinositide metabolism, 185
protein products of, t84
proto-oncogenes in normal and transformed cells, t73, 74–75
  cytoplasmic proteins, 85
  growth factors, 84
  GTP-binding proteins, 85–86
  membrane receptors, 84–85
  nuclear proteins, 86
  protein tyrosine kinases, 84
and viral genes, 72–73
Oncomodulin, 184
Organ specificity for metastases, 161, 167–168
Ornithine decarboxylation, and tumor markers, 196
Ovarian cancer
  anticancer drugs, 299
  chromosome abnormalities, 34
  drug resistance, 314
  drug-induced damage, 290
  and endometrial carcinoma, 214
  hormonal treatment, 221
  melphalan treatment, 297
  monoclonal antibodies, 331, 332
  tumor markers, 195, 199–200
Ovarian follicles, and anticancer drugs, 289–290
Oxygen
  activation, in carcinogenesis, 99
  and biological effects of radiation, 251–253
  enhancement ratio (OER), 251
  in fractionated radiation treatment, 265–266
  high-pressure delivery, 270–271

Pair production, f107, 238
Pancreatic carcinoma
  hormonal treatment, 221
  and smoking, 19, 102
Papillomaviruses, warts and cervical cancer, 60–61
Papovaviruses, 61–62
Paraneoplastic syndrome, 212
Parathyroid hormone, 205, 206
Patients, and diagnostic tests
  numbers of, 371
  spectrum of, 361
Pelvic chrondrosarcoma, ultrasound heating, 351
Perfluorocarbon, 271

About the Editors and Contributors

Ian F. Tannock, MD, PhD, FRCP(C), is a Senior Scientist and Staff Physician at the Ontario Cancer Institute/Princess Margaret Hospital, and Associate Professor, Departments of Medicine and Medical Biophysics at the University of Toronto. He was born in England in 1943 and studied mathematics and physics as an undergraduate at Queens' College, Cambridge. He did postgraduate work at the Institute of Cancer Research, Surrey, England (London University) under the direction of Professor L. Lamerton and Dr G. Steel. His doctoral research involved studies of cell population kinetics in animal tumors. He spent two years as a Postdoctoral Fellow at M.D. Anderson Hospital in Houston, Texas, before entering medical school at the University of Pennsylvania. After receiving his MD he completed his postgraduate medical training in Toronto in internal medicine and medical oncology. He currently divides his time between laboratory-based research and the practice of medical oncology at the Ontario Cancer Institute. His recreational activities include canoeing, camping and cross-country skiing.

Richard P. Hill, PhD, is a Senior Scientist at the Ontario Cancer Institute/Princess Margaret Hospital, and Associate Professor, Department of Medical Biophysics, University of Toronto. He was born in Northern Ireland in 1942 but was raised in England and studied physics at St John's College, Oxford, as an undergraduate. He completed his PhD at the Medical College of St Bartholomew's Hospital (London University) under the direction of Professors P. Lindop and J. Rotblat. His thesis work involved studies of the response of animal tumors to single and fractionated doses of radiation. He then came to the Ontario Cancer Institute in Toronto as a James Picker Foundation Postdoctoral Fellow, where he continued his studies in radiation biology. After three years he returned to England to join the scientific staff of the Institute of Cancer Research. He returned to Toronto in 1973 to become a member of the senior scientific staff of the Ontario Cancer Institute. His major research interests are in radiation biology and the study of metastases. Outside the laboratory he enjoys outdoor activities and is involved in a number of sports, including cricket.

Both of the editors are married and each has three children. They and their families remain close personal friends, despite the hazards of working on the current volume.

THE CONTRIBUTORS

Michael C. Archer, PhD
Senior Scientist, Ontario Cancer Institute/Princess
  Margaret Hospital;
Professor, Dept of Medical Biophysics, University of
  Toronto

Norman F. Boyd, MD, FRCP(C)
Clinical Epidemiologist, Ludwig Institute for Cancer
  Research;
Staff Physician, Ontario Cancer Institute/Princess
  Margaret Hospital;
Associate Professor, Dept of Medicine, University of
  Toronto

Ronald N. Buick, PhD
Senior Scientist, Ontario Cancer Institute/Princess
  Margaret Hospital;
Associate Professor, Dept of Medical Biophysics,
  University of Toronto

Stephen P. Clark, PhD
Visiting Fellow, Laboratory of Molecular Biology,
National Institutes of Arthritis, Diabetes, Digestive
  and Kidney Diseases;
National Institutes of Health, Bethesda, MD.

Charles Erlichman, MD, FRCP(C)
Staff Physician, Ontario Cancer Institute/Princess
    Margaret Hospital;
Assistant Professor, Depts of Medicine and
    Pharmacology, University of Toronto

John W. Hunt, PhD
Senior Scientist, Ontario Cancer Institute/Princess
    Margaret Hospital
Professor, Dept of Medical Biophysics, University of
    Toronto

Tak W. Mak, PhD
Senior Scientist, Ontario Cancer Institute/Princess
    Margaret Hospital
Professor, Dept of Medical Biophysics, University of
    Toronto

Aaron Malkin, MD, PhD, FRCP(C)
Head, Dept of Clinical Biochemistry, Sunnybrook
    Medical Centre
Professor, Depts of Clinical Biochemistry and
    Medicine, University of Toronto

Richard G. Miller, PhD
Senior Scientist, Ontario Cancer Institute/Princess
    Margaret Hospital
Professor and Chairman, Dept of Immunology,
    University of Toronto

Mark D. Minden, MD, PhD, FRCP(C)
Senior Scientist and Staff Physician, Ontario Cancer
    Institute/Princess Margaret Hospital;
Assistant Professor, Depts of Medicine and Medical
    Biophysics, University of Toronto

Robert K. Murray, MD, PhD
Professor, Depts of Biochemistry and Pathology,
    University of Toronto

Robert A. Phillips, PhD
Director of Research, Division of Hematology/
    Oncology, Hospital for Sick Children
Professor, Dept of Medical Biophysics, University of
    Toronto

A. Michael Rauth, PhD
Senior Scientist, Ontario Cancer Institute/Princess
    Margaret Hospital
Professor and Acting Chairman, Dept of Medical
    Biophysics, University of Toronto

Rose Sheinin, PhD, FRSC, D Hum Lett
Professor, Depts of Microbiology and Medical
    Biophysics, University of Toronto

Donald J. A. Sutherland, MD, PhD, FRCP(C)
Staff Physician, Toronto–Bayview Regional Cancer
    Centre and Sunnybrook Medical Centre
Associate Professor, Dept of Medicine, University of
    Toronto